THEORY AND APPLICATION

OF

MATHIEU FUNCTIONS

BY

N. W. McLACHLAN

D.Sc. (Engineering) London

Hon. Member, British Institution of Radio Engineers

Professor of Electrical Engineering, Emeritus,
University of Illinois

Walker-Ames Professor of Electrical Engineering,
University of Washington (in 1954)

DOVER PUBLICATIONS, INC.
NEW YORK

Library of Congress Catalog Card Number 64–16333

Manufactured in the United States of America

Dover Publications, Inc.
180 Varick Street
New York 14, N.Y.

PREFACE TO THE FIRST EDITION

THE purpose of this book is to give the theory of Mathieu functions and to demonstrate its application to representative problems in physics and engineering science. It has been written for the technologist, and *is not addressed in any sense to the pure mathematician*, for whom I am not qualified to write. Between the outlook of the two parties lies a gulf as wide as that between sinner and saint or vice versa! Although, by virtue of necessity, the technologist may occasionally deviate from the narrow path followed rigorously by the pure mathematician, it must not be forgotten that the consequences of such deviation may be practical results of considerable benefit to the community at large. Since the pure mathematician profits by these technological advances, any criticisms of methods used by the technologist should be entirely of a *constructive and helpful* nature.

The text is in two parts, (1) Theory, (2) Applications; but there is no need to peruse the whole of (1) before reading (2). For instance a study of the second half of Chapter IV will enable the reader to cope with most of the applications in Chapter XV. Some theory is associated with computation of parameters, and of coefficients in series. Other parts of it, not applied directly, are included in the hope that future needs will be met. The reader is expected to have an elementary knowledge of (*a*) Bessel functions, because they play an important role in Chapters VIII, X, XI, XIII, XVII–XVIII; (*b*) convergence of infinite series and integrals, and the consequences of uniform convergence, e.g. continuity of a function, term-by-term differentiation and integration of series. If these subjects are unknown, the requisite knowledge should be acquired [see references 203, 214, 215, 221, on pp. 380, 381].

The chapter sequence is such as to reduce forward references to a minimum; unfortunately they are unavoidable. The original memoirs from which information was taken are indicated in [ ], which denotes the number in the reference list on pp. 373–81. The analysis herein is seldom the same as that in the original memoir. In writing the manuscript I realized that there were wide gaps which, if left unfilled, would have rendered the text discontinuous. The filling of these gaps has entailed considerable labour; in fact more than one-third of the text is new. The main part of it is in 'Additional

Results', and in Chapters IV, V, VII–XI, XIII, XIV, XVII, Appendixes I, III. The new method of computing the coefficients in the periodic part of the series representation of fe_m, ge_m, Fe_m, Ge_m in Chapter VII is a joint contribution with W. G. Bickley.

Symbolism. The variety of notations encountered in the literature on the subject, the introduction of new forms of solution, new multipliers, etc., necessitated a careful survey of and a decision on notation. The first item for consideration was the form to be taken by Mathieu's equation. The canonical form chosen is

$$\frac{d^2y}{dz^2} + (a - 2q\cos 2z)y = 0. \tag{1}$$

More than two years after this decision had been made, H. Jeffreys pointed out that the form used by Mathieu in his original memoir [130] was

$$\frac{d^2P}{d\alpha^2} + (R - 2h^2\cos 2\alpha)P = 0. \tag{2}$$

Thus after encircling the point at issue for about three-quarters of a century and encountering many branches, we have at last returned (quite unwittingly) to the initial or starting value! The coincidence seems significant. If we take $k = +q^{\frac{1}{2}}$, the arguments in the Bessel series solutions of (1), and its three other forms, have no fractional factors. Symbols used for various classes of solution have been selected to avoid confusion with other mathematical functions. The basis of the notation is 'e' for elliptic cylinder function, introduced by E. T. Whittaker some thirty-five years ago. He used ce, se, to signify 'cosine-elliptic', 'sine-elliptic', and associated Mathieu's name with these periodic functions. Herein the generic designation 'Mathieu function' applies to all solutions of (1) in its four forms, which have the appropriate multipliers and/or normalization. The functions are classified, for q real, in Appendix III. For second (non-periodic) solutions of (1) which correspond to $ce_m(z, q)$, $se_m(z, q)$, the letters f, g are used. Thus the respective second solutions are written $fe_m(z, q)$, $ge_m(z, q)$. When iz is substituted for z in $ce_m(z, q)$, etc., we follow H. Jeffreys [104] and use capital letters. Accordingly we have $Ce_m(z, q)$, $Se_m(z, q)$, $Fe_m(z, q)$, $Ge_m(z, q)$. There are also second solutions involving the Y- and K-Bessel functions, which take precedence over the two latter. They are designated $Fey_m(z, q)$, $Gey_m(z, q)$, $Fek_m(z, q)$, $Gek_m(z, q)$. $Fey_m(z, q)$ is a *particular* linear combination of the even first solution $ce_m(z, q)$, and the corresponding odd solution $fe_m(z, q)$ of (1), in which z is replaced by iz. For wave propagation problems, combination solutions akin to the Hankel functions have been introduced. They have been allocated the symbols Me, Ne, M being for Mathieu and N the next letter of the alphabet. Owing to the war, it was not till the summer of 1946 that, as a result of correspondence with G. Blanch, I became aware that in references [23, 211], functions represented by series of Y-Bessel functions (similar to some in Chapter VIII), and also combination functions akin to Me, Ne, had been defined.

The Mathieu functions of positive integral order are solutions of (1) in its four forms when the parametric point (a, q) lies *upon* one of the characteristic curves a_m, b_m of Figs. 8 and 11. The functions of fractional order, namely, $ce_{m+\beta}(z, q)$, $se_{m+\beta}(z, q)$, $0 < \beta < 1$, have been introduced to provide standard solutions when (a, q) lies *within* a *stable* region of Figs. 8, 11. If $\beta = p/s$, a rational fraction, *always* presumed to be in its lowest terms, the functions are periodic in z real, with period $2s\pi$, $s \geqslant 2$. The functions $ceu_{m+\mu}(\pm z, q)$ have been introduced to provide standard solutions when (a, q) lies *in* an *unstable* region of Figs. 8, 11. μ is real and positive, and 'u' signifies that the solution pertains to an unstable region. If q is negative imaginary, $ce_m(z, q)$ is a complex function of z, so in Chapter III, $cer_m z$ and $cei_m z$, have been used to denote its real and imaginary parts, respectively. Symbols in heavy type signify 'per unit area', or 'per unit length'; m, n, p, s usually represent positive integers including zero, except in §§ 3.40–3.51 where s is real and positive; r represents any integer; $\simeq$ means 'approximately equal to'; $\sim$ signifies 'asymptotically equal to', 'approaches asymptotically to', or 'asymptotic form'; $R(z)$, $Im(z)$ or $Imag(z)$, indicate the real and imaginary parts of z, respectively; superscripts in $A_{2r+1}^{(2n+1)}$, $B_{2r+2}^{(2n+2)}$ signify the order of the function, while the subscripts denote that of the coefficient itself; the subscripts in a_m, b_m, $a_{m+\beta}$ indicate the order of the function of which a_m, etc., is the characteristic number. Wherever possible a standard summation from 0 to $+\infty$ is used. Other symbols employed are those generally found in advanced mathematical texts in English. References to Fig. 8 are to either 8 A or 8 B, whichever is the more convenient.

Tables. The values of the characteristic numbers $a_0,..., a_5$; $b_1,..., b_6$, computed by Ince, and abbreviated by him to 7 decimal places [95], are given in Appendix II for the range $q = 0$ to 40. For q imaginary, some a_0 computed by Goldstein and Mulholland are given in Table 4, p. 51 [57]. No other tabular values are reproduced, since they are much too extensive for inclusion here. An interpolable table of $a_0, ..., a_{15}$; $b_1, ..., b_{15}$, for the range $q = 0$–25, compiled by the National Bureau of Standards Mathematical Tables Project, became available after completion of the manuscript. By its aid, the stability chart of Fig. 8A may be extended considerably for a positive. To obtain a more uniform vertical spacing (a-axis), $a^{\frac{1}{2}}$ should be plotted instead of a. There are no tabular values of Ce_m, Se_m, Fey_m, Gey_m, Fek_m, Gek_m, and this restricts the use of Mathieu functions in applications. Functions of integral order suitable for tabulation are listed in reference 8. To the list may be added an interpolable table of a, $a^{\frac{1}{2}}$, q, β, μ. This would enable a *large* iso-$\beta\mu$ chart akin to Fig. 11 (but much extended) to be plotted using different coloured inks, thereby rendering visual interpolation possible. If, as mentioned above, $a^{\frac{1}{2}}$ is plotted instead of a, the interpolation is approximately linear when $|q|$ is not too large. A chart of this type would be of inestimable value for solving Mathieu equations.

Acknowledgements. Prof. W. G. Bickley and Mr. T. Lewis undertook the arduous task of reading much of the manuscript. To them I express my sincere thanks for help and advice which has been invaluable. I am indebted to Prof. Bickley for additional terms in (2), (4), (6) § 2.151. My thanks are also due to Prof. T. A. A. Broadbent and Dr. J. C. P. Miller for criticizing certain sections of the manuscript. I take this opportunity of thanking Dr. Gertrude Blanch for pointing out the relations in § 4 of the additional results. She obtained (1)–(6) § 3, and (1), (2) § 8 independently. The whole of the proofs have been read and the analysis checked by Mr. A. L. Meyers. To him I tender my best thanks for the meticulous care which he has exercised, and for his valuable suggestions. I am much indebted to Dr. L. J. Comrie for the loan of books and reprints of papers; also to him and Miss Dorothy Reynolds for checking some of the calculations in Chapter VI, and for computing the numerical data, using analysis in Chapter V, from which the important iso-$\beta\mu$ chart of Figure 11 was plotted. Sir Edmund T. Whittaker kindly loaned me a large number of reprints of papers by various authors, while Mrs. P. Ince kindly gave me copies of the late Prof. E. L. Ince's published works. Prof. A. L. Dixon, Drs. John Dougall, I. M. H. Etherington, Sir Harold Jeffreys, and Miss Ethel M. Harris were good enough to loan me books and memoirs, which I would not have seen otherwise.

It is with pleasure that I acknowledge permission to reproduce the following diagrams and tables in the text:

1. Table 4; *Philosophical Magazine*; paper by S. Goldstein and H. P. Mulholland [57].
2. Figs. 10 A, B; Institute of Radio Engineers (America); paper by F. Maginniss [123].
3. Fig. 25; Institute of Radio Engineers (America); paper by W. L. Barrow, **21**, 1182 (1933).
4. Figs. 41 A, B; Institute of Radio Engineers (America); paper by W. L. Barrow and L. J. Chu, **26**, 1526, 1529 (1938).
5. Fig. 43; Institute of Radio Engineers (America); paper by G. C. Southworth, **25**, 808 (1937).
6. Figs. 44 A, B; *Journal of Applied Physics*; paper by L. J. Chu [22].
7. Figs. 48, 49; *Physical Review*; paper by P. M. Morse and P. J. Rubenstein [144].
8. Appendix II; Mrs. P. Ince and Royal Society, Edinburgh; tables by E. L. Ince [95].

Finally, I wish to thank the Delegates of the Press for their catholicity of outlook in publishing a large book of this kind, at a time when the printing trade has not yet begun to recover from the devastation of war.

N. W. M.

LONDON
October 1946

PREFACE TO THE DOVER EDITION

APART from sundry minor changes, the text is the same as that in the 1951 reprint. Errors and misprints have been corrected, and several references added to Section C on p. 381.

N. W. M.

LONDON
November 1963

CONTENTS

Additional Results, p. 382

Where applicable these should be read in conjunction
with the text

THEORY AND APPLICATION
OF
MATHIEU FUNCTIONS

I

HISTORICAL INTRODUCTION

THE majority of functions used in technical and applied mathematics have originated as the result of investigating practical problems. Mathieu functions were introduced by their originator in 1868 [130], when he determined the vibrational modes of a stretched membrane having an elliptical boundary. The two-dimensional wave equation

$$\frac{\partial^2 V}{\partial x^2} + \frac{\partial^2 V}{\partial y^2} + k_1^2 V = 0 \tag{1}$$

was transformed to elliptical (confocal) coordinates, and then split up into two ordinary differential equations. If $q^{\frac{1}{2}} = \frac{1}{2}k_1 h$, h being the semi-interfocal distance, and a an arbitrary separation constant, the equations take the form

$$\frac{d^2 v}{dz^2} + (a - 2q\cos 2z)v = 0 \tag{2}$$

and

$$\frac{d^2 v}{dz^2} - (a - 2q\cosh 2z)v = 0, \tag{3}†$$

i.e.

$$\frac{d^2 v}{d(iz)^2} + (a - 2q\cos 2zi)v = 0. \tag{4}$$

In Mathieu's problem the parameters a, q were real.

It is evident that (3), the second of the two equations into which (1), expressed in elliptical coordinates, was resolved, may be derived from (2) by writing $\pm zi$ for z, and vice versa. This reciprocal relation is sometimes considered to be a fluke! Equations (2), (3) will be regarded herein as the Mathieu and modified Mathieu equations respectively, for $q > 0$. For the elliptical membrane problem, the appropriate solutions of equation (2) are called (ordinary) Mathieu functions, being periodic in z with period π or 2π. As a consequence of this periodicity, a has special values called characteristic numbers. The corresponding solutions of (3), for the same a as in (2), are known as *modified* Mathieu functions,‡ being derived from the ordinary type

† In reference [103] this is termed the 'modified Mathieu equation'.

‡ Some writers refer to them as 'associated' functions, and others as 'hyperbolic' Mathieu functions. They could be designated Mathieu functions of imaginary argument. In view of the analogy with the derivation of the modified Bessel functions I, K, the term 'modified' seems to be preferable. Also Ince in [85] uses the word 'associated' to define an entirely different set of functions.

by making the argument imaginary. The second independent sets of solutions for the same a are not needed in the membrane problem. They are non-periodic, and those for (2) tend to infinity with z real. Sometimes the solutions of (2), (3) are designated elliptic and hyperbolic cylinder functions, respectively, just as the J-, Y-Bessel functions are termed (circular) cylinder functions.

Following the appearance of Mathieu's work, some ten years elapsed before anything further was published on the subject. In *Kugelfunktionen* [196] Heine (1878) defined the first solutions of integral order of (2) by cosine and sine series, but the coefficients were not calculated. These series fulfil the conditions for Fourier series, but the coefficients are not obtained by integration in the usual way. They have been called Fourier series by many authors. Heine also gave a transcendental equation for the characteristic numbers, pertaining to the first solutions, in the guise of an infinite continued fraction. This form was used to great advantage about half a century later by Goldstein [52], and by Ince [88, 92, 93], for computing the characteristic numbers and the coefficients in the series. Heine also demonstrated that one set of periodic functions of integral order could be expanded in a series of Bessel functions.

G. W. Hill, in a celebrated memoir, investigated the 'Mean motion of the Lunar Perigee' [70] by means of an extended or generalized form of Mathieu equation, namely,

$$\frac{d^2y}{dz^2}+[a-2q\,\psi(2z)]y = 0, \qquad (5)$$

where in Hill's case $-2q\,\psi(2z) = 2[\theta_2\cos 2z+\theta_4\cos 4z+...]$, $a = \theta_0$, the θ being known parameters. The work, done in 1877, was published in 1886. The subject of infinite determinants was introduced into analysis for the first time, and Hill's name is now associated with an equation of form (5).

In 1883 G. Floquet published a general treatment of linear differential equations with periodic coefficients, of which Mathieu's and Hill's equations are cases in point [49]. Lord Rayleigh studied the classical Melde† experiment by aid of Hill's analysis in 1887 [155, 207]. He also dealt with the problem of wave propagation in stratified media, and the oscillations of strings having a periodic distribution of mass [155]. In Melde's experiment one end of a hori-

† *Pogg. Ann.* **109**, 193, 1860.

ːontal thread is fixed, the other being attached to the prong of a massive low-frequency tuning-fork mounted vertically. When the fork moves along the thread, and the tension is suitably adjusted, the thread vibrates at right angles to its length, i.e. transversely, at a frequency *one-half that of the fork*. As we shall see in due course, this *sub-harmonic* of half-frequency is consistent with the periodic solutions of equation (2), of odd integral order, whose period is 2π.

In 1894 Tisserand [213] showed how the solution of (5) could be obtained in the form of a Maclaurin expansion. He also described Lindstedt's method of solving (2) by aid of continued fractions, the convergence of which was investigated by H. Bruns [17]. The theory of Mathieu functions was extended by E. Särchinger in that year [158].

The first appearance of an asymptotic formula for the modified functions in 1898 was due to R. C. Maclaurin [122]. Some years later W. Marshall published a different but more detailed analysis [128]. Neither of these authors obtained the constant multipliers, which are indispensable in numerical work. In 1922, however, Marshall produced the multiplier for his series [129]. D. Hilbert discussed characteristic values and obtained an integral equation, with a discontinuous nucleus, for the periodic solutions of (2) in 1904 [69]. The theory of the functions was treated in certain respects by S. Dannacher in 1906 [26], while W. H. Butts extended the treatment and computed some tabular values in 1908 [19]. In that year B. Sieger published an important paper on the diffraction of electromagnetic waves by an elliptical cylinder. Amongst other topics he dealt with orthogonality, and developed integral equations by means of which he reproduced Heine's solutions in Bessel function series. Using an integral equation with a different nucleus, he derived a solution of equation (3) as a series of Bessel function products, and discussed its convergence [162]. This paper does not seem to have been known to British authors, whose contributions after 1908 sometimes cover similar ground.

It appears that, apart from Sieger's paper, the subject attracted but scant attention in the period 1887–1912, owing possibly to a dearth of physical applications, and to analytical difficulties; for the Mathieu functions cannot be treated in a straightforward way like Bessel or Legendre functions. In 1912, however, E. T. Whittaker started the first systematic study of the subject by a paper read before the International Congress of Mathematicians [184]. Therein he gave an integral equation for one set of the periodic functions of integral order. A similar equation for the modified functions was published in 1908 by Sieger (*supra*), and Whittaker was obviously unaware of this. Next year (1913) Whittaker published a new method of obtaining the general solution of (2) when a is not a characteristic number for a function of integral order [186]. Using this method as a basis, A. W. Young, one of Whittaker's pupils, gave a treatment of general solutions and discussed the question of their stability, i.e. whether the solution tends to zero or to infinity as $z \to +\infty$ [191]. Recurrence formulae for the Mathieu functions cannot be deduced by the direct procedure used for functions of hypergeometric type, e.g. Bessel and Legendre functions. Whittaker, however, evolved a new method, and in 1928 applied it to obtain recurrence relations for the modified Mathieu functions [187].

From 1915 till his early decease in 1941, the chief contributor to the subject was E. L. Ince, a pupil of Whittaker. During this period he published eighteen papers on Mathieu functions and cognate matters. In his first paper (1915) he obtained the second non-periodic solution of equation (2) when a is a characteristic number for the first solution when it has period π, or 2π [80]. Following this he treated Hill's equation on the lines of [186], and obtained formulae different in character from those given by Hill [81-3]. Many aspects of the subject, including characteristic numbers, periodicity, zeros, were covered [87-97]. He introduced the stability chart (Fig. 8A) for functions of integral order in 1925 [88]. The culminating point was perhaps his almost single-handed feat in calculating the characteristic numbers, coefficients in the cosine and sine series for the first solutions of integral order, zeros of these functions, turning-points and values of the functions. The tables occupy some sixty pages of print and appeared in 1932 [95, 96].

A general study of Mathieu's equation was made by J. Dougall in three papers published between 1916 and 1926 [36-8]. As well as a general solution, he obtained asymptotic expansions for the modified functions with large z, and a contour integral which, under certain conditions, degenerates to one for the J-Bessel function. Unaware of Sieger's work in 1908, Dougall derived a solution in terms of Bessel function products. The method of derivation was different from that of Sieger.

Until 1921 the only known periodic solutions of Mathieu's equa-

tion (2) had period π or 2π. In that year E. G. C. Poole generalized
the position and showed that with appropriate values of a for an
assigned q, (2) would admit solutions having period $2s\pi$, s being an
integer $\geqslant 2$ [150]. These solutions *coexist* and their sum, with the
usual arbitrary constant multipliers, constitutes a fundamental
system. About the same time Ince proved that two solutions of
period π or 2π could not coexist (for the same a, q). If the first
solution had period π or 2π, the second would be non-periodic [84].
A different proof of this was given a few years later by Z. Markovic
[126]. He introduced some new integral equations of Volterra type in
1925 [127].

The second solution of (2), a being a characteristic number for
a periodic function (first solution) of integral order, was studied by
S. Dhar in 1921 using a method different from that of Ince [30].
Dhar's publications from 1921 to 1928 cover various aspects of convergence, and integral equations for the second solution [29–35].
Using expansions in Mathieu functions (ordinary and modified), he
reproduced Rayleigh's formula† for the diffraction of electromagnetic
waves due to a long metal cylinder of elliptical cross-section [193].
In 1922 P. Humbert discussed a modified form of Mathieu equation,‡ whose solutions he called 'Mathieu functions of higher order'.
He showed the relation between these and the Gegenbauer polynomials [79].

It often happens that the zeros of functions which occur in practical
applications are essential in connexion with boundary conditions.
The solution for a vibrating circular membrane is expressed in terms
of J-Bessel and circular function products. The zeros of the Bessel
functions determine the vibrational pulsatances and location of the
nodal circles, while those of the circular functions define the positions
of the nodal radii. In the case of an elliptical membrane, the solution
is expressed in terms of modified and ordinary Mathieu function
products. The zeros of the modified functions determine the vibrational pulsatances and confocal nodal ellipses, while those of the
ordinary functions define a system of confocal nodal hyperbolae.
When the eccentricity of the bounding ellipse tends to zero, the nodal
ellipses tend to become nodal circles, and the nodal hyperbolae tend
to nodal radii. Analytically, apart from constant multipliers, the

modified Mathieu functions tend to J-Bessel functions of the same order, and the ordinary functions tend to circular functions.

In 1923 E. Hillé published a lengthy discourse on zeros and cognate matters. He also gave another proof of the non-periodic nature of the second solution of (2), when a is a characteristic number for the first solution of period π or 2π [71]. A table of zeros of eight of these latter functions was published by Ince in 1932 [96]. At the time of writing, there is no table of zeros of the modified functions, but formulae are given herein from which the larger zeros may be computed.

During recent years the problem of frequency modulation in radio transmission has assumed importance, in particular since the frequency was raised to 45 megacycles per second or more. The subject was studied analytically by J. R. Carson in 1922, who dealt with the simple case of a resistanceless oscillatory electrical circuit having a periodically varying capacitance. An approximate differential equation for a circuit with capacitance $C(t) = C_0 + C_1 \cos 2\omega t$, where $C_1 \ll C_0$, is a Mathieu type. Values of the circuital parameters were such that the solution could, with adequate approximation, be expressed as a series of circular functions whose coefficients were J-Bessel functions. These coefficients give the relative amplitudes of the 'side-band frequencies' on each side of the central or 'carrier frequency'. The latter is said to be 'frequency-modulated' [21].

In 1934 A. Erdélyi studied the problem above, when the circuit contained resistance. Solutions were obtained for stable and unstable cases, by aid of integral equations. Both solutions were better approximations than that of Carson, and revealed the fact that 'amplitude modulation' of the 'carrier' occurs as well as 'frequency modulation' [44].

In 1936 Erdélyi obtained a solution of equation (3) by aid of the Laplace integral. He derived another form of asymptotic expansion and gave relationships of the type $y_1(ze^{im\pi}) = e^{\mu m\pi} y_1(z)$, $\mu = ni$, n an integer [47].

In the period 1932–6 W. L. Barrow treated problems on electrical circuits with periodically varying parameters, both analytically and experimentally [2, 3, 4].

Sometimes in applications the parameters of a differential equation are such that it lends itself to approximate methods of solution. In 1923 H. Jeffreys gave an analysis pertaining to approximate solutions of (3). He also obtained asymptotic formulae. The results were applied in an investigation of the vibrational modes of water in a lake whose plan view is elliptical, this problem being of special interest in hydrodynamics. Numerical data were obtained for a number of the lower modes, their periods and the tide heights being computed [101–4].

The making of numerical tables usually receives little encouragement, while the thanks offered by the user are parsimonious rather than plentiful. We have already referred to Ince's philanthropic gesture in computing tabular values. In 1927 S. Goldstein published the results of extensive work on Mathieu functions, and included a set of tables for five of the periodic functions of integral order [52]. Following Heine and Sieger the tabulated functions are defined as sine and cosine series, the coefficients and the characteristic numbers being given for a wide range of q. A new and acceptable normalization of the functions was adopted, this being based upon their orthogonal properties. The same publication contained additional integral equations (akin to those of Sieger and Whittaker), some asymptotic expansions for z large and q large (complete with multipliers), an asymptotic formula for the characteristic numbers,† and formulae for the larger zeros in q of the modified functions. There is also a general discussion relating to the second solution and an extension of Heine's expansions in Bessel function series, the I-type being introduced. In additional papers Goldstein extended Jeffreys's investigation on elliptical lakes, and his own researches on characteristic numbers [53–7].

The problem of eddy currents in a straight conductor of elliptical cross-section was investigated by M. J. O. Strutt in 1927 [167]. He assumed constant current density at the surface. As this is untrue in practice, his analysis is mainly of academic interest. In common with other boundary-condition problems, the wave equation expressed in elliptical coordinates is separable into two Mathieu equations like (2), (3), but in the above problem q is negative imaginary. Strutt has solved a variety of technical problems involving Mathieu functions, e.g. diffraction of plane waves at a slit [173]. In 1929 he published a detailed study of the characteristic exponent μ in Hill's equation (5) [171]. A list of his other works will be found in the references at the end of the book.

† Identical with that found independently by Ince using a different procedure [92, 93].

When experimenting with a moving-coil loud-speaker in 1925, the author found that under certain conditions the coil, although actuated by a sinusoidal current, *moved out of the magnetic field of the magnet.* The analysis, published in 1933, involved a Mathieu equation. Its solution for the axial displacement of the coil was characterized by a dominant term having a period much greater than that of the driving current. Reduction in amplitude of the latter resulted in an increase in the period of the dominant term, and vice versa [202].

Oseen's approximate differential equation is familiar in hydrodynamics. As might be anticipated from this equation, calculation of the vorticity in a viscous fluid flowing past a very long elliptical cylinder in its path necessitates the use of Mathieu functions. This subject was studied by M. Ray in 1936 [154], and by D. Meksyn in 1937 [137]. In 1938 T. Lewis published a general treatment of the problem of circular and elliptical cylinders, and a flat plate in a viscous fluid [116]. He showed that the solution given by Meksyn required modification to avoid infinite circulation of fluid.

About fifty years ago, the transmission of electromagnetic waves within hollow metal cylinders was contemplated by J. J. Thomson.† O. J. Lodge‡ tested the theory experimentally using a hollow metal cylinder having a spark gap and transmitter at one end, the other being open. Three years later Lord Rayleigh§ showed that there was a plurality of modes in which electromagnetic waves could be transmitted within a perfectly conducting uniform circular tube of unlimited length. Using modern electronic devices, it is comparatively easy to incite the transmission modes of lower order within a hollow metal cylinder, now called a 'wave guide'. No cylinder is perfectly circular, so to ascertain the influence of deviation from circularity, L. J. Chu in 1938 investigated the propagation of electromagnetic waves within a hollow cylinder of elliptical cross-section. As might be expected, the final result entailed products of ordinary and modified Mathieu functions of integral order, the former having period π, 2π [22].

† *Recent Researches* (1893).   ‡ *Proc. Roy. Institution,* **14**, 321, 1894.
§ *Phil. Mag.* **43**, 125, 1897.

In 1940 W. G. Bickley published new solutions of (3) with $q < 0$, these being expressed as expansions in I- and K-Bessel functions [6]. He also gave integral and asymptotic formulae for these solutions. During the same year J. G. Brainerd and C. N. Weygandt published data regarding general solutions of equation (2), when a is *not* a characteristic number for functions of integral order. The data were given up to $z = 0\cdot3\pi$, using the Maclaurin method of solution (see § 4.40), with terms as far as $y^{(21)}(0)$. Beyond $z = 0\cdot3\pi$ the solutions, given in the form of curves, were extended by alternative means [12].

What precedes is merely a brief survey of salient matters relating to Mathieu functions and their applications to technical problems. The work of other authors, too extensive to be examined in detail, is given in titular form in the list of references on pp. 373–81.

The occurrence of Mathieu functions in practical applications may be divided into two main categories. First there are the boundary-condition problems arising from solution of the two-dimensional wave equation (1), when expressed in elliptical coordinates. As stated previously, this yields a pair of Mathieu equations like (2), (3).† The appropriate solution of (2) is usually a periodic Mathieu function of integral order, while that of (3), in the cases of the elliptical membrane and the wave guide, is obtained by making the argument of this solution imaginary. Secondly there are what may be regarded as initial-value problems, in which only one equation like (2) is involved. Usually a is not then a characteristic number for a function of integral order having period π or 2π, and the solution is general in type. It may (a) have period $2s\pi$, s an integer $\geqslant 2$, (b) be non-periodic but bounded as $z \to +\infty$, (c) be non-periodic but unbounded as $z \to +\infty$. Frequency modulation and the moving-coil loud-speaker (see Chap. XV) are examples of the class of problem in question. The majority of applications, to date, pertain to the first category and involve the wave equation.

† In the analysis of Melde's experiment, the differential equation is in x and t coordinates, the solutions of the two resulting equations being circular functions in x, and periodic Mathieu functions of integral order in t.

PART I

THEORY OF MATHIEU FUNCTIONS

II

FUNCTIONS OF INTEGRAL ORDER

2.10. Canonical form of Mathieu's equation. In solving the problem of the elliptical membrane [130], Mathieu obtained a differential equation of the type

$$\frac{d^2y}{dz^2} + (a - 2q \cos 2z)y = 0. \tag{1}$$

We shall regard this as the canonical form—ruled by general usage—of the equation. At times it may be expedient to replace $+q$ by k^2. The parameters a, $q = k^2$, will be limited to real numbers, unless stated otherwise, but z is usually unrestricted. The equation is a particular case of a linear type of the second order with periodic coefficients. Its solution takes different forms according to the values of a, q. For the present we shall confine our attention to solutions having period π or 2π in z. In the membranal problem, the displacement from the equilibrium position is a periodic function of one of the coordinates.[†] Thus if q is assigned, y will have period π or 2π in z, provided a has one of an infinite sequence of particular numbers.

2.11. Solution of (1) § 2.10 when $q = 0$. Under this condition the equation becomes

$$\frac{d^2y}{dz^2} + ay = 0, \tag{1}$$

and it is convenient that the solution of (1) § 2.10 should then reduce to $\cos mz$ or $\sin mz$. Accordingly we put $a = m^2$, $m = 1, 2, 3,...$, thereby obtaining the pairs of distinct solutions $+\cos z$, $+\sin z$; $+\cos 2z$, $+\sin 2z$; and so on. When $m = 0$, we take the respective solutions to be $+1$, 0. Also *until* and *unless* stated otherwise, we shall adopt the convention that the coefficient of $\cos mz$ and $\sin mz$ is unity for all q [130].

[†] For a circular membrane the displacement at any radius depends upon $\genfrac{}{}{0pt}{}{\cos}{\sin}(m\theta)$ and is, therefore, a periodic function of θ [202, p. 27]. The displacement of an elliptical membrane is periodic in the elliptical coordinate η (z in (1)), as shown in § 16.11.

2.12. Dependence of a upon q for a periodic solution. When $q \neq 0$, a, q must be interrelated for the solution of (1) § 2.10 to have period π or 2π, so a is a function of q. If we write

$$a = m^2 + \alpha_1 q + \alpha_2 q^2 + \alpha_3 q^3 + ..., \tag{1}$$

the desired form $a = m^2$ is obtained when $q = 0$, and the equation then reduces to

$$\frac{d^2y}{dz^2} + m^2y = 0, \tag{2}$$

whose solutions are $\pm \cos mz$, $\pm \sin mz$. Conventionally we adopt a *positive* sign.

2.13. Periodic solution of the first kind. To illustrate *one* method of finding a particular periodic solution of (1) § 2.10, we take the case where $a = m^2 = 1$ when $q = 0$. Then by (1) § 2.12 we have for $q \gtrless 0$

$$a = 1 + \alpha_1 q + \alpha_2 q^2 + \alpha_3 q^3 + ... \tag{1}$$

Since the solution is to reduce to, say, $\cos z$ when q vanishes, we assume that

$$y = \cos z + q c_1(z) + q^2 c_2(z) + q^3 c_3(z) + ..., \tag{2}†$$

c_1, c_2,... being functions of z to be determined. Substituting (2) into (1) § 2.10 and using the value of a from (1) above, we get

$$\left.\begin{aligned}
y'' &= -\cos z + q c_1'' + q^2 c_2'' + q^3 c_3'' + ...,\\
ay &= \cos z + q(c_1 + \alpha_1 \cos z) + q^2(c_2 + \alpha_1 c_1 + \alpha_2 \cos z) +\\
&\quad + q^3(c_3 + \alpha_1 c_2 + \alpha_2 c_1 + \alpha_3 \cos z) + ...,\\
-(2q \cos 2z)y &= -q(\cos z + \cos 3z) - 2q^2 c_1 \cos 2z -\\
&\quad\quad\quad\quad - 2q^3 c_2 \cos 2z - ....
\end{aligned}\right\} \tag{3}$$

Equating coefficients of like powers of q to zero gives

$$q^0 \qquad\qquad\qquad \cos z - \cos z \equiv 0, \tag{4}$$

$$q \qquad\qquad c_1'' + c_1 - \cos 3z + (\alpha_1 - 1)\cos z = 0, \tag{5}$$

of which the particular integral corresponding to $(\alpha_1 - 1)\cos z$ is the

---

† In ref. [158] it is shown that the solutions of Mathieu's equation, having period π or 2π consist entirely of cosine or sine terms, and not a combination of the two. In ref. [223] it is shown that if one solution is even, the other must be odd. Thus two independent even or two independent odd solutions cannot occur. The only singularity of (1) § 2.10 is an essential one at infinity due to $\cos 2z$. Hence every solution is an integral function of z.

non-periodic function $\frac{1}{2}(1-\alpha_1)z\sin z$. Since y is to be periodic, this term must vanish, so

$$\alpha_1 = 1, \tag{6}$$

while
$$c_1'' + c_1 = \cos 3z. \tag{7}$$

Now the particular integral of $v'' + v = A\cos mz$ is $-A\cos mz/(m^2-1)$ $(m \neq 1)$, so with $A = 1$ and $m = 3$,

$$c_1 = -\frac{1}{8}\cos 3z. \tag{8}$$

Inclusion of $\frac{\sin}{\cos}z$ [complementary function of (7)] in (8) would involve a term in $q\frac{\sin}{\cos}z$ in the solution. By §2.11 the coefficient of $\cos z$ is to be unity for all q; also $\sin z$ is odd. Hence the C.F. of (7) and subsequent equations is omitted.

q^2
$$c_2'' + c_2 + \alpha_1 c_1 - 2c_1\cos 2z + \alpha_2\cos z = 0. \tag{9}$$

Substituting for α_1, c_1 from (6), (8) and expressing $\cos 2z\cos 3z$ as a sum of two cosines, we get

$$c_2'' + c_2 - \frac{1}{8}\cos 3z + \frac{1}{8}\cos 5z + \left(\frac{1}{8} + \alpha_2\right)\cos z = 0. \tag{10}$$

As before, the particular integral pertaining to $(\frac{1}{8} + \alpha_2)\cos z$ is non-periodic, so

$$\alpha_2 = -\frac{1}{8}, \tag{11}$$

while
$$c_2'' + c_2 = \frac{1}{8}\cos 3z - \frac{1}{8}\cos 5z. \tag{12}$$

By aid of the general formula above, the particular integral is

$$c_2 = -\frac{1}{64}\cos 3z + \frac{1}{192}\cos 5z. \tag{13}$$

Proceeding in this way leads to the results:

$$\alpha_3 = -\frac{1}{64}, \qquad c_3 = -\frac{1}{512}\left(\frac{1}{3}\cos 3z - \frac{4}{9}\cos 5z + \frac{1}{18}\cos 7z\right), \tag{14}$$

$$\alpha_4 = -\frac{1}{1536},$$

$$c_4 = \frac{1}{4096}\left(\frac{11}{9}\cos 3z + \frac{1}{6}\cos 5z - \frac{1}{12}\cos 7z + \frac{1}{180}\cos 9z\right), \tag{15}$$

and so on.

Substituting for c_1, c_2,... in (2) gives a solution of Mathieu's

equation, periodic in z, with period 2π. It is denoted by $\text{ce}_1(z,q)$†
and represented by the series

$$\text{ce}_1(z,q) = \cos z - \frac{1}{8}q\cos 3z + \frac{1}{64}q^2\left(-\cos 3z + \frac{1}{3}\cos 5z\right) -$$

$$-\frac{1}{512}q^3\left(\frac{1}{3}\cos 3z - \frac{4}{9}\cos 5z + \frac{1}{18}\cos 7z\right) +$$

$$+\frac{1}{4096}q^4\left(\frac{11}{9}\cos 3z + \frac{1}{6}\cos 5z - \frac{1}{12}\cos 7z + \frac{1}{180}\cos 9z\right) + O(q^5). \quad (16)$$

The value of a necessary to yield this solution is found by substituting the α into (1). Then we get

$$a = 1 + q - \frac{1}{8}q^2 - \frac{1}{64}q^3 - \frac{1}{1536}q^4 + \frac{11}{36864}q^5 + O(q^6). \quad (17)$$

For a given q, the value of a found from (17) is called the *characteristic number* of the Mathieu function $\text{ce}_1(z,q)$. When $q = 0$, $a = 1$,
and the r.h.s. of (16) reduces to $\cos z$.

The notation $\text{ce}_m(z,q)$ signifies a cosine type of Mathieu function
of order m, which reduces to a multiple of $\cos mz$ when $q = 0$. Since
m may be any positive integer, there is an infinite number of solutions of type (16). These functions are even in z, being unchanged
if $-z$ is written for z.

2.14. Another periodic solution of the first kind.
In accor-
dance with our convention in § 2.11, if $m^2 = 1$, the second solution of
(1) § 2.10 reduces to $\sin z$ when $q = 0$. If we assume a solution

$$y = \sin z + q s_1(z) + q^2 s_2(z) + q^3 s_3(z) + \cdots \quad (1)$$

and proceed as in § 2.13, we obtain a sine type of Mathieu function
designated $\text{se}_1(z,q)$.‡ Thus

$$\text{se}_1(z,q) = \sin z - \frac{1}{8}q\sin 3z + \frac{1}{64}q^2\left(\sin 3z + \frac{1}{3}\sin 5z\right) -$$

$$-\frac{1}{512}q^3\left(\frac{1}{3}\sin 3z + \frac{4}{9}\sin 5z + \frac{1}{18}\sin 7z\right) +$$

$$+\frac{1}{4096}q^4\left(-\frac{11}{9}\sin 3z + \frac{1}{6}\sin 5z + \frac{1}{12}\sin 7z + \frac{1}{180}\sin 9z\right) + O(q^5), \quad (2)$$

---

† 'ce' is an abbreviation of 'cosine-elliptic', introduced by E. T. Whittaker.
‡ 'se' is an abbreviation of 'sine-elliptic'.

provided

$$a = 1 - q - \frac{1}{8}q^2 + \frac{1}{64}q^3 - \frac{1}{1536}q^4 - \frac{11}{36864}q^5 + O(q^6). \qquad (3)$$

This particular value of a is the *characteristic number* for the Mathieu function $\mathrm{se}_1(z, q)$, periodic in z with period 2π, which reduces to $\sin z$ when $q = 0$. Since $\mathrm{se}_1(z, q) = -\mathrm{se}_1(-z, q)$, the function is odd in z.

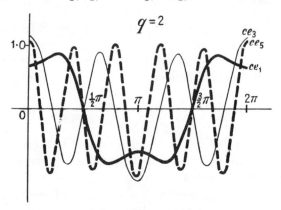

Fig. 1. Graphs of $\mathrm{ce}_1(z, 2)$, $\mathrm{ce}_3(z, 2)$, $\mathrm{ce}_5(z, 2)$ over a period 2π.

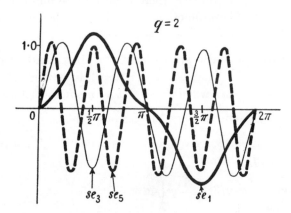

Fig. 2. Graphs of $\mathrm{se}_1(z, 2)$, $\mathrm{se}_3(z, 2)$, $\mathrm{se}_5(z, 2)$ over a period 2π.

If in (16) § 2.13 we write $(\frac{1}{2}\pi - z)$ for z and $-q$ for q, (2) above is reproduced, and vice versa. Since the values of a differ for the two periodic functions ce_1, se_1, these functions are not solutions of the same equation except when $q = 0$. The graphs of these functions for $q = 2$ are shown in Figs. 1, 2.

2.150. Periodic solution of (1) § 2.10 of order m. To derive this, we assume for the cosine type of function that

$$y = \cos mz + q c_1(z) + q^2 c_2(z) + q^3 c_3(z) + \dots \tag{1}$$

and

$$a = m^2 + \alpha_1 q + \alpha_2 q^2 + \alpha_3 q^3 + \dots . \tag{2}$$

The solution obtained is either of the class $ce_{2n}(z, q)$ or $ce_{2n+1}(z, q)$, according as m in (2) is even or odd. If $m = 2$, we find that

$$ce_2(z, q) = \cos 2z - \frac{1}{8} q \left(\frac{2}{3} \cos 4z - 2 \right) + \frac{1}{384} q^2 \cos 6z -$$

$$- \frac{1}{512} q^3 \left(\frac{1}{45} \cos 8z + \frac{43}{27} \cos 4z + \frac{40}{3} \right) +$$

$$+ \frac{1}{4096} q^4 \left(\frac{1}{540} \cos 10z + \frac{293}{540} \cos 6z \right) + O(q^5), \tag{3}$$

with

$$a = 4 + \frac{5}{12} q^2 - \frac{763}{13824} q^4 + \frac{10\,02401}{796\,26240} q^6 + O(q^8). \tag{4}$$

Then a reduces to 4 and ce_2 to $\cos 2z$ when $q = 0$, which is in accordance with our convention in § 2.11. When $q \neq 0$, the function has a constant term whose value is

$$\frac{1}{4} q - \frac{5}{192} q^3 + \frac{1363}{2\,21184} q^5 + O(q^7). \tag{5}$$

The graph of $ce_2(z, 2)$ is shown in Fig. 3. This function is periodic in z with period π.

In the particular case of $m = 0$ in (1), (2), we obtain

$$ce_0(z, q) = 1 - \frac{1}{2} q \cos 2z + \frac{1}{32} q^2 \cos 4z - \frac{1}{128} q^3 \left(\frac{1}{9} \cos 6z - 7 \cos 2z \right) +$$

$$+ \frac{1}{73728} q^4 (\cos 8z - 320 \cos 4z) + O(q^5), \tag{6}$$

with

$$a = - \frac{1}{2} q^2 + \frac{7}{128} q^4 - \frac{29}{2304} q^6 + O(q^8). \tag{7}$$

Then $a = 0$ and $ce_0 = 1$ for $q = 0$. Here again the function has a constant term. In general this holds for all the functions ce_{2n}, but not for ce_{2n+1}.

To derive the sine type function of order m, replace $\cos mz$ in (1) by $\sin mz$ and $c_r(z)$ by $s_r(z)$. The solution obtained is either se_{2n+1} or

se_{2n+2},† according as m is odd or even. If $m = 2$, we have

$$\text{se}_2(z, q) = \sin 2z - \frac{1}{12} q \sin 4z + \frac{1}{384} q^2 \sin 6z -$$

$$- \frac{1}{512} q^3 \left(\frac{1}{45} \sin 8z - \frac{5}{27} \sin 4z \right) +$$

$$+ \frac{1}{4096} q^4 \left(\frac{1}{540} \sin 10z - \frac{37}{540} \sin 6z \right) + O(q^5), \quad (8)$$

with
$$a = 4 - \frac{1}{12} q^2 + \frac{5}{13824} q^4 + O(q^6). \quad (9)$$

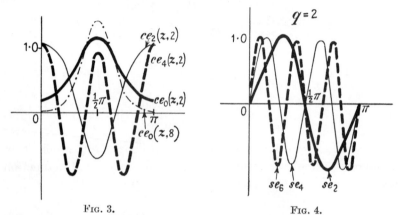

FIG. 3.   FIG. 4.

FIG. 3. Graphs of $\text{ce}_0(z, 2)$, $\text{ce}_0(z, 8)$, $\text{ce}_2(z, 2)$, $\text{ce}_4(z, 2)$ over a period π. For q finite > 0, $\text{ce}_0 > 0$. As $q \to +\infty$, $\text{ce}_0(m\pi, q) \to 0$.

FIG. 4. Graphs of $\text{se}_2(z, 2)$, $\text{se}_4(z, 2)$, $\text{se}_6(z, 2)$ over a period π.

When $q = 0$, a reduces to 4 and $\text{se}_2(z, 0) = \sin 2z$. The function $\text{se}_2(z, q)$ is periodic in z with period π. This is shown graphically in Fig. 4.

2.151. Formulae for a. We designate the characteristic numbers for $\text{ce}_m(z, q)$ and $\text{se}_m(z, q)$ by a_m, b_m respectively. Then

$$a_0 = -\frac{1}{2} q^2 + \frac{7}{128} q^4 - \frac{29}{2304} q^6 + \frac{68687}{188\,74368} q^8 + O(q^{10}). \quad (1)$$

$$b_1 = 1 - q - \frac{1}{8} q^2 + \frac{1}{64} q^3 - \frac{1}{1536} q^4 - \frac{11}{36864} q^5 +$$

$$+ \frac{49}{5\,89824} q^6 - \frac{55}{94\,37184} q^7 - \frac{265}{1132\,46208} q^8 + O(q^9). \quad (2)$$

a_1 = write $-q$ for q in (2). $\qquad\qquad\qquad\qquad\qquad\qquad\qquad$ (3)

† The significance of $2n+2$ in place of $2n$ is that n represents the number of real zeros of ce_{2n}, ce_{2n+1}, se_{2n+1}, se_{2n+2} in the open interval $0 < z < \frac{1}{2}\pi$ (see Chap. XII).

$$b_2 = 4 - \frac{1}{12}q^2 + \frac{5}{13824}q^4 - \frac{289}{796\,26240}q^6 + \frac{21391}{45\,86471\,42400}q^8 + O(q^{10}).$$

(4)

$$a_2 = 4 + \frac{5}{12}q^2 - \frac{763}{13824}q^4 + \frac{10\,02401}{796\,26240}q^6 - \frac{16690\,68401}{45\,86471\,42400}q^8 + O(q^{10}).$$

(5)

$$b_3 = 9 + \frac{1}{16}q^2 - \frac{1}{64}q^3 + \frac{13}{20480}q^4 + \frac{5}{16384}q^5 - \frac{1961}{235\,92960}q^6 +$$

$$+ \frac{609}{1048\,57600}q^7 + O(q^8). \quad (6)$$

$a_3 = $ write $-q$ for q in (6). (7)

$$b_4 = 16 + \frac{1}{30}q^2 - \frac{317}{8\,64000}q^4 + \frac{10049}{27216\,00000}q^6 + O(q^8).$$

(8)

$$a_4 = 16 + \frac{1}{30}q^2 + \frac{433}{8\,64000}q^4 - \frac{5701}{27216\,00000}q^6 + O(q^8).$$

(9)

$$b_5 = 25 + \frac{1}{48}q^2 + \frac{11}{7\,74144}q^4 - \frac{1}{1\,47456}q^5 + \frac{37}{8918\,13888}q^6 + O(q^7). \quad (10)$$

$a_5 = $ write $-q$ for q in (10). (11)

$$b_6 = 36 + \frac{1}{70}q^2 + \frac{187}{439\,04000}q^4 - \frac{58\,61633}{9293\,59872\,00000}q^6 + O(q^8). \quad (12)$$

$$a_6 = 36 + \frac{1}{70}q^2 + \frac{187}{439\,04000}q^4 + \frac{67\,43617}{9293\,59872\,00000}q^6 + O(q^8). \quad (13)$$

When $m \geqslant 7$, the following formula is correct as far as and including the term in q^6:

$$a_m, b_m = m^2 + \frac{1}{2(m^2-1)}q^2 + \frac{5m^2+7}{32(m^2-1)^3(m^2-4)}q^4 +$$

$$+ \frac{9m^4+58m^2+29}{64(m^2-1)^5(m^2-4)(m^2-9)}q^6 + \dots . \quad (14)$$

These formulae may be used to calculate a when q is small enough and of either sign. For equal accuracy, q may increase with increase in m. It must not be inferred from (14) that when $m \geqslant 7$, $a_m = b_m$. Series (12), (13) for b_6, a_6 are identical *up to* $O(q^4)$, but *not* thereafter.† An extension of (14) to higher orders of q would show the same behaviour. As $|q| \to 0$, $a_m \to b_m$, but for $|q| > 0$, $(a_m - b_m) \neq 0$,

† For $m \geqslant 3$, the series for a_m, b_m are identical up to q^{m-1} or q^{m-2} according as m is odd or even.

although it is very small near $q = 0$. Under this condition the characteristic curves for ce_m, se_m are substantially coincident (see Fig. 8). In (14) when m^2 is much greater than any subsequent term, a_m, b_m are almost constant, so the characteristic curves are practically parallel to the q-axis.

2.152. Remarks on the periodic Mathieu functions of integral order.

1. The functions ce_{2n}, $n = 0, 1, 2,...$, have period π. There is a constant term in the series, which is a function of q. As a consequence, ce_0 is never negative, although oscillatory.
2. The functions ce_{2n+1}, $n = 0, 1, 2,...$, have period 2π. There is no constant term in the series.
3. The functions se_{2n+1}, $n = 0, 1, 2,...$, have period 2π. There is no constant term in the series.
4. The functions se_{2n+2}, $n = 0, 1, 2,...$, have period π. There is no constant term in the series.
5. All the above functions have n real zeros in $0 < z < \frac{1}{2}\pi$.

2.153. Dynamical illustration.

The differential equation may be written

$$\frac{d^2y}{dt^2} + ay = (2q\cos 2t)y. \qquad (1)$$

Referring to Fig. 5 (A), if $a = s/m$, $2q = f_0/m$, (1) becomes

$$my'' + sy = (f_0\cos 2t)y, \qquad (2)$$

which is the differential equation of the mechanism illustrated there, provided $y/l \ll 1$, $\omega = 1$. A mass m is fixed to a massless helical spring of stiffness s, and driven along the linear axis of the spring by a force $(f_0\cos 2t)y$, which depends upon the displacement y. If m, s, f_0 have the appropriate values, y may take any of the forms ce_{2n}, ce_{2n+1}, se_{2n+1}, se_{2n+2}. Suppose $y = ce_1(t, q)$, then the motion is described by (16) § 2.13, and the component $\cos t$ is a *sub-harmonic* of $\cos 2t$ in (2) above. This remark applies also if m, s, f_0 are such that $y = se_1(t, q)$, by virtue of the component $\sin t$ in (2) § 2.14. Hence in any system (dynamical, electrical, etc.) represented by (2), if the parameters a, q have certain interrelated values, there will be a sub-harmonic of $f_0\cos 2t$. In any event, so long as the parameters are those for a function having period π, 2π, the displacement (or its equivalent) has an infinite number of harmonic components corresponding to the various terms in the series, e.g. (16) § 2.13, (2) § 2.14, (3) § 2.150. Additional comment is made in §§ 15.40, 15.41.

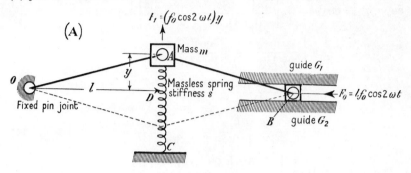

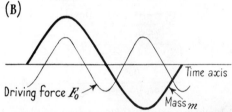

FIG. 5. (A) Schematic diagram (plan) of mechanism illustrating Mathieu's equation. (B) Curves illustrating motion of m and the point B in Fig. (A) when a sub-harmonic of pulsatance ω occurs.

2.16. Mathieu functions of fractional order.†

We define a function of order ν (real but either rational or irrational and positive), to be one which satisfies Mathieu's equation and reduces to $\cos \nu z$, $\sin \nu z$ when $q = 0$. The normalization in this section corresponds to that of § 2.11, so the coefficient of $\cos \nu z$, $\sin \nu z$ is unity for *all* q. If we assume that

$$\mathrm{ce}_\nu(z, q) = \cos \nu z + \sum_{r=1}^{\infty} q^r c_r(z), \tag{1}$$

$$\mathrm{se}_\nu(z, q) = \sin \nu z + \sum_{r=1}^{\infty} q^r s_r(z), \tag{2}$$

$$a = \nu^2 + \sum_{r=1}^{\infty} \alpha_r q^r, \tag{3}$$

† Although the title of this chapter implies functions of integral order only, those of fractional order are introduced here because their expansions *under the normalization of* § 2.11 are obtained in ascending powers of q by a procedure akin to that used for the former. A different definition is given in § 4.71 under the normalization of § 2.21.

and proceed analytically as in §2.13, the following results are obtained:

$$\mathrm{ce}_\nu(z,q) = \cos\nu z - \frac{1}{4}q\left[\frac{\cos(\nu+2)z}{(\nu+1)} - \frac{\cos(\nu-2)z}{(\nu-1)}\right] +$$

$$+\frac{1}{32}q^2\left[\frac{\cos(\nu+4)z}{(\nu+1)(\nu+2)} + \frac{\cos(\nu-4)z}{(\nu-1)(\nu-2)}\right] -$$

$$-\frac{1}{128}q^3\left[\frac{(\nu^2+4\nu+7)\cos(\nu+2)z}{(\nu-1)(\nu+1)^3(\nu+2)} - \frac{(\nu^2-4\nu+7)\cos(\nu-2)z}{(\nu+1)(\nu-1)^3(\nu-2)} +\right.$$

$$\left.+\frac{\cos(\nu+6)z}{3(\nu+1)(\nu+2)(\nu+3)} - \frac{\cos(\nu-6)z}{3(\nu-1)(\nu-2)(\nu-3)}\right] +..., \quad (4)$$

$$\mathrm{se}_\nu(z,q) = \sin\nu z - \frac{1}{4}q\left[\frac{\sin(\nu+2)z}{(\nu+1)} - \frac{\sin(\nu-2)z}{(\nu-1)}\right] +$$

$$+\frac{1}{32}q^2\left[\frac{\sin(\nu+4)z}{(\nu+1)(\nu+2)} + \frac{\sin(\nu-4)z}{(\nu-1)(\nu-2)}\right] -..., \quad (5)$$

$$a = \nu^2 + \frac{1}{2(\nu^2-1)}q^2 + \frac{(5\nu^2+7)}{32(\nu^2-1)^3(\nu^2-4)}q^4 +$$

$$+\frac{9\nu^4+58\nu^2+29}{64(\nu^2-1)^5(\nu^2-4)(\nu^2-9)}q^6 +.... \quad (6)$$

These formulae are suitable for computation when $q^2/2(\nu^2-1) \ll \nu^2$, $\nu > 0$. a has the same value for both solutions for any q, so (4), (5) coexist, and are linearly independent. Thus the complete solution with two arbitrary constants is

$$y = A\,\mathrm{ce}_\nu(z,q) + B\,\mathrm{se}_\nu(z,q), \quad (7)$$

provided ν is non-integral. (4), (5) constitute a fundamental system.

Since (6) is even in q, the characteristic curves, showing the relationship between a, q, for $\mathrm{ce}_\nu(z,q)$, $\mathrm{se}_\nu(z,q)$ are symmetrical about the a-axis. Put $\nu = (m+\beta)$, m being a positive integer, and $0 < \beta < 1$. If $\beta = p/s$, a rational fraction in its lowest terms, the functions have period $2\pi s$ or πs in z, according as p is odd or even, $s \geqslant 2$. If β is irrational, the functions are non-periodic, but they are bounded and tend neither to zero nor infinity as $z \to +\infty$.

2.17. Preferred form of series for $\mathrm{ce}_m(z,q)$, $\mathrm{se}_m(z,q)$. The form of the series given hitherto precludes the application of standard convergence tests. In [180] it is shown that by constructing a 'fonction majorante', the series for $\mathrm{ce}_0(z,q)$ converges if $|4q|^2 < 1$. This is the only case which has been treated. Generally the series *appear*

to converge if q is small, but diverge when it is large enough. The preferred form of the series is given below [52, 88, 95, 162, 197] for q positive:

Characteristic
number

$$\text{ce}_{2n}(z, q) = \sum_{r=0}^{\infty} A_{2r}^{(2n)} \cos 2rz \qquad (a_{2n}) \qquad (1)$$

$$\text{ce}_{2n+1}(z, q) = \sum_{r=0}^{\infty} A_{2r+1}^{(2n+1)} \cos(2r+1)z \qquad (a_{2n+1}) \qquad (2)$$

$$\text{se}_{2n+1}(z, q) = \sum_{r=0}^{\infty} B_{2r+1}^{(2n+1)} \sin(2r+1)z \qquad (b_{2n+1}) \qquad (3)$$

$$\text{se}_{2n+2}(z, q) = \sum_{r=0}^{\infty} B_{2r+2}^{(2n+2)} \sin(2r+2)z \qquad (b_{2n+2}) \qquad (4)$$

In these series A, B are functions of q. This will be evident if we express (16) § 2.13 in the form (2), with $n = 0$. Then

$$\text{ce}_1(z, q) = A_1 \cos z + A_3 \cos 3z + A_5 \cos 5z + ..., \qquad (5)$$

where under the convention of § 2.11

$$A_1 = 1 \text{ for all } q; \quad A_3 = -\frac{1}{8}q\left(1 + \frac{1}{8}q + \frac{1}{192}q^2 - \frac{11}{4608}q^3 + ...\right);$$

$$A_5 = \frac{1}{192}q^2\left(1 + \frac{1}{6}q + \frac{1}{128}q^2 + ...\right), \quad \text{and so on.}$$

When the A, B are obtained by the method used in § 3.13, and the solutions are normalized in accordance with § 2.21, their convergence is readily demonstrated. This is left until § 3.21.

2.18. Changing the sign of q. If in (1) § 2.10 we write $\pm(\frac{1}{2}\pi \pm z)$ for z, it becomes

$$y'' + (a + 2q \cos 2z)y = 0. \qquad (1)$$

Consequently the solutions of (1) § 2.10 with period π, 2π, q being negative, are obtained if the above substitution is made in (1)–(4) § 2.17. Hence, standardizing on $(\frac{1}{2}\pi - z)$, we get [52, 95]:

$$\text{ce}_{2n}(z, -q) = (-1)^n \text{ce}_{2n}(\tfrac{1}{2}\pi - z, q)$$

$$= (-1)^n \sum_{r=0}^{\infty} (-1)^r A_{2r}^{(2n)} \cos 2rz \qquad (a_{2n}), \qquad (2)$$

$$\text{ce}_{2n+1}(z, -q) = (-1)^n \text{se}_{2n+1}(\tfrac{1}{2}\pi - z, q)$$

$$= (-1)^n \sum_{r=0}^{\infty} (-1)^r B_{2r+1}^{(2n+1)} \cos(2r+1)z \qquad (b_{2n+1}), \qquad (3)$$

$$\mathrm{se}_{2n+1}(z, -q) = (-1)^n \, \mathrm{ce}_{2n+1}(\tfrac{1}{2}\pi - z, q)$$

$$= (-1)^n \sum_{r=0}^{\infty} (-1)^r A_{2r+1}^{(2n+1)} \sin(2r+1)z \quad (a_{2n+1}), \quad (4)$$

$$\mathrm{se}_{2n+2}(z, -q) = (-1)^n \, \mathrm{se}_{2n+2}(\tfrac{1}{2}\pi - z, q)$$

$$= (-1)^n \sum_{r=0}^{\infty} (-1)^r B_{2r+2}^{(2n+2)} \sin(2r+2)z \quad (b_{2n+2}). \quad (5)$$

Since $\mathrm{ce}_{2n+1}(z, -q)$, $\mathrm{se}_{2n+1}(z, -q)$ entail cosine and sine series, respectively, they are derived from $\mathrm{se}_{2n+1}(z, q)$ and $\mathrm{ce}_{2n+1}(z, q)$. Accordingly the A, B, and the characteristic numbers are interchanged, i.e. (A, a) and (B, b) accompany each other. The multiplier $(-1)^n$ ensures that when $q = 0$, the functions reduce to $+\cos mz$ or $+\sin mz$ as the case may be.

Any linear differential equation of the second order has two linearly independent solutions, that is to say, they are not proportional. All solutions of integral order obtained hitherto are of the first kind. The second solutions require separate consideration, and being of less practical importance than the first kind, are treated in Chapter VII.

2.19. Orthogonality of the periodic functions ce_m, se_m. Let y_1, y_2 be solutions of

$$y'' + (a - 2q\cos 2z)y = 0, \quad (1)$$

for the same value of q, but usually different values of a, e.g. a_1, a_2. Then

$$y_1'' + (a_1 - 2q\cos 2z)y_1 = 0 \quad \text{and} \quad y_2'' + (a_2 - 2q\cos 2z)y_2 = 0. \quad (2)$$

Multiplying the first of these equations by y_2, the second by y_1, and subtracting, gives

$$y_1'' y_2 - y_2'' y_1 = (a_2 - a_1)y_1 y_2. \quad (3)$$

Integrating both sides of (3) between the limits z_1, z_2, we get

$$\int_{z_1}^{z_2} y_2 \, dy_1' - \int_{z_1}^{z_2} y_1 \, dy_2' = (a_2 - a_1) \int_{z_1}^{z_2} y_1 y_2 \, dz, \quad (4)$$

which after integration by parts becomes

$$[y_1' y_2 - y_2' y_1]_{z_1}^{z_2} = (a_2 - a_1) \int_{z_1}^{z_2} y_1 y_2 \, dz. \quad (5)$$

For a given q, the a corresponding to $y_1 = \mathrm{ce}_m(z, q)$, $y_2 = \mathrm{ce}_p(z, q)$,

$m \neq p$, are different. These functions have period π or 2π, so with $z_1 = 0$, $z_2 = 2\pi$, the l.h.s. of (5) vanishes. Hence, if $m \neq p$,

$$\int_0^{2\pi} \mathrm{ce}_m(z,q)\mathrm{ce}_p(z,q)\,dz = 0. \tag{6}$$

When $m = 2n$, an even integer, from (1) § 2.17, we have

$$\int_0^{2\pi} \mathrm{ce}_{2n}^2(z,q)\,dz = \int_0^{2\pi} \sum_{r=0}^{\infty} [A_{2r}^{(2n)} \cos 2rz]^2\,dz = \sum_{r=0}^{\infty} \int_0^{2\pi} [A_{2r}^{(2n)}]^2 \cos^2 2rz\,dz, \tag{7}$$

since by § 3.21 the series concerned are absolutely and uniformly convergent, term-by-term integration being permissible. The other integrals vanish by virtue of orthogonality of the circular functions. Thus

$$\int_0^{2\pi} \mathrm{ce}_{2n}^2(z,q)\,dz = 2\pi[A_0^{(2n)}]^2 + \pi \sum_{r=1}^{\infty} [A_{2r}^{(2n)}]^2. \tag{8}$$

The results given below may be established in a similar manner:

$$\int_0^{2\pi} \mathrm{ce}_{2n+1}^2(z,q)\,dz = \pi \sum_{r=0}^{\infty} [A_{2r+1}^{(2n+1)}]^2. \tag{9}$$

$$\int_0^{2\pi} \mathrm{se}_m(z,q)\mathrm{se}_p(z,q)\,dz = 0 \quad (m \neq p). \tag{10}$$

$$\int_0^{2\pi} \mathrm{se}_{2n+1}^2(z,q)\,dz = \pi \sum_{r=0}^{\infty} [B_{2r+1}^{(2n+1)}]^2. \tag{11}$$

$$\int_0^{2\pi} \mathrm{ce}_m(z,q)\mathrm{se}_p(z,q)\,dz = 0, \quad m,\ p,\ \text{positive integers.} \tag{12}$$

$$\int_0^{2\pi} \mathrm{se}_{2n+2}^2(z,q)\,dz = \pi \sum_{r=0}^{\infty} [B_{2r+2}^{(2n+2)}]^2. \tag{13}$$

These results are valid for all values of q, and lead us to the important conclusion that $\mathrm{ce}_m(z,q)$, $\mathrm{se}_m(z,q)$ are orthogonal. This fundamental property is used in §§ 4.90, 10.60.

2.191. A fundamental identity. In (5) § 2.19 let y_1, y_2 be independent solutions of (1) § 2.19 for the same a, q. Then with $z_1 = 0$, $z_2 = z$, we get the Wronskian

$$y_1(z)y_2'(z) - y_2(z)y_1'(z) = y_1(0)y_2'(0) - y_2(0)y_1'(0) = c^2, \quad \text{a constant.} \tag{1}$$

If $y_1(0) = y_2'(0) = 1$, and $y_2(0) = y_1'(0) = 0$, $c^2 = 1$ and we obtain

$$y_1(z)y_2'(z) - y_2(z)y_1'(z) \equiv 1. \tag{2}$$

For a given pair of independent solutions, c^2 will in general vary with q.

2.20. Orthogonality of functions of rational fractional order. Since y_1, y_2 in (5) § 2.19 are *any* solutions for the same q, the formula is valid for functions of rational fractional order ν. Then by § 2.16 the period is $2\pi s$, so with $z_1 = 0$, $z_2 = 2\pi s$ in (5) § 2.19, we have

$$\int_0^{2\pi s} \mathrm{ce}_\nu(z, q)\mathrm{ce}_\mu(z, q)\,dz = \int_0^{2\pi s} \mathrm{se}_\nu(z, q)\mathrm{se}_\mu(z, q)\,dz$$

$$= \int_0^{2\pi s} \mathrm{ce}_\nu(z, q)\mathrm{se}_\mu(z, q)\,dz = 0, \tag{1}$$

provided $\nu \neq \mu$ in the first two integrals. Also

$$\int_0^{2\pi s} \mathrm{ce}_\nu^2(z, q)\,dz \neq 0, \qquad \int_0^{2\pi s} \mathrm{se}_\nu^2(z, q)\,dz \neq 0. \tag{2}$$

Hence the *periodic* functions of (rational) fractional order are orthogonal. The value of these integrals is given in § 4.72.

2.21. Normalization of $\mathrm{ce}_m(z, q)$, $\mathrm{se}_m(z, q)$. In § 2.11 we introduced a convention that the coefficients of $\cos mz$, $\sin mz$ should be unity for *all* values of q. Thus in (1)–(4) § 2.17 we should then have $A_m^{(m)} = B_m^{(m)} = 1$ for all q. It will be shown later that constancy of these coefficients leads to undesirable consequences. Accordingly we now introduce an improved convention based upon § 2.19 [52, 95]. We shall make definite or *normalize* the functions $\mathrm{ce}_m(z, q)$, $\mathrm{se}_m(z, q)$ by the stipulation that

$$\frac{1}{\pi}\int_0^{2\pi} \mathrm{ce}_m^2(z, q)\,dz = \frac{1}{\pi}\int_0^{2\pi} \mathrm{se}_m^2(z, q)\,dz = 1, \tag{1}$$

for all real values of q. Then by (1) above and (8) § 2.19, we have

$$2[A_0^{(2n)}]^2 + \sum_{r=1}^{\infty}[A_{2r}^{(2n)}]^2 = 1. \tag{2}$$

Now $\mathrm{ce}_0(z, 0) = 1$ by our convention of § 2.11, so to normalize in

accordance with (1) above, its constant term must be $A_0^{(0)} = 2^{-\frac{1}{2}}$ for $q = 0$, since

$$\frac{1}{\pi} \int_0^{2\pi} dz = 2. \tag{3}$$

For ce_{2n+1}, se_{2n+1}, se_{2n+2} we have, respectively, [52]

$$1 = \sum_{r=0}^{\infty} [A_{2r+1}^{(2n+1)}]^2 = \sum_{r=0}^{\infty} [B_{2r+1}^{(2n+1)}]^2 = \sum_{r=0}^{\infty} [B_{2r+2}^{(2n+2)}]^2. \tag{4}$$

The normalization (1) entails a mean square value of $1/2$ over the interval $(0, 2\pi)$, which is the same as that for the circular functions. It is convenient in applications when the orthogonal properties of the Mathieu functions are used.

The functions of fractional order may be normalized in like manner, but this is postponed till § 4.72.

2.22. Relationships. The following are easily established from what precedes:

$$\begin{matrix}ce_m \\ se_m\end{matrix}(n\pi + z) = \begin{matrix}ce_m \\ -se_m\end{matrix}(n\pi - z), \tag{1}$$

$$\begin{matrix}ce_m \\ se_{m+1}\end{matrix}(\tfrac{1}{2}\pi + z) = (-1)^m \begin{matrix}ce_m \\ se_{m+1}\end{matrix}(\tfrac{1}{2}\pi - z), \tag{2}$$

$$\begin{matrix}ce_m \\ se_m\end{matrix}(\pi + z) = (-1)^m \begin{matrix}ce_m \\ se_m\end{matrix}(z). \tag{3}$$

From these relationships it is seen to be sufficient to give tabular values of the ordinary Mathieu functions in the interval $0 \leqslant z \leqslant \tfrac{1}{2}\pi$ for $q > 0$. When $q < 0$, the appropriate values may be derived from the foregoing by aid of (2)–(5) § 2.18.

Also $ce_{2n+1}(r + \tfrac{1}{2})\pi = se_{2n+1}(r\pi) = se_{2n+2}(\tfrac{1}{2}r\pi) = 0. \tag{4}$

When $z \to \tfrac{1}{2}\pi$

$$(-1)^n ce_{2n}(z, q), \qquad (-1)^n ce_{2n+1}(z, q)/\cos z,$$

$$(-1)^n se_{2n+1}(z, q), \qquad (-1)^n se_{2n+2}(z, q)/\cos z, \tag{5}$$

are positive.

2.23. Transformation of $\dfrac{d^2y}{dz^2} + (a - 2q \cos 2z)y = 0.$

1°. Substitute $x = u(z)$, a continuous function of z, and we get

$$\left(\frac{du}{dz}\right)^2 \frac{d^2y}{du^2} + \frac{d^2u}{dz^2} \frac{dy}{du} + (a - 2q \cos 2z)y = 0. \tag{1}$$

If $u = 2k\cos z$, $q = k^2$, (1) gives the transformed version of Mathieu's equation as

$$(u^2-4k^2)\frac{d^2y}{du^2}+u\frac{dy}{du}+(u^2-a-2k^2)y = 0. \qquad (2)$$

2°. Let $y = u(z)f(z)$, u, f being continuous functions of z, then we obtain

$$u''+2(f'/f)u'+[a+(f''/f)-2q\cos 2z]u = 0. \qquad (3)$$

Take $f(z) = e^{\kappa z}$, then $f'/f = \kappa$, $f''/f = \kappa^2$, so (3) becomes

$$u''+2\kappa u'+[(a+\kappa^2)-2q\cos 2z]u = 0. \qquad (4)$$

The solution of (4) is $u = ye^{-\kappa z}$, where y is a solution of Mathieu's equation.

2.30. Modified Mathieu functions of the first kind of integral order, q positive.

If in (1) § 2.10 we write iz for z, the equation becomes

$$\frac{d^2y}{dz^2} - (a-2q\cosh 2z)y = 0. \qquad (1)$$

This is the canonical form of the second equation found by Mathieu in his analysis of the elliptical membrane. For the values of a corresponding to $\mathrm{ce}_m(z,q)$, $\mathrm{se}_m(z,q)$ the first solutions of (1) are derived by substituting iz for z in (1)–(4) § 2.17. Thus we have

$$\mathrm{Ce}_{2n}(z,q) = \mathrm{ce}_{2n}(iz,q) = \sum_{r=0}^{\infty} A_{2r}^{(2n)}\cosh 2rz \qquad (a_{2n}), \qquad (2)$$

$$\mathrm{Ce}_{2n+1}(z,q) = \mathrm{ce}_{2n+1}(iz,q) = \sum_{r=0}^{\infty} A_{2r+1}^{(2n+1)}\cosh(2r+1)z \qquad (a_{2n+1}), \qquad (3)$$

$$\mathrm{Se}_{2n+1}(z,q) = -i\,\mathrm{se}_{2n+1}(iz,q) = \sum_{r=0}^{\infty} B_{2r+1}^{(2n+1)}\sinh(2r+1)z \qquad (b_{2n+1}), \qquad (4)$$

$$\mathrm{Se}_{2n+2}(z,q) = -i\,\mathrm{se}_{2n+2}(iz,q) = \sum_{r=0}^{\infty} B_{2r+2}^{(2n+2)}\sinh(2r+2)z \qquad (b_{2n+2}). \qquad (5)$$

These are defined to be modified Mathieu functions of the first kind of integral order[†] for $q > 0$. (2), (5) are periodic in z, with period πi, whilst (3), (4) are also periodic with period $2\pi i$.

2.31. Changing the sign of q.

Equation (1) § 2.30 then becomes

$$\frac{d^2y}{dz^2} - (a+2q\cosh 2z)y = 0. \qquad (1)$$

This is obtained if z in (1) § 2.18 is replaced by iz, or if $(\tfrac{1}{2}\pi i+z)$ is

---

[†] The use of capital letters to denote the modified Mathieu functions is due to H. Jeffreys [104, p. 459].

written for z in (1) §2.30. Changing the arguments in either (2)–(5) §2.18 or in (2)–(5) §2.30 leads to the following solutions of (1):

$$\mathrm{Ce}_{2n}(z, -q) = \mathrm{ce}_{2n}(iz, -q)$$

$$= (-1)^n \sum_{r=0}^{\infty} (-1)^r A_{2r}^{(2n)} \cosh 2rz \qquad (a_{2n}), \qquad (2)$$

$$\mathrm{Ce}_{2n+1}(z, -q) = \mathrm{ce}_{2n+1}(iz, -q)$$

$$= (-1)^n \sum_{r=0}^{\infty} (-1)^r B_{2r+1}^{(2n+1)} \cosh(2r+1)z \quad (b_{2n+1}), \qquad (3)$$

$$\mathrm{Se}_{2n+1}(z, -q) = -i\,\mathrm{se}_{2n+1}(iz, -q)$$

$$= (-1)^n \sum_{r=0}^{\infty} (-1)^r A_{2r+1}^{(2n+1)} \sinh(2r+1)z \quad (a_{2n+1}), \qquad (4)$$

$$\mathrm{Se}_{2n+2}(z, -q) = -i\,\mathrm{se}_{2n+2}(iz, -q)$$

$$= (-1)^n \sum_{r=0}^{\infty} (-1)^r B_{2r+2}^{(2n+2)} \sinh(2r+2)z \quad (b_{2n+2}). \qquad (5)$$

(2), (5) have period πi, while (3), (4) have period $2\pi i$ in z. The interchange of the coefficients A, B, and characteristic numbers a_{2n+1}, b_{2n+1}, in (3), (4) §§2.30, 2.31, should be observed—see remarks in §2.18. The multiplier $(-1)^n$ ensures that when $q = 0$, the functions reduce to $+\cosh mz$, or $+\sinh mz$, as the case may be. (2)–(5) may be regarded as modified Mathieu functions of the first kind for q negative.

CALCULATION OF CHARACTERISTIC NUMBERS AND COEFFICIENTS

3.10. Recurrence relations for the coefficients. If each series (1)–(4) § 2.17 is substituted in turn in $y''+(a-2q\cos 2z)y = 0$, and the coefficients of $\cos 2rz$, $\cos(2r+1)z$, $\sin(2r+1)z$, $\sin(2r+2)z$ equated to zero for $r = 0$, 1, 2,..., the following recurrence relations are obtained [52, 88]:

$$\left.\begin{aligned}aA_0-qA_2 &= 0 \\ (a-4)A_2-q(A_4+2A_0) &= 0\dagger \\ (a-4r^2)A_{2r}-q(A_{2r+2}+A_{2r-2}) &= 0\end{aligned}\right\} \begin{aligned}&\text{for ce}_{2n}(z,q), \\ &\ \\ &r \geqslant 2.\end{aligned} \tag{1}$$

$$\left.\begin{aligned}(a-1-q)A_1-qA_3 &= 0 \\ [a-(2r+1)^2]A_{2r+1}-q(A_{2r+3}+A_{2r-1}) &= 0\end{aligned}\right\} \begin{aligned}&\text{for ce}_{2n+1}(z,q), \\ &r \geqslant 1.\end{aligned} \tag{2}$$

$$\left.\begin{aligned}(a-1+q)B_1-qB_3 &= 0 \\ [a-(2r+1)^2]B_{2r+1}-q(B_{2r+3}+B_{2r-1}) &= 0\end{aligned}\right\} \begin{aligned}&\text{for se}_{2n+1}(z,q), \\ &r \geqslant 1.\end{aligned} \tag{3}$$

$$\left.\begin{aligned}(a-4)B_2-qB_4 &= 0 \\ (a-4r^2)B_{2r}-q(B_{2r+2}+B_{2r-2}) &= 0\end{aligned}\right\} \begin{aligned}&\text{for se}_{2n+2}(z,q), \\ &r \geqslant 2.\end{aligned} \tag{4}$$

For simplicity the superscripts $2n$, $2n+1$, $2n+2$ have been omitted from the A and B. The respective recurrence relations for $\text{ce}_{2n}(z, -q)$, etc., $\text{Ce}_{2n}(z,q)$,..., $\text{Ce}_{2n}(z, -q)$,... are identical with those above.‡ To ensure convergence of the series in §§ 2.17, 2.30 it is necessary that $A_m \to 0$, $B_m \to 0$ as $m \to +\infty$.

3.11. Calculation of a and the A, B. If q is small enough, the formulae for a given in § 2.151 may be used. In general, however, a must be calculated using one of the methods illustrated below. We adopt the normalization of § 2.21, thereby entailing coefficients which differ from those obtained using the normalization of § 2.11 [52, 88].

We commence with the function $\text{ce}_0(z, 8)$, i.e. $q = 8$, which is well outside the range of the formulae in Chapter II. First we derive an infinite continued fraction. From the second formula in (1) § 3.10, we have

$$(4-a)A_2+q(A_4+2A_0) = 0. \tag{1}$$

---

† Note the factor 2 for A_0.　　　　　　　‡ Using q or $-q$ as the case may be.

Writing $v_0 = A_2/A_0, v_2 = A_4/A_2$, then $v_0 v_2 = A_4/A_0$. Dividing (1) by A_0 and making these substitutions, gives

$$(4-a)v_0 + q(v_0 v_2 + 2) = 0, \tag{2}$$

so
$$-v_0 = \tfrac{1}{2}q/[1-\tfrac{1}{4}(a-qv_2)]. \tag{3}$$

In the same way from the third formula in (1) § 3.10, with

$$v_{2r-2} = A_{2r}/A_{2r-2}, \qquad v_{2r} = A_{2r+2}/A_{2r},$$

we get
$$(4r^2-a)v_{2r-2} + q(v_{2r}v_{2r-2} + 1) = 0,$$

so $(r \geqslant 2)$
$$-v_{2r-2} = (q/4r^2)/[1-(1/4r^2)(a-qv_{2r})], \tag{4}$$

which may be regarded as an alternative form of recurrence relation. Substituting $r = 2$ in (4) yields

$$-v_2 = (q/16)/[1-\tfrac{1}{16}(a-qv_4)], \tag{5}$$

and on inserting this in (3) we get

$$-v_0 = \tfrac{1}{2}q/\{1-\tfrac{1}{4}a-(q^2/64)/[1-\tfrac{1}{16}(a-qv_4)]\}. \tag{6}$$

Putting $r = 3$ in (4), we obtain a formula for v_4, which is now substituted in (6). Proceeding thus we ultimately get the infinite continued fraction

$$-v_0 = \frac{\tfrac{1}{2}q}{1-\tfrac{1}{4}a-} \; \frac{\tfrac{1}{64}q^2}{1-\tfrac{1}{16}a-} \; \frac{\tfrac{1}{576}q^2}{1-\tfrac{1}{36}a-} \; \frac{\tfrac{1}{2304}q^2}{1-\tfrac{1}{64}a-} \cdots \; \frac{q^2/16r^2(r-1)^2}{1-a/4r^2} - \cdots . \tag{7}$$

From the first formula in (1) § 3.10, $v_0 = A_2/A_0 = a/q$, so (7) becomes

$$a = \frac{-\tfrac{1}{2}q^2}{1-\tfrac{1}{4}a-} \; \frac{\tfrac{1}{64}q^2}{1-\tfrac{1}{16}a-} \; \frac{\tfrac{1}{576}q^2}{1-\tfrac{1}{36}a-} \; \frac{\tfrac{1}{2304}q^2}{1-\tfrac{1}{64}a-} \cdots , \tag{8}$$

which is in effect a transcendental equation for a_{2n}. Since a, q are finite, the denominator of the general term approaches unity as $r \to +\infty$, while the numerator tends to zero. Hence (8) is convergent.

3.12. Computation of a_0 for $q = 8$. We commence by finding an approximate value of a_0 by trial and error. Neglecting all members on the r.h.s. of (8) § 3.11 except the first, we get

$$a_0 = -32/(1-\tfrac{1}{4}a_0),$$

so
$$a_0 = 2\pm(132)^{\frac{1}{2}} \simeq -9{\cdot}5 \text{ or } +13{\cdot}5. \tag{1}$$

Substituting $+13{\cdot}5$ in the first three members on the r.h.s. of (8) § 3.11 gives the following:

$$\left.\begin{array}{l} \tfrac{1}{576}q^2/(1-\tfrac{1}{36}a) = 0{\cdot}178, \\[4pt] \tfrac{1}{64}q^2/(1-\tfrac{1}{16}a-0{\cdot}178) = -43{\cdot}6, \\[4pt] -\tfrac{1}{2}q^2/(1-\tfrac{1}{4}a+43{\cdot}6) = -0{\cdot}776. \end{array}\right\} \tag{2}$$

The great discrepancy between $+13 \cdot 5$ and $-0 \cdot 776$ indicates that we chose the wrong root of (1). Suppose we start with $a_0 = -10$, then to a first approximation

$$a_0 = -\frac{32}{3 \cdot 5} - \frac{1}{1 \cdot 625} - \frac{0 \cdot 111}{1 \cdot 278} = -11 \cdot 2. \tag{3}$$

This is numerically greater than -10, so we now use the average, namely, $-10 \cdot 6$, and repeat the calculation. Before doing so, we shall obtain an estimate of the number of members from (8) § 3.11 to give a reasonable approximation. The general component is

$$\left[q^2/16r^2(r-1)^2\right] \Big/ \left[1 - \frac{1}{4r^2}(a - qv_{2r})\right], \tag{4}$$

and as r increases, we see from (4) § 3.11 that v_{2r-2} decreases, while in (4) the term $|qv_{2r}|/4r^2 \leqslant 1$, provided r is large enough. Taking $r = 6$ in (4) § 3.11, and neglecting $qv_{2r}/4r^2$, we get

$$-v_{10} \simeq (1/18)/[1 + (10 \cdot 6/144)] = 0 \cdot 052, \tag{5}$$

so $|qv_{12}|/4r^2 < |qv_{10}|/4 \times 36 \simeq 0 \cdot 0029$. We shall presume, that for the purpose of illustrating the method of calculation, the accuracy will be adequate if (8) § 3·11 is terminated at the fifth member on the r.h.s. Thus assuming that v_{12} may be neglected, we get [88]

$r = 5$ $[q^2/16r^2(r-1)^2]/(1 - a/4r^2)$

$\qquad = (1/100)/[1 + (10 \cdot 6/100)] = 0 \cdot 00904\ 0,$

$r = 4$ $(1/36)/[1 + (10 \cdot 6/64) - 0 \cdot 00904]$ $= 0 \cdot 02402\ 0,$

$r = 3$ $(1/9)/[1 + (10 \cdot 6/36) - 0 \cdot 02402]$ $= 0 \cdot 08746\ 0,$

$r = 2$ $1/[1 + (10 \cdot 6/16) - 0 \cdot 08746]$ $= 0 \cdot 63490\ 4,$

$r = 1$ $-32/[1 + (10 \cdot 6/4) - 0 \cdot 63490\ 4]$ $= a_0 = -10 \cdot 61326\ 0.$ (6)

The trial value of a_0 was $-10 \cdot 6$, so (6) differs from this in the fourth significant figure. Taking the average† gives $a_0 = -10 \cdot 60663\ 0$. If this is used instead of $-10 \cdot 6$ and the calculation repeated, the new value of a_0 to six significant figures is $-10 \cdot 6067$. A more accurate result may be obtained by using this value of a_0, and repeating the computation with $r = 7$. To seven decimal places

$$a_0 = -10 \cdot 60672\ 92.$$

It is apposite to remark that a formula of the type (7) § 2.150 could

---

† This procedure is not always expedient.

not be used in the present case where $q = 8$. Even for $q = 0.8$ the accuracy would be low.

3.13. Computation of coefficients for $ce_0(z, 8)$. From (5) § 3.12, $v_{10} \simeq -0.052$, so using (4) § 3.11, with $a_0 = -10.6$ to demonstrate the procedure, we obtain

$$r = 5 \qquad -v_8 = (2/25)/[1+(10.6/100)-(2\times 0.052/25)]$$

$$\simeq 0.0726 = -A_{10}/A_8, \quad (1)$$

$$r = 4 \qquad -v_6 = (2/16)/[1+(10.6/64)-(2\times 0.0726/16)]$$

$$\simeq 0.108 = -A_8/A_6, \quad (2)$$

$$r = 3 \qquad -v_4 = (2/9)/[1+(10.6/36)-(2\times 0.108/9)]$$

$$\simeq 0.175 = -A_6/A_4, \quad (3)$$

$$r = 2 \qquad -v_2 = (2/4)/[1+(10.6/16)-(2\times 0.175/4)]$$

$$\simeq 0.318 = -A_4/A_2. \quad (4)$$

By (3) § 3.11 $\qquad -v_0 = 4/[1+(10.6/4)-2\times 0.318]$

$$\simeq 1.327 = -A_2/A_0. \quad (5)$$

Normalizing the function in accordance with the convention of § 2.21, we have

$$1 = 2A_0^2 + A_2^2 + A_4^2 + A_6^2 + ..., \quad (6)$$

so $\qquad 1/A_0^2 = 2 + (A_2/A_0)^2 + (A_4/A_0)^2 + (A_6/A_0)^2 + ... \quad (7)$

From (5), $-A_2 = 1.327A_0$, so by (4)

$$A_4 = 1.327 \times 0.318 A_0 \simeq 0.422 A_0. \quad (8)$$

In the same way we find that

$$\left. \begin{array}{l} A_6 = -0.0739 A_0, \\ A_8 = 0.00798 A_0, \\ A_{10} = -0.00058 A_0. \end{array} \right\} \quad (9)$$

Using these numerical values in (7) leads to

$$1/A_0^2 = 3.9445, \quad \text{so } A_0 = 0.5035, \quad (10)$$

the positive sign being chosen. A more accurate value may be obtained by using $a_0 = -10.6067292$, starting at $r = 6$ and working to, say, eight decimal places. Then $A_0 = 0.5037681$, so our approximate computation errs in the fourth significant figure. We can now calculate the other A, using A_0 at (10), and obtain

$$\left.\begin{aligned}
A_2 &\simeq -0{\cdot}668 \\
A_4 &\simeq 0{\cdot}212 \\
A_6 &\simeq -0{\cdot}037 \\
A_8 &\simeq 0{\cdot}004 \\
A_{10} &\simeq -0{\cdot}00029
\end{aligned}\right\}
\begin{aligned}
&-0{\cdot}66791\ 64,\dagger \\
&0{\cdot}21197\ 32, \\
&-0{\cdot}03707\ 27, \\
&0{\cdot}00400\ 65, \\
&-0{\cdot}00029\ 09.
\end{aligned}
\tag{11}$$

Hence to a first approximation the first and periodic solution (cosine) of

$$y'' + (-10{\cdot}6...-16\cos 2z)y = 0, \tag{12}$$

under the normalization of § 2.21 with $m = 0$, is

$$ce_0(z, 8) = 0{\cdot}504 - 0{\cdot}668\cos 2z + 0{\cdot}212\cos 4z -$$

$$-0{\cdot}037\cos 6z + 0{\cdot}004\cos 8z - 0{\cdot}0003\cos 10z + ... \tag{13}$$

The graph of (13) is shown in Fig. 3.

Checking the solution. To check the solution at $z = 0$, π,..., $n\pi$, we have from the differential equation (12)

$$y''(n\pi) = (16 + 10{\cdot}6...)y(n\pi). \tag{14}$$

From (13),

$$ce_0''(n\pi, 8) \simeq 4 \times 0{\cdot}668 - 16 \times 0{\cdot}212 + 36 \times 0{\cdot}037 -$$

$$-64 \times 0{\cdot}004 + 100 \times 0{\cdot}0003 = 0{\cdot}388, \tag{15}$$

and

$$(26{\cdot}6...)ce_0(n\pi, 8) \simeq 26{\cdot}6...(0{\cdot}504 - 0{\cdot}668 + 0{\cdot}212 -$$

$$-0{\cdot}037 + 0{\cdot}004 - 0{\cdot}0003) = 0{\cdot}391. \tag{16}$$

The results in (15), (16) agree within 1 per cent., which is sufficient for purposes of illustration. The solution may be checked at any other point, e.g. $z = \frac{1}{4}\pi$.

Remarks on the coefficients in (13). There are two salient features: (*a*) beyond a certain term the coefficients decrease rapidly with increase in r, (*b*) they alternate in sign. (*a*) entails the rapid convergence of the series. For $0 \leqslant q < 3{\cdot}2$, tabular values show that $|A_0|$ is the largest coefficient, being $2^{-\frac{1}{2}}$ at $q = 0$. When $q > 3{\cdot}2$ approximately, $|A_2|$ takes precedence, e.g. in (13). The relative values of some of the early coefficients in the series for $ce_2(z, 2)$, $se_3(z, 2)$, $ce_5(z, 2)$ are depicted in Fig. 6.

† The figures in this column are correct to seven decimal places [95].

3.14. Evaluation of a_{2n} for $\mathrm{ce}_{2n}(z,q)$, $n > 0$.

Writing $(r+1)$ for r in (4) §3.11 and multiplying both sides by $q/4r^2$, we get [52]

$$-\frac{qv_{2r}}{4r^2} = \left[q^2/16r^2(r+1)^2\right]\bigg/\left[1 - \frac{1}{4(r+1)^2}(a - qv_{2r+2})\right] \tag{1}$$

$$= \frac{q^2/16r^2(r+1)^2}{1 - a/4(r+1)^2 -} \frac{q^2/16(r+1)^2(r+2)^2}{1 - a/4(r+2)^2} - \frac{q^2/16(r+2)^2(r+3)^2}{1 - a/4(r+3)^2} - \cdots$$

$$= E_{2r}. \tag{2}$$

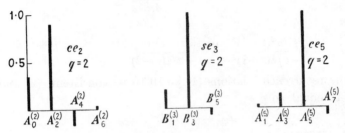

FIG. 6. Relative magnitudes of the coefficients in the series for $\mathrm{ce}_2(z, 2)$, $\mathrm{se}_3(z, 2)$, $\mathrm{ce}_5(z, 2)$. For $q = 2$, the coefficient of functional order is the greatest.

If $a = a_{2n}$, the characteristic number for $\mathrm{ce}_{2n}(z,q)$, $q \neq 0$, none of the denominators in the components of (2) vanish. Then the C.F. is convergent, since the denominator of the general term approaches unity and the numerator tends to zero as $r \to +\infty$.

We shall now derive an alternative terminating C.F. to represent the l.h.s. of (1). After division by $4r^2$, the recurrence formula prior to (4) §3.11 may be written

$$-\frac{qv_{2r}}{4r^2} = 1 - \frac{a}{4r^2} + \frac{q/4r^2}{v_{2r-2}} \tag{3}$$

$$= 1 - \frac{a}{4r^2} + \frac{q^2/16r^2(r-1)^2}{qv_{2r-2}/4(r-1)^2} \quad (r \geqslant 2). \tag{4}$$

Now write $(r-1)$ for r in (4), thereby obtaining a formula for $-qv_{2r-2}/4(r-1)^2$. Substituting this in the third member on the r.h.s. of (4), we get

$$-\frac{qv_{2r}}{4r^2} = 1 - \frac{a}{4r^2} -$$

$$-\left[q^2/16r^2(r-1)^2\right]\bigg/\left[1 - \left[a/4(r-1)^2\right] + \frac{q^2/16(r-1)^2(r-2)^2}{qv_{2r-4}/4(r-2)^2}\right]. \tag{5}$$

Continuing this process leads to the terminating C.F.

$$-\frac{qv_{2r}}{4r^2} = 1 - \frac{a}{4r^2} - \frac{q^2/16r^2(r-1)^2}{1-a/4(r-1)^2-} \; \frac{q^2/16(r-1)^2(r-2)^2}{1-a/4(r-2)^2} -\cdots + \frac{q^2/64}{qv_2/4}.$$

(6)

Since $v_0 = a/q$ by (1) § 3.10, (2) § 3.11 may be written

$$\tfrac{1}{4}qv_2 = -(1-\tfrac{1}{4}a+q^2/2a).$$

(7)

Substituting from (7) into (6) gives

$$-\frac{qv_{2r}}{4r^2} = 1 - \frac{a}{4r^2} - F_{2r},$$

(8)

where

$$F_{2r} = \frac{q^2/16r^2(r-1)^2}{1-a/4(r-1)^2-} \; \frac{q^2/16(r-1)^2(r-2)^2}{1-a/4(r-2)^2} -\cdots - \frac{q^2/64}{1-a/4+} \frac{q^2}{2a}.$$

(9)

For the recurrence relations (1) § 3.10 to be consistent, (2) and (8) must be equal, so

$$E_{2r} = 1-a/4r^2-F_{2r},$$

(10)

and for convenience in computation we may write

$$G_{2r} = 1-a/4r^2-E_{2r}-F_{2r} \quad (r \geqslant 1).$$

(11)

The appropriate value of a corresponds to $G_{2r} = 0$. To obtain a_2, $a_4,\ldots$ for ce_2, $ce_4,\ldots$ we use (11) with $r = 1, 2, 3,\ldots$ initially.

3.15. Evaluation of a_4 for $ce_4(z, 8)$. To start the computation we have to find a trial value of a_4. By (9) § 2.151, $a_4 = 16$ when $q = 0$, and increases with increase in q, so let us assume that $a = 20$ for $q = 8$. In the r.h.s. of (4) § 3.14 take $r = 2$, substitute for $\tfrac{1}{4}qv_2$ from (7) § 3.14, and we get

$$1-\tfrac{1}{16}a-[(q^2/64)/(1-\tfrac{1}{4}a+q^2/2a)] = 1-\tfrac{1}{16}a-F_4 \quad (r = 2). \tag{1}$$

The first two members in (2) § 3.14 give

$$E_4 \simeq \frac{1/9}{1-a/36-} \frac{1/36}{1-a/64}.$$

(2)

Then (1) is approx. $0\cdot166$ while (2) is approx. $0\cdot271$, so

$$G_4 = 0\cdot166-0\cdot271 \simeq -0\cdot105.$$

Examination of the formulae in § 3·14 indicates that $a_4 < 20$, so we now try $a_4 = 19$ and obtain $0\cdot297$ for (1) and $0\cdot26$ for (2), i.e. $G_4 \simeq +0\cdot037$. Thus the value of a_4 lies between 19 and 20. By linear interpolation (see Fig. 7 A), $a_4 \simeq 19+x = 19\cdot26$. Using this value in (1), (2) yields $0\cdot261$, $0\cdot263$ respectively, so $G_4 \simeq -0\cdot002$.

A second linear interpolation gives $a_4 \simeq 19{\cdot}253$. If now, with this value of a_4, we take $r = 7$ in (2), (9) § 3.14 and repeat the computation, the value of a_4 correct to seven decimal places is found to be $19{\cdot}25270\ 51$.

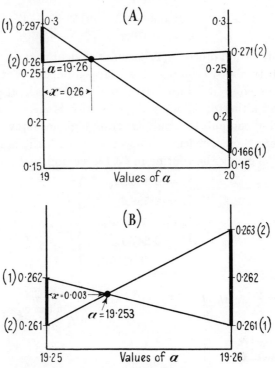

FIG. 7 (A, B). Illustrating linear interpolation.

3.16. Evaluation of coefficients for $ce_4(z, 8)$. By the first recurrence relation in (1) § 3.10

$$v_0 = A_2/A_0 = a_4/q = 19{\cdot}25271/8 \simeq 2{\cdot}4066. \qquad (1)$$

From (7) § 3.14,

$$v_2 = A_4/A_2 = -4(1 - \tfrac{1}{4}a - q^2/2a)/q$$
$$= -(1 - 4{\cdot}8132 + 1{\cdot}6624)/2$$
$$= 1{\cdot}0754. \qquad (2)$$

(3) § 3.14 may be expressed in the form

$$v_{2r} = \frac{1}{q}(a - 4r^2) - \frac{1}{v_{2r-2}} \qquad (r \geqslant 2), \qquad (3)$$

so

$$v_4 = A_6/A_4 = 2 \cdot 4066 - 2 - 0 \cdot 9298 \quad (r = 2)$$
$$= -0 \cdot 5232, \tag{4}$$
$$v_6 = A_8/A_6 = 2 \cdot 4066 - 4 \cdot 5 + 1 \cdot 9113 \quad (r = 3)$$
$$= -0 \cdot 1821, \tag{5}$$
$$v_8 = A_{10}/A_8 = 2 \cdot 4066 - 8 + 5 \cdot 4915 \quad (r = 4)$$
$$= -0 \cdot 1019.\dagger \tag{6}$$

As the computation proceeds, it becomes evident that v_{2r} is the small difference between two comparatively large numbers. For reasonable accuracy, therefore, it is imperative to use more decimal places than we have had hitherto. However, our purpose is merely to illustrate the method of computation, not to attain high accuracy, so we shall now evaluate the coefficients in accordance with the normalization of § 2.21. Following the routine in § 3.13, we find that

$$\left.\begin{aligned} A_2 &= 2 \cdot 4066 A_0, \\ A_4 &= 2 \cdot 589 A_0, \\ A_6 &= -1 \cdot 355 A_0, \\ A_8 &= 0 \cdot 247 A_0, \\ A_{10} &= -0 \cdot 0245 A_0. \end{aligned}\right\} \tag{7}$$

Then by § 2.21

$$1/A_0^2 = 2 + (A_2/A_0)^2 + (A_4/A_0)^2 + (A_6/A_0)^2 + \ldots +$$
$$+ (A_{10}/A_0)^2 + \ldots \simeq 16 \cdot 392, \tag{8}$$

so

$$A_0 = 0 \cdot 247. \tag{9}$$

We now calculate

$$\left.\begin{aligned} A_2 &= 0 \cdot 595, \\ A_4 &= 0 \cdot 639, \\ A_6 &= -0 \cdot 335, \\ A_8 &= 0 \cdot 061, \\ A_{10} &= -0 \cdot 00606. \end{aligned}\right\} \tag{10}$$

The signs of the coefficients are in accordance with the remarks at the end of § 3.33. Inserting these coefficients in (1) § 2.17, the first solution of

$$y'' + (19 \cdot 2527 \ldots - 16 \cos 2z)y = 0, \tag{11}$$

to a first approximation, is the periodic function

$$ce_4(z, 8) = 0 \cdot 247 + 0 \cdot 595 \cos 2z + 0 \cdot 639 \cos 4z -$$
$$- 0 \cdot 335 \cos 6z + 0 \cdot 061 \cos 8z - 0 \cdot 0061 \cos 10z + \ldots. \tag{12}$$

† The value of v_8 correct to five decimal places is $0 \cdot 09971$.

Check on the solution. By (14) § 3.13, we have

$$y''(n\pi) \simeq (16-19 \cdot 253)y(n\pi) = -3 \cdot 253y(n\pi). \tag{13}$$

Now $\mathrm{ce}_4''(n\pi, 8) = -3 \cdot 85$, and $-3 \cdot 253\,\mathrm{ce}_4(n\pi, 8) = -3 \cdot 9$, so the agreement is of the order 1 per cent. To better this, it would be necessary to give the values of the coefficients to more than three decimal places.

3.20. Characteristic numbers and coefficients for ce_{2n+1}, se_{2n+1}, se_{2n+2}. These may be calculated in a similar way to those for ce_{2n}, using appropriate formulae derived from (2)–(4) § 3.10.

For ce_{2n+1}, with $v_{2r+1} = A_{2r+3}^{(2n+1)}/A_{2r+1}^{(2n+1)}$,

$$v_1 = (a-1-q)/q, \tag{1}$$

$$-v_{2r-1} = [q/(2r+1)^2]/[1-a/(2r+1)^2+qv_{2r+1}/(2r+1)^2] \quad (r \geqslant 2). \tag{2}$$

For se_{2n+1}, with $v_{2r+1} = B_{2r+3}^{(2n+1)}/B_{2r+1}^{(2n+1)}$,

$$v_1 = (a-1+q)/q, \tag{3}$$

$$-v_{2r-1} = \text{as at (2) above.} \tag{4}$$

For se_{2n+2}, with $v_{2r} = B_{2r+2}^{(2n+2)}/B_{2r}^{(2n+2)}$,

$$v_2 = (a-4)/q, \tag{5}$$

$$-v_{2r-2} = (q/4r^2)/[1-a/4r^2+qv_{2r}/4r^2] \quad (r \geqslant 3). \tag{6}$$

3.21. Convergence of series for $\mathrm{ce}_m(z, q)$, $\mathrm{se}_m(z, q)$. The third relation at (1) § 3.10 is a linear difference equation. Writing $(r+1)$ for r, we get

$$[a-4(r+1)^2]A_{2r+2}-q(A_{2r+4}+A_{2r}) = 0. \tag{1}$$

Dividing throughout by A_{2r} and putting $v_{2r} = A_{2r+2}/A_{2r}$, gives

$$[a-4(r+1)^2]v_{2r}-q(v_{2r+2}v_{2r}+1) = 0, \tag{2}$$

so

$$v_{2r+2}+\frac{1}{v_{2r}} = [a-4(r+1)^2]q^{-1}. \tag{3}$$

Then $v_{2r+2}+\dfrac{1}{v_{2r}} \to -\infty$ monotonically as $r \to +\infty$, and it is evident that v_{2r} cannot: (1) oscillate boundedly, (2) tend to a unique *finite* limit other than zero. Hence either $v_{2r} \to 0$ or $|v_{2r}| \to \infty$. Now for convergence of the series representing $\mathrm{ce}_{2n}(z, q)$, $A_{2r} \to 0$ as $r \to +\infty$, so v_{2r} must also tend to zero. Consequently, as $r \to +\infty$, one solution of (1) tends to zero, and the other to infinity. In the present instance the latter solution is inadmissible. Thus in (2), when r is large enough, $v_{2r+2}v_{2r} \ll 1$, $a \ll 4(r+1)^2$, and with a, q finite

$$|v_{2r}| \sim q/4(r+1)^2 \to 0 \quad \text{as } r \to +\infty. \tag{4}$$

If z is real, $|\cos 2rz| \leqslant 1$, so it follows by the 'M' test that the series for $\text{ce}_{2n}(z,q)$ is absolutely and uniformly convergent. Moreover, it represents a continuous function for all z real.

In like manner the series for $\text{ce}_{2n+1}(z,q)$, $\text{se}_m(z,q)$ may be proved to have the above properties. Hence all ordinary Mathieu functions are continuous for z real, and the series may be differentiated or integrated term by term provided the resulting series are uniformly convergent. This can be proved to be true. These conclusions apply to the series for $q < 0$.

3.22. Convergence of series for $\text{ce}_m^{(p)}(z, q)$, $\text{se}_m^{(p)}(z, q)$. The pth derivative of $\text{ce}_{2n}(z,q)$ is

$$\frac{d^p}{dz^p}[\text{ce}_{2n}(z,q)] = \sum_{r=1}^{\infty} (2r)^p A_{2r} \begin{matrix} (-1)^{\frac{1}{2}p} \cos 2rz \\ (-1)^{\frac{1}{2}(p+1)} \sin 2rz \end{matrix} \left. \right\} \begin{matrix} p \text{ even,} \\ p \text{ odd.} \end{matrix} \qquad (1)$$

Thus the ratio of the coefficients of the $(r+1)$th and rth terms is

$$\left| \frac{u_{r+1}}{u_r} \right| = \left(\frac{r+1}{r} \right)^p |v_{2r}| = (1+1/r)^p |v_{2r}|. \qquad (2)$$

Then by (4) § 3.21,

$$|u_{r+1}/u_r| \to 0 \quad \text{as } r \to +\infty, \qquad (3)$$

so all derivatives of $\text{ce}_{2n}(z,q)$ are absolutely and uniformly convergent for z real. The same conclusion may be reached in connexion with $\text{ce}_{2n+1}(z,q)$, $\text{se}_m(z,q)$ by similar analysis. This, and proof of the validity of term-by-term integration, are left as exercises for the reader.

3.23. Convergence of series for $\text{Ce}_m(z, q)$, $\text{Se}_m(z, q)$, **and derivatives.** The series are merely those for $\text{ce}_m(z, q)$, $\text{se}_m(z, q)$ with zi written for z. Hence, by (2) § 2.30 and (4) § 3.21,

$$\left| \frac{u_{r+1}}{u_r} \right| \sim \frac{q}{4(r+1)^2} \frac{\cosh(2r+2)z}{\cosh 2rz}. \qquad (1)$$

In § 3.21 we proved that the series for $\text{ce}_{2n}(z,q)$ is absolutely and uniformly convergent for all z real. Hence the series for $\text{Ce}_{2n}(z,q)$ conforms to this when z is imaginary, i.e. $R(z) = 0$. Now when $R(z) \neq 0$, from (1),

$$\left| \frac{u_{r+1}}{u_r} \right| \sim q e^{2|z|}/4(r+1)^2 \to 0 \quad \text{as } r \to +\infty \qquad (2)$$

provided $R(z)$ is finite. Hence the series for $\text{Ce}_{2n}(z,q)$ is absolutely convergent under this condition. By applying the 'M' test it may be proved uniformly convergent. Hence the series is absolutely and uniformly convergent in any finite region of the z-plane or in any closed interval of z real. The same result may be reached for the three remaining functions, and for the pth derivatives of all four functions (see § 3.22).

3.24. Characteristic curves for $\mathrm{ce}_m(z, \pm q)$, $\mathrm{se}_m(z, \pm q)$, q real.

There are tabular values of a_0, a_1,..., a_5 and b_1, b_2,..., b_6 in the range $q = 0$–40, given in Appendix 2 [95]. When these are plotted using cartesian coordinates, the chart of Fig. 8 A is obtained [88]. It is symmetrical about the a-axis. a_{2n}, b_{2n+2}, the characteristic curves for ce_{2n}, se_{2n+2} respectively, are symmetrical about this axis, but a_{2n+1}, b_{2n+1} corresponding to ce_{2n+1}, se_{2n+1} are asymmetrical. Nevertheless the symmetry of the diagram is maintained, since the curves for the functions of odd order, i.e. a_{2n+1}, b_{2n+1} are mutually symmetrical, e.g. a_3, b_3. When q is positive and large enough, the curves a_{2n}, b_{2n+1} approach and are mutually asymptotic, but have no independent linear asymptote. A similar remark pertains to a_m, b_{m+1}. When q is negative and large enough, $a_{2n} \sim a_{2n+1}$, and $b_{2n+1} \sim b_{2n+2}$. It should be noted that of the corresponding pairs of functions one has period π, the other period 2π.

Excepting the curve a_0, which is tangential to the q-axis at the origin in Fig. 8 A, B, all curves intersect this axis twice, one value of q being positive, the other negative. Thus each characteristic has two real zeros in q. For the functions of even order ce_{2n}, se_{2n+2}, the zeros are equal but opposite. The zeros of ce_{2n+1} are equal but opposite to those of se_{2n+1}. Since Mathieu's equation has only one solution of type ce_m or se_m ($q \neq 0$), two characteristic curves cannot intersect.

Approximate values of $q \geqslant 0$ for which a is zero are given in Table 1.

TABLE 1. *Zeros in $q \geqslant 0$ of a_m, b_m*

Characteristic number	a_0	b_1	a_1, b_2	a_2, b_3	$a_m, b_{m+1}, m \geqslant 3$
Value of q	0	0·88	$7·5\frac{1}{7}$	21·28	$0·86(2m+1)^2$†

For $m \geqslant 3$, the q interval between the zeros of a_m and a_{m+1} is $6·88(m+1)$.

† This formula was obtained by taking several terms of (1) § 11.44, putting $a = 0$ and solving for q.

3.25. Continuity of the characteristic numbers as functions

of q. By considering successive convergents, it may be demonstrated

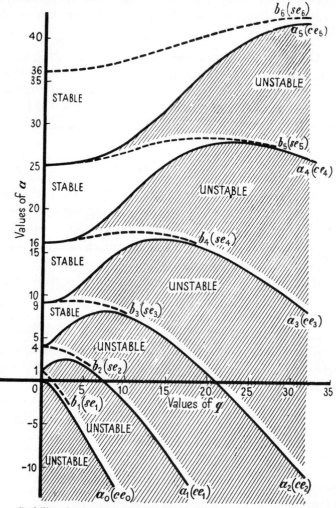

FIG. 8 A . Stability chart for Mathieu functions of integral order. The characteristic curves a_0, b_1, a_1, b_2,... divide the plane into regions of stability and instability. The even-order curves are symmetrical, but the odd-order curves are asymmetrical about the a-axis. Nevertheless the *diagram* is symmetrical about the a-axis.

that the continued fractions for computing the a (see §§ 3.11, 3.14, 3.15) may be expressed as the quotient of two integral functions. The denominator of this quotient cannot vanish if the value of a is a characteristic number for a periodic Mathieu function of integral order. Hence the continued fraction is continuous for any pair of values (a, q) which satisfy the relationship regarded as a transcendental equation for a. It follows, therefore, that a_m, b_m, the characteristic numbers for ce_m, se_m, are continuous† functions of q. Since the transcendental equations for the a are derived primarily

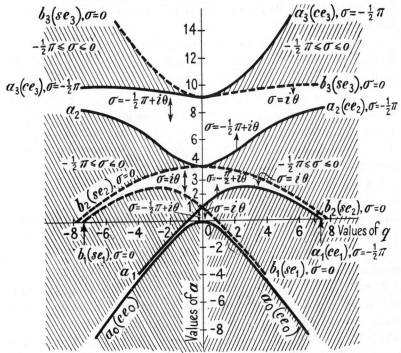

Fig. 8 B. Illustrating variation in the parameter σ (see § 4.30) in stable and unstable regions $q > 0$ and $q < 0$. a_m, b_{m+1} are mutually asymptotic and $\rightarrow -\infty$ as $q \rightarrow +\infty$. a_m, a_{m+1}; b_m, b_{m+1} are mutually asymptotic and $\rightarrow -\infty$ as $q \rightarrow -\infty$ (see § 12.30).

from the recurrence relations, the coefficients A_m, B_m are continuous† functions of q (see Fig. 9).

3.26. Additional comments on normalization. We are now able to comment upon the normalization of § 2.11, where the coefficient of $\cos mz$ in $ce_m(z, q)$, and that of $\sin mz$ in $se_m(z, q)$ is unity for *all* values of q. We shall show that under this convention the remaining coefficients are infinite for certain values of $q \neq 0$ [52].

Consider $ce_2(z, q)$ whose characteristic number is a_2. Then (1) § 3.10 gives

$$q/a_2 = A_0/A_2. \tag{1}$$

† And single-valued.

Now by § 3.24, $a_2 = 0$ for $q_2 \simeq \pm 21 \cdot 28$, so A_0/A_2 is then infinite, and since $A_2 = 1$, $A_0 = \infty$. Also with $a_2 = 0$ in the second formula in (1) § 3.10 we have

$$2qA_0 + 4A_2 + qA_4 = 0, \qquad (2)$$

and since $A_0 = \infty$, $A_2 = 1$, $q \neq 0$, we get $A_4 = -\infty$, and so on. Thus when $q_2 \simeq \pm 21 \cdot 28$, $a_2 = 0$, and all the coefficients except A_2 become infinite.

A similar conclusion may be reached for the coefficients of any Mathieu function of integral order, excepting ce_0, ce_1, se_1, se_2. We shall now examine these singular cases. For ce_0, (1) § 3.10 gives

$$A_0/A_2 = q/a_0. \qquad (3)$$

Since $A_0 = 1$ for all q, and a_0 never vanishes in $q > 0$, A_2 is always finite. It is shown in § 12.30 that $a_0 \sim -2q$ as $q \to \pm \infty$, so $A_0/A_2 \to -\frac{1}{2}$ as $q \to +\infty$. By employing the second recurrence formula for ce_0, we can demonstrate that A_4 is finite, and so on.

For ce_1, (2) § 3.10 gives

$$A_1/A_3 = q/(a_1 - 1 - q), \qquad (4)$$

and since $A_1 = 1$ for all q, while by Appendix 2 $(a_1 - 1 - q) \neq 0$ in $q > 0$, A_3 cannot become infinite. Since $a_1 \sim -2q$ as $q \to +\infty$, $A_1/A_3 \to -\frac{1}{3}$. The functions se_1, se_2 are amenable to similar treatment.

Apart from the above exceptions, it appears—although we have not given a general proof—that for functions of order $2n$, $2n+1$ there are n values of $q > 0$, and an equal number for $q < 0$, for which all coefficients, save that of the same order as the function, become infinite. The positive and negative q are equal numerically. We see, therefore, that the convention of § 2.11 is inadmissible for general purposes, although it is sometimes useful when q is small, and series for ce_m, se_m are given in ascending powers of q (§ 2.13 et seq.). Accordingly we shall now enumerate the advantages of the convention of § 2.21, which is based upon the orthogonal properties of the Mathieu functions.

3.27. Advantages of the normalization of § 2.21.

1°. By (2), (4) § 2.21, none of the coefficients is infinite for any q.

2°. When $q \to 0$, it is shown in § 3.32 that the coefficient of the same order as the function tends to unity,[†] while the remainder tend to zero.[‡] Hence $ce_m(z, q) \to \cos mz$, $se_m(z, q) \to \sin mz$, and these

---

† Except $A_0^{(0)}$ for ce_0 which as shown in § 2.21 is $2^{-\frac{1}{2}}$. In this section $m > 0$.
‡ As stated in § 3.32, this is independent of the normalization.

are the formal solutions of $y'' + ay = 0$, $a = m^2$, which is Mathieu's equation with $q = 0$. The vanishing of the coefficients entails A_{2n}/A_0, A_{2n+1}/A_1, etc., being infinite, but this is inconsequential.

3°. The integrals at (1) §2.21 are independent of q (real).

4°. The mean square value of the function for the interval $(0-2\pi)$ is the same as that of $\cos mz$, $\sin mz$, i.e. $\frac{1}{2}$.

3.30. Properties of the A, B under the normalization of §2.21.

Referring to (12) §3.16, we see that (a) beyond a certain term the

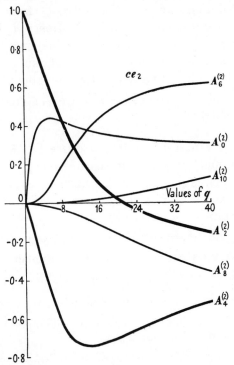

FIG. 9. Illustrating $A_0^{(2)},..., A_{10}^{(2)}$ as single-valued continuous functions of $q \geqslant 0$. When $q \to 0$, $A_0 \propto q$, $A_2 \to 1$, $A_4 \propto -q$, $A_6 \propto q^2$, and so on.

A decrease rapidly in numerical value with increase in r, (b) after the term in $\cos 4z$, they alternate in sign, (c) $|A_4|$ is the largest, but this depends upon the value of q. The values of the A, B vary with q, and by §3.25 the variation is continuous in $q \geqslant 0$. This is illustrated in Fig. 9 by data from [52, 95]. In the range $0 < q \leqslant 40$, tabular data show that $A_2^{(2)}$, $A_3^{(3)}$, $A_4^{(4)}$, $A_5^{(5)}$, $B_4^{(4)}$, $B_5^{(5)}$, $B_6^{(6)}$ each has one zero in q. $B_3^{(3)}$ has a zero in $q > 40$.

1°. *Coefficients in series for* ce_0, ce_1, se_1, se_2. For ce_0, (1) § 3.10 gives
$$A_2/A_0 = a_0/q. \tag{1}$$
From Fig. 8, a_0 is negative in $q > 0$, so the r.h.s. of (1) is negative also. By § 3.27, A_0, A_2 are finite, so neither has a zero in $q > 0$. From the first two relations in (1) § 3.10, we get
$$A_4/A_2 = [(a_0-4)/q] - 2q/a_0. \tag{2}$$
Thus A_4/A_2 will not vanish in $q > 0$ provided $a_0(a_0-4) > 2q^2$. Tabular values show that A_4/A_2 does not vanish in $0 < q \leqslant 1600$ [52]. Beyond this range we take $a_0 \sim -2(q-q^{\frac{1}{2}})$ from (7) § 12.30 and find that the above inequality is satisfied. Hence A_4 has no zero in $q > 0$. Similarly it may be shown that the remaining A have no zeros in $q > 0$. This conclusion is valid for the coefficients in the series for ce_1, se_1, se_2. It is confirmed up to $q = 1600$ by tabular values in [52].

2°. *Real zeros of* $A_{2r}^{(2n)}$, $A_{2r+1}^{(2n+1)}$, $B_{2r+1}^{(2n+1)}$, $B_{2r+2}^{(2n+2)}$ *in* $q > 0$, $n > 0$. For ce_{2n}, (1) § 3.10 gives
$$A_2/A_0 = a_{2n}/q. \tag{1}$$
When $n > 0$, a_{2n} vanishes once in $q > 0$ (see Fig. 8), and since by § 3.27 A_0 is finite, and by (1) above it has no zero in $q > 0$, $A_2 = 0$ when $a_{2n} = 0$. With q large enough, by (7) § 12.30 $a_{2n} \sim -2q + (8n+2)q^{\frac{1}{2}}$, so $A_2/A_0 \to -2$ as $q \to +\infty$, and A_0 never vanishes in $q > 0$. From (1) § 3.10 we obtain
$$A_4/A_2 = -(2q^2 + 4a_{2n} - a_{2n}^2)/qa_{2n}. \tag{2}$$
Then at the *two* intersections of $2q^2 + 4a_{2n} - a_{2n}^2$, and the curve a_{2n} $(q > 0)$, we get
$$A_4/A_2 = 0. \tag{3}$$
Hence A_4 vanishes twice in $q > 0$. Proceeding thus we find that A_6 vanishes thrice in $q > 0$, and so on. The coefficients for other functions may be treated in a similar way.

The zeros of some of the A in ce_2 are given in Table 2. The second zero of $A_4^{(2)}$, the second and third of $A_6^{(2)}$, and all four of $A_8^{(2)}$ lie beyond $q = 1600$. Tabular data indicate that the coefficient of equal order with the function has the smallest zero in q.

TABLE 2

Coefficient	First zero in q (approx.)
$A_2^{(2)}$	21·28
$A_4^{(2)}$	373·6
$A_6^{(2)}$	1352·8
$A_8^{(2)}$	>1600

Although we have not given a general proof, under the normalization of § 2.21 it appears that if $n > 0$, $A_{2r}^{(2n)}$, $A_{2r+1}^{(2n+1)}$, $B_{2r+1}^{(2n+1)}$, $B_{2r+2}^{(2n+2)}$ each has r real zeros in $q > 0$. These correspond to the infinities under the normalization of § 2.11 (see § 3.26). It may be shown that when $r = 0$ none of the above coefficients has a zero in $q > 0$.

3.31. Numerical check on § 3.30. The values of q at the intersections of the straight lines or curves for a null numerator, e.g. as in 2° § 3.30, where $2q^2 + 4a_{2n} - a_{2n}^2 = 0$, and the appropriate characteristic curves a_m, b_m (Fig. 8), were calculated for several functions and are given in Table 3. They are in satisfactory agreement with the zeros in q of the coefficients A, B computed by interpolation from tabular values. The limited range of q in the tables permitted checking of the first zeros only.

TABLE 3. *Approximate zeros in* $0 < q \leqslant 40$ *of* $A_m^{(m)}$, $B_m^{(m)}$

m	$A_m^{(m)}$ for $\mathrm{ce}_m(z, q)$				$B_m^{(m)}$ for $\mathrm{se}_m(z, q)$			
	2	3	4	5	3	4	5	6
q	21·28	15·6	17·4	20·7	>40	37·3	31·4	31·8

$A_0^{(0)}$, $A_1^{(1)}$, $B_1^{(1)}$, $B_2^{(2)}$ have no zeros in $q > 0$.

3.32. Behaviour of coefficients as $q \to 0$. From (1) § 3.10 for $\mathrm{ce}_2(z, q)$

$$A_0 \simeq A_2 q/4, \tag{1}$$

and since A_2 is finite, $A_0 \to 0$ as $q \to 0$. Also

$$(a_2 - 4)A_2 = q(2A_0 + A_4). \tag{2}$$

Substituting for a_2 from (5) § 2.151, and for A_0 from (1) into (2), gives

$$[\tfrac{5}{12}q^2 + O(q^4)]A_2 = \tfrac{1}{2}q^2 A_2 + q A_4, \tag{3}$$

so when q is small

$$A_4 \simeq -\tfrac{1}{12}q A_2 \to 0 \quad \text{as } q \to 0. \tag{4}$$

Again by (1) § 3.10 with $r = 2$,

$$(a_2 - 16)A_4 = q(A_2 + A_6), \tag{5}$$

and by (5) § 2.151 and (4) above

$$-\tfrac{1}{12}A_2[-12 + O(q^2)] = A_2 + A_6. \tag{6}$$

Thus when $q \to 0$, $A_6 \to 0$, and so on for the other coefficients. Now using (2) § 2.21, it follows from above that

$$A_2^{(2)} \to 1 \quad \text{as } q \to 0. \tag{7}$$

In a similar way it may be demonstrated that in (1)–(4) §2.17, $A_m^{(m)} \to 1$, $B_m^{(m)} \to 1$ when $q \to 0$, while all the other A, B tend to zero. The latter result depends upon the recurrence relations, and is independent of the normalization.

3.33. Form of coefficients when q is small. By solving Mathieu's equation as shown in §2.13 et seq. or alternatively, the following results may be derived [215]:

$$A_{2r}^{(0)} = (-1)^r \left[\frac{2}{(r!)^2} t^r - \frac{2r(3r+4)}{[(r+1)!]^2} t^{r+2} + O(t^{r+4}) \right] A_0^{(0)}, \quad t = \tfrac{1}{4}q \quad (r \geqslant 1); \tag{1}$$

$$A_{2r+1}^{(1)} = (-1)^r \left[\frac{1}{r!\,(r+1)!} t^r + \frac{r}{[(r+1)!]^2} t^{r+1} + \frac{1}{4(r-1)!\,(r+2)!} t^{r+2} + \right.$$
$$\left. + O(t^{r+3}) \right] A_1^{(1)}; \tag{2}$$

$$A_0^{(2)} = \left[t - \frac{5}{3} t^3 + \frac{1363}{216} t^5 + O(t^7) \right] A_2^{(2)}; \tag{3}$$

$$A_{2r+2}^{(2)} = (-1)^r \left[\frac{2}{r!\,(r+2)!} t^r + \frac{r(47r^2 + 222r + 247)}{18(r+2)!\,(r+3)!} t^{r+2} + O(t^{r+4}) \right] A_2^{(2)}; \tag{4}$$

$$B_{2r+1}^{(1)} = (-1)^r \left[\frac{1}{r!\,(r+1)!} t^r - \frac{r}{[(r+1)!]^2} t^{r+1} + \frac{1}{4(r-1)!\,(r+2)!} t^{r+2} + \right.$$
$$\left. + O(t^{r+3}) \right] B_1^{(1)}; \tag{5}$$

$$B_{2r+2}^{(2)} = (-1)^r \left[\frac{2}{r!\,(r+2)!} t^r - \frac{r(r+1)(7r+23)}{18(r+2)!\,(r+3)!} t^{r+2} + O(t^{r+4}) \right] B_2^{(2)}. \tag{6}$$

Either by obtaining formulae similar to (1)–(6) or by using recurrence relations, and the expansions of a in terms of q, it may be deduced that if q is small enough, $A_{2r}^{(2n)}$, $A_{2r+1}^{(2n+1)}$, $B_{2r+1}^{(2n+1)}$, $B_{2r+2}^{(2n+2)}$, are $O(q^{n-r})$ or $O(q^{r-n})$ according as $n \lessgtr r$. To illustrate this point, we find for $ce_5(z, q)$ that when q is small enough, the recurrence relations give

$$A_1^{(5)} \simeq \frac{1}{384} q^2 A_5^{(5)}, \qquad A_3^{(5)} \simeq \frac{1}{16} q A_5^{(5)}, \qquad A_5^{(5)} \simeq 1,$$

$$A_7^{(5)} \simeq -\frac{1}{24} q A_5^{(5)}, \quad \text{and} \quad A_9^{(5)} \simeq \frac{1}{1344} q^2 A_5^{(5)}.$$

Since $\sum\limits_{r=0}^{\infty} [A_{2r+1}^{(5)}]^2 = 1$, we obtain

$$A_5^{(5)} \simeq 1 - \frac{13}{4608} q^2 + O(q^4). \tag{7}$$

From [28] we get the general formulae $(r \geqslant 0, m > 0)$,

$$A^{(m)}_{m+2r} \simeq (-1)^r \frac{m!}{r!\,(m+r)!} t^r, \tag{8}$$

and

$$A^{(m)}_{m-2r} \simeq \frac{(m-r-1)!}{r!\,(m-1)!} t^r. \tag{9}$$

When q is not too large, we infer from (8) that the A of order greater than m are alternately negative and positive, while (9) shows that all those of order less than m are positive. $A^{(m)}_m$ is positive. These statements are borne out by tabular values, from which they are seen to be invalid when q exceeds a certain value [95].

3.34. Behaviour of coefficients as $q \to +\infty$.

We use the recurrence relations in § 3.10, and $a \sim -2q$ from § 12.30. Then for ce_{2n},

$$aA_0 - qA_2 = 0, \tag{1}$$

so

$$A_2/A_0 \to -2 \quad \text{as } q \to +\infty. \tag{2}$$

Also

$$(a-4)A_2 - q(A_4 + 2A_0) = 0, \tag{3}$$

so substituting for a, A_2,

$$-4A_0 + A_4 + 2A_0 = 0, \quad \text{giving } A_4/A_0 \to 2 \text{ as } q \to +\infty. \tag{4}$$

In general we find that

$$A^{(2n)}_{2r}/A^{(2n)}_0 \to (-1)^r 2 \quad \text{as } q \to +\infty. \tag{5}$$

By (2) § 2.21 it follows that for $n \geqslant 0$, all the $A^{(2n)} \to 0$ as $q \to +\infty$, in a manner compatible therewith. Similar analysis yields the same conclusion for the $A^{(2n+1)}$, $B^{(m)}$. The results corresponding to (5) are, for $n \geqslant 0$,

$$A_{2r+1}/A_1 \to (-1)^r(2r+1); \qquad B_{2r+1}/B_1 \to (-1)^r;$$
$$B_{2r+2}/B_2 \to (-1)^r(r+1). \tag{6}$$

Numerical illustration. When $q = 1600$, from [52], $A_2/A_0 \simeq -1.95$ for ce_0, and -1.75 for ce_2, as against -2 as $q \to +\infty$. Using $a \sim -2q + (8n+2)q^{\frac{1}{2}}$ from § 12.30 in the recurrence relations, we obtain -1.95, -1.75 for $q = 1600$. For ce_1, $A_3/A_1 \simeq -2.85$, and with the better asymptotic form of a we get -2.85. As $q \to +\infty$, the ratio $\to -3$. The accuracy of the values calculated in the above way decreases with increase in the order of the function.

$A^{(2n)}_{2r}$ *as a function of* q. By § 3.33 it is $O(q^p)$ in the neighbourhood of $q = 0$, with $p \geqslant 0$; by § 3.30 it has r real zeros in $q > 0$; and from above it tends to zero as $q \to +\infty$. Thus we surmise that in general $A_{2r}^{(2n)}$ is an alternating non-periodic function of q which ultimately tends to zero asymptotically. The same conclusion pertains to the other coefficients.

3.35. Behaviour of coefficients as $n \to +\infty$. When a is very large, positive, and much greater than q, $a_{2n} \sim 4n^2$. From (1) § 3.10

$$A_0/A_2 = q/a \sim q/4n^2 \to 0 \quad \text{as } n \to +\infty. \tag{1}$$

Hence $A_0 \to 0$. From (1) § 3.10

$$A_2/A_4 = q/(a-4) \to 0 \quad \text{as } n \to +\infty. \tag{2}$$

Hence $A_2 \to 0$. In like manner it can be shown that all the $A \to 0$ except $A_{2n}^{(2n)}$ which tends to unity. The same conclusion applies to the coefficients for the other functions of integral or fractional order.

3.40. Solution of $y''+(a-2q\cos 2z)y = 0$, when q is negative imaginary. In the problem of eddy current effects in § 17.10, q takes the form $-is$, s being real and positive. In numerical work it is preferable to work with $q = +is$, and then obtain the solution for $q = -is$ by writing $(\frac{1}{2}\pi - z)$ for z. The value of a is real or complex according to conditions. For q moderate, the series for a_m, b_m in § 2.151 are convergent, and may be used for computation. The series for a_{2n}, b_{2n} proceed in powers of q^2, while those for a_{2n+1}, b_{2n+1} proceed in powers of q. Hence a_{2n}, b_{2n} are real, but a_{2n+1}, b_{2n+1} are complex. When $s > s_0$, s_0 depending upon n and the function, a_{2n}, b_{2n} are complex. In the sections following, the method of calculating characteristic numbers and coefficients is exemplified.

3.41. Calculation of a_0 and coefficients in the series for $ce_0(z, -0.16i)$. We take $s = 0.16$ in (1) § 2.151, so with $q = is$

$$a_0 = \frac{1}{2}s^2 + \frac{7}{128}s^4 + \frac{29}{2304}s^6 + \dots \tag{1}$$

$$= 0.0128 + 0.00003\ 584 + 0.0^621$$

$$= 0.01283\ 6 \quad \text{to six decimal places.} \tag{2}$$

By (1) § 3.10,

$$v_0 = A_2/A_0 = a_0/is = -0.01283\ 6i/0.16$$

$$= -0.08022\ 5i,$$

so

$$A_2 = -0.08022\ 5iA_0. \tag{3}$$

From (2) §3.11,

$$v_2 = (a_0 - 4 - 2q/v_0)/q \tag{4}$$
$$= [0{\cdot}01283\ 6 - 4 + (0{\cdot}32i/0{\cdot}08022\ 5i)]/0{\cdot}16i$$
$$= -0{\cdot}01011\ 2i. \tag{5}$$

Thus

$$A_4 = -0{\cdot}01011\ 2iA_2 = -0{\cdot}01011\ 2 \times 0{\cdot}08022\ 5A_0$$
$$= -0{\cdot}00081\ 1A_0. \tag{6}$$

Hence

$$\mathrm{ce}_0(z, +0{\cdot}16i) \simeq A_0[1 - 0{\cdot}0802i \cos 2z - 0{\cdot}0008 \cos 4z + \ldots], \tag{7}$$

and by writing $(\tfrac{1}{2}\pi - z)$ for z on the r.h.s. of (7),[†] we get

$$\mathrm{ce}_0(z, -0{\cdot}16i) \simeq A_0[1 + 0{\cdot}0802i \cos 2z - 0{\cdot}0008 \cos 4z + \ldots]. \tag{8}$$

An approximate check on the A may be obtained by using the formula (6) §2.150, namely,

$$\mathrm{ce}_0(z, q) \simeq 1 - \left(\frac{1}{2}q - \frac{7}{128}q^3 + \ldots\right)\cos 2z + \left(\frac{1}{32}q^2 - \frac{5}{1152}q^4 + \ldots\right)\cos 4z -$$
$$- \left(\frac{1}{1152}q^3 - \ldots\right)\cos 6z + \left(\frac{1}{73728}q^4 - \ldots\right)\cos 8z + \ldots. \tag{9}$$

$v_4 = A_6/A_4$ may be calculated by aid of (4) §3.11 expressed in the form

$$v_{2r} = (a - 4r^2 - q/v_{2r-2})/q \quad (r \geqslant 2), \tag{10}$$

but the numbers involved are such that unless each is given to more decimal places than we have used above, a large error will occur. It is preferable to write (10) in the form

$$v_{2r-2} = q/(a - 4r^2 - qv_{2r}), \tag{11}$$

and as an approximation to assume that v_{2r} vanishes to an adequate number of decimal places. Then with $r = 3$ in (11), we get

$$v_4 \simeq 0{\cdot}16i/(0{\cdot}0128 - 36) = -0{\cdot}00444\ 6i, \tag{12}$$

so

$$A_6 = -0{\cdot}00444\ 6iA_4 = 0{\cdot}00444\ 6i \times 0{\cdot}00081\ 1A_0,$$
$$= 0{\cdot}00000\ 36iA_0. \tag{13}$$

To the same number of decimal places this value is obtained from (9), i.e. $-q^3/1152$, with $q = 0{\cdot}16i$. The value of A_6 in (7) is given at (13), but in (8) its sign will be negative.

---

† When the A are either real or imaginary, but not complex, (8) is obtained by changing the sign of i in (7).

3.42. a_2 and the A in the series for $ce_2(z, -0.16i)$. From (5) §2.151 we have, with $q = is$,

$$a_2 = 4 - \frac{5}{12}s^2 - \frac{763}{13824}s^4 - \frac{10\ 02401}{796\ 26240}s^6 + \dots \tag{1}$$

$$= 4 - 0.01066\ 667 - 0.00003\ 617 - 0.0^621$$

$$= 3.98929\ 7. \tag{2}$$

Proceeding as in §3.41, we find that

$$ce_2(z, 0.16i) = A_0[1 - 25i\cos 2z - 0.328\cos 4z + 0.00164i\cos 6z + \dots] \tag{3}$$

and

$$ce_2(z, -0.16i) = A_0[1 + 25i\cos 2z - 0.328\cos 4z - 0.00164i\cos 6z + \dots]. \tag{4}$$

When q is moderate and real, $|A_{2n}|$ is the largest coefficient in the series for $ce_{2n}(z, q)$. This is true if q is moderate but imaginary, as is exemplified by the A in (4).

3.43. Calculation of a_0 and the A in $ce_0(z, -4.8i)$. Here $s = 4.8$, which is too large for (1) §3.41 to give an adequately accurate result. Instead of using this formula, we obtain an approximation to a_0 by means of two asymptotic formulae. The first is (1) §11.44, and for brevity we designate the r.h.s. by Γ_m. The second is in reference [56], and takes the form

$$b_{m+1} - a_m \sim \frac{2^{4m+5}}{m!}\left(\frac{2}{\pi}\right)^{\frac{1}{2}}q^{\frac{1}{2}(m+\frac{3}{2})}e^{-4q^{\frac{1}{2}}}(1 + c_1 q^{-\frac{1}{2}} + c_2 q^{-1} + \dots) \equiv \Delta_m, \tag{1}$$

where $c_1 = -0.225, -0.849, -1.765, -2.925$ correspond respectively to $m = 0, 1, 2, 3$, and the value of $|q|$ is large enough for terms involving $c_2, c_3, \dots$ to be neglected. In reference [57] it is explained that $\Gamma_m - \frac{1}{2}\Delta_m$ is a suitable approximation to a for starting a computation, provided s is large enough. We take $q = is$, s real and positive, and finally write $(\frac{1}{2}\pi - z)$ for z in the $ce_0(z, 4.8i)$ series, thereby obtaining that for $ce_0(z, -4.8i)$. In the formulae for Γ_m, Δ_m we take $\pm i = e^{\pm\frac{1}{2}\pi i}$, $i^{\pm\frac{3}{2}} = e^{\pm\frac{3}{4}\pi i}$, and so on. Values for $m = 0$ are given in Table 4 [57].

We commence the computation by assuming that the tabular value of a_0 for $s = 4.8$ is an adequate approximation, and apply the recurrence relation (4) §3.11 in the form

$$v_{2r-2} = q/(a - 4r^2 - qv_{2r}) \quad (r \geqslant 2). \tag{2}$$

TABLE 4

s	Γ_0	Δ_0	$\Gamma_0 - \tfrac{1}{2}\Delta_0 \simeq a_0$
1·6	1·52624 0 − 1·38491 6i	−0·56 −0·68i	1·80624 0 − 1·04491 6i
3·2	2·26885 6 − 3·85346 8i	−0·2848 +0·2132i	2·41125 6 − 3·96006 8i
4·8	2·83878 8 − 6·48850 8i	+0·0356 +0·1528i	2·82098 8 − 6·56490 8i
6·4	3·31939 2 − 9·21146 8i	+0·07016 +0·02744i	3·28431 2 − 9·22518 8i
8·0	3·74247 2 −11·99053 6i	+0·03416 8 −0·01775 6i	3·72538 8 −11·98165 8i
9·6	4·12486 0 −14·80972 0i	+0·00656 0 −0·01960 8i	4·12158 0 −14·79991 6i
11·2	4·47642 8 −17·65937 2i	−0·00432 4 −0·01071 2i	4·47859 0 −17·66472 8i
12·8	4·80360 0 −20·53316 8i	−0·00574 4 −0·00336 8i	4·80647 2 −20·53148 4i
14·4	5·11084 8 −23·42672 0i	−0·00393 2 +0·00033 0i	5·11281 4 −23·42688 5i
16·0	5·40142 4 −26·33682 0i	−0·00178 0 +0·00148 8i	5·40231 4 −26·33756 4i

To illustrate the procedure, high accuracy is waived: we take $v_6 = 0$, and $a_0 = 2 \cdot 821 - 6 \cdot 565i$ in (2), thereby obtaining

$$v_4 = 4 \cdot 8i/(2 \cdot 821 - 6 \cdot 565i - 36) = -4 \cdot 8i/(33 \cdot 179 + 6 \cdot 565i)$$

$$= -(0 \cdot 0276 + 0 \cdot 139i). \tag{3}$$

Applying (2) with $r = 2$, we have

$$v_2 = 4 \cdot 8i/[2 \cdot 821 - 6 \cdot 565i - 16 + 4 \cdot 8i(0 \cdot 0276 + 0 \cdot 139i)]$$

$$= -4 \cdot 8i/(13 \cdot 85 + 6 \cdot 433i)$$

$$= -(0 \cdot 132 + 0 \cdot 285i). \tag{4}$$

Also
$$v_0 = 2q/(a_0 - 4 - qv_2) \tag{5}$$

$$= 9 \cdot 6i/[2 \cdot 821 - 6 \cdot 565i - 4 + 4 \cdot 8i(0 \cdot 132 + 0 \cdot 285i)]$$

$$= -9 \cdot 6i/(2 \cdot 547 + 5 \cdot 931i)$$

$$= -(1 \cdot 367 + 0 \cdot 588i). \tag{6}$$

We can now calculate the coefficients A_2, A_4,... in terms of A_0, but before doing so, we shall investigate the accuracy of the assumed value of a_0.

3.44. Closer approximations to a_0 and the v. The first recurrence relation in (1) § 3.10 may be written

$$L = qv_0 - a_0 = 0. \tag{1}$$

Thus if a_0 and v_0 are calculated very accurately, the l.h.s. of (1) should be correspondingly small. Moreover, the magnitude of L will be an index of the error incurred due to the assumed value of a_0 and in taking $v_6 = 0$. The numerical results in § 3.43 are not accurate enough to permit the calculation of L. However, we can show the method of obtaining a closer approximation to a_0 and the v symbolically.

Since the v are functions of a_0, by (1) we have, with q constant,

$$L(a_0) = qv_0 - a_0. \tag{2}$$

Then if δa_0 is small enough, by Taylor's theorem

$$L(a_0 + \delta a_0) \simeq L(a_0) + \delta a_0 \frac{\partial L(a_0)}{\partial a_0}. \tag{3}$$

We presume that $L(a_0 + \delta a_0) \simeq 0$, so we have Newton's well-known approximation

$$\delta a_0 = L(a_0) \Big/ \left[-\frac{\partial L(a_0)}{\partial a_0} \right]. \tag{4}$$

Our next step is to derive an expression for $-\partial L(a_0)/\partial a_0$ in terms of $v_0, v_2, v_4, \ldots$. Then from (2)

$$-\frac{\partial L}{\partial a_0} = 1 - \frac{\partial(qv_0)}{\partial a_0}. \tag{5}$$

Also, by (2) §3.11, $v_0 = 2q/(a_0 - 4 - qv_2)$, $\tag{6}$

so $\dfrac{\partial v_0}{\partial a_0} = \dfrac{-2q}{(a_0 - 4 - qv_2)^2} \dfrac{\partial}{\partial a_0}(a_0 - 4 - qv_2)$, $\tag{7}$

and, therefore, $-\dfrac{\partial(qv_0)}{\partial a_0} = \tfrac{1}{2}v_0^2\left[1 - \dfrac{\partial(qv_2)}{\partial a_0}\right]$. $\tag{8}$

Again, by (2) §3.43, $v_2 = q/(a_0 - 16 - qv_4)$, $\tag{9}$

so $-\dfrac{\partial(qv_2)}{\partial a_0} = v_2^2\left[1 - \dfrac{\partial(qv_4)}{\partial a_0}\right]$. $\tag{10}$

Substituting the r.h.s. of (10) into that of (8) yields

$$-\frac{\partial(qv_0)}{\partial a_0} = \tfrac{1}{2}v_0^2\left[1 + v_2^2\Big\{1 - \frac{\partial(qv_4)}{\partial a_0}\Big\}\right]. \tag{11}$$

In general $-\dfrac{\partial(qv_{2r-2})}{\partial a_0} = v_{2r-2}^2\left[1 - \dfrac{\partial(qv_{2r})}{\partial a_0}\right], r > 1$ $\tag{12}$

so by inserting the expression for $-\partial(qv_4)/\partial a_0$ in (11), and repeating the process, we are led to

$$-\frac{\partial(qv_0)}{\partial a_0} = \tfrac{1}{2}v_0^2[1 + v_2^2 + v_2^2 v_4^2 + v_2^2 v_4^2 v_6^2 + \ldots]. \tag{13}$$

Accordingly, by (5), (13)

$$-\frac{\partial L}{\partial a_0} = 1 + \tfrac{1}{2}[v_0^2 + v_0^2 v_2^2 + v_0^2 v_2^2 v_4^2 + \ldots] \tag{14}$$

$$= 1 + \frac{1}{2A_0^2}[A_2^2 + A_4^2 + A_6^2 + \ldots]. \tag{15}$$

Hence

$$-2A_0^2 \frac{\partial L}{\partial a_0} = 2A_0^2 + \sum_{r=1}^{\infty} A_{2r}^2 = \frac{1}{\pi} \int_0^{2\pi} \mathrm{ce}_{2n}^2(z, q)\, dz. \qquad (16)\dagger$$

We calculate L from (2) using adequately accurate values of v_0, a_0. Let the result be $L = x_0 + iy_0$. Now calculate $-\partial L/\partial a_0$ from (14) using the v. Let $-\partial L/\partial a_0 = x_1 + iy_1$. Then from (4)

$$\delta a_0 \simeq (x_0 + iy_0)/(x_1 + iy_1) = x_2 + iy_2, \qquad (17)$$

so

$$a_0 + \delta a_0 \simeq (2\text{·}82098\ 8 + x_2) - (6\text{·}56490\ 8 - y_2)i, \qquad (18)$$

which is a closer approximation to the characteristic number than that in §3.43. This new value of a_0 is used to recalculate the v, as in §3.43. The process may be repeated, but the number of decimal places required for increasing accuracy will increase at each repetition, owing to decrease in the real and imaginary parts of L.

3.45. The series for $\mathrm{ce}_0(z, -4\text{·}8i)$. For this we use the v calculated in §3.43. Then

$$A_2 = v_0 A_0, \qquad A_4 = v_0 v_2 A_0, \qquad A_6 = v_0 v_2 v_4 A_0,$$

and we find approximately that

$$\left. \begin{array}{l} A_2 = -(1\text{·}367 + 0\text{·}588i)A_0, \\ A_4 = (0\text{·}013 + 0\text{·}468i)A_0, \\ A_6 = (0\text{·}065 - 0\text{·}015i)A_0. \end{array} \right\} \qquad (1)$$

Thus to a first approximation, we obtain

$$\mathrm{ce}_0(z, 4\text{·}8i) = A_0[1 - (1\text{·}367 + 0\text{·}588i)\cos 2z +$$
$$+ (0\text{·}013 + 0\text{·}468i)\cos 4z + (0\text{·}065 - 0\text{·}015i)\cos 6z + \ldots]. \qquad (2)$$

Writing $(\tfrac{1}{2}\pi - z)$ for z in (2) leads to

$$\mathrm{ce}_0(z, -4\text{·}8i) = A_0[1 + (1\text{·}367 + 0\text{·}588i)\cos 2z +$$
$$+ (0\text{·}013 + 0\text{·}468i)\cos 4z - (0\text{·}065 - 0\text{·}015i)\cos 6z + \ldots]. \qquad (3)$$

It may be remarked that (3) is not (2) with the sign of i changed (see footnote to §3.41).

3.46. a_2 **and the** A **for** $\mathrm{ce}_2(z, -4\text{·}8i)$. It is found by computation [57] that when $s > 1\text{·}4688\ldots$, a_0 is complex, and its conjugate is a_2.‡ By applying §3.44 to the value of a_0 in Table 4, we obtain

$$a_0 = 2\text{·}82120\ 8 - 6\text{·}56266\ 8i, \qquad (1)$$

so

$$a_2 = 2\text{·}82120\ 8 + 6\text{·}56266\ 8i. \qquad (2)$$

† This has not been equated to unity because q is imaginary (see § 2.21).
‡ No formal proof of this has yet been published.

The v for ce_2 are obtained from those for ce_0 by merely altering the signs of the real parts—a procedure whose validity is easily established. Thus from (3), (4), (6) § 3.43, we get

$$v_0 = 1\cdot367 - 0\cdot588i, \\ v_2 = 0\cdot132 - 0\cdot285i, \\ v_4 = 0\cdot0276 - 0\cdot139i, \qquad (3)$$

these data being approximate for purposes of illustration. The A may be calculated from formulae at the beginning of § 3.45, but they can be found immediately by changing the signs of the real and imaginary parts in alternate A in (1) § 3.45. Thus for ce_2 we have

$$A_2 = (1\cdot367 - 0\cdot588i)A_0, \\ A_4 = (0\cdot013 - 0\cdot468i)A_0, \\ A_6 = -(0\cdot065 + 0\cdot015i)A_0. \qquad (4)$$

Hence we find that

$$ce_2(z, 4\cdot8i) = A_0[1 + (1\cdot367 - 0\cdot588i)\cos 2z + \\ + (0\cdot013 - 0\cdot468i)\cos 4z - (0\cdot065 + 0\cdot015i)\cos 6z + ...], \quad (5)$$

and, therefore, writing $(\tfrac{1}{2}\pi - z)$ for z,

$$ce_2(z, -4\cdot8i) = A_0[1 - (1\cdot367 - 0\cdot588i)\cos 2z + \\ + (0\cdot013 - 0\cdot468i)\cos 4z + (0\cdot065 + 0\cdot015i)\cos 6z + ...]. \quad (6)$$

3.47. Characteristic numbers for other functions when s is positive. When $s > s_0 > 0$ and the characteristic numbers are complex, numerical values indicate the following results [57]:

$$a_0 \text{ is conjugate to } a_2, \\ a_1 \quad ,, \qquad ,, \quad b_1, \\ a_3 \quad ,, \qquad ,, \quad b_3, \\ b_2 \quad ,, \qquad ,, \quad b_4.$$

If s is large enough, numerical values indicate that [57]:

$$a_0 \sim b_1, \\ a_3 \sim b_4, \\ \tfrac{1}{2}(a_0 + b_1) \sim \Gamma_0, \\ \tfrac{1}{2}(a_3 + b_4) \sim \Gamma_1, \\ b_1 - a_0 \sim \Delta_0, \\ b_4 - a_3 \sim \Delta_1.$$

See § 3.43 for meaning of symbols.

It may be remarked that when s varies from $0 \cdot 16$ to $1 \cdot 44$, a_0 varies from $0 \cdot 012836$ to $1 \cdot 689280$, whilst a_2 varies from $3 \cdot 989297$ to $2 \cdot 481324$. Thus the variation in $(a_0 + a_2)$ is from $4 \cdot 002132$ to $4 \cdot 170604$, so $(a_0 + a_2)$ is in the neighbourhood of 4 when s is in the range $0 \cdot 16 \leqslant s \leqslant 1 \cdot 44$, i.e. the two a are real. This is readily explained by aid of (1) §3.41 and (1) §3.42. From these formulae when s is moderate

$$(a_0 + a_2) = 4 + \left(\frac{1}{2} - \frac{5}{12}\right) s^2 + \left(\frac{7}{128} - \frac{763}{13824}\right) s^4 - \ldots \tag{1}$$

$$= 4 + \frac{1}{12} s^2 - \frac{7}{13824} s^4 - \ldots, \tag{2}$$

so the dominant term is 4. Numerical data show that as $s \to +1 \cdot 4688\ldots$, $a_0 \to (2-0)$, and $a_2 \to (2+0)$.

Since the series for a_0, a_2 at (1) §3.41, (1) §3.42 proceed in powers of s^2, all the terms are real. The fact that a_0, a_2 are both complex when $s > 1 \cdot 4688\ldots$ indicates, therefore, that the series cannot hold then, i.e. they appear to be divergent.

3.50. cer, cei, ser, sei **functions.** In § 3.40 et seq. we have seen that $\mathrm{ce}_m(z, -is)$ is a complex function of z, so we may put

$$\mathrm{ce}_m(z, -is) = \mathrm{cer}_m z + i\, \mathrm{cei}_m z. \tag{1}$$

Writing the complex coefficients in polar form, we take

$$A_p^{(m)} = |A_p^{(m)}| e^{i\varphi_p}.$$

Thus, if $\mathrm{ce}_{2n}(z, +is) = \sum_{r=0}^{\infty} A_{2r}^{(2n)} \cos 2rz$, by (2) §2.18 we have

$$\mathrm{ce}_{2n}(z, -is) = (-1)^n \sum_{r=0}^{\infty} (-1)^r A_{2r}^{(2n)} \cos 2rz$$

$$= (-1)^n \sum_{r=0}^{\infty} (-1)^r |A_{2r}^{(2n)}| e^{i\varphi_{2r}} \cos 2rz \tag{2}$$

$$= (-1)^n \Big[\sum_{r=0}^{\infty} (-1)^r |A_{2r}^{(2n)}| \cos \varphi_{2r} \cos 2rz +$$

$$+ i \sum_{r=0}^{\infty} (-1)^r |A_{2r}^{(2n)}| \sin \varphi_{2r} \cos 2rz \Big], \tag{3}$$

so

$$\mathrm{cer}_{2n} z = (-1)^n \sum_{r=0}^{\infty} (-1)^r |A_{2r}^{(2n)}| \cos \varphi_{2r} \cos 2rz \tag{4}$$

$$= (-1)^n |A_0^{(2n)}| \{ 1 - |v_0| \cos \varphi_2 \cos 2z +$$

$$+ |v_0 v_2| \cos \varphi_4 \cos 4z - |v_0 v_2 v_4| \cos \varphi_6 \cos 6z + \ldots \}, \tag{5}$$

and

$$\text{cei}_{2n}\,z = (-1)^n \sum_{r=0}^{\infty} (-1)^r |A_{2r}^{(2n)}| \sin\varphi_{2r}\cos 2rz \tag{6}$$

$$= (-1)^n |A_0^{(2n)}|\,\{1 - |v_0|\sin\varphi_2\cos 2z +$$

$$+ |v_0\,v_2|\sin\varphi_4\cos 4z - |v_0\,v_2\,v_4|\sin\varphi_6\cos 6z + ...\}. \tag{7}$$

These series are absolutely and uniformly convergent in any finite region of the z-plane. The series for cer_{2n+1}, cei_{2n+1}, ser_m, sei_m may be found by procedure akin to that above. The modified functions Cer_m, Cei_m, etc., are derived from the foregoing by writing iz for z.

3.51. Bessel series for cer, cei, ser, sei. Writing $k = (is)^{\frac{1}{2}} = i^{\frac{1}{2}}l$ in (2) § 8.20, using the complex A from § 3.50, and the relation $I_{2r}(u) = (-1)^r J_{2r}(iu)$, we obtain

$$\text{ce}_{2n}(z, is) = \frac{\text{ce}_{2n}(0, is)}{A_0^{(2n)}} \sum_{r=0}^{\infty} A_{2r}^{(2n)} J_{2r}(2i^{\frac{3}{2}}l\sin z). \tag{1}$$

Writing $(\frac{1}{2}\pi - z)$ for z gives

$$\text{ce}_{2n}(z, -is) = (-1)^n \frac{\text{ce}_{2n}(0, is)}{A_0^{(2n)}} \sum_{r=0}^{\infty} A_{2r}^{(2n)} J_{2r}(2i^{\frac{3}{2}}l\cos z). \tag{2}$$

By [203, pp. 121, 122], we have

$$J_{2r}(i^{\frac{3}{2}}u) = \text{ber}_{2r}u + i\,\text{bei}_{2r}u = M_{2r}(u)e^{i\theta_{2r}(u)}. \tag{3}$$

Let $\text{ce}_{2n}(0, is)/A_0 = E_{2n}e^{i\psi_{2n}}$, and use (3) in (2); then we find that

$$\text{ce}_{2n}(z, -is) = (-1)^n E_{2n} \sum_{r=0}^{\infty} |A_{2r}^{(2n)}| M_{2r} e^{i(\theta_{2r} + \varphi_{2r} + \psi_{2n})}, \tag{4}$$

so

$$\text{cer}_{2n}\,z = (-1)^n E_{2n} \sum_{r=0}^{\infty} |A_{2r}^{(2n)}| M_{2r}\cos(\theta_{2r} + \varphi_{2r} + \psi_{2n}), \tag{5}$$

and

$$\text{cei}_{2n}\,z = (-1)^n E_{2n} \sum_{r=0}^{\infty} |A_{2r}^{(2n)}| M_{2r}\sin(\theta_{2r} + \varphi_{2r} + \psi_{2n}), \tag{6}$$

the argument of M, θ being $u = 2l\cos z$. These series have the same convergence properties as in § 3.50. Series for the other functions may be derived in a similar way, while those for Cer_m, etc., may be obtained if iz be written for z.

By replacing k_1^2 in (3) § 2, Appendix 1, with $-ik_1^2$, it will be found that when the fundamental ellipse tends to a circle, Cer, Cei, etc., degenerate to constant multiples of the ber and bei functions.

GENERAL THEORY: FUNCTIONS OF FRACTIONAL ORDER: SOLUTION OF EQUATIONS

4.10. Introduction. The discussion in this and in the next eight sections applies to any linear differential equation of the second order with single-valued periodic coefficients, e.g. (2), (5) Chapter I, these being Mathieu's and Hill's equations respectively.

Let $y_1(z)$, $y_2(z)$ be any two solutions which constitute a fundamental system. The complete solution is

$$y = Ay_1(z) + By_2(z), \tag{1}$$

A, B being arbitrary constants. If we write $(z+\pi)$ for z, then $y_1(z+\pi)$, $y_2(z+\pi)$ are solutions also, π being the period of the coefficients. In accordance with the theory in [49], we have

$$y_1(z+\pi) = \alpha_1 y_1(z) + \alpha_2 y_2(z), \tag{2}$$

and
$$y_2(z+\pi) = \beta_1 y_1(z) + \beta_2 y_2(z), \tag{3}$$

where α_1, α_2, β_1, β_2 are constants determinable from the conditions at, say, $z = 0$. It is convenient in this discussion to choose the initial conditions $y_1(0) = 1$, $y_1'(0) = 0$, $y_2(0) = 0$, $y_2'(0) = 1$. Substituting the first and third of these in (2), (3) yields

$$\alpha_1 = y_1(\pi), \qquad \beta_1 = y_2(\pi). \tag{4}$$

Differentiating (2), (3) with respect to z, we get

$$y_1'(z+\pi) = \alpha_1 y_1'(z) + \alpha_2 y_2'(z), \tag{5}$$

and
$$y_2'(z+\pi) = \beta_1 y_1'(z) + \beta_2 y_2'(z); \tag{6}$$

so insertion of the second and fourth conditions leads to

$$\alpha_2 = y_1'(\pi), \qquad \beta_2 = y_2'(\pi). \tag{7}$$

If y_1 were an even function of z, and y_2 an odd one, on writing $z = -\pi$ in (3) we should get

$$y_2(0) = 0 = \beta_1 y_1(\pi) - \beta_2 y_2(\pi) = \beta_1(\alpha_1 - \beta_2). \tag{8}$$

Since $\beta_1 \neq 0$, it follows that $\alpha_1 = \beta_2$, i.e.

$$y_1(\pi) = y_2'(\pi). \tag{9}$$

4.11. Relationship between $y(z)$ **and** $y(z+\pi)$. From (1)–(3)
§ 4.10 we have

$$y(z+\pi) = Ay_1(z+\pi)+By_2(z+\pi) \tag{1}$$
$$= A\{\alpha_1 y_1(z)+\alpha_2 y_2(z)\}+B\{\beta_1 y_1(z)+\beta_2 y_2(z)\}$$
$$= (A\alpha_1+B\beta_1)y_1(z)+(A\alpha_2+B\beta_2)y_2(z). \tag{2}$$

Thus, if φ, a constant, can be found such that $(A\alpha_1+B\beta_1) = \varphi A$,
and $(A\alpha_2+B\beta_2) = \varphi B$, then by (1) § 4.10, (2) above may be written
in the form
$$y(z+\pi) = \varphi y(z). \tag{3}$$
This necessitates

$$A(\alpha_1-\varphi)+B\beta_1 = 0, \quad \text{or} \quad -A/B = \beta_1/(\alpha_1-\varphi), \tag{4}$$
and $\qquad A\alpha_2+B(\beta_2-\varphi) = 0, \quad \text{or} \quad -A/B = (\beta_2-\varphi)/\alpha_2. \tag{5}$

Accordingly, if A, B are non-zero, we must have

$$(\alpha_1-\varphi)(\beta_2-\varphi) = \alpha_2\beta_1, \tag{6}$$
or $\qquad \varphi^2-(\alpha_1+\beta_2)\varphi+(\alpha_1\beta_2-\alpha_2\beta_1) = 0. \tag{7}$

Since $\alpha_1,\ldots, \beta_2$ were determined in § 4.10, the two values of φ which
satisfy (7) may be expressed in terms of $y_1(\pi)$, $y_1'(\pi)$, $y_2(\pi)$, $y_2'(\pi)$.

4.12. Introduction of the index μ. Let $\varphi = e^{\mu\pi}$, where μ is a
number dependent upon the parameters in the equation, i.e. a, q in
(1) § 2.10. Also take $\phi(z) = e^{-\mu z}y(z)$, both of these being definitions.
Writing $(z+\pi)$ for z gives

$$\phi(z+\pi) = e^{-\mu(z+\pi)}y(z+\pi) \tag{1}$$
$$= e^{-\mu(z+\pi)}\varphi y(z),$$
by (3) § 4.11, $\qquad = e^{-\mu z}y(z) = \phi(z). \tag{2}$

Hence $\phi(z)$ is periodic in z with period π. Since $y(z)$ is a solution of
the type of differential equation under consideration, it follows that
$e^{\mu z}\phi(z)$ is a solution.

4.13. Complete solution of equation. For our specific purpose
we fix attention upon the equations

$$\frac{d^2y}{dz^2}+(a-2q\cos 2z)y = 0, \tag{1}$$

and $\qquad \dfrac{d^2y}{dz^2}+[a-2q\,\psi(z)]y = 0. \tag{2}$

$\psi(z)$ is an even, differentiable† function of z, periodic therein with

† See footnote on p. 127.

period π, e.g. $\psi(z) = \sum\limits_{r=1}^{\infty} \theta_{2r} \cos 2rz.\dagger$ By virtue of periodicity π, we take

$$\phi(z) = \sum_{r=-\infty}^{\infty} c_{2r} e^{2rzi}, \tag{3}$$

and

$$\phi(-z) = \sum_{r=-\infty}^{\infty} c_{2r} e^{-2rzi}. \tag{4}$$

Then by § 4.12, if $\mu = \alpha + i\beta$, α, β real, $e^{\mu z}\phi(z)$ is a formal solution of (1) or of (2). Since both of these equations are unchanged,‡ if $-z$ be written for z, $e^{-\mu z}\phi(-z)$ is an independent solution, provided either $\alpha \neq 0$, or when $\alpha = 0$, β is non-integral. Hence the complete solutions of equations of type (1), (2) may be expressed in the form

$$y(z) = A e^{\mu z} \sum_{r=-\infty}^{\infty} c_{2r} e^{2rzi} + B e^{-\mu z} \sum_{r=-\infty}^{\infty} c_{2r} e^{-2rzi}, \tag{5}$$

A, B being arbitrary constants. The above analysis is based on [215].

4.14. Stability of solutions, z real.

(a) A solution is defined to be unstable if it tends to $\pm\infty$ as $z \to +\infty$.

(b) A solution is defined to be stable if it tends to zero or remains bounded as $z \to +\infty$.

(c) A solution with period π, 2π is said to be neutral, but may be regarded as a special case of a stable solution.

Cases (a), (b) are non-periodic.§ In (5) § 4.13, since the sigma terms are both periodic in z, the stability depends upon $e^{\mu z}$, i.e. upon μ. It may, in general, have any real, imaginary, or complex value. If real and positive > 0, $e^{\mu z} \to +\infty$ with z. Hence the A member of (5) § 4.13 tends to $\pm\infty$ as $z \to +\infty$, while the B member approaches zero. Thus the first part of the solution is unstable, but the second is stable, so the complete solution is unstable. If μ is real and negative, instability arises from the B member.

When $\mu = i\beta$, β non-integral (5) § 4.13 gives the stable solution

$$y(z) = A \sum_{r=-\infty}^{\infty} c_{2r} e^{(2r+\beta)zi} + B \sum_{r=-\infty}^{\infty} c_{2r} e^{-(2r+\beta)zi}. \tag{1}$$

If β is a rational fraction p/s, p and s being prime to each other,

† In § 6.20 the θ_{2r} must be such that $\psi(z)$, $\psi'(z)$,... are uniformly convergent and, therefore, ψ, ψ',... are differentiable term by term. In a practical application, the number of terms would usually be finite. It may sometimes be expedient for $\psi(z)$ to have additional properties specified in § 6.10, with $\omega = 1$.

‡ With ψ as above. § Except as in (1) when the period is $2s\pi$.

the Σ members are both periodic, with period $2s\pi$. When β is irrational, the solution is oscillatory but bounded and non-periodic, i.e. it never repeats itself exactly at any interval. The Σ members in (1) are independent solutions of (1), (2) §4.13.

If $\mu = \alpha+i\beta$, where α, β are real and non-zero, (5) §4.13 assumes the form

$$y(z) = Ae^{\alpha z} \sum_{r=-\infty}^{\infty} c_{2r}\, e^{(2r+\beta)zi} + Be^{-\alpha z} \sum_{r=-\infty}^{\infty} c_{2r}\, e^{-(2r+\beta)zi}, \qquad (2)$$

and from what precedes, this is an unstable type. In numerical work it is possible, however, to arrange that μ shall be either real or imaginary (according as the solution is unstable or stable), but not complex; also that $0 < \beta < 1$ for convenience (see §4.70).

Recapitulation.

(a) The solution is unstable if μ is any real number $\neq 0$.

(b) The solution is unstable if $\mu = \alpha+i\beta$, $|\alpha| > 0$, $|\beta| > 0$.

(c) The solution is stable and periodic if $\mu = i\beta$, β a rational fraction.

(d) The solution is stable but non-periodic if $\mu = i\beta$, β irrational. In (a)–(d) the *complete* solution is implied.

4.15. Alternative forms of solution. In accordance with the theory of linear differential equations, we may choose as a first solution

$$y_1(z) = \tfrac{1}{2}A\left\{e^{\mu z} \sum_{r=-\infty}^{\infty} c_{2r}\, e^{2rzi} + e^{-\mu z} \sum_{r=-\infty}^{\infty} c_{2r}\, e^{-2rzi}\right\} \qquad (1)$$

$$= \tfrac{1}{2}Ac_0(e^{\mu z}+e^{-\mu z}) + \tfrac{1}{2}Ae^{\mu z}\left\{\sum_{r=1}^{\infty} (c_{2r}\, e^{2rzi}+c_{-2r}\, e^{-2rzi})\right\} +$$

$$+ \tfrac{1}{2}Ae^{-\mu z}\left\{\sum_{r=1}^{\infty} (c_{2r}\, e^{-2rzi}+c_{-2r}\, e^{2rzi})\right\} \qquad (2)$$

$$= Ac_0\cosh\mu z + A\sum_{r=1}^{\infty}\{c_{2r}\cosh(\mu+2ri)z + c_{-2r}\cosh(\mu-2ri)z\}$$

$$= A\sum_{r=-\infty}^{\infty} c_{2r}\cosh(\mu+2ri)z. \qquad (3)$$

As in §4.10 suppose $y_1(0) = 1$, then $A = 1\Big/\sum_{-\infty}^{\infty} c_{2r}$ and, therefore,

$$\alpha_1 = y_1(\pi) = \cosh\mu\pi, \qquad y_1(n\pi) = \cosh\mu n\pi, \qquad (4)$$

for all finite values of μ.

Starting with a negative sign within the r.h.s. of (1), we obtain a second independent solution, namely,

$$y_2(z) = B \sum_{r=-\infty}^{\infty} c_{2r} \sinh(\mu+2ri)z. \tag{5}$$

As in § 4.10, let $y_2'(0) = 1$, then $B = 1 \big/ \sum_{-\infty}^{\infty} (\mu+2ri)c_{2r}$, so

$$\beta_2 = y_2'(\pi) = \cosh\mu\pi, \qquad y_2'(n\pi) = \cosh\mu n\pi, \tag{6}$$

provided (5) is uniformly convergent for differentiation of the series to be permissible (see § 4.77).

From (4), (6) we get

$$y_1(\pi) = y_2'(\pi), \quad \text{or} \quad \alpha_1 = \beta_2, \tag{7}$$

and

$$y_1(n\pi) = y_2'(n\pi) = \cosh\mu n\pi. \tag{8}$$

Again, from (3)

$$y_1'(z) = A \sum_{r=-\infty}^{\infty} (\mu+2ri)c_{2r} \sinh(\mu+2ri)z,$$

provided (3) is uniformly convergent (see § 4.77). Then with $z = \pi$,

$$\alpha_2 = y_1'(\pi) = A \sinh\mu\pi \sum_{-\infty}^{\infty} (\mu+2ri)c_{2r}$$

$$= \frac{A}{B}\sinh\mu\pi. \tag{9}$$

Also

$$y_1'(n\pi) = \frac{A}{B}\sinh\mu n\pi. \tag{10}$$

Writing $z = \pi$ in (5) leads to

$$\beta_1 = y_2(\pi) = \frac{B}{A}\sinh\mu\pi. \tag{11}$$

Also

$$y_2(n\pi) = \frac{B}{A}\sinh\mu n\pi, \tag{12}$$

so

$$\alpha_2\beta_1 = y_1'(\pi)y_2(\pi) = \sinh^2\mu\pi, \qquad y_1'(n\pi)y_2(n\pi) = \sinh^2\mu n\pi. \tag{13}$$

From (4), (6)

$$\alpha_1\beta_2 = y_2'(\pi)y_1(\pi) = \cosh^2\mu\pi, \qquad y_2'(n\pi)y_1(n\pi) = \cosh^2\mu n\pi. \tag{14}$$

By (13), (14)

$$\alpha_1\beta_2 - \alpha_2\beta_1 = y_2'(\pi)y_1(\pi) - y_1'(\pi)y_2(\pi) = 1, \tag{15}†$$

and

$$y_2'(n\pi)y_1(n\pi) - y_1'(n\pi)y_2(n\pi) = 1. \tag{16}†$$

Substituting from (4), (6), (15) into (7) § 4.11, we find that

$$\varphi_1 = e^{\mu\pi}, \qquad \varphi_2 = e^{-\mu\pi}, \qquad \varphi_1\varphi_2 = 1, \qquad \varphi_1 = 1/\varphi_2.$$

† These are (2) § 2.191 with $z = \pi$ and $n\pi$, respectively.

These results are valid for $\mu = \alpha+i\beta$, $\alpha \neq 0$, or if $\alpha = 0$, β is non-integral: also $y_1(z)$ is even in z, whilst $y_2(z)$ is odd therein. This restriction is removed in § 4.152.

4.151. Extension of § 4.11. Reverting now to (3) § 4.11, if $y_1(z)$ be a solution of either (1), (2) § 4.13, then

$$y_1(z\pm\pi) = e^{\pm\mu\pi}y_1(z). \tag{1}$$

Also, if $y_2(z)$ is a linearly independent solution,

$$y_2(z\pm\pi) = e^{\mp\mu\pi}y_2(z). \tag{2}$$

From (1) $$e^{\pm\mu\pi} = y_1(z\pm\pi)/y_1(z). \tag{3}$$

Hence $${\cosh \atop \sinh}\Big\}\mu\pi = [y_1(z+\pi)\pm y_1(z-\pi)]/2y_1(z). \tag{4}$$

If $z = 0$, and $y_1(r\pi) \neq 0$, (4) gives

$${\cosh \atop \sinh}\Big\}\mu\pi = [y_1(\pi)\pm y_1(-\pi)]/2y_1(0). \tag{5}$$

Similarly (2) yields the formulae

$${\cosh \atop \sinh}\Big\}\mu\pi = [y_2(z-\pi)\pm y_2(z+\pi)]/2y_2(z), \tag{6}$$

when $z = \pi$, $$= [y_2(0)\pm y_2(2\pi)]/2y_2(\pi), \tag{7}$$

provided $y_2(0) \neq 0$. Since $\phi(z)$ has period π, $y_2(0) = 0$ entails $y_2(n\pi) = 0$, so (7) would then be indeterminate.

4.152. A more general case. From § 4.12 the solutions of (1), (2) § 4.13 have the form

$$y = e^{\mu z}\phi(z), \tag{1}$$

where for convenience we shall take 2π as the period of $\phi(z)$. Then $\phi(-\pi) = \phi'(\pi)$, and

$$y(-\pi) = e^{-\mu\pi}\phi(\pi), \qquad y(\pi) = e^{\mu\pi}\phi(\pi), \tag{2}$$

so $$y(\pi)-e^{2\mu\pi}y(-\pi) = 0. \tag{3}$$

Similarly we obtain

$$y'(\pi)-e^{2\mu\pi}y'(-\pi) = 0. \tag{4}$$

Let $y_1(z)$ and $y_2(z)$ be *any* two linearly independent solutions, and substitute $y = Ay_1(z)+By_2(z)$ in (3), (4). Then we get

$$A[y_1(\pi)-e^{2\mu\pi}y_1(-\pi)]+B[y_2(\pi)-e^{2\mu\pi}y_2(-\pi)] = 0 \tag{5}$$

and $$A[y_1'(\pi)-e^{2\mu\pi}y_1'(-\pi)]+B[y_2'(\pi)-e^{2\mu\pi}y_2'(-\pi)] = 0. \tag{6}$$

For A, B non-zero, we must have

$$[y_1(\pi)-e^{2\mu\pi}y_1(-\pi)][y_2'(\pi)-e^{2\mu\pi}y_2'(-\pi)]-$$
$$-[y_2(\pi)-e^{2\mu\pi}y_2(-\pi)][y_1'(\pi)-e^{2\mu\pi}y_1'(-\pi)] = 0, \quad (7)$$

i.e. $$e^{4\mu\pi}-\frac{D}{c^2}e^{2\mu\pi}+1 = 0, \tag{8}$$

where

$$D = y_1(-\pi)y_2'(\pi)+y_1(\pi)y_2'(-\pi)-y_2(-\pi)y_1'(\pi)-y_2(\pi)y_1'(-\pi),$$

and

$$y_1(\pi)y_2'(\pi)-y_2(\pi)y_1'(\pi) = y_1(-\pi)y_2'(-\pi)-y_2(-\pi)y_1'(-\pi) = c^2$$

(see § 2.191). Solving (8) leads to

$$\cosh 2\mu\pi = D/2c^2. \tag{9}$$

It may be remarked that conditions respecting oddness and evenness of the solutions have not been imposed. This is useful in connexion with problems like that in § 6.40 where the solutions are neither odd nor even. The preceding formulae are valid if $n\pi$ is written for π, $n \geqslant 2$.

If we assign the initial conditions

$$y_1(-\pi) = y_2'(-\pi) = 1, \qquad y_2(-\pi) = y_1'(-\pi) = 0,$$

(9) becomes $$\cosh 2\mu\pi = [y_1(\pi)+y_2'(\pi)]/2, \tag{10}$$

and, as before, π may be replaced by $n\pi$.

4.153. Functions having period 2π. Apart from § 4.152 the analysis in this chapter has been based upon a solution of the type $e^{\mu z}\phi(z)$, with $\phi(z) = \sum\limits_{r=-\infty}^{\infty} c_{2r} e^{2rzi}$, which has period π. It is preferable that μ should be real or imaginary ($\mu = i\beta$, $0 < \beta < 1$), but not complex. To obtain this objective when the parametric point (a, q) lies in certain regions of the (a, q)-plane (see Fig. 8), which are specified later in § 4.70, it is essential that $\phi(z)$ has period 2π. The results in §§ 4.10–4.151 are applicable if for π we write 2π, and take

$$\phi(z) = \sum_{r=-\infty}^{\infty} c_{2r+1} e^{(2r+1)zi}; \tag{1}$$

also in all infinite series we change $2r$ to $(2r+1)$. The relation corresponding to (4), (8) § 4.15 is now

$$y_1(n\pi) = y_2'(n\pi) = (-1)^n \cosh\mu n\pi. \tag{2}$$

4.16. Form of solution when $\mu = i\beta$, $0 < \beta < 1$. In (3) § 4.15 write $\mu = i\beta$, and it becomes

$$y_1(z) = A \sum_{r=-\infty}^{\infty} c_{2r} \cos(2r+\beta)z, \tag{1}$$

while the same substitution in (5) § 4.15 gives the linearly independent solution

$$y_2(z) = B \sum_{r=-\infty}^{\infty} c_{2r} \sin(2r+\beta)z, \tag{2}$$

the i being dropped, since it is merely a constant multiplier. Hence the complete solution of

$$y'' + (a - 2q \cos 2z)y = 0, \tag{3}$$

takes the form

$$y(z) = A \sum_{r=-\infty}^{\infty} c_{2r} \cos(2r+\beta)z + B \sum_{r=-\infty}^{\infty} c_{2r} \sin(2r+\beta)z, \tag{4}$$

and this constitutes a fundamental system.

Corresponding to (4), (8), (13) § 4.15, we have

$$y_1(n\pi) = y_2'(n\pi) = \cos\beta n\pi \tag{5}$$

and

$$y_1'(n\pi)y_2(n\pi) = -\sin^2\beta n\pi. \tag{6}$$

These are readily checked by using (1), (2) and the initial conditions $y_1(0) = y_2'(0) = 1$, $y_2(0) = y_1'(0) = 0$.

Additional forms of solution. Replacing $2r$ by $(2r+1)$ in (1), (2), (4) in accordance with § 4.153, leads to the solutions (independent of each other)

$$y_1(z) = A \sum_{r=-\infty}^{\infty} c_{2r+1} \cos(2r+1+\beta)z, \tag{7}$$

and

$$y_2(z) = B \sum_{r=-\infty}^{\infty} c_{2r+1} \sin(2r+1+\beta)z, \tag{8}$$

giving for the complete solution

$$y(z) = A \sum_{r=-\infty}^{\infty} c_{2r+1} \cos(2r+1+\beta)z + B \sum_{r=-\infty}^{\infty} c_{2r+1} \sin(2r+1+\beta)z. \tag{9}$$

Corresponding to (2) § 4.153, we have

$$y_1(n\pi) = y_2'(n\pi) = (-1)^n \cos\beta n\pi, \tag{10}$$

which can be confirmed by using (7), (8).

It may be remarked that the A, B are quite arbitrary, and need not have the values obtained in § 4.15, using the initial conditions stated there, i.e. any appropriate initial conditions may be chosen.

4.17. Solution when $\beta = 0$ or 1. Consider any point (a, q), $q > 0$, in a stable region of Fig. 8 A near a_{2n} but not upon it. Then (3) § 4.16 has two independent coexistent solutions, namely, (1), (2) § 4.16. On a_{2n}, $\beta = 0$ and (2) § 4.16 ceases to be a solution.† Substituting either (1) or (2) § 4.16 into (3) § 4.16 and equating the coefficient of $\cos(2r+\beta)z$ or $\sin(2r+\beta)z$ to zero for $r = -\infty$ to ∞, we obtain the recurrence relation

$$[a-(2r+\beta)^2]c_{2r}-q(c_{2r+2}+c_{2r-2}) = 0. \tag{1}$$

With $\beta = 0$, (1) becomes

$$(a-4r^2)c_{2r}-q(c_{2r+2}+c_{2r-2}) = 0. \tag{2}$$

Writing $-r$ for r yields

$$(a-4r^2)c_{-2r}-q(c_{-2r-2}+c_{-2r+2}) = 0. \tag{3}$$

Then (2), (3) are compatible provided $c_0 \neq 0$ and $c_{2r} = c_{-2r}$, $r \geqslant 1$. Hence, when $\beta = 0$ and $a = a_{2n}$, (1) § 4.16 may be written

$$y_1(z) = A\Big[c_0+2\sum_{r=1}^{\infty}c_{2r}\cos 2rz\Big], \tag{4}$$

which is a constant multiple of $ce_{2n}(z, q)$ as defined at (1) § 2.17.

When $\beta = 1$, (a, q) is on b_{2n+1}, and (1) § 4.16 ceases to be a solution. The recurrence relation is now

$$[a-(2r+1)^2]c_{2r}-q(c_{2r+2}+c_{2r-2}) = 0. \tag{5}$$

Writing $-(r+1)$ for r in (5) gives

$$[a-(2r+1)^2]c_{-2r-2}-q(c_{-2r}+c_{-2r-4}) = 0. \tag{6}$$

Then (5), (6) are compatible if $c_{2r} = -c_{-2r-2}$, e.g. $c_0 = -c_{-2}$, $c_2 = -c_{-4}$. Hence (2) § 4.16 may be written

$$y_2(z) = 2B\sum_{r=0}^{\infty}c_{2r+1}\sin(2r+1)z, \tag{7}$$

where c_{2r+1} has been substituted for c_{2r}. This is a constant multiple of $se_{2n+1}(z, q)$ defined at (3) § 2.17.

With $\beta = 0$ in (7), (8) § 4.16, $y_2(z)$ is not a solution since (a, q) is on a_{2n+1}. Then as above it can be shown that

$$y_1(z) = 2A\sum_{r=0}^{\infty}c_{2r+1}\cos(2r+1)z, \tag{8}$$

which is a constant multiple of $ce_{2n+1}(z, q)$. Similarly with $\beta = 1$ in

† See § 2.13 et seq. The characteristic numbers for ce_m, se_m are different.

(7), (8) § 4.16, $y_1(z)$ ceases to be a solution, since (a, q) is on b_{2n+2}. Then we find that

$$y_2(z) = 2B \sum_{r=0}^{\infty} c_{2r+2} \sin(2r+2)z, \tag{9}$$

which is a constant multiple of $\mathrm{se}_{2n+2}(z, q)$.

4.18. Changing the sign of q. Except in § 4.17, the sign of q has not been specified. Assuming, however, that the various solutions are for $q > 0$, those for the same a but $q < 0$ may be derived if $(\frac{1}{2}\pi - z)$ is written for z.

4.19. General relationships between the solutions. We commence with (2), (3) § 4.10, and use the values of α_1, α_2, β_1, β_2 and the initial conditions stated therein. Then if y_1, y_2 are independent solutions of (1) or of (2) § 4.13,

$$y_1(\pi+z) = y_1(\pi)y_1(z)+y_1'(\pi)y_2(z) \tag{1}$$

and

$$y_2(\pi+z) = y_2(\pi)y_1(z)+y_1(\pi)y_2(z). \tag{2}$$

Writing $-z$ for z, and postulating that y_1 is even and y_2 odd in z, (1), (2) yield

$$y_1(\pi-z) = y_1(\pi)y_1(z)-y_1'(\pi)y_2(z) \tag{3}$$

and

$$y_2(\pi-z) = y_2(\pi)y_1(z)-y_1(\pi)y_2(z). \tag{4}$$

Formulae (2), (4) are analogous to those for the circular functions. Four additional relationships are obtained if (1)–(4) are differentiated with respect to z.

Writing $(z-\pi)$ for z in (1), (2), and $(\pi+z)$ for z in (3), (4) leads to

$$y_1(z) = y_1(\pi)y_1(\pi \mp z)-y_1'(\pi)y_2(\pi \mp z) \tag{5}$$

and

$$y_2(z) = \pm y_2(\pi)y_1(\pi \mp z) \mp y_1(\pi)y_2(\pi \mp z). \tag{6}$$

Differentiating (3), (4) with respect to z and using (2) § 2.191, we obtain

$$y_1'(\pi) = y_1(z)y_1'(\pi-z)+y_1'(z)y_1(\pi-z) \tag{7}$$

and

$$y_2(\pi) = y_2(z)y_2'(\pi-z)+y_2'(z)y_2(\pi-z). \tag{8}$$

The following may be derived from (1)–(4):

$$y_1(z)y_2(\pi-u) \pm y_2(z)y_1(\pi-u) = y_1(u)y_2(\pi \pm z)-y_2(u)y_1(\pi \pm z) \tag{9}$$

and

$$y_1(z)y_2(\pi+u) \pm y_2(z)y_1(\pi+u) = y_1(u)y_2(\pi \pm z)+y_2(u)y_1(\pi \pm z). \tag{10}$$

If y_1 and/or y_2 is periodic, the above relationships may be simplified. It may be remarked that if y_1 is periodic in z with period π or 2π,

y_2 is non-periodic. But if y_1 has period $2s\pi$, $s \geqslant 2$, y_2 also has this period (see § 4.71).

4.20. Determination of μ when q is small. Dividing (1) $1°$ § 4.750 by $[(2r-i\mu)^2-a]$ and writing $\xi_{2r} = q/[(2r-i\mu)^2-a]$ leads to

$$c_{2r}+\xi_{2r}(c_{2r+2}+c_{2r-2}) = 0. \tag{1}$$

With $r = ...-2, -1, 0, 1, 2,...$ we obtain the system of linear equations:

$$\left.\begin{array}{l}
.\;\;\;.\quad\;\; .\quad\;\;\;\;\; .\quad\;\;\;\;\; .\quad\;\;\; .\quad\;\;\; .\quad\;\;\; .\quad\;\;\; . \\
.\;\; 0+\xi_{-4}c_{-6}+\;\; c_{-4}\; +\xi_{-4}c_{-2}+\;\; 0\;\; +\; 0\; +\; 0\; +\; 0\; +\;\; . \\
.\;\; 0+\;\; 0\;\; +\xi_{-2}c_{-4}+\;\; c_{-2}\; +\xi_{-2}c_0+\; 0\; +\; 0\; +\; 0\; +\;\; . \\
.\;\; 0+\;\; 0\;\; +\;\; 0\;\; +\xi_0c_{-2}+\;\; c_0\; +\xi_0c_2+\; 0\; +\; 0\; +\;\; . \\
.\;\; 0+\;\; 0\;\; +\;\; 0\;\; +\;\; 0\;\; +\xi_2c_0\; +\; c_2\; +\xi_2c_4+\; 0\; +\;\; . \\
.\;\; 0+\;\; 0\;\; +\;\; 0\;\; +\;\; 0\;\; +\;\; 0\;\; +\xi_4c_2+\; c_4\; +\xi_4c_6+\;\; . \\
.\;\;\;.\quad\;\; .\quad\;\;\;\;\; .\quad\;\;\;\;\; .\quad\;\;\; .\quad\;\;\; .\quad\;\;\; .\quad\;\;\; .
\end{array}\right\} = 0. \tag{2}$$

For (1) $2°$ § 4.70 to be a solution of Mathieu's equation, (2) must be a consistent system of equations, i.e. they must be satisfied simultaneously, so the eliminating determinant for the c (variables of the equations) must vanish. Thus we get the infinite determinant

$$\Delta(i\mu) = \begin{vmatrix}
. & . & . & . & . & . & . & . & . \\
. & \xi_{-4} & 1 & \xi_{-4} & 0 & 0 & 0 & 0 & . \\
. & 0 & \xi_{-2} & 1 & \xi_{-2} & 0 & 0 & 0 & . \\
. & 0 & 0 & \xi_0 & \boxed{1} & \xi_0 & 0 & 0 & . \\
. & 0 & 0 & 0 & \xi_2 & 1 & \xi_2 & 0 & . \\
. & 0 & 0 & 0 & 0 & \xi_4 & 1 & \xi_4 & . \\
. & . & . & . & . & . & . & . & .
\end{vmatrix} = 0. \tag{3}$$

When expanded this constitutes an equation for μ. If in the ξ we write $\mu = 0$, the determinant $\Delta(0)$ is obtained.

4.21. Convergence of (3) § 4.20. An infinite determinant is absolutely convergent if (a) the product of the diagonal elements is absolutely convergent, (b) the sum of the non-diagonal elements is absolutely convergent. (a) is satisfied, since the product is unity, while for (b) we have to demonstrate the convergence of

$$\sum_{r=-\infty}^{\infty} |1/[(2r-i\mu)^2-a]| = \frac{1}{4}\sum_{r=-\infty}^{\infty}\frac{1}{r^2}\left|1\middle/\left[\left(1-\frac{i\mu}{2r}\right)^2 - \frac{a}{4r^2}\right]\right|. \tag{1}$$

When $|r|$ is large enough, the terms under the sigma sign on the r.h.s.
of (1) are each $< |r|^{-p}$, $1 < p < 2$. Now the series $\sum_1^\infty 1/r^p$ is known
to converge, so (3) § 4.20 converges absolutely for all finite a and μ,
provided no denominator of one of the ξ_r vanishes, i.e.

$$(2r-i\mu) \neq \pm a^{\frac{1}{2}}.$$

4.22. $\Delta(i\mu)$ as a function of the complex variable.

(a) (i) Writing $-\mu$ for μ and $-r$ for r leaves $\Delta(i\mu)$ unaltered, since
$(2r-i\mu)^2 = (-2r+i\mu)^2$.

    (ii) r takes all integral values from $-\infty$ to $+\infty$, so that trans-
position of the elements with $+r$ and $-r$ leaves $\Delta(i\mu)$ unaltered.
Hence $\Delta(i\mu) = \Delta(-i\mu)$, so that $\Delta(i\mu)$ is an even function of μ.
Further, if a, q are real, so also is $\Delta(i\mu)$.

(b) $[2r+i(\mu+2i)]^2 = [2(r-1)+i\mu]^2$, so replacing $(r-1)$ by r in the
second bracket gives $(2r+i\mu)^2$, the determinant is unchanged
and $\Delta(i\mu) = \Delta[i(\mu+2i)]$. Hence Δ is periodic in μ with period
$2i$, so its behaviour everywhere is deducible from that in the
infinite strip of the μ-plane, $0 \leqslant \mathrm{Im}(\mu) \leqslant 1$.

(c) The only singularities of Δ are simple poles which occur when
$[(2r-i\mu)^2-a] = 0$, i.e. $\mu = i(a^{\frac{1}{2}}-2r)$ and $-i(a^{\frac{1}{2}}+2r)$. Now
the function $\chi(i\mu) = 1/(\cos i\mu\pi - \cos \pi a^{\frac{1}{2}})$ has simple poles at
these values of μ,† while its period is that of $\Delta(i\mu)$.

(d) From (c) it follows that the function

$$\psi(i\mu) = \Delta(i\mu) - C\chi(i\mu) \tag{1}$$

will have no singularities if C is suitably chosen, so by Liouville's theorem it must be a constant.

(e) To determine C we proceed as follows: When $\mu \to \infty$, all the
ξ in (3) § 4.20 tend to zero, and the diagonal elements alone
remain. Thus $\lim_{\mu\to\infty} \Delta(i\mu) = 1$. Also $\lim_{\mu\to\infty} \chi(i\mu) = 0$, and, therefore, $\psi(i\mu) = 1$. Then

$$C\chi(i\mu) = \Delta(i\mu) - 1,$$

or $$C = [\Delta(i\mu)-1]/\chi(i\mu). \tag{2}$$

When $\mu = 0$, $\chi(0) = 1/(1-\cos \pi a^{\frac{1}{2}})$, while the value of (3) § 4.20 is
$\Delta(0)$, the ξ_r being $q/(4r^2-a)$, $a \neq 4r^2$, to avoid an infinity. Hence
by (2)

$$C = [\Delta(0)-1][1-\cos \pi a^{\frac{1}{2}}]. \tag{3}$$

† We assume that $a \neq 4r^2$, so $\mu = 0$ is not a pole.

With this value of C, (1) is devoid of singularities in the μ-plane. The preceding analysis is based upon [215].

4.23. Solution of (3) § 4.20. This determinantal equation is satisfied if μ be such that $\Delta(i\mu) = 0$. Substituting this for Δ in (2) § 4.22 and equating to (3) § 4.22, we have

$$1/\chi(i\mu) = [1 - \Delta(0)][1 - \cos \pi a^{\frac{1}{2}}]. \tag{1}$$

Now $1/\chi(i\mu) = \cos i\mu\pi - \cos \pi a^{\frac{1}{2}}$, so by (1) we get

$$\cos i\mu\pi = \cos \pi a^{\frac{1}{2}} + [1 - \Delta(0)][1 - \cos \pi a^{\frac{1}{2}}]$$
$$= 1 - \Delta(0)[1 - \cos \pi a^{\frac{1}{2}}] \tag{2}$$

or $\qquad \sin^2 \tfrac{1}{2} i\mu\pi = \Delta(0)\sin^2 \tfrac{1}{2}\pi a^{\frac{1}{2}} \quad (a \neq 4r^2). \tag{3}$

This result is obtained in [213] without recourse to the complex variable.

The values of μ which satisfy (3) above, satisfy (3) § 4.20 also. Hence μ is determined if $\Delta(0)$ can be evaluated. If q is small,† by aid of [213] we find that

$$\Delta(0) \simeq 1 - \frac{\pi q^2 \cot \tfrac{1}{2}\pi a^{\frac{1}{2}}}{4a^{\frac{1}{2}}(a-1)}, \tag{4}$$

so (2) may be written

$$\cos i\mu\pi \simeq \cos \pi a^{\frac{1}{2}} + [\pi q^2 \sin \pi a^{\frac{1}{2}}/4a^{\frac{1}{2}}(a-1)] \quad (a \neq m^2). \tag{5}$$

4.24. The roots of (3) § 4.20. The determinant being an even function of $i\mu$, if $i\mu_0$ is a root of $\Delta(i\mu) = 0$, so is $-i\mu_0$. Since a linear D.E. of the second order has no more than two independent solutions, $\pm i\mu_0$ are the only *distinctive* roots. Now the non-diagonal elements are $\xi_{2r} = q/[(2r - i\mu)^2 - a]$, and if we write $i\mu = (i\mu_0 - 2r)$ in the elements on either side of the origin where $r = 0$, ξ_{2r} above is obtained. The result of treating all non-diagonal elements in this way is merely to shift the origin, and to leave $\Delta(i\mu)$ unchanged. It follows that the roots are $i\mu = \pm i\mu_0 - 2r$, r being any integer. If μ_0 is real, the roots occur in conjugate complex pairs $i\mu_0 - 2r$, $-i\mu_0 - 2r$. If μ_0 is imaginary $(= i\beta)$, the roots occur in the real pairs $\pm\beta - 2r$. For $\mu_0 = \alpha + i\beta$, $i\mu_0 = i\alpha - \beta$. Since r is any integer, we have the conjugate pair $i\alpha - \beta - 2r$, and $-i\alpha + \beta - 2(r+\beta) = -i\alpha - \beta - 2r$, provided β is an integer. Hence μ may be complex if its imaginary part is integral.

---

† It suffices if the term in q^2 in (4) is small compared with unity.

Recapitulation.

(a) If μ_0 is real and $r = 0$, $\mu = \pm\mu_0$ is real.

(b) If μ_0 is real and $r \neq 0$, μ is complex.

(c) If μ_0 is imaginary, μ is imaginary for all r.

(d) If $\mu_0 = \alpha + i\beta$, β an integer, μ is complex for all r.

As shown in § 4.70 the form of solution may be chosen to make μ either real or imaginary (according to the position of a, q in the plane, Fig. 8), but not complex. These remarks apply to all real values of a, q finite. The determinantal method of finding μ is unsuitable for numerical evaluation unless q is small. When q exceeds, say, q_0, the methods exemplified in Chapter V should be used to get accurate results.

4.30. Alternative form of general solution [186]. For the first solution we take

$$y_1(z) = e^{\mu z}\phi(z, \sigma), \tag{1}$$

ϕ being periodic in z with period π or 2π, and σ a new parameter. When (a, q) lies between a_0, b_2 in Fig. 8, we shall obtain the form

$$\phi(z, \sigma) = \sin(z-\sigma) + s_3\sin(3z-\sigma) + s_5\sin(5z-\sigma) + ... +$$
$$+ c_3\cos(3z-\sigma) + c_5\cos(5z-\sigma) + ..., \tag{2}$$

σ being dependent upon a, q, as also are the c, s. ϕ has no term in $\cos(z-\sigma)$ as its inclusion would introduce a *non-periodic* term, as shown below. For convenience the coefficient of $\sin(z-\sigma)$ is taken as unity for all q. Since σ, a, q are interrelated, we assume that

$$a = 1 + qf_1(\sigma) + q^2f_2(\sigma) + q^3f_3(\sigma) + ...; \tag{3}$$

also

$$\mu = qg_1(\sigma) + q^2g_2(\sigma) + q^3g_3(\sigma) + ..., \tag{4}$$

there being no term devoid of q, and we take

$$\phi(z, \sigma) = \sin(z-\sigma) + qh_1(z, \sigma) + q^2h_2(z, \sigma) + q^3h_3(z, \sigma) + ..., \tag{5}$$

where f, g are functions of σ, the h being functions of z, σ, *periodic* in z. Substituting the r.h.s. of (1) into $y'' + (a - 2q\cos 2z)y = 0$ gives

$$e^{\mu z}[\phi'' + 2\mu\phi' + (\mu^2 + a - 2q\cos 2z)\phi] = 0,$$

and by the aid of (3)–(5) we get

$$e^{\mu z}\left\{\begin{array}{l} -\sin(z-\sigma) + qh_1'' + q^2h_2'' + q^3h_3'' + ... + \\ + 2(qg_1 + q^2g_2 + q^3g_3 + ...)[\cos(z-\sigma) + qh_1' + q^2h_2' + q^3h_3' + ...] + \\ + [(qg_1 + q^2g_2 + q^3g_3 + ...)^2 + 1 + qf_1 + q^2f_2 + ... - 2q\cos 2z] \times \\ \qquad\qquad\qquad \times [\sin(z-\sigma) + qh_1 + q^2h_2 + ...] \end{array}\right\} = 0. \tag{6}$$

Taking
$$2 \cos 2z \sin(z-\sigma) = [\sin(3z-\sigma) - \sin(z+\sigma)]$$
$$= [\sin(3z-\sigma) - \sin(z-\sigma)\cos 2\sigma - \cos(z-\sigma)\sin 2\sigma],$$
and equating coefficients of q^0, q, q^2,... to zero we obtain

q^0: $-\sin(z-\sigma)+\sin(z-\sigma) = 0$ identically;   (7)

q: $h_1''+h_1+f_1 \sin(z-\sigma)+2g_1 \cos(z-\sigma)-2\sin(z-\sigma)\cos 2z = 0$.

Thus
$$h_1''+h_1+(2g_1+\sin 2\sigma)\cos(z-\sigma)+$$
$$+(f_1+\cos 2\sigma)\sin(z-\sigma)-\sin(3z-\sigma) = 0. \qquad (8)$$

Now the particular integrals corresponding to $\cos(z-\sigma)$, $\sin(z-\sigma)$ are $\frac{1}{2}z \sin(z-\sigma)$ and $-\frac{1}{2}z \cos(z-\sigma)$. These are non-periodic and tend to $\pm\infty$ as $z \to +\infty$. Since ϕ is to be periodic, the coefficients of $\cos(z-\sigma)$, $\sin(z-\sigma)$ must be zero. Hence we must have $g_1 = -\frac{1}{2}\sin 2\sigma$, $f_1 = -\cos 2\sigma$, leaving $h_1''+h_1 = \sin(3z-\sigma)$, so

$$h_1 = -\tfrac{1}{8}\sin(3z-\sigma). \qquad (9)$$

q^2: $h_2''+h_2+2g_2 \cos(z-\sigma)-\frac{3}{4}g_1 \cos(3z-\sigma)+(g_1^2+f_2)\sin(z-\sigma)+$
$$+\tfrac{1}{8}\sin(3z-\sigma)\cos 2\sigma+\tfrac{1}{4}\sin(3z-\sigma)\cos 2z = 0,$$

so
$$h_2''+h_2+2g_2 \cos(z-\sigma)+\tfrac{3}{8}\cos(3z-\sigma)\sin 2\sigma+(\tfrac{1}{4}\sin^2 2\sigma+\tfrac{1}{8}+f_2)\sin(z-\sigma)+$$
$$+\tfrac{1}{8}\sin(3z-\sigma)\cos 2\sigma+\tfrac{1}{8}\sin(5z-\sigma) = 0. \quad (10)$$

To avoid non-periodic terms we take $g_2 = 0$, $f_2 = -\frac{1}{4}+\frac{1}{8}\cos 4\sigma$, leaving the equation
$$h_2''+h_2+\tfrac{3}{8}\cos(3z-\sigma)\sin 2\sigma+\tfrac{1}{8}\sin(3z-\sigma)\cos 2\sigma+\tfrac{1}{8}\sin(5z-\sigma) = 0,$$
of which the particular integral is
$$h_2 = [3 \sin 2\sigma \cos(3z-\sigma)+\cos 2\sigma \sin(3z-\sigma)+\tfrac{1}{3}\sin(5z-\sigma)]/64. \quad (11)$$

Proceeding in this way, on substituting for the various functions in (3), (4) we obtain

$$a = 1-q \cos 2\sigma+\frac{1}{4}q^2\left(-1+\frac{1}{2}\cos 4\sigma\right)+\frac{1}{64}q^3 \cos 2\sigma+$$
$$+\frac{1}{16}q^4\left(\frac{1}{3}-\frac{11}{32}\cos 4\sigma\right)-\frac{1}{32}q^5\left(\frac{1}{9}\cos 2\sigma-\frac{13}{128}\cos 6\sigma\right)+$$
$$+\frac{1}{8192}q^6\left(-\frac{893}{27}+\frac{9181}{216}\cos 4\sigma-\frac{35}{4}\cos 8\sigma\right)-... \qquad (12)$$
$$= 1-q \cos 2\sigma-\mu^2+qs_3. \qquad (13)\dagger$$

† This result was obtained by substituting (1) in the differential equation $y''+(a-2q \cos 2z)y = 0$, using ϕ at (2), and equating to zero the coefficient of $\sin(z-\sigma)$.

$$\mu = -\frac{1}{2}q\sin 2\sigma + \frac{3}{128}q^3\sin 2\sigma - \frac{3}{1024}q^4\sin 4\sigma -$$

$$-\frac{1}{4096}q^5\left(\frac{137}{9}\sin 2\sigma - \frac{9}{2}\sin 6\sigma\right) +$$

$$+\frac{1}{16384}q^6\left(\frac{337}{27}\sin 4\sigma - \frac{15}{4}\sin 8\sigma\right) + \dots \quad (14)$$

$$= \tfrac{1}{2}q(-\sin 2\sigma + c_3). \qquad (15)\dagger$$

Also

$$s_3 = -\frac{1}{8}q + \frac{1}{64}q^2\cos 2\sigma - \frac{1}{512}q^3\left(-\frac{14}{3} + 5\cos 4\sigma\right) +$$

$$+\frac{1}{4096}q^4\left(-\frac{74}{9}\cos 2\sigma + 7\cos 6\sigma\right) - \dots \quad (16)$$

$$c_3 = \frac{3}{64}q^2\sin 2\sigma - \frac{3}{512}q^3\sin 4\sigma + \frac{1}{4096}q^4\left(-\frac{274}{9}\sin 2\sigma + 9\sin 6\sigma\right) - \dots \quad (17)$$

$$s_5 = \frac{1}{192}q^2 - \frac{1}{1152}q^3\cos 2\sigma + \frac{1}{4096}q^4\left(-\frac{155}{54} + \frac{82}{27}\cos 4\sigma\right) - \dots \quad (18)$$

$$c_5 = -\frac{7}{2304}q^3\sin 2\sigma + \frac{11}{27648}q^4\sin 4\sigma - \dots \quad (19)$$

$$s_7 = -\frac{1}{9216}q^3 + \frac{1}{49152}q^4\cos 2\sigma - \dots \quad (20)$$

$$c_7 = \frac{35}{4\,42368}q^4\sin 2\sigma - \dots \quad (21)$$

$$s_9 = \frac{1}{7\,37280}q^4 - \dots \quad (22)$$

$\cdot$ $\cdot$ $\cdot$ $\cdot$ $\cdot$ $\cdot$ $\cdot$ $\cdot$ $\cdot$ $\cdot$ $\cdot$ $\cdot$ $\cdot$ $\cdot$ $\cdot$ $\cdot$

It may be remarked that in (2) the coefficients of $\cos(3z-\sigma)$, $\cos(5z-\sigma),\dots$ are expressed in terms of $\sin 2\sigma$, $\sin 4\sigma,\dots$, while those of $\sin(3z-\sigma),\dots$ are expressed in terms of $\cos 2\sigma$, $\cos 4\sigma,\dots$.

If in (12) we write $-\sigma$ for σ, it is unchanged because a is an even function of σ. Making this change in (14) alters the sign of μ, since it is an odd function of σ. Thus referring to (1), we see that the

† This result was obtained by substituting (1) in the differential equation $y'' + (a - 2q\cos 2z)y = 0$, using ϕ at (2), and equating to zero the coefficient of $\cos(z-\sigma)$.

second independent solution of Mathieu's equation may take the form

$$y_2 = e^{-\mu z}\phi(z, -\sigma). \tag{23}$$

y_1, y_2 constitute a fundamental system, and the complete solution, with two arbitrary constants, is [186]

$$y = Ae^{\mu z}\phi(z, \sigma) + Be^{-\mu z}\phi(z, -\sigma). \tag{24}$$

4.31. Degeneration of (1) § 4.30 to $ce_1(z, q)$ and $se_1(z, q)$. When $\sigma = -\frac{1}{2}\pi$, $\mu = 0$, $c_3 = c_5 = \ldots = 0$, and the series for a becomes that for a_1 at (3) § 2.151. Also

$$s_3 = -\frac{1}{8}q - \frac{1}{64}q^2 - \frac{1}{1536}q^3 + \frac{11}{36864}q^4 - \ldots, \tag{1}$$

and so on, while

$$\sin[(2n+1)z + \tfrac{1}{2}\pi] = \cos(2n+1)z. \tag{2}$$

Substituting in (1), (2) § 4.30, we obtain (16) § 2.13, the series for $ce_1(z, q)$. Similarly, when $\sigma = 0$, (1), (2) § 4.30 yield (2) § 2.14, the series for $se_1(z, q)$.

4.32. Useful range of formulae in § 4.30. The series for a, μ, and the coefficients are similar in type to those in § 2.13 et seq. Such series probably diverge when q, real and positive, exceeds a certain value. The first term of (12) § 4.30 is unity, so if this series were used to compute a_5 for $ce_5(z, 0.4)$, which exceeds 25, $\cos 2\sigma$ would be correspondingly large, and low accuracy would ensue. This remark applies also to the series for μ and the coefficients. Moreover, for computation the formulae in § 4.30 may be used when q is moderate and the point (a, q) lies between the characteristics for ce_0 and se_2 in Fig. 8.

If (a, q) were between the characteristics for se_2, ce_2, a more suitable form of solution would be obtained by taking

$$\phi(z, \sigma) = \sin(2z - \sigma) + s_4 \sin(4z - \sigma) + s_6 \sin(6z - \sigma) + \ldots +$$
$$+ c_4 \cos(4z - \sigma) + c_6 \cos(6z - \sigma) + \ldots \tag{1}$$

$$= \sin(2z - \sigma) + qh_1(z, \sigma) + q^2 h_2(z, \sigma) + \ldots, \tag{2}$$

there being no term in $\cos(2z - \sigma)$, to avoid a non-periodic term of the type $z\sin(2z - \sigma)$ in the solution. If we assume that

$$a = 4 + qf_1(\sigma) + q^2 f_2(\sigma) + \ldots, \tag{3}$$

we find that $f_1(\sigma) = 0$, while

$$f_2(\sigma) = \tfrac{1}{6} - \tfrac{1}{4}\cos 2\sigma, \tag{4}$$

so $$a = 4 + \tfrac{1}{2}q^2(\tfrac{1}{3} - \tfrac{1}{2}\cos 2\sigma) + \dots. \tag{5}$$

Owing to the presence of 4 in (5), the coefficients of the terms in powers of q will be less than those in (12) § 4.30 if a is, say, 4·6.

In general the solution preferably has the forms at $1°$ (3), (6), $2°$ (2), (4) § 4.70, the corresponding series for a being of type (3) above, the leading term for ce_{2n}, se_{2n} being $4n^2$, while that for ce_{2n+1}, se_{2n+1} is $(2n+1)^2$.

4.40. Maclaurin series solution. If y is a solution of

$$y'' + (a - 2q\cos 2z)y = 0, \tag{1}$$

then by Maclaurin's theorem

$$y(z) = y(0) + zy'(0) + \frac{1}{2!}z^2 y''(0) + \frac{1}{3!}z^3 y'''(0) + \dots + \frac{1}{n!}z^n y^{(n)}(0) + R_n, \tag{2}$$

the derivatives being obtained by successive differentiation of (1) and insertion of $z = 0$. Although the procedure is simple, the solution so obtained has serious drawbacks:

1. The form, a power series in z, is markedly inferior in applications to those given previously. If (2) were periodic, its periodicity would be difficult to establish. Also it is unsuitable for interpreting the physical behaviour of a system, e.g. stability and instability.
2. If convergent, the rate of convergence is very slow and in many cases the number of terms needed to obtain accuracy for even moderate values of z, e.g. $\tfrac{1}{2}\pi$, would be prohibitive: see [12].
3. The convergence is difficult to establish.

4.50. Relation between solutions in § 4.153 and § 4.30. The respective forms are

$$\bar{y}_1(z) = e^{\mu z} \sum_{r=-\infty}^{\infty} \bar{c}_{2r+1}\, e^{(2r+1)zi} \tag{1}$$

and

$$y_1(z) = e^{\mu z}[\sin(z-\sigma) + s_3\sin(3z-\sigma) + s_5\sin(5z-\sigma) + \dots + \\ + c_3\cos(3z-\sigma) + c_5\cos(5z-\sigma) + \dots], \tag{2}$$

μ having the same value in both cases (see §4.70). Omitting the common factor $e^{\mu z}$, we expand the r.h.s. of (2) and obtain

$$\phi(z) = \sin z \cos \sigma - \cos z \sin \sigma + s_3(\sin 3z \cos \sigma - \cos 3z \sin \sigma) +$$

$$+ s_5(\sin 5z \cos \sigma - \cos 5z \sin \sigma) + \ldots + c_3(\cos 3z \cos \sigma + \sin 3z \sin \sigma) +$$

$$+ c_5(\cos 5z \cos \sigma + \sin 5z \sin \sigma) + \ldots \quad (3)$$

$$= \cos \sigma(\sin z + s_3 \sin 3z + s_5 \sin 5z + \ldots + c_3 \cos 3z + c_5 \cos 5z + \ldots) -$$

$$- \sin \sigma(\cos z + s_3 \cos 3z + s_5 \cos 5z + \ldots - c_3 \sin 3z - c_5 \sin 5z - \ldots) \quad (4)$$

$$= \sum_{r=0}^{\infty} [K_{2r+1} \cos(2r+1)z + L_{2r+1} \sin(2r+1)z], \quad (5)$$

where

$$K_{2r+1} = (c_{2r+1} \cos \sigma - s_{2r+1} \sin \sigma) \quad (r > 0), \qquad K_1 = -\sin \sigma;$$

$$L_{2r+1} = (s_{2r+1} \cos \sigma + c_{2r+1} \sin \sigma) \quad (r > 0), \qquad L_1 = \cos \sigma.$$

Writing the circular functions in (5) in exponentials, we get

$$\phi(z) = \tfrac{1}{2} \sum_{r=0}^{\infty} [(K_{2r+1} - iL_{2r+1})e^{(2r+1)zi} + (K_{2r+1} + iL_{2r+1})e^{-(2r+1)zi}]. \quad (6)$$

Now

$$\sum_{r=-\infty}^{\infty} \bar{c}_{2r+1} e^{(2r+1)zi} = \sum_{r=0}^{\infty} [\bar{c}_{2r+1} e^{(2r+1)zi} + \bar{c}_{-2r-1} e^{-(2r+1)zi}]. \quad (7)$$

Hence by (6), (7) the two forms of solution are identical, provided

$$\bar{c}_{2r+1} = \tfrac{1}{2}\bar{Z}_0(K_{2r+1} - iL_{2r+1}) \quad \text{and} \quad \bar{c}_{-2r-1} = \tfrac{1}{2}\bar{Z}_0(K_{2r+1} + iL_{2r+1}), \quad (8)$$

$\bar{Z}_0$ being a constant. It follows from (8) that $\bar{c}_{2r+1} \bar{Z}_0^{-1}$ and $\bar{c}_{-2r-1} \bar{Z}_0^{-1}$ are conjugate complex numbers, while $|c_{2r+1}| = |c_{-2r-1}|$.† By adding the two parts of (8), we get

$$\bar{Z}_0 K_{2r+1} = \bar{c}_{2r+1} + \bar{c}_{-2r-1}, \quad (9)$$

and by subtracting, we have

$$\bar{Z}_0 L_{2r+1} = i(\bar{c}_{2r+1} - \bar{c}_{-2r-1}). \quad (10)$$

Writing $r = 0$ in (9), (10), and substituting the values of K_1, L_1 from above, leads to

$$\bar{Z}_0 = -(\bar{c}_1 + \bar{c}_{-1})/\sin \sigma = i(\bar{c}_1 - \bar{c}_{-1})/\cos \sigma. \quad (11)$$

---

† Write $\qquad \bar{Z}_0 = M_0 e^{i\theta_0}, \qquad \bar{c}_{2r+1} = \rho_{2r+1} e^{i\psi_{2r+1}},$

then $\quad \bar{c}_{2r+1} \bar{Z}_0^{-1} = M_0^{-1} \rho_{2r+1} e^{i(\psi_{2r+1} - \theta_0)}, \qquad \bar{c}_{-2r-1} \bar{Z}_0^{-1} = M_0^{-1} \rho_{2r+1} e^{i(\psi_{-2r-1} - \theta_0)}.$

By virtue of the conjugate property,

$$\psi_{2r+1} - \theta_0 = -(\psi_{-2r-1} - \theta_0) - 2s\pi,$$

so $\qquad\qquad\qquad \theta_0 = \tfrac{1}{2}(\psi_{2r+1} + \psi_{-2r-1}) + s\pi,$

s being integral. $\bar{c}_{2r+1} \bar{Z}_0^{-1}$ and $\bar{c}_{-2r-1} \bar{Z}_0^{-1}$ are complex conjugate only if σ is real, i.e. when (a, q) lies in an unstable region of Fig. 8.

By squaring and adding both sides of (9), (10) we obtain

$$\bar{Z}_0 = 2(\bar{c}_{2r+1}\,\bar{c}_{-2r-1})^{\frac{1}{2}}/(K^2_{2r+1}+L^2_{2r+1})^{\frac{1}{2}}, \tag{12}$$

and, with $r = 0$, $\qquad \bar{Z}_0 = 2(\bar{c}_1\,\bar{c}_{-1})^{\frac{1}{2}}.$ \hfill (13)

We have proved, therefore, that, save for a constant multiplier, the solutions in §§ 4.153, 4.30 are identical. A similar conclusion applies in connexion with the solution $e^{\mu z}\sum_{r=-\infty}^{\infty}\bar{c}_{2r}\,e^{2rzi}$ and its alternative form. These results are to be expected, since the solution of Mathieu's equation must be unique.

4.60. Division of the (a, q)-plane into stable and unstable regions.

Fig. 8 shows the 'charted' part of the plane, i.e. that portion for which the characteristic curves a_m, b_m for the Mathieu functions of integral order have been computed. Consider the region in Fig. 8 B lying between a_1 and b_2. On the curve a_1, $\sigma = -\frac{1}{2}\pi$ in (12) § 4.30. Now if $\sigma = -\frac{1}{2}\pi+i\theta$, $\cos 2\sigma = -\cosh 2\theta$, whatever the sign of θ, so if $q > 0$ is fixed, (12) § 4.30 shows that a increases with increase in θ until b_2 is reached. On this curve from [191] we have

$$a = 4+\tfrac{1}{2}q^2(\tfrac{1}{3}-\tfrac{1}{2}\cos 2\sigma)+\dots \tag{1}$$

with $\sigma = 0$. If in (1) we write $\sigma = i\theta$, a decreases with increase in θ until a_1 is regained. Thus between a_1, b_2 with $q > 0$, σ is complex or imaginary according as (12) § 4.30 or (1) is used. If we take $\sigma = -\frac{1}{2}\pi+i\theta$, then $\sin 2\sigma = -i\sinh 2\theta$, and (14) § 4.30 shows that μ is imaginary and, therefore, by § 4.14 the solution is stable.

Starting from b_2', where $\sigma = 0$ in (1), if for fixed $q > 0$, σ (real) decreases, then a increases until a_2 is reached where $\sigma = -\frac{1}{2}\pi$. Since σ is real in the intervening region, the series for μ (like (14) § 4.30) may be shown to contain $\sin 2\sigma$, $\sin 4\sigma$, etc. Thus μ is real, and by § 4.14 an unstable solution is obtained for any (a, q) in the region.

Now consider the region between a_2, b_3 with fixed $q > 0$. On the former $\sigma = -\frac{1}{2}\pi$ in (1), so the term in $\cos 2\sigma$ is positive. If we take $\sigma = (-\frac{1}{2}\pi+i\theta)$, then $\cos 2\sigma = -\cosh 2\theta$, and by increasing θ from zero in (1), b_3 will ultimately be reached. Using the procedure suggested in § 4.32, we obtain [191]

$$a = 9+\tfrac{1}{16}q^2-\tfrac{1}{64}q^3\cos 2\sigma+\dots \tag{2}$$

for the region in question, and on b_3, $\sigma = 0$. Taking $\sigma = i\theta$ in (2) and increasing θ from zero, a_2 will eventually be regained. Thus between a_2, b_3, σ is complex or imaginary according as (1) or (2) is used. Since the series for μ contains $\sin 2\sigma$, $\sin 4\sigma$, etc., μ is imaginary in the region, so the solution of Mathieu's equation for an assigned (a, q) is stable.

In this way the (a, q)-plane, for q positive, may be divided into zones or regions in which the solution of Mathieu's equation corresponding to a point (a, q) is either stable or unstable. On the characteristic curves for the functions of integral order, the first solution is neutral, but the second solution treated in Chapter VII is unstable. When q is negative, by writing $-q$ for q in the above series and using a similar argument, the plane may be divided up as illustrated in Figs. 8, 11. The series for the a hold if $|q| < q_0$, but the results may be established for the whole range of q.

Summary. (1) When (a, q), $q > 0$ lies between a_m, b_{m+1} in Figs. 8, 11, μ is imaginary, and the two solutions of Mathieu's equation are stable.

(2) When (a, q), $q > 0$ lies between b_m, a_m, μ is real provided the appropriate form of solution is taken (see 2° § 4.70), and the complete solution of Mathieu's equation is unstable.

Apparatus for illustrating stability is described in [202] chap. XIV, also in § 15.40 et seq.

4.70. Form of solution for different regions of (a, q)-plane.

Certain advantages accrue by assuming different forms of solution corresponding to various regions in which the point (a, q) may lie in Figs. 8, 11. By adopting the convention given below, μ will be either real as in 2°, or imaginary as in 1°, but never complex. It will then have the same value for the two forms of solution in 2° (real), and the three forms in 1° (imaginary). z is assumed to be real.

1°. *Stable solution, q small and positive.* When (a, q) lies *between* a_{2n}, b_{2n+1}, for the first solution we take

$$y_1(z) = e^{i\beta z} \sum_{r=-\infty}^{\infty} c_{2r} e^{2rzi} = e^{i\beta z}\phi(z)_{2r} \tag{1}$$

$$\text{or} \quad y_1(z) = \sum_{r=-\infty}^{\infty} c_{2r} \cos(2r+\beta)z \tag{2}$$

$$\text{or} \quad y_1(z) = e^{i\beta z}[\sin(2nz-\sigma)+s_2\sin(2z-\sigma)+s_4\sin(4z-\sigma)+...+$$
$$+c_2\cos(2z-\sigma)+c_4\cos(4z-\sigma)+...], \tag{3}$$

there being no term in $\cos(2nz-\sigma)$, e.g. if $n = 1$, $c_2 = 0$, for the reason given in § 4.30. In these series β is real and $0 < \beta < 1$. If

$n \geqslant 1$, formulae for a, $i\beta = \mu$, and the coefficients c_{2r}, s_{2r} may be developed as shown in § 4.30.

When (a, q) lies *between* a_{2n+1}, b_{2n+2}, for the first solution we take

$$y_1(z) = e^{i\beta z} \sum_{r=-\infty}^{\infty} c_{2r+1} e^{(2r+1)zi} = e^{i\beta z}\phi(z)_{2r+1} \qquad (4)$$

or $\quad y_1(z) = \sum_{r=-\infty}^{\infty} c_{2r+1} \cos(2r+1+\beta)z \qquad (5)$

or $\quad y_1(z) = e^{i\beta z}[\sin\{(2n+1)z-\sigma\}+s_1\sin(z-\sigma)+s_3\sin(3z-\sigma)+...+$
$$+c_1\cos(z-\sigma)+c_3\cos(3z-\sigma)+...], \qquad (6)$$

there being no term in $\cos\{(2n+1)z-\sigma\}$, e.g. if $n = 1$, $c_3 = 0$, for the reason given in § 4.30. If $n \geqslant 1$, formulae for a, $i\beta = \mu$, and the coefficients c_{2r+1}, s_{2r+1} may be developed as shown in § 4.30.

The second solution is obtained by writing $-z$ for z in (1), (4); sin for cos in (2), (5); $-\beta$ for β, $-\sigma$ for σ in (3), (6). In each case the two solutions are linearly independent, provided β is in the range $0 < \beta < 1$, and constitute a fundamental system. When the initial conditions are specified, all forms of solution yield an identical result, since the solution is unique.

2°. *Unstable solution, q small and positive.* When (a, q) lies *between* b_{2n+2}, a_{2n+2} for the first solution we take

$$y_1(z) = e^{\mu z} \sum_{r=-\infty}^{\infty} c_{2r} e^{2rzi} = e^{\mu z}\phi(z)_{2r} \qquad (1)$$

or $\quad y_1(z) = e^{\mu z}[\sin(2nz-\sigma)+s_2\sin(2z-\sigma)+s_4\sin(4z-\sigma)+...+$
$$+c_2\cos(2z-\sigma)+c_4\cos(4z-\sigma)+...], \qquad (2)$$

where μ (real) > 0. See remarks below (3) 1°.

When (a, q) lies *between* b_{2n+1}, a_{2n+1}, for the first solution we take

$$y_1(z) = e^{\mu z} \sum_{r=-\infty}^{\infty} c_{2r+1} e^{(2r+1)zi} = e^{\mu z}\phi(z)_{2r+1} \qquad (3)$$

or $\quad y_1(z) = e^{\mu z}[\sin\{(2n+1)z-\sigma\}+s_1\sin(z-\sigma)+s_3\sin(3z-\sigma)+...+$
$$+c_1\cos(z-\sigma)+c_3\cos(3z-\sigma)+...]. \qquad (4)$$

See remarks below (6) 1°.

The second solution is derived by making the substitutions stated in 1°. The period of $\phi(z)_{2r}$ is π, while that of $\phi(z)_{2r+1}$ is 2π. Observe remark at end of 1°.

3°. *Stable solution, q moderate and positive.* See (1), (2), (4), (5) in 1°. The form at (3), (6) 1° is usually unsuitable for computation when $q > 0.4$ approx.

4°. *Unstable solution, q moderate and positive.* As at (1), (3) in 2°.

5°. *Any solution, q negative.* In the solution for $q > 0$, write $(\tfrac{1}{2}\pi - z)$ for z.

4.71. Mathieu functions of real fractional order [134].

In § 4.16 (1), (2) represent coexistent solutions of Mathieu's equation, i.e. for an assigned value of q they have the same value of a. Consider the region in Fig. 11 between the curves a_m, b_{m+1} with $m = 1$. Take any line parallel to the a-axis and terminating on these curves. Hereon $0 \leqslant \beta \leqslant 1$. If for any assigned β, say 0·8, the a are calculated for q increasing from zero in small steps, and the points plotted, the characteristic curve $\beta = 0\cdot8$ is obtained. Lying between those for ce$_1$, se$_2$, we shall define it as that for the Mathieu function of·real fractional order $(1+\beta)$. In general, if (a, q) lies between the curves a_m, b_{m+1}, the order of the function will be $(m+\beta)$, and the value of a on any curve is that for ce$_{m+\beta}(z, q)$ and se$_{m+\beta}(z, q)$. Moreover, by computing a series of curves at intervals of, say, $\beta = 0\cdot1$, we can plot an iso-β chart,† of the type depicted in Fig. 11.

For $q > 0$, $0 < \beta < 1$, β real, we adopt the definitions [134]

$$\left. \begin{aligned} \text{ce}_{2n+\beta}(z, q) &= \sum_{r=-\infty}^{\infty} A_{2r}^{(2n+\beta)} \cos(2r+\beta)z, \\ \text{se}_{2n+\beta}(z, q) &= \sum_{r=-\infty}^{\infty} A_{2r}^{(2n+\beta)} \sin(2r+\beta)z, \end{aligned} \right\} \begin{aligned} &\text{coexistent solutions with} \quad (1) \\ &a = a_{2n+\beta}: (a, q) \text{ between} \\ &a_{2n} \text{ and } b_{2n+1}; \quad\quad\quad (2) \end{aligned}$$

$$\left. \begin{aligned} \text{ce}_{2n+1+\beta}(z, q) &= \sum_{r=-\infty}^{\infty} A_{2r+1}^{(2n+1+\beta)} \cos(2r+1+\beta)z, \\ \text{se}_{2n+1+\beta}(z, q) &= \sum_{r=-\infty}^{\infty} A_{2r+1}^{(2n+1+\beta)} \sin(2r+1+\beta)z, \end{aligned} \right\} \begin{aligned} &\text{coexistent solutions} \quad (3) \\ &\text{with } a = a_{2n+1+\beta}: \\ &(a, q) \text{ between } a_{2n+1} \\ &\text{and } b_{2n+2}. \quad\quad\quad (4) \end{aligned}$$

$q < 0$. Writing $(\tfrac{1}{2}\pi - z)$ for z in (1), (2), we obtain

$$\text{ce}_{2n+\beta}(\tfrac{1}{2}\pi - z, q) = \cos\tfrac{1}{2}\beta\pi \sum_{r=-\infty}^{\infty} (-1)^r A_{2r}^{(2n+\beta)} \cos(2r+\beta)z +$$

$$+ \sin\tfrac{1}{2}\beta\pi \sum_{r=-\infty}^{\infty} (-1)^r A_{2r}^{(2n+\beta)} \sin(2r+\beta)z, \quad (5)$$

$$\text{se}_{2n+\beta}(\tfrac{1}{2}\pi - z, q) = \sin\tfrac{1}{2}\beta\pi \sum_{r=-\infty}^{\infty} (-1)^r A_{2r}^{(2n+\beta)} \cos(2r+\beta)z -$$

$$- \cos\tfrac{1}{2}\beta\pi \sum_{r=-\infty}^{\infty} (-1)^r A_{2r}^{(2n+\beta)} \sin(2r+\beta)z. \quad (6)$$

† Using an argument similar to that in § 3.25, it may be shown that the iso-β curves are single-valued and continuous.

If we adopt the definitions

$$\left.\begin{aligned}\text{ce}_{2n+\beta}(z, -q) &= (-1)^n \sum_{r=-\infty}^{\infty} (-1)^r A_{2r}^{(2n+\beta)} \cos(2r+\beta)z, \\ \text{se}_{2n+\beta}(z, -q) &= (-1)^n \sum_{r=-\infty}^{\infty} (-1)^r A_{2r}^{(2n+\beta)} \sin(2r+\beta)z,\end{aligned}\right\} \begin{aligned}&\text{coexistent} \quad (7) \\ &\text{solutions with} \\ &a = a_{2n+\beta}, \quad (8)\end{aligned}$$

each function is a linearly independent solution of Mathieu's equation, and when $q \to 0$ it degenerates to the appropriate form given in § 4.73. The functions corresponding to (3), (4) are obtained by writing $(1+\beta)$ for β in (7), (8) and using $A_{2r+1}^{(2n+1+\beta)}$ for $A_{2r}^{(2n+\beta)}$. If the tabular values of (1), (2) are known, those of (7), (8) may be calculated therefrom by aid of the following relationships derived from (5)–(8):

$$\text{ce}_{2n+\beta}(z, -q)$$
$$= (-1)^n[\cos\tfrac{1}{2}\beta\pi\,\text{ce}_{2n+\beta}(\tfrac{1}{2}\pi - z, q) + \sin\tfrac{1}{2}\beta\pi\,\text{se}_{2n+\beta}(\tfrac{1}{2}\pi - z, q)] \quad (9)$$

and

$$\text{se}_{2n+\beta}(z, -q)$$
$$= (-1)^n[\sin\tfrac{1}{2}\beta\pi\,\text{ce}_{2n+\beta}(\tfrac{1}{2}\pi - z, q) - \cos\tfrac{1}{2}\beta\pi\,\text{se}_{2n+\beta}(\tfrac{1}{2}\pi - z, q)]. \quad (10)$$

A similar remark applies concerning (3), (4).

The relationships for functions of order $(2n+1+\beta)$ are derived from (9), (10) as described above with regard to (7), (8).

If the functions are defined as

$$\begin{aligned}\text{ce}_{2n+\beta}(z, +q) &= \sec\tfrac{1}{4}\beta\pi \sum_{r=-\infty}^{\infty} A_{2r}^{(2n+\beta)} \cos[(2r+\beta)z - \tfrac{1}{4}\beta\pi], \\ \text{se}_{2n+\beta}(z, +q) &= \sec\tfrac{1}{4}\beta\pi \sum_{r=-\infty}^{\infty} A_{2r}^{(2n+\beta)} \sin[(2r+\beta)z - \tfrac{1}{4}\beta\pi],\end{aligned} \quad (11)$$

then for $q < 0$, the substitution $(\tfrac{1}{2}\pi - z)$ for z yields (11), but with $(-1)^r$ within the sigma sign (see (7) and (8)). Although the functions defined thus are well suited for tabulation, since $\text{ce}_{2n+\beta}(z, -q)$ is then equal to $\text{ce}_{2n+\beta}(\tfrac{1}{2}\pi - z, q)$, they have the following disadvantages: (a) they are neither odd nor even, (b) they do not reduce to $\cos(m+\beta)z$, $\sin(m+\beta)z$ when $q \to 0$, (c) they are more complicated than (1)–(4), (7), (8). These comments apply also to (5), (6).

As in § 3.21, all the above series may be proved absolutely and uniformly convergent in any real closed interval $z_1 \leqslant z \leqslant z_2$, or in any closed rectangle of the z-plane (see § 4.77).

For the pairs of functions (1), (7); (2), (8); etc. the iso-β curves are symmetrical about the a-axis of Fig. 11. No two of these intersect; for if they did, the equation would have more than two independent solutions corresponding to the point of intersection (a, q), which is impossible. If $\beta = p/s$, a rational fraction less than unity, p, s being prime to each other, and z is real, the function has period $2s\pi$, $s \geqslant 2$. When β is irrational, the function is not periodic, and tends neither to zero nor to infinity as $z \to +\infty$. By appropriate choice of (a, q) the function may have any real period $2s\pi$. An argument akin to that in § 3.25 may be used to show that the characteristic numbers and coefficients are continuous in q.†

Modified functions of fractional order. These are solutions of (1) §§ 2.30, 2.31, respectively, being defined as follows:

$$\begin{matrix} \mathrm{Ce} \\ \mathrm{Se}_{m+\beta} \end{matrix} (z, \pm q) = \begin{matrix} \mathrm{ce} \\ -i\,\mathrm{se}_{m+\beta} \end{matrix} (iz, \pm q) \quad (a_{m+\beta}). \tag{12}$$

The series representations may be derived from above by writing iz for z.

4.711. Behaviour of the coefficients as $\beta \to 0$ and 1.

Consider a point (a, q) in a stable region of Figs. 8 or 11 between a_{2n} and b_{2n+1}; then $0 < \beta < 1$. With $q > 0$ fixed, let a_{2n} be approached so that $\beta \to 0$. Then by § 4.17

$$\mathrm{ce}_{2n+\beta}(z, q) \to \mathrm{ce}_{2n}(z, q), \qquad \mathrm{se}_{2n+\beta}(z, q) \to 0; \tag{1}$$

so we must have

$$A_{-2r}^{(2n+\beta)} \to A_{2r}^{(2n+\beta)} \to \tfrac{1}{2}A_{2r}^{(2n)}, \qquad A_0^{(2n+\beta)} \to A_0^{(2n)}; \; a_{2n+\beta} \to a_{2n}. \tag{2}$$

Similarly, as $\beta \to 1$,

$$\mathrm{se}_{2n+\beta}(z, q) \to \mathrm{se}_{2n+1}(z, q), \qquad \mathrm{ce}_{2n+\beta}(z, q) \to 0; \tag{3}$$

$$-A_{-2r-2}^{(2n+\beta)} \to A_{2r}^{(2n+\beta)} \to \tfrac{1}{2}B_{2r+1}^{(2n+1)}; \; a_{2n+\beta} \to b_{2n+1}. \tag{4}$$

For (a, q) between a_{2n+1} and b_{2n+2}, as $\beta \to 0$,

$$\mathrm{ce}_{2n+1+\beta}(z, q) \to \mathrm{ce}_{2n+1}(z, q), \qquad \mathrm{se}_{2n+1+\beta}(z, q) \to 0; \tag{5}$$

$$A_{-2r-1}^{(2n+1+\beta)} \to A_{2r+1}^{(2n+1+\beta)} \to \tfrac{1}{2}A_{2r+1}^{(2n+1)}; \; a_{2n+1+\beta} \to a_{2n+1}. \tag{6}$$

As $\beta \to 1$

$$\mathrm{se}_{2n+1+\beta}(z, q) \to \mathrm{se}_{2n+2}(z, q), \qquad \mathrm{ce}_{2n+1+\beta}(z, q) \to 0; \tag{7}$$

$$-A_{-2r-3}^{(2n+1+\beta)} \to A_{2r+1}^{(2n+1+\beta)} \to \tfrac{1}{2}B_{2r+2}^{(2n+2)}, \qquad A_{-1} \to 0; \; a_{2n+1+\beta} \to b_{2n+2}. \tag{8}$$

$r \geqslant 0$ except in (2), where $r \geqslant 1$.

† They are single-valued also.

4.72. Normalization of $ce_{m+\beta}(z, q)$, $se_{m+\beta}(z, q)$.

$1°$. $\beta = p/s$, *a rational fraction in its lowest terms.* Since the functions have period $2s\pi$, we take

$$\frac{1}{s\pi} \int_0^{2s\pi} ce_{m+\beta}^2(z, q)\, dz = 1, \qquad \frac{1}{s\pi} \int_0^{2s\pi} se_{m+\beta}^2(z, q)\, dz = 1. \qquad (1)$$

Inserting the series (1)–(4) § 4.71 in these integrals leads to

$$\sum_{r=-\infty}^{\infty} [A_{2r}^{(2n+\beta)}]^2 = \sum_{r=-\infty}^{\infty} [A_{2r+1}^{(2n+1+\beta)}]^2 = 1. \qquad (2)$$

$2°$. β *an irrational number,* $0 < \beta < 1$. If in (1), $s \to +\infty$, (2) follows, so we normalize accordingly.

Comparison of (1), (2) § 4.16 and (1), (2) § 4.71 shows that we may write $A_{2r}^{(2n+\beta)} = Kc_{2r}$, where K is a constant. Then from (2) we get

$$K^2 \sum_{r=-\infty}^{\infty} c_{2r}^2 = 1, \quad \text{so } K = 1 \Big/ \Big[\sum_{-\infty}^{\infty} c_{2r}^2\Big]^{\frac{1}{2}}. \qquad (3)\dagger$$

If the c are found as in § 5.20 et seq., K may be computed, e.g. § 5.311.

4.73. Form of solution when $q = 0$. At the intersection of an iso-β curve with the a-axis in Fig. 11, $q = 0$. Then

$$a = m^2 + \Delta a = (m+\beta)^2,$$

m being the order of the function whose characteristic curve intersects the a-axis at the point $a = m^2$. Thus the differential equation reduces to

$$y'' + (m+\beta)^2 y = 0, \qquad (1)$$

whose formal solutions are $\cos(m+\beta)z$, $\sin(m+\beta)z$.

By analysis akin to that in § 3.32 it can be shown that as $q \to 0$, all the A in (1), (2) § 4.71 except $A_{2n}^{(2n+\beta)}$ tend to zero. By § 4.72 $A_{2n}^{(2n+\beta)} = 1$ when $q = 0$. A similar conclusion applies to (3), (4) § 4.71. Hence, when $q = 0$, the functions of fractional order become $\cos(m+\beta)z$, $\sin(m+\beta)z$, so (1) is satisfied.

4.74. Formula for β **[134].** When the parametric point lies in a stable region of Figs. 8 or 11, formula (6) § 2.16 may be adapted to calculate β. When $q > 0$, if the curves bounding the region are a_m (lower), b_{m+1} (upper), $m \geqslant 0$, we take $\nu = m+\beta$. Then from (6) § 2.16

$$\nu^2 = a - \frac{1}{2(\nu^2-1)}q^2 - \frac{(5\nu^2+7)}{32(\nu^2-1)^3(\nu^2-4)}q^4 -$$
$$- \frac{9\nu^4+58\nu^2+29}{64(\nu^2-1)^5(\nu^2-4)(\nu^2-9)}q^6 + O(q^8). \qquad (1)$$

† This formula is valid when β is a rational fraction.

This formula is usable under the condition that $|a| \gg |q^2/2(v^2-1)|$, and that the ratio of each of the terms in q^{2r} to its predecessor is small. For a first approximation we have $v^2 = a$. Inserting this in the term in q^2 and omitting the others, the second approximation is

$$v^2 = a - q^2/2(a-1). \tag{2}$$

Substituting from (2) into the second term on the r.h.s. of (1) and $v^2 = a$ in the third and fourth, yields the third approximation, namely,

$$v^2 = a - \frac{(a-1)}{[2(a-1)^2 - q^2]} q^2 - \frac{(5a+7)}{32(a-1)^3(a-4)} q^4 -$$
$$- \frac{9a^2 + 58a + 29}{64(a-1)^5(a-4)(a-9)} q^6 + O(q^8). \tag{3}$$

Since $v^2 = (m+\beta)^2$, we obtain (whatever the sign of q)

$$\beta \simeq \left[a - \frac{(a-1)}{[2(a-1)^2 - q^2]} q^2 - \frac{(5a+7)}{32(a-1)^3(a-4)} q^4 - \right.$$
$$\left. - \frac{9a^2 + 58a + 29}{64(a-1)^5(a-4)(a-9)} q^6 \right]^{\frac{1}{2}} - m, \tag{4}$$

provided no denominator vanishes. If $v_1 = (m+\beta_1)$ calculated from (4) is fairly accurate, a closer result may be obtained by substituting v_1 for v on the r.h.s. of (1), and recalculating v.

The accuracy obtained from (4) increases with decrease in q, a being assigned. Broadly, for moderate accuracy we must have $|a/q| \gg 1$. Thus, if a is large enough, q also may be large, e.g. if $a = 1000$, q might be 50. For lower accuracy the term in q^6 may be omitted. When a, q are such that adequate accuracy cannot be obtained with (4), the procedure described in §§ 5.11–5.14, 5.32 may be employed.

4.750. Conjugate properties of the coefficients, μ real, (a, q) in an unstable region.

1°. When (a, q) lies between b_{2n} and a_{2n}, the recurrence relation is

$$[a - (2r - i\mu)^2] c_{2r} - q(c_{2r+2} + c_{2r-2}) = 0. \tag{1}$$

Writing $-r$ for r, (1) becomes

$$[a - (2r + i\mu)^2] c_{-2r} - q(c_{-2r-2} + c_{-2r+2}) = 0. \tag{2}$$

Since a, q, μ are real, it follows from (1), (2) that c_{2r} and c_{-2r} expressed in terms of c_0 (real) are conjugate complex numbers.

2°. When (a, q) lies between b_{2n+1} and a_{2n+1}, the recurrence relation is

$$[a-(2r+1-i\mu)^2]c_{2r+1}-q(c_{2r+3}+c_{2r-1}) = 0. \tag{1}$$

Writing $-(r+1)$ for r in (1) gives

$$[a-(2r+1+i\mu)^2]c_{-2r-1}-q(c_{-2r-3}+c_{-2r+1}) = 0. \tag{2}$$

Suppose that the c_{2r+1} are expressed in terms of c_1, and the c_{-2r-1} in terms of c_{-1}. Then c_{2r+1} and $(c_1/c_{-1})c_{-2r-1}†$ are conjugate. In §4.751 it is shown that $|c_{2r+1}| = |c_{-2r-1}|$, so $|c_1| = |c_{-1}|$.

The conjugate property of the coefficients is useful for checking purposes in numerical solutions. If this species of checking is waived, computation of c_{2r}, $r = 1, 2,...$, in terms of c_0, and c_{2r+1}, $r = -1, 1, 2,...$, in terms of c_1 is sufficient.

4.751. Alternative form of solution in unstable region.

1°. By 2° §4.70, when (a, q) lies between b_{2n+1} and a_{2n+1}, the form of solution

$$y_1(z) = e^{\mu z} \sum_{r=-\infty}^{\infty} c_{2r+1} e^{(2r+1)zi} \tag{1}$$

ensures the reality of μ. If $\mu > 0$, $y_1 \to 0$ as $z \to -\infty$. Since a, q are real, the c are complex. Then it may be shown that if z is real, save for a constant complex multiplier, say Z_0, there is a real solution which tends to zero as $z \to -\infty$.

Let $\qquad c_{2r+1} = Z_0 d_{2r+1}, \qquad Z_0 = e^{i\theta_0}, \qquad |Z_0| = 1,$

$$c_1 = 1, \qquad d_{2r+1} = \rho_{2r+1} e^{i\phi_{2r+1}} \tag{2}$$

for all r. We shall now demonstrate that d_{2r+1} and d_{-2r-1} are conjugate complex numbers. Substituting from (2) into (1) leads to

$$Z_0^{-1}y_1(z) = e^{\mu z} \sum_{r=-\infty}^{\infty} \rho_{2r+1}\{\cos[(2r+1)z+\phi_{2r+1}]+i\sin[(2r+1)z+\phi_{2r+1}]\}. \tag{3}$$

For a real solution, the imaginary part of the r.h.s. of (3) must vanish identically. Hence

$$\rho_{2r+1}\sin[(2r+1)z+\phi_{2r+1}]-\rho_{-2r-1}\sin[(2r+1)z-\phi_{-2r-1}] \equiv 0, \tag{4}$$

and, therefore,

$$\rho_{2r+1} = \rho_{-2r-1}, \quad \text{and} \quad \phi_{2r+1} = -(\phi_{-2r-1}+2s\pi), \tag{5}$$

s being an integer. It follows that d_{2r+1} and d_{-2r-1} are conjugate, so (3) may be written

$$y_1(z) = 2Z_0 e^{\mu z} \sum_{r=0}^{\infty} \rho_{2r+1} \cos[(2r+1)z+\phi_{2r+1}]. \tag{6}$$

† By aid of 1°, 4.751, it may be shown that $(c_1/c_{-1}) = e^{-2i\theta_0}$.

The second independent solution is

$$y_2(z) = y_1(-z) = 2Z_0 e^{-\mu z} \sum_{r=0}^{\infty} \rho_{2r+1} \cos[(2r+1)z - \phi_{2r+1}]. \tag{7}$$

Then (6) $\to 0$ as $z \to -\infty$ if $\mu > 0$, while (7) $\to \pm\infty$ as $z \to -\infty$.

Determination of Z_0. For all integral values of r

$$c_{2r+1} = Z_0 d_{2r+1}, \quad \text{with } |Z_0| = 1. \tag{8}$$

Since d_{2r+1} and d_{-2r-1} are conjugate, it follows that

$$|c_{2r+1}| = |c_{-2r-1}|. \tag{9}$$

Thus we may write $c_{2r+1} = \rho_{2r+1} e^{i\psi_{2r+1}}$, $c_{-2r-1} = \rho_{2r+1} e^{i\psi_{-2r-1}}$. Then

$$Z_0 = e^{i\theta_0} = c_{2r+1}/d_{2r+1} = e^{i(\psi_{2r+1} - \phi_{2r+1})} \tag{10}$$

$$= c_{-2r-1}/d_{-2r-1} = e^{i(\psi_{-2r-1} + \phi_{2r+1} + 2s\pi)}, \tag{11}$$

by (5). Hence

$$2\theta_0 = (\psi_{2r+1} - \phi_{2r+1}) + (\psi_{-2r-1} + \phi_{2r+1} + 2s\pi),$$

so

$$\theta_0 = \tfrac{1}{2}(\psi_{2r+1} + \psi_{-2r-1}) + s\pi. \tag{12}$$

It follows from the footnote in § 4.50 that $\bar{Z}_0 = M_0 Z_0$, i.e. $\bar{Z}_0$ and Z_0 have equal angles.

$2°$. When (a, q) lies between b_{2n}, a_{2n}, by $2°$ § 4.70 μ is real if

$$y_1(z) = e^{\mu z} \sum_{r=-\infty}^{\infty} c_{2r} e^{2rzi}. \tag{1}$$

Take $c_{2r} = \rho_{2r} e^{i\phi_{2r}}$, $c_0 = 2\rho_0$ real, then for a real solution it may be shown that $\rho_{2r} = \rho_{-2r}$, $\phi_{2r} = -(\phi_{-2r} + 2s\pi)$, so if $r \geqslant 1$, c_{2r} and c_{-2r} are conjugate. Also

$$y_1(z) = 2e^{\mu z}\Big\{\rho_0 + \sum_{r=1}^{\infty} \rho_{2r} \cos(2rz + \phi_{2r})\Big\}, \tag{2}$$

and

$$y_2(z) = y_1(-z) = 2e^{-\mu z}\Big\{\rho_0 + \sum_{r=1}^{\infty} \rho_{2r} \cos(2rz - \phi_{2r})\Big\}. \tag{3}$$

In this case $Z_0 = 1$.

4.752. Example illustrating analysis in § 4.751. We shall consider the solution of

$$y'' + (1 - 0\cdot32 \cos 2z)y = 0, \tag{1}$$

obtained in § 5.33. The parametric point $a = 1$, $q = 0\cdot16$, lies in an unstable region between b_1 and a_1. From $2°$ § 5.33 we have

$$\left.\begin{aligned}
c_1 &= 1, \\
c_{-1} &= (5\cdot95 \times 10^{-2} + 0\cdot998i); \\
c_3 &= -(1\cdot994 \times 10^{-2} + 1\cdot198 \times 10^{-3}i), \\
c_{-3} &= -(2\cdot38 \times 10^{-3} + 1\cdot978 \times 10^{-2}i); \\
c_5 &= (1\cdot325 \times 10^{-4} + 1\cdot24 \times 10^{-5}i), \\
c_{-5} &= (2\cdot024 \times 10^{-5} + 1\cdot313 \times 10^{-4}i).
\end{aligned}\right\} \tag{2}$$

1°. We find that $|c_1| \simeq |c_{-1}|$, $|c_3| \simeq |c_{-3}|$, $|c_5| \simeq |c_{-5}|$.

2°. (a) $\psi_1 = 0$, $\psi_{-1} = \tan^{-1}(0\cdot998/0\cdot0595) = 86\cdot56^\circ$.

Hence by (12), 1° §4.751 with $s = 0$,

$$\theta_0 = \tfrac{1}{2}(\psi_1 + \psi_{-1}) = 43\cdot28^\circ. \tag{1}$$

  (b) $\psi_3 = \tan^{-1}(-1\cdot198/-19\cdot94) = 183\cdot44^\circ$,

  $\psi_{-3} = \tan^{-1}(-1\cdot978/-0\cdot238) = 263\cdot12^\circ$.

Hence by (12), 1° §4.751 with $s = -1$,

$$\theta_0 = \tfrac{1}{2}(\psi_3 + \psi_{-3}) - 180^\circ = 43\cdot28^\circ. \tag{2}$$

  (c) $\psi_5 = \tan^{-1}(0\cdot124/1\cdot325) = 5\cdot37^\circ$,

  $\psi_{-5} = \tan^{-1}(1\cdot313/0\cdot2024) = 81\cdot25^\circ$.

Hence by (12), 1° §4.751 with $s = 0$,

$$\theta_0 = \tfrac{1}{2}(\psi_5 + \psi_{-5}) = 43\cdot31^\circ. \tag{3}$$

The agreement at (1), (2), (3) is satisfactory for the purpose of illustration.

3°. $$Z_0 = e^{43\cdot28^\circ i} = 0\cdot728 + 0\cdot686i$$

and $$|Z_0| = 1.$$

4°.
$$\left.\begin{aligned} d_1 &= c_1 e^{-43\cdot28^\circ i} = e^{-43\cdot28^\circ i} \\ d_{-1} &= c_{-1} e^{-43\cdot28^\circ i} = e^{43\cdot28^\circ i} \end{aligned}\right\} \text{ conjugate.} \tag{1}$$

$$\left.\begin{aligned} d_3 &= c_3 e^{-43\cdot28i} = |c_3| e^{140\cdot16i} \\ d_{-3} &= c_{-3} e^{-43\cdot28i} = |c_3| e^{219\cdot84i} \end{aligned}\right\} \text{ conjugate.} \tag{2}$$

$$\left.\begin{aligned} d_5 &= c_5 e^{-43\cdot28i} = |c_5| e^{-37\cdot91i} \\ d_{-5} &= c_{-5} e^{-43\cdot28i} = |c_5| e^{37\cdot97i} \end{aligned}\right\} \text{ conjugate.} \tag{3}$$

As an exercise, the reader may check the remark in §4.750 that c_{2r+1} and $(c_1/c_{-1})c_{-2r-1}$ are conjugate.

5°.
$$\left.\begin{aligned} \rho_1 &= 1, & \phi_1 &= -43\cdot28^\circ; \\ \rho_3 &= 2 \times 10^{-2}, & \phi_3 &= 140\cdot16^\circ; \\ \rho_5 &= 1\cdot33 \times 10^{-4}, & \phi_5 &= -37\cdot91^\circ. \\ & \text{By } 1^\circ \text{ §5.33 } \mu = 0\cdot08. \end{aligned}\right\} \tag{1}$$

6°. Two approximate independent solutions of (1) §4.752 are

$$y_1(z) \simeq 2Z_0 e^{\mu z}\left\{\sum_{r=0}^{2} \rho_{2r+1} \cos[(2r+1)z + \phi_{2r+1}]\right\} \tag{1}$$

and

$$y_2(z) = y_1(-z) \simeq 2Z_0 e^{-\mu z}\left\{\sum_{r=0}^{2} \rho_{2r+1} \cos[(2r+1)z - \phi_{2r+1}]\right\}. \tag{2}$$

By combining these linearly independent solutions, we obtain the *even* solution

$$\frac{1}{4Z_0}(y_1+y_2) = \bar{y}_1 \simeq \cosh \mu z \sum_{r=0}^{2} \rho_{2r+1} \cos(2r+1)z \cos \phi_{2r+1} -$$

$$-\sinh \mu z \sum_{r=0}^{2} \rho_{2r+1} \sin(2r+1)z \sin \phi_{2r+1}, \quad (3)$$

and the *odd* solution

$$\frac{1}{4Z_0}(y_1-y_2) = \bar{y}_2 \simeq \sinh \mu z \sum_{r=0}^{2} \rho_{2r+1} \cos(2r+1)z \cos \phi_{2r+1} -$$

$$-\cosh \mu z \sum_{r=0}^{2} \rho_{2r+1} \sin(2r+1)z \sin \phi_{2r+1}. \quad (4)$$

In practical applications (3), (4) have the disadvantage that *both* tend to infinity with z.

4.753. Formula for μ when $a < 0$. μ may be calculated for (a, q) below a_0 in Figs. 8, 11, by means of (4) § 4.74 with $m = 0$. Then $\mu = -i\beta$. The remarks on accuracy in the last paragraph of § 4.74 apply here also. As shown later, (7) § 4.91 may be used when (a, q) lies in an unstable region between b_m and a_m, $m > 0$.

4.760. The iso-μ curves in Fig. 11. Consider the segment of any line between the curves b_m, a_m, parallel to the a-axis, i.e. in an unstable region. The convention of § 4.70 ensures the reality of μ. On b_m and a_m, $\mu = 0$, while at some point on the segment of the line, μ attains a maximum value. This is true also for points on the segment of a line parallel to the q-axis and terminating on a_m. Thus if the turning-point (nearest the a-axis) on an iso-μ curve is $q = q_0$, there are two values of a for any $q > q_0$ on the curve. Moreover, the coefficients in the solutions corresponding to the two a are different, except at the turning-point. No two iso-μ curves intersect for the reason stated in § 4.71 regarding the same property of iso-β curves. The iso-μ curves are asymptotic to the characteristic curves b_m, a_m which bound the unstable region where they lie, and they have no linear asymptotes.

If the numerical data were available, families of iso-μ curves akin to those depicted in Fig. 11 could be plotted. Tabulation of a, $a^{\frac{1}{2}}$, q, μ would permit the value of the latter being found immediately, or by interpolation. The solution of an equation with (a, q) in a 'charted' unstable region would then be completed by computing the coefficients in (1) or (3), 2° § 4.70, using the procedure in 2° § 5.33 and § 5.34.

4.761. Functions of order $m+\mu$, q positive. When (a, q) lies in an unstable region between b_{2n} and a_{2n}, we define the functions of order $(2n+\mu)$ by aid of (2), (3), $2°$ § 4.751. Thus

$$\mathrm{ceu}_{2n+\mu}(\pm z, q) = Ke^{\pm\mu z}\left\{\rho_0 + \sum_{r=1}^{\infty} \rho_{2r}\cos(2rz \pm \phi_{2r})\right\} \quad (b_{2n+\mu}). \quad (1, 2)$$

For the region between b_{2n+1}, a_{2n+1} we use (6), (7) $1°$ § 4.751, so

$$\mathrm{ceu}_{2n+1+\mu}(\pm z, q) = K_1 e^{\pm\mu z}\sum_{r=0}^{\infty} \rho_{2r+1}\cos[(2r+1)z \pm \phi_{2r+1}] \quad (b_{2n+1+\mu}),$$
$$(3, 4)$$

where K and K_1 are normalizing constants defined in § 4.764. The above forms of solution are preferable in applications to those at (3), (4), $6°$ § 4.752 for the following reasons:

(i) One solution tends to zero, the other to infinity with z, whereas the even and odd solutions *both* tend to infinity with z.

(ii) In numerical work, tables of e^z, e^{-z} are better to use than those of $\sinh z$, $\cosh z$.

(iii) Analytical work using (1)–(4) is likely to be simpler than that involving the even and odd solutions.

It is of interest to remark that if we substitute

$$Z_0^{-1}(A_{2r+1}^{(2n+1-i\mu)} + A_{-2r-1}^{(2n+1-i\mu)}) = \rho_{2r+1}\cos\phi_{2r+1}, \quad (5)$$

and $\qquad -iZ_0^{-1}(A_{2r+1}^{(2n+1-i\mu)} - A_{-2r-1}^{(2n+1-i\mu)}) = \rho_{2r+1}\sin\phi_{2r+1}, \quad (6)$

in the r.h.s. of

$$\left.\begin{array}{c}\mathrm{ce}\\ i\,\mathrm{se}\end{array}\right\}_{2n+1-i\mu}(z, q) = \sum_{r=-\infty}^{\infty} A_{2r+1}^{(2n+1-i\mu)}\begin{array}{c}\cos\\ i\sin\end{array}(2r+1-i\mu)z, \quad (7, 8)†$$

the r.h.s. of (3), (4), $6°$ § 4.752 are reproduced, with $r = 0$ to $+\infty$. Since μ is real, $2n+1-i\mu$ is complex, so (7), (8), and the corresponding functions derived by writing $2n$, $2r$ for $(2n+1)$, $(2r+1)$, respectively, may be designated functions of complex order.

Discrimination between solutions for the same q but different a. We refer to § 4.760. On the upper and lower parts, and at the turning-point of an iso-μ curve, we use the symbols

$$\mathrm{ceu}_{m+\bar{\mu}}, \quad \mathrm{ceu}_{m+\underline{\mu}}, \quad \mathrm{ceu}_{m+\breve{\mu}}, \quad \text{respectively.} \quad (9)$$

For example, if (a, q) lies on the upper part of the curve between b_{2n} and a_{2n}, we write

$$\mathrm{ceu}_{2n+\bar{\mu}}(\pm z, q) = Ke^{\pm\bar{\mu}z}\left\{\bar{\rho}_0 + \sum_{r=1}^{\infty} \bar{\rho}_{2r}\cos(2rz \pm \bar{\phi}_{2r})\right\}. \quad (10, 11)$$

† The r.h.s. of (7), (8) are the series for $\mathrm{ce}_{2n+1+\beta}(z, q)$ and $\mathrm{se}_{2n+1+\beta}(z, q)$ with $-i\mu$ written for β.

Symbolism for solutions with the same a but different q may be devised by the reader.

4.762. Degenerate forms of (1)–(4) § 4.761. If a remains constant as (a, q) moves towards a_{2n}† in Fig. 11, $\bar{\mu} \to 0$, and in (1), (2) §4.761 $K\bar{\rho}_0 \to A_0^{(2n)}$, $K\bar{\rho}_{2r} \to A_{2r}^{(2n)}$, and $\bar{\phi}_{2r} \to 0$, $r \geqslant 1$. When $\bar{\mu} = 0$, by proper choice of K, we obtain $ce_{2n}(z, q)$. As (a, q) moves towards b_{2n}, $\underline{\mu} \to 0$, and $\rho_0 \to 0$, $K\rho_{2r} \to B_{2r}^{(2n)}$, $\phi_{2r} \to -\frac{1}{2}\pi$, $r \geqslant 1$, so with $\mu = 0$ we get $\pm se_{2n}(z, q)$. Similarly the degenerate forms of (3), (4) § 4.761 are $ce_{2n+1}(z, q)$ and $\pm se_{2n+1}(z, q)$. These forms may also be derived from (3), (4) 6° § 4.752.

4.763. Functions of order $m+\mu$, $q < 0$. These are defined as follows:

$$ceu_{2n+\mu}(\pm z, -q) = (-1)^n e^{\mp \frac{1}{2}\pi\mu} \, ceu_{2n+\mu}[\pm(\tfrac{1}{2}\pi - z), q] \quad (b_{2n+\mu})$$
$$(1, 2)$$

$$= (-1)^n K e^{\mp \mu z} \Big\{ \rho_0 + \sum_{r=1}^{\infty} (-1)^r \rho_{2r} \cos(2rz \mp \phi_{2r}) \Big\}.$$
$$(3, 4)$$

$$ceu_{2n+1+\mu}(\pm z, -q) = (-1)^n e^{\mp \frac{1}{2}\pi\mu} \, ceu_{2n+1+\mu}[\pm(\tfrac{1}{2}\pi - z), q] \quad (a_{2n+1+\mu})$$
$$(5, 6)$$

$$= (-1)^n K_1 e^{\mp \mu z} \sum_{r=0}^{\infty} (-1)^r \rho_{2r+1} \sin[(2r+1)z \mp \phi_{2r+1}].$$
$$(7, 8)$$

The r.h.s. of (7), (8) may be expressed in a cosine series by altering the argument in [ ] to $[(2r+1)z - \frac{1}{2}\pi \mp \phi_{2r+1}]$. The definition would then be in keeping with the notation ceu. When $\bar{\mu} = 0$ in (3), (4), (7), (8) the functions degenerate to $ce_{2n}(z, -q)$, $se_{2n+1}(z, -q)$; when $\underline{\mu} = 0$, we get $\mp se_{2n}(z, -q)$, $\pm ce_{2n+1}(z, -q)$, as may be expected from Fig. 11, where $q < 0$. The multiplier $(-1)^n$ ensures that the signs of the degenerate forms are in accordance with the definitions in § 2.18, provided the upper signs are taken in the case $\mu = 0$.

4.764. Normalization. The rules must be such that the degenerate forms of the functions are those given in §§ 4.762, 4.763. Then we must have

$$K^2 \Big[2\rho_0^2 + \sum_{r=1}^{\infty} \rho_{2r}^2 \Big] = 1, \quad \text{or} \quad K = 1 \Big/ \Big[2\rho_0^2 + \sum_{r=1}^{\infty} \rho_{2r}^2 \Big]^{\frac{1}{2}}, \quad (1)$$

and $$K_1^2 \sum_{r=0}^{\infty} \rho_{2r+1}^2 = 1, \quad \text{or} \quad K_1 = 1 \Big/ \Big[\sum_{r=0}^{\infty} \rho_{2r+1}^2 \Big]^{\frac{1}{2}}. \quad (2)$$

---

† Except at $a = m^2$, $q = 0$, the direction of approach to a_{2n} is immaterial, e.g. in § 4.711 the approach is with q constant.

4.77. Convergence of solutions. Substituting (1) $2°$ §4.70 into Mathieu's equation and equating the coefficient of e^{2rzi} to zero for $r = -\infty$ to $+\infty$, yields the recurrence relation (1) §4.750. This is a linear difference equation which may be treated on the lines of §3.21. We find that

$$|u_{2r}| \sim q/4(r+1)^2 \to 0 \quad \text{as } r \to +\infty, \tag{1}$$

where $u_{2r} = c_{2r+2}/c_{2r}$. A similar result is obtained for r negative. Then as in §§3.21–3.23 it may be shown that (1) $2°$ §4.70 and its derivatives are absolutely and uniformly convergent in any closed region of the z-plane. Hence the series, differentiable term by term, represent continuous functions. They may also be proved integrable term by term. These conclusions are valid for stable and also for unstable regions of the (a, q)-plane. Similar conclusions may also be drawn respecting the solutions given in §§4.761, 4.763.

4.80. Solution of $y'' + (a - 2q \cos 2z)y = 0$, a **very large** $\gg q > 0$. The equation may be written

$$y'' + ay = (2q \cos 2z)y. \tag{1}$$

Neglecting the r.h.s., which is relatively small, by hypothesis, the formal solutions are $\cos za^{\frac{1}{2}}$, $\sin za^{\frac{1}{2}}$. Substituting $\cos za^{\frac{1}{2}}$ for y on the r.h.s. of (1) leads to

$$y'' + ay = q[\cos(a^{\frac{1}{2}}+2)z + \cos(a^{\frac{1}{2}}-2)z], \tag{2}$$

of which the particular integral is

$$-\tfrac{1}{4}q\left[\frac{\cos(a^{\frac{1}{2}}+2)z}{a^{\frac{1}{2}}+1} - \frac{\cos(a^{\frac{1}{2}}-2)z}{a^{\frac{1}{2}}-1}\right], \tag{3}$$

provided $a \neq 1$. Using this for y in the r.h.s. of (1) and solving again, the particular integral has terms in $\cos(a^{\frac{1}{2}}\pm4)z$, and so on. Hence the first solution of (1) may be expressed in the form

$$y_1 = \sum_{r=-\infty}^{\infty} c_r \cos(a^{\frac{1}{2}}-2r)z \quad (a^{\frac{1}{2}} \text{ non-integral}). \tag{4}$$

If we use $\sin a^{\frac{1}{2}}z$ and proceed as above, the second solution is found to be

$$y_2 = \sum_{r=-\infty}^{\infty} c_r \sin(a^{\frac{1}{2}}-2r)z. \tag{5}$$

Substituting either (4) or (5) in the differential equation yields the recurrence relation

$$[a - (a^{\frac{1}{2}}-2r)^2]c_r - q(c_{r-1}+c_{r+1}) = 0, \tag{6}$$

or $$4r(a^{\frac{1}{2}}-r)c_r-q(c_{r-1}+c_{r+1}) = 0. \tag{7}$$

If $a^{\frac{1}{2}} \gg r$, we get the approximate relation

$$4rc_r-(q/a^{\frac{1}{2}})(c_{r-1}+c_{r+1}) = 0. \tag{8}$$

As in §3.21, for convergence of (4), (5) we must have $c_r \to 0$ as $r \to \pm\infty$.

Now a recurrence relation for the J-Bessel function is

$$4rJ_r(u)-2u(J_{r-1}+J_{r+1}) = 0, \tag{9}$$

and since $J_r \to 0$ as $r \to \pm\infty$, $c_r = \text{constant} \times J_r$. If we take the constant to be unity (for simplicity) we get

$$c_r = J_r(q/2a^{\frac{1}{2}}). \tag{10}$$

When $q/2a^{\frac{1}{2}} \ll r$, the B.F. may be represented by the first term of its expansion, so $c_r \simeq (q/4a^{\frac{1}{2}})^r/r!$ giving $c_r/c_{r-1} = q/4ra^{\frac{1}{2}}$. Thus the coefficients decrease with increase in r and may be neglected if $r > r_0$, where $a^{\frac{1}{2}} \gg r_0$. Accordingly, approximate solutions of Mathieu's equation, subject to the conditions a very large $\gg q > 0$, $a^{\frac{1}{2}} \gg r_0$, are

$$y_1 \simeq \sum_{r=-r_0}^{r_0} J_r(q/2a^{\frac{1}{2}})\cos(a^{\frac{1}{2}}-2r)z \tag{11}$$

and $$y_2 \simeq \sum_{r=-r_0}^{r_0} J_r(q/2a^{\frac{1}{2}})\sin(a^{\frac{1}{2}}-2r)z. \tag{12}†$$

Hence the approximate complete solution with two arbitrary constants is

$$y \simeq Ay_1+By_2 = C \sum_{r=-r_0}^{r_0} J_r(q/2a^{\frac{1}{2}})\cos[(a^{\frac{1}{2}}-2r)z-\alpha], \tag{13}$$

where $C = (A^2+B^2)^{\frac{1}{2}}$, $\alpha = \tan^{-1}(B/A)$. Since (13) is bounded in z, the point (a,q) must lie in a stable region of the plane (see Fig. 8).

4.81. Transformation of Mathieu's equation to a Riccati type.

Write $y = e^{\nu \int^z w\,dz}$, where $\nu = a^{\frac{1}{2}}$, and $w(z)$ is a differentiable function of z. Then

$$dy/dz = \nu wy, \qquad d^2y/dz^2 = \nu y(dw/dz+\nu w^2). \tag{1}$$

If we put $[1-(2q/a)\cos 2z] = \rho^2$, Mathieu's equation becomes

---

† If r covered the range $-\infty$ to $+\infty$, it is easy to show by aid of formulae (6), (7), p. 42, reference [203], that the respective representations of (11), (12), would be ${\cos \atop \sin}\left[a^{\frac{1}{2}}\left(z-\dfrac{q}{2a}\sin 2z\right)\right]$. This form is obtained at (7), (8) § 4.81 by a different method.

$y'' + a\rho^2 y = 0$. Using the above substitution it is transformed to the Riccati type [133]

$$\frac{1}{\nu}\frac{dw}{dz} + w^2 + \rho^2 = 0, \tag{2}$$

since $y \not\equiv 0$. Now if $a \gg q > 0$, a being very large, the first member of (2) may be neglected, and we get

$$w = \pm i\rho = \pm i\left(1 - \frac{2q}{a}\cos 2z\right)^{\frac{1}{2}} \tag{3}$$

$$\simeq \pm i\left(1 - \frac{q}{a}\cos 2z\right). \tag{4}$$

Hence

$$\nu\int^z w\,dz \simeq \pm ia^{\frac{1}{2}}\left(z - \frac{q}{2a}\sin 2z\right), \tag{5}$$

and, therefore,

$$y = e^{\nu\int^z w\,dz} \simeq e^{\pm ia^{\frac{1}{2}}[z - (q/2a)\sin 2z]}. \tag{6}$$

Then by the theory of linear differential equations, we may combine the two solutions in (6) as follows:

$$y_1 \simeq \tfrac{1}{2}\{e^{ia^{\frac{1}{2}}[z - (q/2a)\sin 2z]} + e^{-ia^{\frac{1}{2}}[z - (q/2a)\sin 2z]}\} = \cos\left[a^{\frac{1}{2}}\left(z - \frac{q}{2a}\sin 2z\right)\right],$$

and

$$\tag{7}$$

$$y_2 \simeq \frac{1}{2i}\{e^{ia^{\frac{1}{2}}[z - (q/2a)\sin 2z]} - e^{-ia^{\frac{1}{2}}[z - (q/2a)\sin 2z]}\} = \sin\left[a^{\frac{1}{2}}\left(z - \frac{q}{2a}\sin 2z\right)\right].$$

$$\tag{8}$$

Combining (7), (8) with two arbitrary constants leads to

$$y = \bar{A}y_1 + \bar{B}y_2 = \bar{C}\cos\left[a^{\frac{1}{2}}\left(z - \frac{q}{2a}\sin 2z\right) - \bar{\alpha}\right], \tag{9}$$

where $\bar{C} = (\bar{A}^2 + \bar{B}^2)^{\frac{1}{2}}$, and $\bar{\alpha} = \tan^{-1}(\bar{B}/\bar{A})$. Expanding (9) gives

$$y \simeq \bar{C}\left\{\cos\left(\frac{q}{2a^{\frac{1}{2}}}\sin 2z\right)\cos(a^{\frac{1}{2}}z - \bar{\alpha}) + \sin\left(\frac{q}{2a^{\frac{1}{2}}}\sin 2z\right)\sin(a^{\frac{1}{2}}z - \bar{\alpha})\right\}. \tag{10}$$

Expressing the first factor of each member of the r.h.s. in B.F. series [203, p. 42], we get, with $h = (q/2a^{\frac{1}{2}})$, which may be $\gg 1$,

$$y \simeq \bar{C}\left\{\left[J_0(h) + 2\sum_{r=1}^{\infty}J_{2r}(h)\cos 4rz\right]\cos(a^{\frac{1}{2}}z - \bar{\alpha}) + \right.$$

$$\left. + \left[2\sum_{r=0}^{\infty}J_{2r+1}(h)\sin(4r+2)z\right]\sin(a^{\frac{1}{2}}z - \bar{\alpha})\right\}, \tag{11}$$

$$= \bar{C}\sum_{r=-\infty}^{\infty}J_r(h)\cos[(a^{\frac{1}{2}} - 2r)z - \bar{\alpha}]. \tag{12}$$

This has the same form as (13) §4.80, but in (12) the summation covers a doubly infinite range of r. Owing to the rapid decrease in $J_r(h)$ beyond $r = r_0$, a finite range of r is adequate in applications.

The approximate solution of $y'' + (a + 2q \cos 2z)y = 0$ is obtained from (12) by writing $-h$ for h. Since $J_r(-h) = (-1)^r J_r(h)$, we get

$$y \simeq \bar{C} \sum_{r=-\infty}^{\infty} (-1)^r J_r(h) \cos[(a^{\frac{1}{2}} - 2r)z - \bar{\alpha}]. \tag{13}$$

As in §4.80 the point (a, q) must lie in a stable region of Fig. 8.

4.82. More accurate approximate solution of

$$y'' + (a - 2q \cos 2z)y = 0.$$

The solution at (9) §4.81 is a circular function with periodically varying argument, but constant amplitude factor $\bar{C}$. We shall now derive a closer approximation in which the amplitude factor is periodic in z. We start with (2) §4.81, and assume that [133]

$$w = w_0 + \frac{1}{\nu}w_1 + \frac{1}{\nu^2}w_2 + ..., \tag{1}$$

the $w(z)$ being differentiable functions of z. Then

$$w^2 = w_0^2 + \frac{2}{\nu}w_0 w_1 + \frac{1}{\nu^2}(w_1^2 + 2w_0 w_2) + ..., \tag{2}$$

$$\frac{1}{\nu}\frac{dw}{dz} = \frac{1}{\nu}w_0' + \frac{1}{\nu^2}w_1' + \frac{1}{\nu^3}w_2' + ... \tag{3}$$

Substituting (2), (3) into (2) §4.81 gives

$$w_0^2 + \rho^2 + \frac{1}{\nu}(w_0' + 2w_0 w_1) + \frac{1}{\nu^2}(w_1' + w_1^2 + 2w_0 w_2) + ... = 0. \tag{4}$$

Equating the coefficients of ν^0, ν^{-1}, ν^{-2},... to zero yields

$$w_0^2 + \rho^2 = 0, \tag{5}$$

$$w_0' + 2w_0 w_1 = 0, \tag{6}$$

$$w_1' + w_1^2 + 2w_0 w_2 = 0, \tag{7}$$

$$\cdot \quad \cdot \quad \cdot \quad \cdot \quad \cdot \quad \cdot$$

From (5), $w_0 = \pm i\rho$,   so $\nu \int^z w_0 \, dz = \pm i\nu \int^z \rho \, dz.$ (8)

From (6),

$$w_1 = -\frac{1}{2}\frac{w_0'}{w_0}, \quad \text{so} \int^z w_1 \, dz = -\frac{1}{2}\int^z \frac{dw_0}{w_0} + \text{constant}$$

$$= \log A w_0^{-\frac{1}{2}} = \log(A\rho^{-\frac{1}{2}}) \mp \frac{1}{4}\pi i. \tag{9}$$

From (7),

$$w_2 = -\left(\frac{w_1' + w_1^2}{2w_0}\right) = \frac{1}{4}\left[\frac{w_0''}{w_0^2} - \frac{3}{2}\frac{w_0'^2}{w_0^3}\right]$$

$$= \mp\frac{i}{8\rho^3}(2\rho\rho'' - 3\rho'^2),$$

so
$$\frac{1}{\nu}\int^z w_2\,dz = \mp\frac{i}{8\nu}\int^z \left(\frac{2\rho\rho'' - 3\rho'^2}{\rho^3}\right)dz. \tag{10}$$

Then by (1), (8)–(10), if $|a| \gg 1$, $|a| > |2q|$, to a second approximation

$$\nu\int^z w\,dz = \pm i\nu\int^z \rho\,dz + \log(A\rho^{-\frac{1}{2}}) \mp \tfrac{1}{4}\pi i \mp \frac{ia^{-\frac{1}{2}}}{8}\int^z \left(\frac{2\rho\rho'' - 3\rho'^2}{\rho^3}\right)dz. \tag{11}$$

Hence

$$e^{\nu\int^z w\,dz} = Be^{\nu\int_0^z w\,dz} \simeq (\text{constant})\rho^{-\frac{1}{2}}e^{\pm ia^{\frac{1}{2}}\int_0^z[\rho-(2\rho\rho''-3\rho'^2)/8a\rho^3]\,dz}, \tag{12}$$

the factor $e^{\mp\frac{1}{4}\pi i}$ being absorbed in the constant.

Combining the two solutions as in § 4.81 we get

$$\begin{matrix}y_1\\y_2\end{matrix}(z) \simeq \text{constant } \rho^{-\frac{1}{2}}\begin{matrix}\cos\\\sin\end{matrix}\left[a^{\frac{1}{2}}\int_0^z \varphi(z)\,dz\right], \tag{13}$$

where $\varphi(z) = \rho - (2\rho\rho'' - 3\rho'^2)/8a\rho^3$. Then (13) are independent solutions of $y'' + a\rho^2 y = 0$. Representative graphs are given in Fig. 10 A.

If $a \gg 1$, $a > 2q > 0$, both real, the solutions (13) are bounded, so the point (a, q) must lie in a stable region of Fig. 8. If $|a| \gg 1$, $|a| \gg |2q|$, and the argument in [ ] is imaginary or complex, the solutions are unstable, so (a, q) then lies in an unstable region of Fig. 8.

Omitting the terms in ρ', ρ'' in $\varphi(z)$, we get

$$a^{\frac{1}{2}}\int_0^z \phi(z)\,dz = \int^z (a - 2q\cos 2z)^{\frac{1}{2}}\,dz$$

$$= (a + 2q)^{\frac{1}{2}}\int_0^z (1 - \lambda^2\cos^2 u)^{\frac{1}{2}}\,du$$

$$= (a + 2q)^{\frac{1}{2}}[E(\lambda, \tfrac{1}{2}\pi) - E(\lambda, \tfrac{1}{2}\pi - z)]$$

$$= (a + 2q)^{\frac{1}{2}}E_1(\lambda, z), \tag{14}$$

where $E(\lambda, z)$ is an incomplete elliptic integral of the second kind with modulus $\lambda = 2[q/(a+2q)]^{\frac{1}{2}} < 1$. Then we may write (13) in the form

$$\begin{matrix} y_1 \\ y_2 \end{matrix}(z) \simeq \frac{\text{constant}}{(a-2q\cos 2z)^{\frac{1}{4}}} \begin{matrix} \cos \\ \sin \end{matrix}[(a+2q)^{\frac{1}{2}}E_1(\lambda, z)]. \tag{15}$$

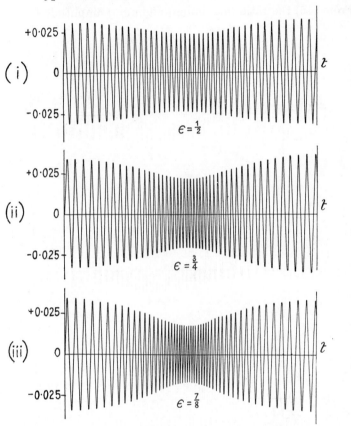

Fig. 10 A. Curves showing combined amplitude and frequency modulation; see (13) § 4.82 and (4) § 15.25.

When $|2q| \gg |a|$ the approximate solution of Mathieu's equation may be derived as shown in 2° § 6.20.

The argument of the circular functions in (15) is periodic, so the frequency of repetition of the function fluctuates. It is defined to be

$$f = \omega/2\pi = \frac{1}{2\pi}\frac{d}{dz}[(a+2q)^{\frac{1}{2}}E_1(\lambda, z)]$$

$$= \frac{1}{2\pi}(a+2q)^{\frac{1}{2}}(1-\lambda^2\cos^2 z)^{\frac{1}{2}}. \tag{16}$$

The 'periodicity' or reciprocal of the frequency is

$$1/f = 2\pi/(a+2q)^{\frac{1}{2}}(1-\lambda^2\cos^2 z)^{\frac{1}{2}}, \tag{17}$$

which differs from that when $q = 0$, namely, $2\pi a^{-\frac{1}{2}}$.

From (15) the ratio (maximum/minimum) amplitude factor is

$$[(a+2q)/(a-2q)]^{\frac{1}{4}}. \tag{18}$$

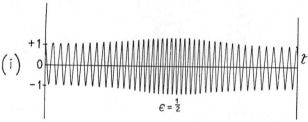

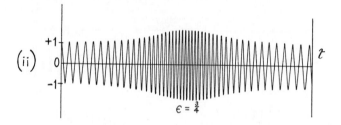

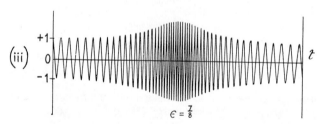

Fig. 10 B . As at Fig. 10A, but for the derivative, e.g. $I_1(t)$ in (9) § 15.25.

4.83. Equation of the type $y''+2\kappa y'+(\bar{a}-2q\cos 2z)y = 0$.
Assume that κ, $\bar{a}$, q are real, with $\kappa \geqslant 0$, $q \geqslant 0$. Substituting $y = e^{-\kappa z}u(z)$ into the equation, we obtain the Mathieu equation

$$u''+(a-2q\cos 2z)u = 0, \tag{1}$$

with $a = (\bar{a}-\kappa^2)$. If the parametric point (a, q) lies within a stable region of Fig. 8, the solution of the original equation takes the form (see (2), (5), 1° § 4.70)

$$y_1(z) = e^{-\kappa z} \sum_{r=-\infty}^{\infty} c_{2r} \cos(2r+\beta)z \quad \text{or} \quad e^{-\kappa z} \sum_{r=-\infty}^{\infty} c_{2r+1} \cos(2r+1+\beta)z, \quad (2)$$

and

$$y_2(z) = e^{-\kappa z} \sum_{r=-\infty}^{\infty} c_{2r} \sin(2r+\beta)z \quad \text{or} \quad e^{-\kappa z} \sum_{r=-\infty}^{\infty} c_{2r+1} \sin(2r+1+\beta)z$$

$$(0 < \beta < 1, \ \beta \ \text{real}). \quad (3)$$

The solutions (2), (3) are proportional to $e^{-\kappa z} \operatorname{ce}_{m+\beta}(z, q)$ and $e^{-\kappa z} \operatorname{se}_{m+\beta}(z, q)$ respectively. These may be regarded as damped Mathieu functions of fractional order.

If (a, q) lies in an unstable region of Fig. 8, the solution of (1) takes the form at (1) or (3), 2° § 4.70. Thus the solution of the original equation is given by

$$y_1(z) = e^{(\mu-\kappa)z} \sum_{r=-\infty}^{\infty} c_{2r} e^{2rzi} \quad \text{or} \quad e^{(\mu-\kappa)z} \sum_{r=-\infty}^{\infty} c_{2r+1} e^{(2r+1)zi} \quad (4)$$

and

$$y_2(z) = e^{-(\mu+\kappa)z} \sum_{r=-\infty}^{\infty} c_{2r} e^{-2rzi} \quad \text{or} \quad e^{-(\mu+\kappa)z} \sum_{r=-\infty}^{\infty} c_{2r+1} e^{-(2r+1)zi}. \quad (5)$$

y_1 is stable and $\to 0$ as $z \to +\infty$, if $\kappa > \mu > 0$.

y_1 is unstable and $\to \pm\infty$ as $z \to +\infty$, if $0 \leqslant \kappa < \mu$.

y_1 is neutral and periodic with period π or 2π, if $\kappa = \mu > 0$.

y_2 is stable and $\to 0$ as $z \to +\infty$ in each case.

Conditions of solution are assumed (see 2° § 4.70) such that μ is real. If it is complex, $R(\mu)$ is to be understood above; also z is real.

4.84. Iso-$\beta\mu$ stability chart. This is illustrated in Fig. 11. The iso-β curves lie in the stable regions for Mathieu's equation, while the iso-μ curves lie in the unstable regions. Each iso-β curve is single-valued in q, but except for the region below a_0, each iso-μ is double-valued in q. For constant μ, q at the turning-point of the iso-μ curve increases with increase in a, e.g. if $\mu = 0.1$, $q \simeq 0.21$ when $a \simeq 1$, but $q \simeq 1.3$ when $a \simeq 4.22$.

Suppose that in (1) § 4.83, $a = 1$, $q \simeq 0.21$, then (a, q) lies *on* the iso-μ curve $\mu = 0.1$ between b_1 and a_1. Thus the solution of the equation is unstable. Referring to the original equation, if $\kappa > 0.1$, the solution is stable and tends to zero as $z \to +\infty$. Since $(1, 0.21)$ lies between the characteristics for se_1 and ce_1, by 2° § 4.70 the solutions take the form at the extreme right of (4), (5) § 4.83. If $\kappa = 0.1$, $(\mu - \kappa) = 0$, so one solution is periodic with period 2π, while the other

$\rightarrow 0$ as $z \rightarrow +\infty$. The iso-μ curve $\mu = 0{\cdot}1$ is its characteristic or boundary curve separating the stable and unstable regions. Thus for

$$y'' + 0{\cdot}2y' + (\bar{a} - 2q \cos 2z)y = 0, \tag{1}$$

the stable regions are larger than those for Mathieu's equation, by

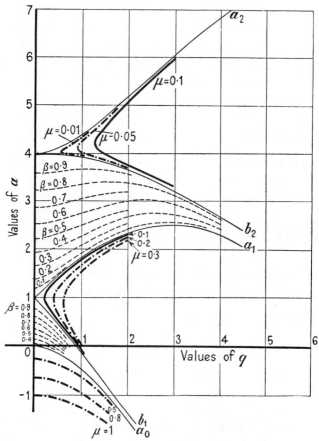

FIG. 11. Iso-$\beta\mu$ stability chart for Mathieu functions of fractional order. The iso-β and iso-μ curves are symmetrical about the a-axis.

the areas included between the iso-μ curves $\mu = 0{\cdot}1$ and the b_m, a_m curves to which they are asymptotic. The range of μ is $-\infty < \mu < \infty$: if positive it is $0 \leqslant \mu < \infty$.

4.85. Solution of $y'' + 2\kappa y' + (\bar{a} - 2q \cos 2z)y = 0$, **when** $\bar{a} \gg 2q > 0$, $\bar{a} \gg \kappa^2$. We assume that the point $[(\bar{a} - \kappa^2), q]$ lies in a stable region of Figs. 8 or 11. Then by §4.83 $y = e^{-\kappa z}u(z)$, $u(z)$ being a solution of

(1) § 4.83. Hence its value is given by § 4.81 with $a = \bar{a} - \kappa^2$. Accordingly, with $h_1 = q/2(\bar{a} - \kappa^2)^{\frac{1}{2}}$, we get

$$y \simeq C_1 \sum_{r=-\infty}^{\infty} J_r(h_1) e^{-\kappa z} \cos[\{(\bar{a} - \kappa^2)^{\frac{1}{2}} - 2r\}z - \alpha_1]. \tag{1}$$

4.86. More accurate approximate solution of equation in § 4.85. It is evident that the required solution may be derived on writing $(\bar{a} - \kappa^2)$ for a in (15) § 4.82 and multiplying by $e^{-\kappa z}$. Thus we get

$$\begin{matrix} y_1 \\ y_2 \end{matrix}(z) \simeq \frac{\text{a constant } e^{-\kappa z}}{(\bar{a} - \kappa^2 - 2q \cos 2z)^{\frac{1}{4}}} \begin{matrix} \cos \\ \sin \end{matrix}[(\bar{a} - \kappa^2 + 2q)^{\frac{1}{2}} E_1(\lambda_1, z)], \tag{1}$$

where $\lambda_1^2 = 4q/(\bar{a} - \kappa^2 + 2q)$, and the conditions respecting (a, q) in § 4.82 obtain. In the foregoing cases, when q is negative the solution is obtained by writing $(\frac{1}{2}\pi - z)$ for z in that already given, excepting the exponential index.

4.90. Solution of $y'' + (a - 2q \cos 2z)y = 0$ in an unstable region of the (a, q)-plane. In § 4.12 et seq the solution was shown to have the form

$$\begin{matrix} y_1 \\ y_2 \end{matrix}(z) = \left. \begin{matrix} e^{\mu z}\phi(z), \\ e^{-\mu z}\phi(-z). \end{matrix} \right\} \tag{1}$$

Now $\phi(z)$ is periodic in z with period π or 2π, so it can be expressed in a series of Mathieu functions se_{2p}, ce_{2p} or se_{2p+1}, ce_{2p+1}. In accordance with 2° § 4.70, for (a, q) in an unstable region between the curves b_{2p} and a_{2p}, we write

$$\phi(z) = \sum_{p=0}^{\infty} [C_{2p} \, ce_{2p}(z, q) + S_{2p} \, se_{2p}(z, q)]; \tag{2}$$

and for (a, q) in an unstable region between b_{2p+1} and a_{2p+1} we write

$$\phi(z) = \sum_{p=0}^{\infty} [C_{2p+1} \, ce_{2p+1}(z, q) + S_{2p+1} \, se_{2p+1}(z, q)], \tag{3}$$

the C, S being determinable constants. Putting $r = 2p$ or $2p+1$, as the case may be, our proposed solution takes the form

$$\begin{matrix} y_1 \\ y_2 \end{matrix}(z) = e^{\pm \mu z} \sum_{p=0}^{\infty} [C_r \, ce_r(z, q) \pm S_r \, se_r(z, q)]. \tag{4}$$

Substituting $y_1(z)$ from (1) into Mathieu's equation yields

$$\phi'' + 2\mu\phi' + (a + \mu^2 - 2q \cos 2z)\phi = 0. \tag{5}$$

From (2), (3) with $r = 2p$ or $2p+1$, assuming uniform convergence,

$$\phi''(z) = \sum_{p=0}^{\infty} (C_r \, ce_r'' + S_r \, se_r'')$$

$$= \sum_{p=0}^{\infty} [C_r(2q \cos 2z - a_r)ce_r + S_r(2q \cos 2z - b_r)se_r], \tag{6}$$

where a_r, b_r are the characteristic numbers for ce_r, se_r, respectively, corresponding to the value of q used in the equation. Also

$$\phi'(z) = \sum_{p=0}^{\infty} (C_r \mathrm{ce}'_r + S_r \mathrm{se}'_r). \tag{7}$$

Substituting from (2), (3), (6), (7) into (5) leads to

$$\sum_{p=0}^{\infty} [C_r(2q\cos 2z - a_r)\mathrm{ce}_r + S_r(2q\cos 2z - b_r)\mathrm{se}_r] + 2\mu \sum_{p=0}^{\infty} (C_r \mathrm{ce}'_r + S_r \mathrm{se}'_r) +$$

$$+ (a + \mu^2 - 2q\cos 2z) \sum_{p=0}^{\infty} (C_r \mathrm{ce}_r + S_r \mathrm{se}_r) = 0. \tag{8}$$

The series being assumed absolutely convergent, (8) may be written

$$\sum_{p=0}^{\infty} C_r(a - a_r + \mu^2)\mathrm{ce}_r + \sum_{p=0}^{\infty} S_r(a - b_r + \mu^2)\mathrm{se}_r + 2\mu \sum_{p=0}^{\infty} (C_r \mathrm{ce}'_r + S_r \mathrm{se}'_r) = 0. \tag{9}$$

Multiplying (9) by ce_s and integrating with respect to z from 0 to 2π, by aid of §§ 2.19, 2.21, 14.42, we get

$$\pi C_s(a - a_s + \mu^2) + 2\mu \int_0^{2\pi} \sum_{p=0}^{\infty} S_r \mathrm{se}'_r \mathrm{ce}_s \, dz = 0, \tag{10}$$

or

$$\pi C_s(a - a_s + \mu^2) + 2\mu \sum_{p=0}^{\infty} S_r K_{rs} = 0, \tag{11}$$

where

$$K_{rs} = \int_0^{2\pi} \mathrm{se}'_r \mathrm{ce}_s \, dz.$$

Multiplying (9) by se_s and integrating as above leads to

$$\pi S_s(a - b_s + \mu^2) + 2\mu \int_0^{2\pi} \sum_{p=0}^{\infty} C_r \mathrm{ce}'_r \mathrm{se}_s \, dz = 0. \tag{12}$$

By (2) § 14.42, $\int_0^{2\pi} \mathrm{ce}'_r \mathrm{se}_s \, dz = -\int_0^{2\pi} \mathrm{se}'_s \mathrm{ce}_r \, dz = -K_{sr}$, and by virtue of uniform convergence (12) may be written

$$\pi S_s(a - b_s + \mu^2) - 2\mu \sum_{p=0}^{\infty} C_r K_{sr} = 0, \tag{13}$$

so

$$\pi S_r(a - b_r + \mu^2) - 2\mu \sum_{j=0}^{\infty} C_s K_{rs} = 0, \tag{14}$$

with $s = 2j$ or $2j+1$, as the case may be. Writing m for s in (11) and substituting for S_r from (14) yields

$$\pi^2 C_m(a - a_m + \mu^2) + 4\mu^2 \sum_{p=0}^{\infty} \sum_{j=0}^{\infty} [C_s K_{rs} K_{rm}/(a - b_r + \mu^2)] = 0. \tag{15}$$

The eliminant of this set of equations is—in effect—an equation from which μ may be determined (compare (3) § 4.20).

4.91. Approximate solution when $a \gg q$ real > 0.

In this case we see from Fig. 8 that a lies in a narrow unstable region where $b_m < a < a_m$. It is to be expected, therefore, that the dominant terms in (2), (3) § 4.90 will be of order m. Accordingly as an approximation we shall take

$$\phi(z) \simeq C_m \, \mathrm{ce}_m(z, q) + S_m \, \mathrm{se}_m(z, q), \tag{1}$$

the other C, S being assumed negligible by comparison. Then by (1) and (1) § 4.90

$$y_1(z) \simeq e^{\mu z}[C_m \, \mathrm{ce}_m(z, q) + S_m \, \mathrm{se}_m(z, q)] \tag{2}$$

and

$$y_2(z) \simeq e^{-\mu z}[C_m \, \mathrm{ce}_m(z, q) - S_m \, \mathrm{se}_m(z, q)]. \tag{3}$$

Thus (15) § 4.90 may be written

$$C_m[\pi^2(a - a_m + \mu^2) + 4\mu^2 K_{mm}^2/(a - b_m + \mu^2)] = 0. \tag{4}$$

Now $C_m \neq 0$, so (4) gives

$$\frac{4\mu^2}{\pi^2} K_{mm}^2 + (a - a_m + \mu^2)(a - b_m + \mu^2) = 0. \tag{5}$$

Neglecting μ^4, on the assumption that $|\mu| \ll 1$, we obtain from (5)

$$\mu^2 = (a_m - a)(a - b_m) \Big/ \left(\frac{4}{\pi^2} K_{mm}^2 + 2a - a_m - b_m \right). \tag{6}$$

When q is small enough, by §§ 3.32, 14.42 and tabular values of the coefficients A, B [95], we find that $K_{mm}^2 \simeq \pi^2 m^2$, while

$$(2a - a_m - b_m) \ll 4m^2.$$

Hence we may express (6) in the approximate form

$$\mu \simeq \pm[(a_m - a)(a - b_m)]^{\frac{1}{2}}/2m. \tag{7}$$

In Fig. 12, $(a_2 - a)$, $(a - b_2)$ are the segments of the line $a_2 b_2$. Their product is a maximum when a is the mid-point. Then for an assigned q

$$\mu_{\max} \simeq (a_m - b_m)/4m. \tag{8}$$

By virtue of this property, when q is small enough the turning-point of an iso-μ curve occurs approximately midway between the bounding curves for the region, i.e. b_{2n}, a_{2n} or b_{2n+1}, a_{2n+1} as the case may be. Also, when q is small enough, the series for a_m, b_m in § 2.151 may be used in computing μ, as exemplified in § 4.92.

To the degree of approximation in (1), equations (11), (13) § 4.90 become

$$\pi C_s(a-a_s+\mu^2)+2\mu S_m K_{ms} = 0 \tag{9}$$

and

$$\pi S_s(a-b_s+\mu^2)-2\mu C_m K_{sm} = 0. \tag{10}$$

In particular when $s = m$, we get

$$\pi C_m(a-a_m+\mu^2)+2\mu S_m K_{mm} = 0 \tag{11}$$

and

$$\pi S_m(a-b_m+\mu^2)-2\mu C_m K_{mm} = 0. \tag{12}$$

From (12) $\quad S_m = 2\mu C_m K_{mm}/\pi(a-b_m+\mu^2). \tag{13}$

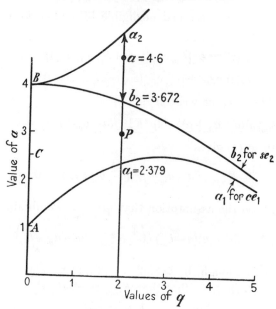

FIG. 12. Illustrating calculation of β, μ.

Substituting for $2\mu K_{mm}/\pi$ from (5) into (13) yields

$$S_m = C_m\left(\frac{a_m-a-\mu^2}{a-b_m+\mu^2}\right)^{\frac{1}{2}}. \tag{14}$$

Substituting for μ from (5) and for S_m from (13) into (9), we obtain

$$C_s = -C_m\frac{K_{ms}}{K_{mm}}\left(\frac{a_m-a-\mu^2}{a-a_s+\mu^2}\right). \tag{15}$$

Substituting for μ from (5) into (10) leads to

$$S_s = C_m\frac{K_{sm}}{K_{mm}}\frac{[(a_m-a-\mu^2)(a-b_m+\mu^2)]^{\frac{1}{2}}}{(a-b_s+\mu^2)}. \tag{16}$$

In (15), (16) it may be remarked that s corresponds to r in (4) § 4.90.

4.92. Example. Find a first approximation to $y_1(z)$ for the equation $y'' + (1 - 0.32 \cos 2z)y = 0$.

Here $a = 1$, $q = 0.16$, and the point (a, q) lies in an unstable region of the plane between the curves b_1, a_1 in Fig. 8. Then from (2), (3) § 2.151

$$b_1 \simeq 1 - q - \tfrac{1}{8}q^2 \tag{1}$$

and

$$a_1 \simeq 1 + q - \tfrac{1}{8}q^2. \tag{2}$$

Thus

$$\left.\begin{array}{l} (a - b_1) \simeq q + \tfrac{1}{8}q^2, \\ (a_1 - a) \simeq q - \tfrac{1}{8}q^2, \end{array}\right\} \quad \text{so } (a_1 - a)(a - b_1) \simeq q^2 - \tfrac{1}{64}q^4 \simeq q^2. \tag{3}$$

Hence from (3) above, and (7) § 4.91 with $m = 1$, we obtain

$$\mu \simeq \pm \tfrac{1}{2}q = \pm 0.08, \tag{4}$$

which is the value calculated in $2°$ § 5.33 using an entirely different method.

Substituting for the various quantities in (14) § 4.91 with $m = 1$, we have

$$S_1 \simeq C_1 \left(\frac{q - \tfrac{1}{8}q^2 - \tfrac{1}{4}q^2}{q + \tfrac{1}{8}q^2 + \tfrac{1}{4}q^2} \right)^{\tfrac{1}{2}} = C_1 \left(\frac{1 - \tfrac{3}{8}q}{1 + \tfrac{3}{8}q} \right)^{\tfrac{1}{2}}$$

$$\simeq 0.94 C_1.\dagger \tag{5}$$

Substituting for μ, S_1, q in (2) § 4.91 gives a first approximation to $y_1(z)$, namely,

$$y_1(z) \simeq C_1 e^{0.08z}[\mathrm{ce}_1(z, 0.16) + 0.94\,\mathrm{se}_1(z, 0.16)], \tag{6}$$

C_1 being arbitrary. Also writing $-z$ for z, the second solution is

$$y_2(z) \simeq C_1 e^{-0.08z}[\mathrm{ce}_1(z, 0.16) - 0.94\,\mathrm{se}_1(z, 0.16)], \tag{7}$$

and the complete solution with two arbitrary constants is, therefore,

$$y \simeq A e^{-0.08z}[\mathrm{ce}_1 - 0.94\,\mathrm{se}_1] + B e^{0.08z}[\mathrm{ce}_1 + 0.94\,\mathrm{se}_1], \tag{8}$$

the constant C_1 being absorbed in A, B.

4.93. Solution of $y'' + (a - 2q \cos 2z)y = f(z)$. This is given by (13) § 6.22 to which section reference should be made.

4.94. Solution of $y'' + 2\kappa y' + (\bar{a} - 2q \cos 2z)y = f(z)$. The substitution $y = e^{-\kappa z}u(z)$ transforms the equation to

$$u'' + (a - 2q \cos 2z)u = e^{\kappa z}f(z), \tag{1}$$

with $a = (\bar{a} - \kappa^2)$. Then the solution of (1) is given by (13) § 6.22.

If $q < 0$, or if cosh be written for cos, $-\infty < q < \infty$, in this section and in § 4.93, the procedure is first to obtain the solution with the r.h.s. zero, and then use (13) § 6.22.

† The sign of this term is that of (13) § 4.91, where we assume μ is positive.

NUMERICAL SOLUTION OF EQUATIONS

5.10. Calculation of β, μ, with q small and positive. Provided $a \neq m^2$, (4) § 4.74 or (2) § 4.23 may be used. Also (14) § 4.30, or one of that type suited to the region of the (a, q)-plane where a, q lies, is valid for a integral or fractional, provided q is not too large. If an iso-$\beta\mu$ stability chart of the type in Fig. 11, but 2 or 3 feet square, and covering a greater range of a were available, β, μ could be obtained directly. If $a^{\frac{1}{2}}$ and q were plotted, the vertical spacing would be more uniform than that in Fig. 11, while interpolation near the $a^{\frac{1}{2}}$-axis would be almost linear. Tabular values of $a^{\frac{1}{2}}$, q, and β would serve the same purpose and facilitate interpolation.

1°. *Calculate β for* $y'' + (2 - 0.32\cos 2z)y = 0$. Here $a = 2$, $q = 0.16$ and the parametric point lies in a stable region of Figs. 8, 11, between a_1 and b_2. First we obtain an approximation. On the a-axis β = fractional part of $a^{\frac{1}{2}}$, so taking $a = 2$, $\beta = 2^{\frac{1}{2}} - 1 \simeq 0.414$. This is an approximation to β at $q = 0.16$. In Fig. 11 the β const. curve through $(2, 0.16)$ meets the a-axis where $a < 2$. Thus the correct value of $\beta < 0.414$.

Method 1. Using (4) § 4.74 and omitting the term in q^6, we get

$$1 + \beta = \left[2 - \frac{0.16^2}{2 - 0.16^2} + \frac{17 \times 0.16^4}{32 \times 2}\right]^{\frac{1}{2}} = 1.9872^{\frac{1}{2}},$$

so
$$\beta = 0.4097. \tag{1}$$

As we shall see in § 5.20, this is a fairly close result.

Method 2. We apply (14) § 4.30, but have to calculate $\sin 2\sigma$ first. Then (12) § 4.30 may be abbreviated and written in the approximate form

$$\frac{1}{4}q^2\left(1 - \frac{11}{64}q^2\right)\cos^2 2\sigma - q\left(1 - \frac{1}{64}q^2\right)\cos 2\sigma + \frac{65}{1536}q^4 - \frac{3}{8}q^2 + 1 - a = 0. \tag{2}$$

Substituting $a = 2$, $q = 0.16$ gives

$$\cos^2 2\sigma - 25.1\cos 2\sigma - 158.5 = 0,$$

so
$$\cos 2\sigma = -5.2 \text{ or } +30.3. \tag{3}$$

Referring to Fig. 8 B, we see that in (3), $\sigma = -\frac{1}{2}\pi + i\theta$ for the region in which the point $(2, 0 \cdot 16)$ lies.† Then

$$\cos(-\pi + 2i\theta) = -\cosh 2\theta = -5 \cdot 2,$$

this root of (3) being chosen since the positive one is inadmissible. Now $|\cos 2\sigma| > 1$, so

$$\sin 2\sigma = \pm i(\cos^2 2\sigma - 1)^{\frac{1}{2}} = \pm 5 \cdot 11i, \tag{4}$$

and by (14) §4.30 we obtain

$$\mu \simeq \pm 0 \cdot 4085i, \quad \text{so } \beta = 0 \cdot 4085, \tag{5}$$

where the positive sign is used conventionally. Thus (1), (5) differ in the third decimal place. In §5.20 the former result is shown to be the more accurate.

2°. *Example.* Calculate β for $y'' + (6 \cdot 25 - 1 \cdot 6 \cos 2z)y = 0$. Here $a = 6 \cdot 25$, $q = 0 \cdot 8$, so the parametric point lies in a stable region of Figs. 8, 11, between the curves a_2 and b_3. Then $6 \cdot 25^{\frac{1}{2}} = 2 \cdot 5$, so taking the fractional part, $0 \cdot 5$ is a rough approximation to the value of β. In accordance with our remarks in 1°, $\beta < 0 \cdot 5$.

Method 1. From (4) §4.74, omitting the term in q^6 (for purposes of illustration)

$$2 + \beta = \left[6 \cdot 25 - \frac{5 \cdot 25 \times 0 \cdot 8^2}{2 \times 5 \cdot 25^2 - 0 \cdot 64} - \frac{(31 \cdot 25 + 7) \times 0 \cdot 8^4}{32 \times 5 \cdot 25^3 \times 2 \cdot 25} \right]^{\frac{1}{2}}, \tag{1}$$

$$= 6 \cdot 1869^{\frac{1}{2}} = 2 \cdot 4873.$$

Hence $\qquad\qquad\qquad \beta = 0 \cdot 4873. \tag{2}$

Method 2. Using (14) §4.30 and (2) 1°,

$$\mu \simeq (-0 \cdot 4 + 0 \cdot 012 + 0 \cdot 0096 - 0 \cdot 00122 + 0 \cdot 0227)\sin 2\sigma \tag{3}$$

$$\simeq \pm 1 \cdot 385i, \quad \text{so } \beta \simeq 0 \cdot 385. \tag{4}$$

In this case unity is present, because (14) §4.30 has been used outside the region stipulated in §4.32. The value $\beta = 0 \cdot 385$ is in marked disagreement with (2), the former being in error, since q is too large for (12), (14) §4.30 to yield accurate results. This is indicated by the fact that $0 \cdot 0227$ exceeds the three prior terms numerically.

3°. *Example.* Calculate μ for the equation

$$y'' + (1 - 0 \cdot 64 \cos 2z)y = 0.$$

The point $a = 1$, $q = 0 \cdot 32$ lies in an unstable region of Fig. 8 between b_1 and a_1. Here (2) §4.23 does not apply, since $a = m^2 = 1$, so we fall back on (12), (14) §4.30. From the former

$$\cos^2 2\sigma - 12 \cdot 72 \cos 2\sigma - 1 \cdot 512 = 0,$$

† As shown in §4.60 this value of σ applies to (2) for the region concerned. For (1) §4.60, $\sigma = i\theta$.

giving $\qquad \cos 2\sigma = -0 \cdot 115$ or $+12 \cdot 835.$ $\qquad\qquad$ (1)

Referring to Fig. 8 B, we see that σ is real, so $|\cos 2\sigma| \leqslant 1$ and, therefore, we choose the negative root. The reality of σ entails $\sin 2\sigma = \pm (1 - \cos^2 2\sigma)^{\frac{1}{2}}$, so

$$\sin 2\sigma = \pm 0 \cdot 9934. \qquad (2)$$

By (14) § 4.30 we find that

$$\mu = \pm 0 \cdot 158 \quad \text{(see Fig. 11).} \qquad (3)$$

The above examples illustrate various formulae and their limitations. If μ is real, $|\cos 2\sigma|$ and $|\sin 2\sigma| \leqslant 1$, but if imaginary they exceed unity. Hence for equal accuracy, q in (12), (14) § 4.30 may be greater when the solution is unstable than when it is stable (μ imaginary).

If μ is computed using (6) § 4.91, the result is $0 \cdot 16$, being less accurate than (3).

5.11. Calculation of β using continued fractions, $q > 0$. When a, q are such that (4) § 4.74 does not give sufficient accuracy, the method below may be used. Applying the procedure in § 3.11 to (1) § 4.17 we get the infinite continued fraction [94, 134]

$$\frac{c_{2r}}{c_{2r-2}} = \frac{-q/(2r+\beta)^2}{1 - a/(2r+\beta)^2 -} \frac{q^2/(2r+\beta)^2(2r+2+\beta)^2}{1 - a/(2r+2+\beta)^2 -}$$
$$- \frac{q^2/(2r+2+\beta)^2(2r+4+\beta)^2}{1 - a/(2r+4+\beta)^2} - \cdots \quad (1)$$

The next step is to derive an alternative continued fraction for c_{2r}/c_{2r-2}. In (1) § 4.17 we replace r by $(r-1)$, divide throughout by qc_{2r-2}, and obtain

$$c_{2r}/c_{2r-2} = [a - (2r-2+\beta)^2 - q(c_{2r-4}/c_{2r-2})]/q, \qquad (2)$$

so $\quad c_{2r-2}/c_{2r} = -q/[(2r-2+\beta)^2 - a + q(c_{2r-4}/c_{2r-2})] \qquad (3)$

$$= \frac{-q/(2r-2+\beta)^2}{1 - a/(2r-2+\beta)^2 -} \frac{q^2/(2r-2+\beta)^2(2r-4+\beta)^2}{1 - a/(2r-4+\beta)^2} - \cdots \quad (4)$$

But (2) may be expressed in the form

$$c_{2r}/c_{2r-2} = \{[-(2r-2+\beta)^2 + a]/q\} - (c_{2r-4}/c_{2r-2}). \qquad (5)$$

Writing $(r-1)$ for r in (4) and substituting it for the third member of (5) yields the alternative continued fraction

$$c_{2r}/c_{2r-2} = \frac{-(2r-2+\beta)^2 + a}{q} + \frac{q/(2r-4+\beta)^2}{1 - a/(2r-4+\beta)^2 -}$$
$$- \frac{q^2/(2r-4+\beta)^2(2r-6+\beta)^2}{1 - a/(2r-6+\beta)^2} - \cdots \quad (6)$$

Then (1), (6) are equal for all r provided β has its correct value. Thus with $r = 1$, we get, respectively,

$$v_0 = c_2/c_0 = \frac{-q/(\beta+2)^2}{1-a/(\beta+2)^2-} \frac{q^2/(\beta+2)^2(\beta+4)^2}{1-a/(\beta+4)^2-} \frac{q^2/(\beta+4)^2(\beta+6)^2}{1-a/(\beta+6)^2-} \cdots,$$

(7)

$$\bar{v}_0 = c_2/c_0 = \frac{a-\beta^2}{q} + \frac{q/(\beta-2)^2}{1-a/(\beta-2)^2-} \frac{q^2/(\beta-2)^2(\beta-4)^2}{1-a/(\beta-4)^2-} \cdots.$$

(8)

(7), (8) are based upon the form of solution (2) 1° §4.70 which progresses in even orders of r. Consequently they are suited for computing β when (a, q) lies in a stable region between a_{2n} and b_{2n+1}. If (a, q) lies between a_{2n+1}, b_{2n+2} the appropriate solution is (5) 1° §4.70, so we use the recurrence relation

$$[a-(2r+1+\beta)^2]c_{2r+1}-q(c_{2r+3}+c_{2r-1}) = 0,$$

(9)

which is (1) §4.17 with $(\beta+1)$ for β and c_{2r+1} for c_{2r}. Making this substitution for β in (7), (8) gives

$$v_1 = \frac{-q/(\beta+3)^2}{1-a/(\beta+3)^2-} \frac{q^2/(\beta+3)^2(\beta+5)^2}{1-a/(\beta+5)^2-} \frac{q^2/(\beta+5)^2(\beta+7)^2}{1-a/(\beta+7)^2-} \cdots, \quad (10)$$

$$\bar{v}_1 = \frac{a-(\beta+1)^2}{q} + \frac{q/(\beta-1)^2}{1-a/(\beta-1)^2-} \frac{q^2/(\beta-1)^2(\beta-3)^2}{1-a/(\beta-3)^2-} \cdots. \quad (11)$$

The correct value of β in (7), (8) or in (10), (11) is that for which $v_0 = \bar{v}_0$, or $v_1 = \bar{v}_1$, $0 < \beta < 1$. In practice we aim to make $v_0-\bar{v}_0$, or $v_1-\bar{v}_1$, vanish to an adequate number of decimal places. Convergence of the C.F. may be considered as in §3.14. A numerical example is given in §5.13 et seq.

5.12. Calculation of μ, q moderate and positive, solution unstable. When the parametric point lies in an unstable region of Figs. 8, 11 between b_{2n+2} and a_{2n+2}, μ is real and we write $\beta = -i\mu$ in (7), (8) §5.11. Then $-v_0$ and $\bar{v}_0-(a+\mu^2)/q$ are seen to be conjugate complex numbers. Let $v_0 = -(x+iy)$, and $\bar{v}_0-(a+\mu^2)/q = x-iy$. When $(v_0-\bar{v}_0) = 0$, the imaginary part vanishes and

$$2R(v_0) = -2x = (a+\mu^2)/q.$$

(1)

It is possible to satisfy this equality by evaluating v_0 alone such that twice its real part is equal to $(a+\mu^2)/q$, i.e.

$$2x+(a+\mu^2)/q = 0.$$

(2)

When the parametric point lies between b_{2n+1} and a_{2n+1}, β in (10), (11) §5.11 is replaced by $-i\mu$. The conditions for correct μ are

$$R(v_1) = R(\bar{v}_1) \quad \text{and} \quad I(v_1) = I(\bar{v}_1). \tag{3}$$

5.13. Calculation of β for $y''+(3-4\cos 2z)y = 0$. Before using the formulae in § 5.11, we have to find a trial value of β to start the calculation. (4) §4.74 may be used for this purpose if a/q is large enough. Here $a/q = 1.5$ is too small, and in consequence the term in q^6 is too large. An iso-$\beta\mu$ chart of the type in Fig. 11, or the tabular values corresponding thereto, may be used if available. We proceed now as follows: In Fig. 8 the point $(3, 2)$ lies in a stable region between a_1 and b_2. For $q = 2$, we find from Appendix 2 that $a_1 \simeq 2.379$, $b_2 \simeq 3.672$. Referring to Fig. 12, we divide $BA = (4-1)$ on the a-axis in the ratio

$$(3^{\frac{1}{2}}-2.379^{\frac{1}{2}})/(3.672^{\frac{1}{2}}-2.379^{\frac{1}{2}}) = 0.508.$$

Thus $AC = 3 \times 0.508 = 1.524$, so at C, $a = 2.524$ and, therefore, $\beta = 2.524^{\frac{1}{2}}-1 = 0.589$. This is our trial β, and we shall see later that it is in error by $+0.00956...$.

Since (a, q) lies between a_1, b_2 we employ (10), (11) § 5.11, and to *demonstrate* the procedure, choose a less accurate value of β than 0.589. We take $\beta = 0.56$. Neglecting components in (10) §5.11 beyond the third, and in (11) § 5.11 beyond the fourth—the computation being merely by way of illustration—we get

$$\frac{q^2/(\beta+5)^2(\beta+7)^2}{1-a/(\beta+7)^2} = \frac{4/5.56^2 \times 7.56^2}{1-3/7.56^2} = 0.0024,$$

$$\frac{q^2/(\beta+3)^2(\beta+5)^2}{1-a/(\beta+5)^2-0.0024} = \frac{4/3.56^2 \times 5.56^2}{1-3/5.56^2-0.0024} = 0.0114,$$

$$\frac{-q/(\beta+3)^2}{1-a/(\beta+3)^2-0.0114} = \frac{-2/3.56^2}{1-3/3.56^2-0.0114} = -0.209 = v_1, \tag{1}$$

$$\frac{q^2/(\beta-3)^2(\beta-5)^2}{1-a/(\beta-5)^2} = \frac{4/2.44^2 \times 4.44^2}{1-3/4.44^2} = 0.0402,$$

$$\frac{q^2/(\beta-1)^2(\beta-3)^2}{1-a/(\beta-3)^2-0.0402} = \frac{4/0.44^2 \times 2.44^2}{1-3/2.44^2-0.0402} = 7.64,$$

$$\frac{q/(\beta-1)^2}{1-a/(\beta-1)^2-7.64} = \frac{2/0.44^2}{1-3/0.44^2-7.64} = -0.466,$$

$$[a-(\beta+1)^2]/q = (3-1.56^2)/2 = 0.285,$$

so

$$\bar{v}_1 = 0.285-0.466 = -0.181. \tag{2}$$

Since $v_1 \neq \bar{v}_1$ in (1), (2), we now repeat the computation with $\beta = 0.58$ and obtain $v_1 = -0.207$, $\bar{v}_1 = -0.208$. Whether β should be increased or decreased to bring v_1, $\bar{v}_1$ closer to equality in (1), (2) may be ascertained by examining the continued fractions.

5.14. Interpolation. Next we use interpolation as illustrated graphically in Fig. 13 A. In this case the crossing-point is near

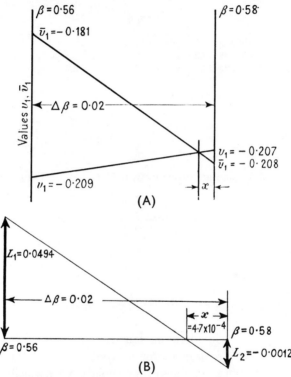

FIG. 13 (A), (B). Illustrating linear interpolation for β.

one extremity of the range of β, which is likely to improve the accuracy of the result. To a first approximation—a higher one not being justifiable with three decimal places—we have

$$\frac{x}{0.02-x} = \frac{0.001}{0.028}, \quad \text{so } x = 0.0007. \tag{1}$$

Hence to three decimal places

$$\beta = 0.58 - 0.0007 = 0.579_3. \tag{2}$$

Using $\beta = 0.5793$, if we repeat the calculation with five component fractions for v_1, six for $\bar{v}_1$, and work to nine decimal places, a more accurate result will be obtained. Thereafter the accuracy may be improved by interpolation, and so on until the desired number of decimal places is reached.

To illustrate the procedure, in Table 5 we give the results of a calculation using two values of β different from those employed hitherto [94].

TABLE 5

β	0·5766	0·5794	$\Delta\beta =$	0·0028	
v_1	$-0·20726\ 88$	$-0·20683\ 52$	$\Delta v_1 =$	0·00043 36	$v_1-\bar{v}_1 = -0·00004\ 29$
$\bar{v}_1$	$-0·20348\ 13$	$-0·20679\ 23$	$\Delta\bar{v}_1 =$	$-0·00331\ 10$	$\Delta\bar{v}_1-\Delta v_1 = -0·00374\ 46$

Then to a closer approximation

$$\beta = 0·5794 + \left(\frac{v_1-\bar{v}_1}{\Delta\bar{v}_1-\Delta v_1}\right)\Delta\beta,$$

$$= 0·57943\ 2. \tag{3}$$

Continuing the calculation we obtain the data in Table 6 [94].

TABLE 6

β	0·5794	0·57943 2	$\Delta\beta = 3·2\times10^{-5}$		
v_1	$-0·20683\ 52$	$-0·20683\ 049$	$\Delta v_1 = 4·71\times10^{-6}$		$v_1-\bar{v}_1 = -3·2\times10^{-7}$
$\bar{v}_1$	$-0·20679\ 23$	$-0·20683\ 017$	$\Delta\bar{v}_1 = -3·787\times10^{-5}$		$\Delta\bar{v}_1-\Delta v_1 = -4·26\times10^{-5}$

To eight decimal places

$$\beta = 0·57943\ 2 + \left(\frac{v_1-\bar{v}_1}{\Delta\bar{v}_1-\Delta v_1}\right)\Delta\beta = 0·57943\ 224. \tag{4}$$

In interpolating, it will often be found that $|\Delta\bar{v}_1/\Delta\beta| \gg |\Delta v_1/\Delta\beta|$ or vice versa. It is essential, therefore, to ensure that the portions of the curves between the points of interpolation are sensibly linear. A check may be made by calculating v_1, $\bar{v}_1$ at an equal small interval $\delta\beta$ on each side of the crossing-point. The points so obtained should lie on the original lines.

5.15. Trial values of β. We shall now compare trial values of β found by the method used in §5.13, and also by (4) §4.74. The former may be crystallized in the empirical formula

$$\beta = m\left\{\left[1+\left(\frac{2m+1}{m^2}\right)\phi\right]^{\frac{1}{2}}-1\right\}, \tag{1}$$

where $\phi = (a^{\frac{1}{2}}-a_m^{\frac{1}{2}})/(b_{m+1}^{\frac{1}{2}}-a_m^{\frac{1}{2}}) < 1$, the values of a_m, b_{m+1} being for the q in the differential equation. If $[(2m+1)/m^2]\phi$ is small enough, a first approximation to (1) is

$$\beta \simeq \left(1 + \frac{1}{2m}\right)\phi. \tag{2}$$

TABLE 7. *Trial values of β calculated from different formulae*

a	q	Formula used			More accurate value of β
		β (1)	β (2)	β (4) § 4.74	
3 ($m = 1$)	2	0·589	m too small	inapplicable: see § 5.13	0·5794
6 ($m = 2$)	2	0·27	0·29	0·35	0·34
8 ($m = 2$)	3	0·67	0·79	0·72	0·70
36 ($m = 5$)	16	0·51	0·54	0·62	0·583

In the second, third, and fourth rows of Table 7 the superiority of (4) § 4.74 is evident, although a/q is comparatively small. If in the fourth row q were 3, $a/q = 12$ instead of 2·25, and the accuracy would be improved appreciably. Wherever *possible*, the use of (4) § 4.74 is preferable to obtain the best trial value.

Although we have concentrated our attention on the evaluation of β, since it is needed in differential equations, the same principles may be used to calculate a if β, q are assigned. First we obtain a trial a using either (6) § 2.16 or (1) § 5.15 suitably transformed, and then (if necessary) proceed with the method of continued fractions as in § 5.13 et seq. to obtain $v_0 = \bar{v}_0$, or $v_1 = \bar{v}_1$.

5.20. Solution of equations [134]. The methods adopted may be shown most readily by a series of numerical examples. We commence with the equation

$$y'' + (2 - 0·32 \cos 2z)y = 0, \tag{1}$$

whose parametric point ($a = 2, q = 0·16$) lies in a stable region of Fig. 8 between a_1 and b_2. Accordingly we choose the form of solution at (4) 1° § 4.70. Substituting it into (1), equating the coefficient of $e^{(2r+1+\beta)zi}$ to zero, $r = -\infty$ to $+\infty$, and taking $\beta = 0·409$ from § 5.10, we obtain the recurrence relation

$$[2 - (2r + 1·409)^2]c_{2r+1} - 0·16(c_{2r+3} + c_{2r-1}) = 0. \tag{2}$$

We have taken $\beta = 0·409$ instead of the more accurate value 0·4097 to illustrate a check later on. In § 4.77 when r is large enough we showed that $|c_{2r+2}/c_{2r}| \sim q/4(r+1)^2$, so that after a certain r is reached the $|c|$ decrease very rapidly. To start the computation we assume that c_{2r+3} vanishes to the number of decimal places required in the solution. Taking $r = 3$ in (2) and neglecting c_9, we get

$$c_{2r-1} = [2-(2r+1\cdot409)^2]c_{2r+1}/0\cdot16, \tag{3}$$

so
$$c_5 = (2-7\cdot409^2)6\cdot25c_7$$
$$= -330c_7. \tag{4}$$

With $r = 2$ in (2)

$$c_3 = -(2-5\cdot409^2)6\cdot25\times330c_7-c_7$$
$$= 5\cdot62\times10^4c_7. \tag{5}$$

With $r = 1$ in (2)

$$c_1 = (2-3\cdot409^2)6\cdot25\times5\cdot62\times10^4c_7+330c_7$$
$$= -3\cdot38\times10^6c_7. \tag{6}$$

Thus
$$c_7 = -2\cdot96\times10^{-7}c_1. \tag{7}$$

Using (7) in (4), (5) yields

$$\left. \begin{array}{l} c_3 = -1\cdot661\times10^{-2}c_1, \\ c_5 = 9\cdot77\times10^{-5}c_1, \\ c_7 = -2\cdot96\times10^{-7}c_1. \end{array} \right\} \tag{8} \tag{9} \tag{7}$$

These numerical values illustrate the rapid decrease in the c with increase in r, when $a = 2$, $q = 0\cdot16$.

To calculate c_{-2r-1} we use the above method, and in the present instance commence by neglecting c_{-9}. Then with $r = -4$ and $c_{-9} = 0$ in (2)

$$c_{-5} = (2-6\cdot591^2)6\cdot25c_{-7}$$
$$= -259c_{-7}. \tag{10}$$

With $r = -3$

$$c_{-3} = -(2-4\cdot591^2)6\cdot25\times259c_{-7}-c_{-7}$$
$$= 3\cdot1\times10^4c_{-7}. \tag{11}$$

$r = -2 \quad c_{-1} = (2-2\cdot591^2)6\cdot25\times3\cdot1\times10^4c_{-7}+259c_{-7}$
$$= -9\cdot12\times10^5c_{-7}. \tag{12}$$

$r = -1 \quad c_1 = -(2-0\cdot591^2)6\cdot25\times9\cdot12\times10^5c_{-7}-3\cdot1\times10^4c_{-7}$
$$= -9\cdot44\times10^6c_{-7}. \tag{13}$$

Thus
$$c_{-7} = -1\cdot06\times10^{-7}c_1, \tag{14}$$

and since $|c_{-7}/c_{-5}| < 4 \times 10^{-3}$, we may anticipate that

$$|c_{-9}/c_{-7}| < 4 \times 10^{-3},$$

so by (14), $|c_{-9}| < 4 \times 10^{-10} c_1$. Using (14) in (10)–(12) yields

$$c_{-1} = -9 \cdot 12 \times 10^5 c_{-7} = \quad 9 \cdot 67 \times 10^{-2} c_1, \tag{15}$$
$$c_{-3} = \quad 3 \cdot 1 \times 10^4 c_{-7} = -3 \cdot 286 \times 10^{-3} c_1, \tag{16}$$
$$c_{-5} = -259 c_{-7} \qquad\quad = \quad 2 \cdot 72 \times 10^{-5} c_1, \tag{17}$$
$$c_{-7} = -1 \cdot 06 \times 10^{-7} c_1. \tag{18}$$

Check on β. Writing $r = 0$ in (2) gives

$$(2 - 1 \cdot 409^2) c_1 = 0 \cdot 16 (c_3 + c_{-1}). \tag{19}$$

Using (8), (15), the two sides of (19) are

$$1 \cdot 472 \times 10^{-2} c_1 \quad \text{and} \quad 1 \cdot 28 \times 10^{-2} c_1, \quad \text{respectively,} \tag{20}$$

from which it follows that the value $\beta = 0 \cdot 409$ is a little too small. Now an error in the fourth decimal place in β causes a trifling error in $0 \cdot 16(c_3 + c_{-1})$, so we may write

$$2 - (1 + \beta)^2 = 1 \cdot 28 \times 10^{-2}, \tag{21}$$

and an improved value of β is then found to be

$$\beta = 0 \cdot 4097, \tag{22}$$

which is in accord with (1) § 5.10.

5.21. Solution of $y'' + (2 - 0 \cdot 32 \cos 2z)y = 0$. By (4) 1° § 4.70,

$$y = \sum_{r=-\infty}^{\infty} c_{2r+1} e^{(2r+1 \cdot 41)zi}, \tag{1}$$

where we have taken $\beta \simeq 0 \cdot 41$. Substituting for c_{2r+1} from § 5.20 in (1), we obtain

$$y(z) = c_1[\ldots - 1 \cdot 06 \times 10^{-7} e^{-6 \cdot 59 zi} + 2 \cdot 72 \times 10^{-5} e^{-4 \cdot 59 zi} -$$
$$- 3 \cdot 286 \times 10^{-3} e^{-2 \cdot 59 zi} + 9 \cdot 67 \times 10^{-2} e^{-0 \cdot 59 zi} + e^{1 \cdot 41 zi} -$$
$$- 1 \cdot 661 \times 10^{-2} e^{3 \cdot 41 zi} + 9 \cdot 77 \times 10^{-5} e^{5 \cdot 41 zi} - 2 \cdot 96 \times 10^{-7} e^{7 \cdot 41 zi} + \ldots].$$
$$\tag{2}$$

This form is inconvenient, so we refer to (5) 1° § 4.70. If the latter is substituted in the above differential equation, the recurrence relation (2) § 5.20 is obtained. Hence, apart from a constant multiplier, the coefficients c_{2r+1} must be the same in both cases. Accordingly a first solution of the equation is

$$y_1(z) = \sum_{r=-\infty}^{\infty} c_{2r+1} \cos(2r+1+\beta) \tag{3}$$

$$\begin{aligned}= c_1[&...-1{\cdot}06 \times 10^{-7} \cos 6{\cdot}59z + 2{\cdot}72 \times 10^{-5} \cos 4{\cdot}59z - \\ &-3{\cdot}286 \times 10^{-3} \cos 2{\cdot}59z + 9{\cdot}67 \times 10^{-2} \cos 0{\cdot}59z + \\ &+\cos 1{\cdot}41z - 1{\cdot}661 \times 10^{-2} \cos 3{\cdot}41z + 9{\cdot}77 \times 10^{-5} \cos 5{\cdot}41z - \\ &-2{\cdot}96 \times 10^{-7} \cos 7{\cdot}41z + ...].\end{aligned} \tag{4}$$

The second solution is derived by writing sin for cos in the $\sum$ terms in (3), but not in (4), since the terms corresponding to negative values of r would then have the wrong signs. Thus we get

$$\begin{aligned}y_2(z) = c_1[&...+1{\cdot}06 \times 10^{-7} \sin 6{\cdot}59z - 2{\cdot}72 \times 10^{-5} \sin 4{\cdot}59z + \\ &+3{\cdot}286 \times 10^{-3} \sin 2{\cdot}59z - 9{\cdot}67 \times 10^{-2} \sin 0{\cdot}59z + \sin 1{\cdot}41z - \\ &-1{\cdot}661 \times 10^{-2} \sin 3{\cdot}41z + 9{\cdot}77 \times 10^{-5} \sin 5{\cdot}41z - \\ &-2{\cdot}96 \times 10^{-7} \sin 7{\cdot}41z + ...].\end{aligned} \tag{5}$$

If (2) is expressed in circular functions, (4) is the real and (5) the imaginary part, i.e. the real and imaginary parts are linearly independent solutions of the equation, which is to be expected.

The complete solution, using (4), (5), is

$$y = Ay_1 + By_2, \tag{6}$$

where A, B are arbitrary constants, real or complex, and this defines a fundamental system. In an application, A, B would be obtained from the initial conditions.

Check on the solution. (4) may be checked as in §§ 3.13, 3.16, by aid of the relationship

$$y''(0) = (2q-a)y(0) = -1{\cdot}68y(0).$$

To an adequate approximation we find that each side has the value $-1{\cdot}81$. If greater accuracy is needed, β should be computed as shown in § 5.13 commencing with the value $0{\cdot}4097$. The coefficients c_{2r+1} may then be found to the same degree of accuracy as β, if r is increased and more significant figures used in the calculation.

5.22. Second method of solving $y'' + (2 - 0{\cdot}32 \cos 2z)y = 0$. Here we use the analysis in § 4.30 and refer to § 5.10. Then $\mu = 0{\cdot}41i$† in (5) 1° § 5.10 corresponds to $\sin 2\sigma = -5{\cdot}11i$, $\cos 2\sigma = -5{\cdot}2$, $\sigma = (-\frac{1}{2}\pi + i\theta)$. Substituting in (16), (17) § 4.30 we find that

---

† In accordance with (22) § 5.20 we have taken this approximate value of βi.

$s_3 = -0\cdot02478$, $c_3 = -0\cdot00817i$. Thus by (1), (2) §4.30 the first solution is

$$y_1(z) = e^{0\cdot41zi}[\sin(z-i\theta+\tfrac{1}{2}\pi)-0\cdot02478\sin(3z-i\theta+\tfrac{1}{2}\pi)-$$
$$-0\cdot00817i\cos(3z-i\theta+\tfrac{1}{2}\pi)+...] \quad (1)$$

$$= e^{0\cdot41zi}[\cos(z-i\theta)-0\cdot02478\cos(3z-i\theta)+$$
$$+0\cdot00817i\sin(3z-i\theta)+...]. \quad (2)$$

Expressing the circular functions in exponentials, (2) becomes

$$y_1(z) = \tfrac{1}{2}e^{\theta}[(\cos 1\cdot41z+i\sin 1\cdot41z)-1\cdot661\times10^{-2}(\cos 3\cdot41z+$$
$$+i\sin 3\cdot41z)+e^{-2\theta}\{(\cos 0\cdot59z-i\sin 0\cdot59z)-$$
$$-3\cdot295\times10^{-2}(\cos 2\cdot59z-i\sin 2\cdot59z)+...\}]. \quad (3)$$

Now $\sin 2\sigma = \sin(-\pi+2i\theta) = -i\sinh 2\theta = -5\cdot11i$, so θ is positive and it has the value $1\cdot166$. Then $e^{-2\theta} = 9\cdot7\times10^{-2}$, and (3) becomes

$$y_1(z) = A_1[(\cos 1\cdot41z+i\sin 1\cdot41z)-1\cdot661\times10^{-2}(\cos 3\cdot41z+$$
$$+i\sin 3\cdot41z)+...+9\cdot7\times10^{-2}(\cos 0\cdot59z-i\sin 0\cdot59z)-$$
$$-3\cdot2\times10^{-3}(\cos 2\cdot59z-i\sin 2\cdot59z)+...], \quad (4)$$

with $A_1 = \tfrac{1}{2}e^{\theta}$. Making allowance for the reduced number of terms, (4) is seen to be a linear combination of (4), (5) §5.21. For apart from the multipliers A_1, iA_1, the coefficients agree well enough for the purpose of illustration. Also, since the real and imaginary parts of (4) are linearly independent solutions of the equation, apart from arbitrary constants, (4) contains the complete solution given at (6) §5.21.

Proceeding to find $y_2(z)$, as shown in §4.30, we write $-\sigma$ for σ. Since $\cos 2\sigma$ is even but $\sin 2\sigma$ is odd, we get

$$\mu = -0\cdot41i, \qquad s_3 = -0\cdot02478, \qquad c_3 = 0\cdot00817i.$$

Thus the second solution is

$$y_2(z) = e^{-0\cdot41zi}[\cos(z+i\theta)-0\cdot02478\cos(3z+i\theta)-$$
$$-0\cdot00817i\sin(3z+i\theta)+...], \quad (5)$$

which is merely (2) above with the sign of i changed. It follows, therefore, that the solutions obtained herein have the forms

$$y_1(z) = A_1[f_1(z)+if_2(z)] \quad (6)$$

and
$$y_2(z) = A_1[f_1(z)-if_2(z)]. \quad (7)$$

In applications these forms will usually be inconvenient. Thus when μ is imaginary, the forms at (4), (5) §5.21 are preferable. They may, of course, be derived from above, since $f_1(z)$, $f_2(z)$ are linearly independent solutions of the differential equation. Then the complete solution may be written

$$y(z) = Af_1(z) + Bf_2(z), \tag{8}$$

where A, B are arbitrary constants.

5.23. Relation between solutions of types § 4.13 and § 4.30.

Although in § 4.50 we demonstrated symbolically that the solutions are alike, as they must be for uniqueness, it is interesting to ascertain whether or not the two expressions for $\bar{Z}_0$ in (11) § 4.50 yield identical numerical results. From § 5.20, $\bar{c}_{-1} = 9 \cdot 67 \times 10^{-2} \bar{c}_1$,[†] and from § 5.10, $\sin 2\sigma = -5 \cdot 11i$, $\cos 2\sigma = -5 \cdot 2$. Then $2\cos^2\sigma - 1 = -5 \cdot 2$, so $\cos\sigma = \pm 1 \cdot 449i$. Now $\sigma = (-\tfrac{1}{2}\pi + i\theta)$, $\theta = 1 \cdot 166$, so $\cos(-\tfrac{1}{2}\pi + i\theta) = i\sinh\theta = +1 \cdot 449i$. Also $\sin\sigma = \sin 2\sigma / 2\cos\sigma = -1 \cdot 763$. Substituting these values in (11) § 4.50, we obtain

$$\bar{Z}_0 = -(\bar{c}_1 + \bar{c}_{-1})/\sin\sigma = \bar{c}_1 \times 1 \cdot 0967/1 \cdot 763 = 0 \cdot 622\bar{c}_1 \tag{1}$$

and

$$\bar{Z}_0 = i(\bar{c}_1 - \bar{c}_{-1})/\cos\sigma = \bar{c}_1 \times 0 \cdot 9033/1 \cdot 449 = 0 \cdot 623\bar{c}_1. \tag{2}$$

The approximate agreement of (1), (2) is sufficient to illustrate the point in question. Here $\bar{Z}_0$ is real, since the $\bar{c}$ are real by virtue of the parametric point of the equation lying in a stable region of the (a, q)-plane of Fig. 11.

5.30. Example: Solve $y'' + (3 - 4\cos 2z)y = 0$.

In § 5.14 we calculated β for this equation to a high degree of accuracy, but for the purpose of illustration we shall take $\beta = 0 \cdot 58$. Adopting the scheme outlined in § 5.20, we neglect c_{13} et seq. Then with $r = 5$ in the recurrence relation

$$[3 - (2r+1 \cdot 58)^2]c_{2r+1} - 2(c_{2r+3} + c_{2r-1}) = 0, \tag{1}$$

we get

$r = 5$
$$c_9 = \tfrac{1}{2}(3 - 11 \cdot 58^2)c_{11}$$
$$= -65 \cdot 5c_{11}; \tag{2}$$

$r = 4$
$$c_7 = -\tfrac{1}{2}(3 - 9 \cdot 58^2) \times 65 \cdot 5c_{11} - c_{11}$$
$$= 2 \cdot 899 \times 10^3 c_{11}; \tag{3}$$

$r = 3$
$$c_5 = \tfrac{1}{2}(3 - 7 \cdot 58^2) \times 2899c_{11} - c_9$$
$$= -7 \cdot 893 \times 10^4 c_{11}; \tag{4}$$

$r = 2$
$$c_3 = -\tfrac{1}{2}(3 - 5 \cdot 58^2) \times 78930c_{11} - c_7$$
$$= 1 \cdot 102 \times 10^6 c_{11}; \tag{5}$$

† To conform with the notation in § 4.50, bars have been placed above the c.

$r = 1$
$$c_1 = \tfrac{1}{2}(3 - 3{\cdot}58^2) \times 1{\cdot}102 \times 10^6 c_{11} - c_5$$
$$= -5{\cdot}331 \times 10^6 c_{11}. \tag{6}$$

Thus
$$c_3 = -0{\cdot}2068 c_1 \dagger \qquad (-0{\cdot}20683\ 0c_1), \tag{7}$$
$$\bullet \quad c_5 = 0{\cdot}01478 c_1 \qquad (0{\cdot}01474\ 4c_1), \tag{8}$$
$$c_7 = -0{\cdot}00054\ 3c_1 \qquad (-0{\cdot}00054\ 2c_1), \tag{9}$$
$$c_9 = 0{\cdot}00001\ 228c_1 \qquad (0{\cdot}00001\ 2c_1), \tag{10}$$
$$c_{11} = -0{\cdot}00000\ 01875c_1 \qquad -\!. \tag{11}$$

To calculate c_{-2r-1}, we commence by neglecting c_{-13} et seq.; so with

$r = -6$
$$c_{-9} = \tfrac{1}{2}(3 - 10{\cdot}42^2) c_{-11}$$
$$= -52{\cdot}7 c_{-11}; \tag{12}$$

$r = -5$
$$c_{-7} = -\frac{(3 - 8{\cdot}42^2)}{2} 52{\cdot}7 c_{-11} - c_{-11}$$
$$= 1{\cdot}78 \times 10^3 c_{-11}; \tag{13}$$

$r = -4$
$$c_{-5} = \frac{(3 - 6{\cdot}42^2)}{2} 1780 c_{-11} - c_{-9}$$
$$= -3{\cdot}405 \times 10^4 c_{-11}; \tag{14}$$

$r = -3$
$$c_{-3} = -\frac{(3 - 4{\cdot}42^2)}{2} 3{\cdot}405 \times 10^4 c_{-11} - c_{-7}$$
$$= 2{\cdot}807 \times 10^5 c_{-11}; \tag{15}$$

$r = -2$
$$c_{-1} = \frac{(3 - 2{\cdot}42^2)}{2} 2{\cdot}807 \times 10^5 c_{-11} - c_{-5}$$
$$= -3{\cdot}674 \times 10^5 c_{-11}; \tag{16}$$

$r = -1$
$$c_1 = -\frac{(3 - 0{\cdot}42^2)}{2} 3{\cdot}674 \times 10^5 c_{-11} - c_{-3}$$
$$= -8 \times 10^5 c_{-11}. \tag{17}$$

Thus
$$c_{-1} = 0{\cdot}4592 c_1 \qquad (0{\cdot}45952\ 7c_1), \tag{18}$$
$$c_{-3} = -0{\cdot}3509 c_1 \qquad (-0{\cdot}35134\ 9c_1), \tag{19}$$
$$c_{-5} = 0{\cdot}04256 c_1 \qquad (0{\cdot}04275\ 2c_1), \tag{20}$$
$$c_{-7} = -0{\cdot}00222\ 5c_1 \qquad (-0{\cdot}00224\ 0c_1), \tag{21}$$
$$c_{-9} = 0{\cdot}00006\ 6c_1 \qquad (0{\cdot}00006\ 6c_1), \tag{22}$$
$$c_{-11} = -0{\cdot}00000\ 125c_1 \qquad -\!. \tag{23}$$

† The ratio $c_3/c_1 = -0{\cdot}2068$ should be equal to v_1 in § 5.14. They differ in the fifth decimal place. The values in (   ) were obtained by machine using an elaborate method of computation [94].

Check on calculation. This may be effected by computing c_{-1} for $r = 0$. Then from (1)

$$c_{-1} = \frac{(3-1 \cdot 58^2)}{2} c_1 - c_3$$

$$= (0 \cdot 252 + 0 \cdot 2068)c_1$$

$$= 4 \cdot 588 \times 10^{-1}c_1, \tag{24}$$

which differs from (18) in the third decimal place. More accurate c than those we have computed are given in brackets at the r.h.s. In (18), (24), c_{-1} is slightly too small. This defect could be rectified by using a more accurate β, and working to six or eight significant figures.

5.310. Solution of $y'' + (3 - 4 \cos 2z)y = 0$. Since the point $a = 3$, $q = 2$ lies in a stable region between the curves a_1, b_2 in Fig. 8, the preferred form of solution is

$$y_1(z) = \sum_{r=-\infty}^{\infty} c_{2r+1} \cos(2r+1+\beta)z \tag{1}$$

$$\simeq 0 \cdot 459 \cos 0 \cdot 42z + \cos 1 \cdot 58z - 0 \cdot 351 \cos 2 \cdot 42z -$$

$$- 0 \cdot 207 \cos 3 \cdot 58z + 0 \cdot 043 \cos 4 \cdot 42z + 0 \cdot 015 \cos 5 \cdot 58z -$$

$$- 0 \cdot 002 \cos 6 \cdot 42z - \ldots \tag{2}$$

with $c_1 = 1$. The second solution is (1) with sin for cos, so

$$y_2(z) \simeq - 0 \cdot 459 \sin 0 \cdot 42z + \sin 1 \cdot 58z + 0 \cdot 351 \sin 2 \cdot 42z -$$

$$- 0 \cdot 207 \sin 3 \cdot 58z - 0 \cdot 043 \sin 4 \cdot 42z + 0 \cdot 015 \sin 5 \cdot 58z +$$

$$+ 0 \cdot 002 \sin 6 \cdot 42z - \ldots \tag{3}$$

The complete solution with two arbitrary constants is

$$y(z) = Ay_1(z) + By_2(z). \tag{4}$$

5.311. The Mathieu functions $\mathrm{ce}_{1 \cdot 58}(z, 2)$, $\mathrm{se}_{1 \cdot 58}(z, 2)$. Referring to §4.72, we have to compute the normalizing constant

$$K = 1 \Big/ \Big[\sum_{r=-\infty}^{\infty} c_{2r+1}^2 \Big]^{\frac{1}{2}}. \tag{1}$$

Using the c in §5.30, we find that $K \simeq 0 \cdot 852/c_1$. Now c_1 in §5.310 is unity, so by §§4.71, 4.72

$$\mathrm{ce}_{1 \cdot 58}(z, 2) \simeq 0 \cdot 852 y_1(z) \tag{2}$$

and $$\mathrm{se}_{1 \cdot 58}(z, 2) \simeq 0 \cdot 852 y_2(z). \tag{3}$$

5.32. Alternative method of calculating β, μ [134]. The method of checking β in § 5.20 suggests how it may be calculated. Suppose the equation to be solved is that in § 5.30. First we obtain a trial β as in § 5.13, say, 0·56. Then we use (1) § 5.30 with $r = 0$, β for 0·58, and get

$$[3-(1+\beta)^2]c_1 = 2(c_3+c_{-1}). \tag{1}$$

Analysis as in §§ 5.20, 5.30 leads to the values of c_3, c_{-1} in terms of c_1. Neglecting c_9, c_{-9} and coefficients of higher orders, we obtain

$$[3-(1+\beta)^2]c_1 = 2(-0·2095+0·468)c_1, \tag{2}$$

so

$$\beta = 0·576, \tag{3}$$

choosing the positive root. The process may now be repeated using more significant figures in the working, and commencing with, say, c_{15}, c_{-15}. The result will be more accurate than before. Repetition may continue until the desired accuracy has been attained. It may be preferable, however, to use interpolation. From (1) with $\beta = 0·56$ and by aid of (2), we have

$$(3-1·56^2)c_1-2(-0·2095+0·468)c_1 = L_1 c_1, \tag{4}$$

giving

$$L_1 = 0·0494. \tag{5}$$

Taking $\beta = 0·58$, we get c_3, c_{-1} from § 5.30, and on substitution in (1) we have

$$(3-1·58^2)c_1-2(-0·2068+0·4592)c_1 = L_2 c_1, \tag{6}$$

so

$$L_2 = -0·0012. \tag{7}$$

Having obtained values of L on each side of zero, we interpolate and calculate β when L is zero. Thus (Fig. 13 B)

$$x = \frac{(0·58-0·56)0·0012}{0·0494+0·0012} \simeq 0·00047. \tag{8}$$

Hence

$$\beta \simeq 0·58-0·00047 = 0·5795. \tag{9}$$

This may be improved by repetition and application of procedure similar to that in § 5.14, where an accuracy to eight decimal places is achieved.

The foregoing method is applicable to the determination of μ (real) when (a, q) lies in an unstable region of Figs. 8, 11, but the starting value of μ would need to be assumed, unless a rough trial value could be obtained from (6), (7) § 4.91, or as in 3° § 5.10, 1° § 5.33. Also, if β or μ is assigned for a given q, the value of a may be calculated.

5.33. Example. Solve $y''+(1-0{\cdot}32\cos 2z)y = 0.$†

1°. From Fig. 8 we see that the point $a = 1$, $q = 0{\cdot}16$ lies in an unstable region between b_1 and a_1. Thus σ, μ will be real and $|\cos 2\sigma| < 1$. Using (2) 1° § 5.10 we obtain the approximate equation

$$\cos^2 2\sigma - 25\cos 2\sigma - 1{\cdot}5 = 0, \tag{1}$$

so
$$\cos 2\sigma = 12{\cdot}5 \pm 12{\cdot}56$$

$$= -0{\cdot}06 \text{ or } +25{\cdot}06. \tag{2}$$

Since $|\cos 2\sigma| < 1$, we take

$$\cos 2\sigma = -0{\cdot}06,$$

so
$$\sin 2\sigma = \mp(1-\cos^2 2\sigma)^{\frac{1}{2}} = \mp 0{\cdot}9982.$$

By Fig. 8 B, $-\tfrac{1}{2}\pi \leqslant \sigma \leqslant 0$, so

$$\sigma = -46{\cdot}72° = -0{\cdot}815 \text{ radian.} \tag{3}$$

Using (14) § 4.30 we obtain

$$\mu \simeq \pm 0{\cdot}08 \quad \text{(compare (4) § 4.92).} \tag{4}$$

Also by (16), (17) § 4.30

$$s_3 \simeq -0{\cdot}02, \qquad c_3 \simeq -0{\cdot}0012. \tag{5}$$

Substituting σ, μ, etc., into (1), (2) § 4.30 yields the first solution, namely,

$$y_1(z) \simeq e^{0{\cdot}08z}[\sin(z+0{\cdot}815) - 0{\cdot}02\sin(3z+0{\cdot}815) -$$
$$-0{\cdot}0012\cos(3z+0{\cdot}815)+...]. \tag{6}$$

To derive the second independent solution we write $-\sigma$ for σ. Then μ, c_3 being odd functions of σ, change sign. Thus

$$y_2(z) \simeq e^{-0{\cdot}08z}[\sin(z-0{\cdot}815) - 0{\cdot}02\sin(3z-0{\cdot}815) +$$
$$+0{\cdot}0012\cos(3z-0{\cdot}815)+...]. \tag{7}$$

Now $y_1 \to \pm\infty$ as $z \to +\infty$, so this part of the complete solution is
unstable,

$y_2 \to 0$ as $z \to +\infty$, so this part of the complete solution is stable.

Hence the complete solution, with arbitrary constants A, B, namely,

$$y = Ay_1 + By_2, \tag{8}$$

is unstable and tends to $\pm\infty$ as $z \to +\infty$.

† See § 4.92 for a different method of solution.

2°. We shall now obtain the solution in the form given at (3), 2° §4.70, namely,

$$y_1(z) = e^{\mu z} \sum_{r=-\infty}^{\infty} c_{2r+1} e^{(2r+1)zi}, \tag{1}$$

using the value of μ at (4), 1°. The recurrence formula for the c is (1), 2° §4.750, which may be written

$$\{a+[\mu+(2r+1)i]^2\}c_{2r+1}-q(c_{2r+3}+c_{2r-1}) = 0. \tag{2}$$

Putting $\mu = 0\cdot08$,† $a = 1$, $q = 0\cdot16$ in (2) gives

$$\{1+[0\cdot08+(2r+1)i]^2\}c_{2r+1}-0\cdot16(c_{2r+3}+c_{2r-1}) = 0. \tag{3}$$

To illustrate the procedure in calculating the c, assume that the real and imaginary parts of c_7 vanish to an adequate number of decimal places, i.e. in the computation we put $c_7 = 0$. Then with

$$r = 2 \qquad\qquad c_3 = -5(30-i)c_5, \tag{4}$$

where $0\cdot08^2/0\cdot16 = 0\cdot04$ has been neglected in comparison with -150. With

$$r = 1 \qquad c_1 = (-50+3i)c_3-c_5$$
$$\text{and by (4)} \qquad = 5(1496-140i)c_5,$$
$$\text{so} \qquad c_5 = (1\cdot325\times10^{-4}+1\cdot24\times10^{-5}i)c_1. \tag{5}$$

From (4), (5) $\quad c_3 = -(1\cdot994\times10^{-2}+1\cdot198\times10^{-3}i)c_1.$ (6)

To calculate the c_{-2r+1}, neglect c_{-7}, and with

$$r = -3 \text{ in (3)}, \qquad c_{-3} = -5(30+i)c_{-5}, \tag{7}$$
$$r = -2 \qquad c_{-1} = -(50+3i)c_{-3}-c_{-5}$$
$$= 5(1496+140i)c_{-5}, \tag{8}$$
$$r = -1 \qquad c_1 = (0\cdot04-i)c_{-1}-c_{-3}$$
$$= 5(229\cdot84-1489\cdot4i)c_{-5}, \tag{9}$$

the $0\cdot04$, omitted previously, being included here. Thus

$$c_{-1} = (5\cdot95\times10^{-2}+0\cdot998i)c_1, \tag{10}$$
$$c_{-3} = -(2\cdot38\times10^{-3}+1\cdot978\times10^{-2}i)c_1, \tag{11}$$
$$c_{-5} = (2\cdot024\times10^{-5}+1\cdot313\times10^{-4}i)c_1. \tag{12}$$

† When μ cannot be calculated with adequate accuracy by the method used in 1°, or by the formulae in §4.91, the procedure outlined in either §5.11 (continued fractions) or §5.34 (recurrence relation) may be used. The latter is the simpler of the two. To obtain a rough indication of the order of μ to start a computation (trial μ) as in §5.34, formula (7) §4.91 may be used beyond its normal range. Having found μ to the required accuracy, the solution is obtained as shown in the present section. It may, if desired, be expressed in the form given in §4.751.

As a check we shall find c_{-1} by taking $r = 0$ in (3). Then

$$c_{-1} = [(0.08+i)^2+1]6.25c_1-c_3$$
$$= (5.994 \times 10^{-2}+1.001i)c_1, \tag{13}$$

which differs slightly from (10). Alternatively, from (2) with $r = 0$

$$(\mu+i)^2+1 = 0.16(c_3+c_{-1})/c_1. \tag{14}$$

Substituting for the c, on equating real and imaginary parts, we find in each case that μ is nearly 0.08.

3°. *The solution.* Substituting the values of μ and the c in $y_1 = e^{\mu z} \sum c_{2r+1} e^{(2r+1)zi}$ gives the first solution:

$$y_1(z) = c_1 e^{0.08z}[(1.06+0.998i)\cos z-(2.232+2.1i)10^{-2}\cos 3z+$$
$$+(1.529+1.44i)10^{-4}\cos 5z-...+(0.998+0.94i)\sin z-$$
$$-(1.86+1.752i)10^{-2}\sin 3z+(1.189+1.123i)10^{-4}\sin 5z-...]$$
$$\tag{1}$$

$$= c_1 e^{0.08z}[1.06+0.998i][\cos z-2.1 \times 10^{-2}\cos 3z+$$
$$+1.44 \times 10^{-4}\cos 5z-...+0.94\sin z-1.75 \times 10^{-2}\sin 3z+$$
$$+1.12 \times 10^{-4}\sin 5z-...]. \tag{2}$$

The second solution is obtained by changing the sign of z in (2). The exponential becomes $e^{-0.08z}$, while the sine terms alter sign.

4°. *Odd and even solutions.* The solutions in 3° are neither odd nor even. Nevertheless such solutions may be constructed using linear combinations of those in 3°. Omitting external multipliers, the solutions in 3° may be written

$$e^{0.08z}[\sum \cos+ \sum \sin] \quad \text{and} \quad e^{-0.08z}[\sum \cos- \sum \sin]. \tag{1}$$

By addition we get the *even* solution

$$\bar{y}_1 = 2[\cosh 0.08z \sum \cos+\sinh 0.08z \sum \sin], \tag{2}$$

and by subtraction we get the *odd* solution

$$\bar{y}_2 = 2[\sinh 0.08z \sum \cos+\cosh 0.08z \sum \sin]. \tag{3}$$

The complete solution is

$$y = A\bar{y}_1+B\bar{y}_2, \tag{4}$$

where A, B are arbitrary constants, determinable from the initial conditions. The utility of such solutions in practical problems is doubtful since they both tend to infinity with z.

5°. *Relationship between* (6) 1° *and* (2) 3°. This is expressed by $\bar{Z}_0$ in (11) § 4.50. The two formulae for $\bar{Z}_0$ should give the same result, which ought to be a multiple of $(1 \cdot 06 + 0 \cdot 998i)$ in (2) 3°. Then by (11) §4.50, with $c_1 = \bar{c}_1 = 1$,

$$\bar{Z}_0 = -(1 \cdot 0595 + 0 \cdot 998i)/\sin \sigma \quad \text{and} \quad \bar{Z}_0 = (0 \cdot 9405i + 0 \cdot 998)/\cos \sigma. \tag{1}$$

Now from 1°, $\sigma = -46 \cdot 72^\circ$, so $\sin \sigma = -0 \cdot 728$ and $\cos \sigma = 0 \cdot 686$. Substituting these into the two fractions in (1), we find that they are in good agreement, having the value

$$\bar{Z}_0 \simeq 1 \cdot 37(1 \cdot 06 + 0 \cdot 998i)$$
$$= 1 \cdot 99e^{43 \cdot 28^\circ i}. \tag{2}$$

The angle of $\bar{Z}_0$ is the same as that of Z_0 in 3° §4.752, and since by §4.751, $\bar{Z}_0 = M_0 Z_0$, it follows that

$$M_0 = 1 \cdot 99. \tag{3}$$

Reference should be made to §4.752, where the conjugate properties of the coefficients in 2° are discussed and another form of solution is given.

5.34. Example. Solve $y'' - (1 \cdot 25 + 2 \cos 2z)y = 0$. From Figs. 8, 11, we see that the parametric point $a = -1 \cdot 25$, $q = 1$, lies in an unstable region below a_0, where the iso-μ curves are asymptotic to a_0 as $q \to \pm\infty$. When $q = 0$, $\mu = ia^{\frac{1}{2}}$, taking the positive root, so the curvature of the iso-μ curve through the point $(-1 \cdot 25, 1)$ is less than that of a_0 ($q = 1$). On this basis we proceed to find a *trial* μ to start the computation. A few assumed iso-μ curves, which may be drawn in pencil on a large version of Fig. 8 A, show that the curve through $(-1 \cdot 25, 1)$ will *probably* intersect the a-axis between $-(0 \cdot 81)^{\frac{1}{2}}$ and -1, i.e. $-0 \cdot 9$ and -1, if $ia^{\frac{1}{2}}$ is plotted instead of a.† Thus our trial μ lies between 0.9 and 1, so we shall choose 0.95.‡

The recurrence relation for the coefficients in the solution of type (1) 2° §4.70 is (1) 1° §4.750. Inserting $a = -1 \cdot 25$, $q = 1$, $\mu = 0 \cdot 95$ therein, we get

$$-[1 \cdot 25 + (2r - 0 \cdot 95i)^2]c_{2r} - (c_{2r+2} + c_{2r-2}) = 0. \tag{1}$$

Let $r = 3$, neglect c_8, and (1) gives (using a 10-inch slide-rule as we are merely demonstrating the procedure)

$$c_4 = -[1 \cdot 25 + (6 - 0 \cdot 95i)^2]c_6 = -36 \cdot 35(1 - 0 \cdot 314i)c_6. \tag{2}$$

† When $a > 0$, $a^{\frac{1}{2}}$ is plotted.

‡ If (4) §4.74 is used to calculate μ, as indicated in §4.753, the value $1 \cdot 002$ is obtained. As shown later, this is a better value than 0.95. The purpose of the above procedure, however, is to illustrate what may sometimes be done when the formula cannot be used.

$$r = 2 \quad c_2 = -[1\cdot25+(4-0\cdot95i)^2]c_4-c_6 = 506(1-0\cdot914i)c_6. \tag{3}$$

$$r = 1 \quad c_0 = -[1\cdot25+(2-0\cdot95i)^2]c_2-c_4 = 3929(-0\cdot107+i)c_6. \tag{4}$$

Then

from (4), $\qquad c_6 = -2\cdot52\times10^{-4}(0\cdot107+i)c_0,$ (5)

from (2), (5), $\qquad c_4 = 9\cdot53\times10^{-3}(0\cdot421+0\cdot966i)c_0,$ (6)

from (3), (5), $\qquad c_2 = -(0\cdot13+0\cdot115i)c_0.$ (7)

To check the trial μ we put $r = 0$ in (1), thereby obtaining

$$-[1\cdot25-0\cdot95^2]c_0 \text{ for the l.h.s.}$$

and $\qquad c_2+c_{-2} = 2R(c_2)$ for the r.h.s., (8)

since by § 4.750, c_2 and c_{-2} are conjugate. Thus the l.h.s. is $-0\cdot35c_0$, and the r.h.s. is $-0\cdot26c_0$. Hence the trial μ is too small, and a better value is found by substituting μ for $0\cdot95$ and solving the resulting equation. By so doing we find that $\mu \simeq 0\cdot995$, taking the positive root.† We now repeat the computation using $\mu = 1$, and obtain the following results:

$$\left. \begin{array}{l} c_2 = -(0\cdot124+0\cdot119i)c_0, \\ c_4 = (3\cdot20+8\cdot93i)10^{-3}c_0, \\ c_6 = -(6\cdot23+248i)10^{-6}c_0. \end{array} \right\} \tag{9}$$

The remainder of the solution is left as an exercise for the reader. Since c_{2r} and c_{-2r} are conjugate, c_{-2}, c_{-4}, c_{-6} follow immediately from (9) by changing the sign of i. The *computation* of these coefficients would constitute a check. A partial check is obtained by repeating the procedure at (8). Then with $\mu = 1$, we get

$$-[1\cdot25-1]c_0 = -0\cdot25c_0 \text{ for the l.h.s.}$$

and $\qquad 2R(c_2) = -0\cdot248c_0$ for the r.h.s. (10)

Solving for μ as before, we have

$$(a+\mu^2)c_0 = 2qR(c_2), \tag{11}$$

so $\qquad \mu^2 = -0\cdot248+1\cdot25 = 1\cdot002$

and, therefore, $\qquad \mu \simeq 1\cdot001,$ (12)

taking the positive root. Thus the results are accurate enough for

† This procedure should be used only when the difference between the two values of μ is a small fraction of the trial value. When this is not so, a better trial μ must be chosen.

the purpose of illustration. Greater accuracy may be obtained by increasing r at the beginning, e.g. take $r = 5$, neglect c_{12}, and work to (say) seven decimal places,† with $\mu = 1{\cdot}001$. An improved value of μ will follow, the computation is repeated, and interpolation then used as in § 5.32. The requisite technique is gradually acquired by practice.

5.35. Solutions with $q < 0$. In the solutions with q positive write $(\tfrac{1}{2}\pi - z)$ for z. In the case of unstable solutions like (2), 3° § 5.33, the constant multiplier $e^{\pm\frac{1}{2}\pi\mu}$ may be omitted.

5.40. Solutions of $y'' + (a \mp 2q \sin 2z)y = 0$. If in

$$y'' + (a - 2q \cos 2z)y = 0$$

we write $(\tfrac{1}{4}\pi \mp z)$ for z, it takes the form of the first equation. Hence if q is positive, the solutions of the equation are derived from those of $y'' + (a - 2q \cos 2z)y = 0$ by writing $(\tfrac{1}{4}\pi \mp z)$ for z.

5.41. Solutions of $y'' + [a - 2q \cos(2z \pm \theta)]y = 0$. If we write $(\tfrac{1}{2}\theta \pm z)$ for z in Mathieu's equation, the above form is reproduced. Accordingly for q positive, solutions of the first equation may be derived from those of the second by making this change of variable. When $q < 0$, write $[\tfrac{1}{2}(\pi + \theta) \pm z]$ for z in the solution of Mathieu's equation.

5.50. Example. Solve $y'' - (3 - 4 \cosh 2z)y = 0$. If in § 5.30 we write iz for z, the equation there takes this form. Hence the first solution is (2) § 5.310 with cosh written for cos, while the second solution is (3) § 5.310 with sinh written for sin, the multiplier i being omitted as it is a constant.

5.51. Example. Solve $y'' - (3 + 4 \cosh 2z)y = 0$. The solutions derived by writing $(\tfrac{1}{2}\pi i + z)$ for z in those of the equation in § 5.50 are unduly complicated. The simplest procedure is that given in § 4.71 for q negative, i.e. change alternate signs in § 5.50.

5.60. Example. Solve $y'' + 4y' + (5 - 0{\cdot}32 \cos 2z)y = 0$. By § 4.83 we have $\kappa = 2$, $\bar{a} = 5$, $a = \bar{a} - \kappa^2 = 1$, $q = 0{\cdot}16$, so the auxiliary equation is

$$u'' + (1 - 0{\cdot}32 \cos 2z)u = 0. \tag{1}$$

The point $a = 1$, $q = 0{\cdot}16$ lies in an unstable region of Fig. 8 between

---

† Using a machine.

the curves b_1, a_1, and the first solution of (1) is given by (2), 3° § 5.33. Then $y_1(z) = e^{-2z}u_1(z)$, so

$$y_1(z) = c_1[1\cdot06+0\cdot998i]e^{-1\cdot92z}(\cos z - 2\cdot1\times10^{-2}\cos 3z+...+$$
$$+0\cdot94\sin z-1\cdot75\times10^{-2}\sin 3z+...). \quad (2)$$

The second solution is derived from (2), 3° § 5.33 by writing $-z$ for z and multiplying by e^{-2z}. Thus

$$y_2(z) = c_1[1\cdot06+0\cdot998i]e^{-2\cdot08z}(\cos z-2\cdot1\times10^{-2}\cos 3z+...-$$
$$-0\cdot94\sin z+1\cdot75\times10^{-2}\sin 3z-...). \quad (3)$$

In (2), (3) we may write $C = c_1[1\cdot06+0\cdot998i]$, a constant multiplier. Both solutions tend to zero as $z \to +\infty$, and are, therefore, stable but non-periodic. The complete solution, with two arbitrary constants, is

$$y = Ay_1+By_2, \quad (4)$$

and this constitutes a fundamental system.

HILL'S EQUATION

6.10. Form of equation. For general purposes this may be taken as

$$\frac{d^2y}{dz^2} + [a - 2q\,\psi(\omega z)]y = 0, \tag{1}$$

where $\psi(\omega z)$ is a periodic differentiable function of z,† such that $|\psi(\omega z)|_{\max}^{\min} = 1$. Usually $\psi(\omega z)$ is even in z with

$$\int_0^{2\pi} \psi(\omega z)\, dz = 0.$$

Sometimes $|\psi(\omega z)|_{\max} \neq |\psi(\omega z)|_{\min}$, but this case is not considered herein. We assume a, q to be real. When $\psi(\omega z) = \cos 2z$, (1) becomes the standard Mathieu equation. In certain applications it is convenient to write (1) in the form

$$\frac{d^2y}{dz^2} + \Big(\theta_0 + 2\sum_{r=1}^{\infty} \theta_{2r}\cos 2rz\Big)y = 0, \tag{2}$$

where θ_0, θ_2, θ_4,... are assigned parameters and $\sum_{r=1}^{\infty}|\theta_{2r}|$ converges.

The theory in §§ 4.10–4.16 applies to (1), (2). Stability is discussed in §§ 4.14, 6.50.

6.11. Solution of (2) § 6.10. In accordance with § 4.13, we take a solution of the form [215]—see comments in § 6.31—

$$y_1(z) = e^{\mu z} \sum_{r=-\infty}^{\infty} c_{2r} e^{2rzi}, \tag{1}$$

where μ may be real, imaginary, or complex. Substituting the r.h.s. of (1) into (2) § 6.10, we obtain

$$\sum_{-\infty}^{\infty}(\mu+2ri)^2 c_{2r} e^{2rzi} + \theta_0 \sum_{-\infty}^{\infty} c_{2r} e^{2rzi} + \theta_2 \sum_{-\infty}^{\infty} c_{2r}[e^{2(r+1)zi} + e^{2(r-1)zi}] +$$

$$+ \theta_4 \sum_{-\infty}^{\infty} c_{2r}[e^{2(r+2)zi} + e^{2(r-2)zi}] + \theta_6 \sum_{-\infty}^{\infty} c_{2r}[e^{2(r+3)zi} + e^{2(r-3)zi}] + \dots. \tag{2}$$

---

† $\psi(\omega z)$ may also be periodic and finitely discontinuous (piecewise continuous), but it cannot be differentiated at its discontinuities. The saw-tooth function treated in § 6.40 is a case in point.

Equating the coefficient of e^{2rzi} to zero, $r = -\infty$ to ∞, we get

$$(\mu+2ri)^2 c_{2r} + \theta_0 c_{2r} + \theta_2(c_{2r-2}+c_{2r+2}) + \theta_4(c_{2r-4}+c_{2r+4}) +$$
$$+ \theta_6(c_{2r-6}+c_{2r+6}) + \ldots = 0, \quad (3)$$

or

$$(\mu+2ri)^2 c_{2r} + \sum_{m=-\infty}^{\infty} \theta_{2m} c_{2r+2m} = 0, \quad (4)$$

with the convention that $\theta_{2m} = \theta_{-2m}$. As in § 4.20 we have a set of equations, infinite in number, giving relations between the coefficients c_{2r}. Dividing (3) throughout by

$$(\mu+2ri)^2 + \theta_0 = \theta_0 - (2r-i\mu)^2 = \phi_{2r}, \quad (5)$$

we obtain

$$c_{2r} + \frac{\theta_2}{\phi_{2r}}(c_{2r-2}+c_{2r+2}) + \frac{\theta_4}{\phi_{2r}}(c_{2r-4}+c_{2r+4}) + \ldots = 0. \quad (6)$$

Giving r the values $\ldots -1, 0, 1, \ldots$ in succession leads to the set of equations

$$\left.\begin{array}{l} \cdot \; + \dfrac{\theta_4}{\phi_{-2}}c_{-6} + \dfrac{\theta_2}{\phi_{-2}}c_{-4} + \Big(c_{-2} + \dfrac{\theta_2}{\phi_{-2}}c_0 + \dfrac{\theta_4}{\phi_{-2}}c_2 \Big) + \dfrac{\theta_6}{\phi_{-2}}c_4 + \cdot = 0 \\[2mm] \cdot \; + \dfrac{\theta_6}{\phi_0}c_{-6} + \dfrac{\theta_4}{\phi_0}c_{-4} + \Big(\dfrac{\theta_2}{\phi_0}c_{-2} + c_0 + \dfrac{\theta_2}{\phi_0}c_2 \Big) + \dfrac{\theta_4}{\phi_0}c_4 + \cdot = 0 \\[2mm] \cdot \; + \dfrac{\theta_8}{\phi_2}c_{-6} + \dfrac{\theta_6}{\phi_2}c_{-4} + \Big(\dfrac{\theta_4}{\phi_2}c_{-2} + \dfrac{\theta_2}{\phi_2}c_0 + c_2 \Big) + \dfrac{\theta_2}{\phi_2}c_4 + \cdot = 0 \end{array}\right\} \quad (7)$$

The eliminant for the c is

$$\Delta(i\mu) = \begin{vmatrix} \cdot & \cdot & \cdot & \cdot & \cdot & \cdot & \cdot \\ \cdot & 1 & \theta_2/\phi_{-4} & \theta_4/\phi_{-4} & \theta_6/\phi_{-4} & \theta_8/\phi_{-4} & \cdot \\ \cdot & \theta_2/\phi_{-2} & 1 & \theta_2/\phi_{-2} & \theta_4/\phi_{-2} & \theta_6/\phi_{-2} & \cdot \\ \cdot & \theta_4/\phi_0 & \theta_2/\phi_0 & \boxed{1} & \theta_2/\phi_0 & \theta_4/\phi_0 & \cdot \\ \cdot & \theta_6/\phi_2 & \theta_4/\phi_2 & \theta_2/\phi_2 & 1 & \theta_2/\phi_2 & \cdot \\ \cdot & \theta_8/\phi_4 & \theta_6/\phi_4 & \theta_4/\phi_4 & \theta_2/\phi_4 & 1 & \cdot \\ \cdot & \cdot & \cdot & \cdot & \cdot & \cdot & \cdot \end{vmatrix} = 0, \quad (8)$$

provided $\theta_0 \neq (2r-i\mu)^2$.

6.12. Evaluation of (8) § 6.11. Adopting the procedure in § 4.21, we can show that the determinant is absolutely convergent, provided none of ϕ_{2r} vanishes. Then by an argument akin to that in §§ 4.22,

4.23, we find that [215]

$$\cos i\mu\pi = 1 - \Delta(0)[1 - \cos \pi\theta_0^{\frac{1}{2}}] \tag{1}$$

or
$$\sin^2 \tfrac{1}{2} i\mu\pi = \Delta(0)\sin^2 \tfrac{1}{2}\pi\theta_0^{\frac{1}{2}}, \tag{2}$$

where $\Delta(0)$ is (8) § 6.11 with $\mu = 0$, and $\theta_0 \neq 4r^2$. Thus
$\Delta(0) =$

$$
\begin{vmatrix}
\cdot & \cdot & \cdot & \cdot & \cdot & \cdot \\
\cdot & 1 & \theta_2/(\theta_0-16) & \theta_4/(\theta_0-16) & \theta_6/(\theta_0-16) & \theta_8/(\theta_0-16) & \cdot \\
\cdot & \theta_2/(\theta_0-4) & 1 & \theta_2/(\theta_0-4) & \theta_4/(\theta_0-4) & \theta_6/(\theta_0-4) & \cdot \\
\cdot & \theta_4/\theta_0 & \theta_2/\theta_0 & \boxed{1} & \theta_2/\theta_0 & \theta_4/\theta_0 & \cdot \\
\cdot & \theta_6/(\theta_0-4) & \theta_4/(\theta_0-4) & \theta_2/(\theta_0-4) & 1 & \theta_2/(\theta_0-4) & \cdot \\
\cdot & \theta_8/(\theta_0-16) & \theta_6/(\theta_0-16) & \theta_4/(\theta_0-16) & \theta_2/(\theta_0-16) & 1 & \cdot \\
\cdot & \cdot & \cdot & \cdot & \cdot & \cdot
\end{vmatrix}
\tag{3}
$$

The remarks in § 4.24 on the roots of (3) § 4.20 apply equally to those of (8) § 6.11. When θ_2, θ_4, θ_6,... are small enough, it can be shown by aid of the expansion for $\cot x$ that

$$\Delta(0) \simeq 1 + \frac{\pi \cot \tfrac{1}{2}\pi\theta_0^{\frac{1}{2}}}{4\theta_0^{\frac{1}{2}}}\left[\frac{\theta_2^2}{1-\theta_0} + \frac{\theta_4^2}{2^2-\theta_0} + \frac{\theta_6^2}{3^2-\theta_0} + \cdots\right]. \tag{4}$$

A less accurate formula can be obtained by expanding the third-order determinant in (3) about the origin. Then if θ_2, θ_4,... are small enough

$$\Delta(0) \simeq 1 + \frac{2\theta_2^2}{\theta_0(2^2-\theta_0)} + \frac{2\theta_2^2\theta_4}{\theta_0(2^2-\theta_0)^2} - \frac{\theta_4^2}{(2^2-\theta_0)^2}. \tag{5}$$

6.13. Example. In the lunar perigee problem [70] which gave rise to Hill's equation, the following data were used:

$$\theta_0 = \quad 1\cdot15884\ 39396\ 0,$$
$$\theta_2 = -0\cdot05704\ 40187\ 5,$$
$$\theta_4 = \quad 0\cdot00038\ 32380\ 0,$$
$$\theta_6 = -0\cdot00000\ 91732\ 9.$$

Calculate the value of μ.

1°. We shall get a first approximation using (5) § 6.12. The last two terms will be neglected, since they are of order $\leqslant 10^{-7}$. Then

$$\Delta(0) \simeq 1 + [2\theta_2^2/\theta_0(4-\theta_0)] = 1\cdot00197, \tag{1}$$

so
$$[\Delta(0)]^{\frac{1}{2}} \simeq \pm 1\cdot00098\ 5; \quad \text{also } \theta_0^{\frac{1}{2}} \simeq 1\cdot07649\ 6. \tag{2}$$

Thus $\qquad \sin \tfrac{1}{2}\pi i\mu = [\Delta(0)]^{\frac{1}{2}} \sin \tfrac{1}{2}\pi\theta_0^{\frac{1}{2}}$

$$\simeq \pm 1\cdot00098\ 5\cos(\tfrac{1}{2}\pi \times 0\cdot07649\ 6)$$

$$= \pm 1\cdot00098\ 5\cos 0\cdot12016\ 0$$

$$= \pm 1\cdot00098\ 5 \times 0\cdot99278\ 9$$

$$= \pm 0\cdot99376\ 7. \qquad (3)$$

We find that

$$\tfrac{1}{2}\pi i\mu = \pm 1\cdot45909\ 1 \quad \text{or} \quad \pm 1\cdot68250\ 1 \text{ radian},$$

so $\qquad \mu \simeq \pm 0\cdot92888\ 6i \quad \text{or} \quad \pm 1\cdot07111\ 4i, \qquad (4)$

the sum being $\pm 2i$. Since (5) § 6.12 is not a very accurate formula, we are not justified in giving the value of μ to more than three decimal places. Thus we take

$$\mu \simeq \pm 0\cdot929i \quad \text{or} \quad \pm 1\cdot071i. \qquad (5)$$

2°. We shall now obtain a more accurate value of μ using (4) § 6.12. Then

$$\theta_0^{\frac{1}{2}} = \quad 1\cdot07649\ 61400\ 8 \qquad \frac{\pi \cot \tfrac{1}{2}\pi\theta_0^{\frac{1}{2}}}{4\theta_0^{\frac{1}{2}}} = -0\cdot08809\ 15080\ 2$$

$$\tfrac{1}{2}\pi\theta_0^{\frac{1}{2}} = \quad 1\cdot69095\ 61826\ 5$$

$$\cot \tfrac{1}{2}\pi\theta_0^{\frac{1}{2}} = -0\cdot12074\ 15203\ 9 \qquad \theta_2^2/(1-\theta_0) = -0\cdot02048\ 56419\ 7$$

$$\sin \tfrac{1}{2}\pi\theta_0^{\frac{1}{2}} = \quad 0\cdot99278\ 94864\ 7 \qquad \theta_4^2/(4-\theta_0) = \quad 0\cdot \qquad\quad 516\ 9$$

$$[\qquad] = -0\cdot02048\ 55902\ 7 \qquad \theta_6^2/(9-\theta_0) = \quad 0\cdot \qquad\qquad\quad 1$$

Thus $\qquad\qquad \Delta(0) = \quad 1\cdot00180\ 46065\ 4 \qquad\qquad\qquad (1)$

and $\qquad\qquad [\Delta(0)]^{\frac{1}{2}} = \pm 1\cdot00090\ 18965\ 6. \qquad\qquad (2)$

$$\sin \tfrac{1}{2}\pi i\mu = [\Delta(0)]^{\frac{1}{2}} \sin \tfrac{1}{2}\pi\theta^{\frac{1}{2}}$$

$$= \pm 0\cdot99368\ 48798\ 9, \qquad\qquad (3)$$

so $\qquad \mu = \pm 0\cdot92841\ 62006\ 3i \quad \text{or} \quad \pm 1\cdot07158\ 37993\ 7i. \qquad (4)$

These values of μ are correct to six decimal places. More accurate values may be calculated by aid of (7) § 6.30 which gives

$$\mu = \pm 0\cdot92841\ 67276i \quad \text{and} \quad \pm 1\cdot07158\ 32724i. \qquad (5)$$

6.14. Calculation of coefficients in (1) § 6.11. Having found μ, if $\theta_2, \theta_4, \dots$ are small enough compared with θ_0, an approximate solution may be obtained by neglecting all c except, say, $c_{-4}, c_{-2}, c_0, c_2, c_4$. In (7) § 6.11 the five equations, the central one with two immediately above and below it, each containing only $c_{-4}, \dots, c_4$, are solved in the usual way. A rough approximation may be got by solving the three equations within the broken-line rectangle, which include only c_{-2},

c_0, c_2. In any case, unless θ_2, θ_4, θ_6,... are small enough compared with θ_0, the solution is troublesome. Additional methods are given below.

6.20. Transformation of Hill's equation to a Riccati type.

1°. The form of (1) § 6.10 is such that the analysis in § 4.82 may be applied provided $\psi(\omega z)$ be written for $\cos 2z$. Thus the Riccati type of equation is (2) § 4.81, where $\rho^2 = [1-(2q/a)\psi(\omega z)]$; and if $|a| \gg q > 0$, $|\psi(\omega z)|_{\max} = 1$, its solution is (13) § 4.82. In terms of ψ we have [133]

$$y_1(z) \simeq \frac{\text{constant}}{[1-(2q/a)\psi(\omega z)]^{\frac{1}{4}}} \frac{\cos}{\sin}\left[a^{\frac{1}{2}} \int\limits_0^z \left(1-\frac{2q}{a}\psi\right)^{\frac{1}{2}} dz + \right.$$
$$\left. y_2 \qquad +\frac{\omega^2 q}{4a^{\frac{3}{2}}} \int\limits_0^z \left\{\psi''+\frac{5q}{2a}\frac{\psi'^2}{[1-(2q/a)\psi]}\right\}\frac{dz}{[1-(2q/a)\psi]^{\frac{3}{2}}}\right]. \quad (1)$$

As in § 4.82, the argument of the circular functions is periodic, the frequency of repetition being

$$f = \frac{1}{2\pi}\frac{d}{dz}\left[\qquad\qquad\right]$$
$$= \frac{1}{2\pi}\left[a^{\frac{1}{2}}\left(1-\frac{2q}{a}\psi\right)^{\frac{1}{2}}+\frac{\omega^2 q}{4a^{\frac{3}{2}}}\left\{\frac{\psi''}{[1-(2q/a)\psi]^{\frac{3}{2}}}+\frac{5q\psi'^2}{2a[1-(2q/a)\psi]^{\frac{5}{2}}}\right\}\right]. \quad (2)$$

Under the conditions $|a| \gg q > 0$, $|\psi(\omega z)|_{\max} = 1$, we derive from (2) the approximation

$$f \simeq \frac{1}{2\pi}[a^{\frac{1}{2}}-qa^{-\frac{1}{2}}\psi+\tfrac{1}{4}\omega^2 qa^{-\frac{3}{2}}\{\psi''(1+3qa^{-1}\psi)+\tfrac{5}{2}qa^{-1}\psi'^2(1+5qa^{-1}\psi)\}]. \quad (3)$$

The periodicity is the reciprocal of (3).

The solution of (2) § 6.10 is obtained if in (13) § 4.82 we write θ_0 for a, and take $\rho^2 = [1+(2/\theta_0)\sum\limits_{r=1}^{\infty}\theta_{2r}\cos 2rz]$. As a first approximation, with $\varphi(z) = \rho$ we get

$$y_1(z) \simeq \frac{\text{constant}}{[1+(2/\theta_0)\sum\limits_{r=1}^{\infty}\theta_{2r}\cos 2rz]^{\frac{1}{4}}} \frac{\cos}{\sin}\left[\theta_0^{\frac{1}{2}} \int\limits_0^z \left\{1+(2/\theta_0)\sum\limits_{r=1}^{\infty}\theta_{2r}\cos 2rz\right\}^{\frac{1}{2}} dz\right]. \quad (4)$$

This solution rests on the assumption that $|\theta_0| \gg 2\sum\limits_{r=1}^{\infty}|\theta_{2r}|$, and in common with (1) its boundedness implies stability, i.e. (4) does not hold for an unstable region of the a, q-plane for Hill's equation.

2°. $2q \gg a > 0$, $|\psi(\omega z)|_{\max} = 1$. We now write (1) § 6.10 in the form

$$y'' + 2q\left[\frac{a}{2q} - \psi(\omega z)\right]y = 0. \qquad (5)$$

Substituting $y = e^{\gamma \int^z w\,dz}$ with $\gamma^2 = 2q$, we get

$$\frac{d^2y}{dz^2} = \gamma y\left(\frac{dw}{dz} + \gamma w^2\right), \qquad (6)$$

so from (5), (6), if $\xi^2 = [(a/2q) - \psi]$, (5) transforms to

$$\frac{1}{\gamma}\frac{dw}{dz} + w^2 + \xi^2 = 0. \qquad (7)$$

On comparison with (2) § 4.81, the approximate solution of (5) is obtained by writing γ for ν, and ξ for ρ in (13) § 4.82. Thus

$$\begin{matrix} y_1 \\ y_2 \end{matrix}(z) \simeq (\text{constant})\xi^{-\frac{1}{2}}\begin{matrix}\cos\\\sin\end{matrix}\left[(2q)^{\frac{1}{2}}\int\limits_0^z \{\xi - (2\xi\xi'' - 3\xi'^2)/16q\xi^3\}\,dz\right]. \qquad (8)$$

By omitting the terms in ξ', ξ'', we get

$$\begin{matrix} y_1 \\ y_2 \end{matrix}(z) \simeq \frac{\text{constant}(2q)^{\frac{1}{4}}}{[a - 2q\psi(\omega z)]^{\frac{1}{4}}}\begin{matrix}\cos\\\sin\end{matrix}\left[\int\limits_0^z \{a - 2q\psi(\omega z)\}^{\frac{1}{2}}\,dz\right]. \qquad (9)$$

The solution of Mathieu's equation under the above conditions is found from (9) by writing $\cos 2z$ for $\psi(\omega z)$.

6.21. Solution of (2) § 6.10 involving Mathieu functions.
The equation may be written

$$y'' + (\theta_0 + 2\theta_2 \cos 2z)y = -2\left[\sum_{r=2}^\infty \theta_{2r}\cos 2rz\right]y. \qquad (1)$$

If for a first approximation the r.h.s. of (1) may be neglected, and if μ is imaginary, the solutions are

$$y_1(z) = \text{ce}_{m+\beta}(z, -q) \quad \text{and} \quad y_2(z) = \text{se}_{m+\beta}(z, -q), \qquad (2)$$

provided θ_0 is not a characteristic number for ce_m, se_m, $0 < \beta < 1$ and $q = +\theta_2$.† For a second approximation to the first solution we

---

† If θ_0 is a characteristic number, then $\beta = 0$ or 1, and with $\theta_2 > 0$, by Chapters II, VII, the solutions are

$$y_1 = \text{ce}_m(z, -q), \qquad y_2 = \text{fe}_m(z, -q) \quad (\theta_0 = a_m),$$

or $\qquad y_1 = \text{se}_m(z, -q), \qquad y_2 = \text{ge}_m(z, -q) \quad (\theta_0 = b_m).$

With $\theta_2 < 0$, $-q$ becomes $+q$, and $(-1)^s$ is absent from the second Σ in (3). See § 4.71.

use $y_1(z)$ for y on the r.h.s. of (1). Then we get

$$y'' + (\theta_0 + 2\theta_2 \cos 2z)y$$
$$= (-1)^{n+1}2\left[\sum_{r=2}^{\infty}\theta_{2r}\cos 2rz\right]\sum_{s=-\infty}^{\infty}(-1)^s A_{\substack{2s\\2s+1}}^{(m+\beta)}\left\{\cos\binom{2s+\beta}{2s+1+\beta}z\right\}, \quad (3)$$

β or $(\beta+1)$ being used in accordance with §§ 4.70, 4.71. Taking only the important terms on the r.h.s. of (3), the equation now to be solved may be written

$$\frac{d^2y}{dz^2} + (\theta_0 + 2\theta_2\cos 2z)y = f(z). \quad (4)$$

6.22. Solution of (4) § 6.21.
We write the equation in the form

$$\frac{d^2y}{dz^2} + (a+2q\cos 2z)y = f(z). \quad (1)$$

When $f(z) = 0$, we take the complete solution as the sum of two Mathieu functions $y_1(z)$, $y_2(z)$ with the arbitrary constants A, B. Thus

$$y(z) = Ay_1 + By_2. \quad (2)$$

When the r.h.s. of (1) has the value $f(z)$, suppose that

$$y = Ay_1 + By_2 + A_1(z)y_1 + B_2(z)y_2 \quad (3)$$

and

$$0 = y_1\frac{dA_1}{dz} + y_2\frac{dB_2}{dz}, \quad (4)$$

where $A_1(z)$, $B_2(z)$ are variable parameters (functions of z) added to the respective arbitrary constants in (2). Differentiating (3), we get

$$\frac{dy}{dz} = Ay_1' + By_2' + A_1y_1' + B_2y_2' + A_1'y_1 + B_2'y_2. \quad (5)$$

Using (4) in (5) gives

$$\frac{dy}{dz} = (A+A_1)y_1' + (B+B_2)y_2', \quad (6)$$

so

$$\frac{d^2y}{dz^2} = (A+A_1)y_1'' + (B+B_2)y_2'' + A_1'y_1' + B_2'y_2'. \quad (7)$$

Substituting (7) into (1) and using (3) leads to

$$(A+A_1)[y_1'' + (a+2q\cos 2z)y_1] +$$
$$+ (B+B_2)[y_2'' + (a+2q\cos 2z)y_2] + A_1'y_1' + B_2'y_2' = f(z). \quad (8)$$

Now the [ ] are both zero, so (8) reduces to

$$A_1'y_1' + B_2'y_2' = f(z). \quad (9)$$

Solving (4), (9) gives

$$A_1' = y_2f(z)/(y_2y_1' - y_1y_2'). \quad (10)$$

By § 2.191 the value of the denominator in (10) is $-c^2$, so

$$A_1' = -y_2 f(z)/c^2, \quad \text{or} \quad A_1 = -\frac{1}{c^2} \int^z y_2 f(z)\, dz. \tag{11}$$

Also

$$B_2' = y_1 f(z)/c^2, \quad \text{or} \quad B_2 = \frac{1}{c^2} \int^z y_1 f(z)\, dz. \tag{12}$$

Substituting for A_1, B_2 from (11), (12) into (3) yields the complete solution of (1). Hence

$$y = [Ay_1 + By_2] - \frac{1}{c^2}\left[y_1(z) \int^z y_2(u) f(u)\, du - y_2(z) \int^z y_1(u) f(u)\, du \right] \tag{13}$$

$$= \text{complementary function} + \text{particular integral.} \tag{14}$$

This solution is valid if $-q$ be written for q in (1), provided y_1, y_2 are then solutions of $y'' + (a - 2q\cos 2z)y = 0$, and c^2 is calculated therefrom. If (a, q) lies in a stable region of Fig. 8, these solutions are $\mathrm{ce}_{m+\beta}(z, q)$, $\mathrm{se}_{m+\beta}(z, q)$.

When the point (a, q) in (1) lies in an unstable region of Fig. 8, so long as y_1, y_2 can be found, (13) gives the solution of (1). The method in § 4.90 for solving Mathieu's equation in terms of Mathieu functions is applicable to Hill's equation. Reference may also be made to § 10.70 et seq., where integral equations and their solution in connexion with Hill's equation are discussed.

6.30. Solution of $y'' + \left[\theta_0 + 2\sum_{r=1}^{\infty} \theta_{2r} \cos 2rz\right]y = 0$ **by method of § 4.30 [81–3].** We assume a solution

$$y_1 = e^{\mu z}\phi(z, \sigma), \tag{1}$$

where

$$\begin{aligned}
\mu = {} & \theta_2\psi_2(\sigma) + \theta_4\psi_4(\sigma) + \theta_6\psi_6(\sigma) + \ldots + \\
& + \theta_2^2\xi_2(\sigma) + \theta_4^2\xi_4(\sigma) + \ldots + \\
& + \theta_2\theta_4\xi_{2,4}(\sigma) + \theta_2\theta_6\xi_{2,6}(\sigma) + \theta_4\theta_6\xi_{4,6}(\sigma) + \ldots + \\
& + \theta_2^3\chi_2(\sigma) + \ldots + \\
& + \ldots .
\end{aligned} \tag{2}$$

$$\begin{aligned}
\phi(z, \sigma) = {} & \sin(z - \sigma) + \theta_2 f_2(z, \sigma) + \theta_4 f_4(z, \sigma) + \ldots + \\
& + \theta_2^2 g_2(z, \sigma) + \theta_4^2 g_4(z, \sigma) + \ldots + \\
& + \theta_2\theta_4 g_{2,4}(z, \sigma) + \ldots + \\
& + \theta_2^3 h_2(z, \sigma) + \ldots + \\
& + \ldots \quad \text{a periodic function,}
\end{aligned} \tag{3}$$

σ being found from the relation

$$\begin{aligned}
\theta_0 = 1 &+ \theta_2\,\alpha_2(\sigma) + \theta_4\,\alpha_4(\sigma) + \theta_6\,\alpha_6(\sigma) + \ldots + \\
&+ \theta_2^2\beta_2(\sigma) + \theta_4^2\beta_4(\sigma) + \ldots + \\
&+ \theta_2\theta_4\beta_{2,4}(\sigma) + \ldots + \\
&+ \theta_2^3\gamma_2(\sigma) + \ldots .
\end{aligned} \tag{4}$$

Substituting (1) into the differential equation yields

$$\phi'' + 2\mu\phi' + \left[\mu^2 + \theta_0 + 2\sum_{r=1}^{\infty}\theta_{2r}\cos 2rz\right]\phi = 0. \tag{5}$$

Inserting the series (2)–(4) into (5) and proceeding as in §4.30 to get a periodic solution for ϕ, we derive expressions for θ_0, μ, f_2, g_2, etc. The analysis is much too extensive, however, for inclusion here, so the original memoir should be consulted. Expressions for θ_0 and μ are given below for making a computation. Then

$$\begin{aligned}
\theta_0 = 1 &- \frac{1}{4}\theta_2^2 - \frac{1}{6}\theta_4^2 - \frac{11}{192}\theta_2^2\theta_4 - \frac{13}{192}\theta_2\theta_4\theta_6 + \frac{1}{48}\theta_2^4 - \frac{893}{2\,21184}\theta_2^6 + \ldots + \\
&+ \cos 2\sigma\left[\theta_2 + \frac{1}{4}\theta_2\theta_4 + \frac{1}{12}\theta_4\theta_6 - \frac{1}{64}\theta_2^3 + \frac{5}{192}\theta_2^2\theta_6 - \right. \\
&\qquad\qquad \left. - \frac{1}{144}\theta_2\theta_4^2 - \frac{175}{9612}\theta_2^3\theta_4 + \frac{1}{288}\theta_2^5 + \ldots\right] + \\
&+ \cos 4\sigma\left[\frac{1}{8}\theta_2^2 + \frac{5}{64}\theta_2^2\theta_4 + \frac{13}{576}\theta_2\theta_4\theta_6 - \frac{11}{512}\theta_2^4 + \frac{9181}{17\,69472}\theta_2^6 + \ldots\right] + \\
&+ \cos 6\sigma\left[\frac{7}{512}\theta_2^3\theta_4 - \frac{13}{4096}\theta_2^5 + \ldots\right] + \\
&+ \cos 8\sigma\left[-\frac{35}{32768}\theta_2^6 + \ldots\right] + \ldots .
\end{aligned} \tag{6}$$

$$\begin{aligned}
\mu = \sin 2\sigma&\left[\frac{1}{2}\theta_2 + \frac{1}{8}\theta_2\theta_4 + \frac{1}{24}\theta_4\theta_6 - \frac{3}{128}\theta_2^3 + \frac{5}{384}\theta_2^2\theta_6 + \right. \\
&\qquad\qquad \left. + \frac{7}{288}\theta_2\theta_4^2 - \frac{211}{9216}\theta_2^3\theta_4 + \frac{137}{36864}\theta_2^5 + \ldots\right] + \\
&+ \sin 4\sigma\left[\frac{1}{128}\theta_2^2\theta_4 + \frac{1}{1152}\theta_2\theta_4\theta_6 - \frac{3}{1024}\theta_2^4 + \frac{337}{4\,42368}\theta_2^6 + \ldots\right] + \\
&+ \sin 6\sigma\left[\frac{5}{1024}\theta_2^3\theta_4 - \frac{9}{8192}\theta_2^5 + \ldots\right] + \\
&+ \sin 8\sigma\left[-\frac{15}{65536}\theta_2^6 + \ldots\right] + \ldots .
\end{aligned} \tag{7}$$

6.31. Calculation of μ. Using the numerical values of θ_0, θ_2,... given in § 6.13, we find from (6) § 6.30 that [81]

$$1 \cdot 15884\ 39396\ 0 = 1 - 0 \cdot 00081\ 33804\ 9 - 0 \cdot 05704\ 65855\ 7 \cos 2\sigma +$$
$$+ 0 \cdot 00040\ 66226\ 27 \cos 4\sigma + 0 \cdot 0^9 945 \cos 6\sigma -$$
$$- 0 \cdot 0^{10} 368 \cos 8\sigma. \qquad (1)$$

Thus

$$\cos 2\sigma = -2 \cdot 79871\ 82492\ 1 + 0 \cdot 00712\ 79047\ 3 \cos 4\sigma +$$
$$+ 0 \cdot 0^7 165\ 65 \cos 6\sigma - 0 \cdot 0^8 64\ 51 \cos 8\sigma. \qquad (2)$$

Expressing the r.h.s. of (2) in terms of $\cos 2\sigma$ leads to the equation

$$0 \cdot 0^7 516\ 08 \cos^4 2\sigma - 0 \cdot 0^7 662\ 60 \cos^3 2\sigma - 0 \cdot 01425\ 58603\ 6 \cos^2 2\sigma +$$
$$+ \cos 2\sigma + 2 \cdot 80584\ 60209\ 7 = 0. \qquad (3)$$

Using six significant figures and the last three terms of (3), we obtain the first approximation $\cos 2\sigma \simeq -2 \cdot 70178$. Then by the process of successive approximation it is found that

$$\cos 2\sigma = -2 \cdot 70178\ 48031\ 8. \qquad (4)$$

Since $|\cos 2\sigma| > 1$, by § 4.60, $\sigma = -\frac{1}{2}\pi + i\alpha$, and from four-figure tables $\alpha = 0 \cdot 8255$, so $\sigma = -\frac{1}{2}\pi + 0 \cdot 8255i$. Also

$$\sin 2\sigma = \mp i (\cos^2 2\sigma - 1)^{\frac{1}{2}} \qquad = \mp 2 \cdot 50990\ 86064\ 0i, \qquad (5)$$
$$\sin 4\sigma = 2 \sin 2\sigma \cos 2\sigma \qquad = \pm 13 \cdot 56247i, \qquad (6)$$
$$\sin 6\sigma = \sin 2\sigma (4 \cos^2 2\sigma - 1) \qquad = \mp 70 \cdot 7758i, \qquad (7)$$
$$\sin 8\sigma = 4 \sin 2\sigma (2 \cos^3 2\sigma - \cos 2\sigma) = \pm 368 \cdot 8i. \qquad (8)$$

Inserting the values of θ_2, θ_4, θ_6 in (7) § 6.30 we get

$$\mu = -0 \cdot 02852\ 03942\ 5 \sin 2\sigma - 0 \cdot 0^7 212\ 52 \sin 4\sigma +$$
$$+ 0 \cdot 0^9 3\ 162 \sin 6\sigma - 0 \cdot 0^{13} 26 \sin 8\sigma. \qquad (9)$$

Using (5)–(8) in (9) leads to the result

$$\mu = \pm 0 \cdot 07158\ 32724i. \qquad (10)$$

By aid of the formulae in [81], f_2, f_4, g_2, etc., in (3) § 6.30 may be found, so the first solution in the form (1) § 6.30 is obtained. The second solution is derived therefrom by changing σ to $-\sigma$ and $+\mu$ to $-\mu$. Since μ is imaginary the solution is stable, and if the number of decimal places is fixed (conventionally) it is periodic. It may of course be expressed in the form (4) 1° § 4.70 if desired. In this connexion we remark that the values of μ in (10) differ by $\pm i$ from those at 2° § 6.13 (up to the seventh decimal place), because in § 6.11

we assumed the form of solution at (1) $1°$ §4.70. Without a stability chart for Hill's equation—like Figs. 8, 11—the particular form of solution required to keep μ in the range $0 < \mu < i$ is not always predictable. In the present instance, however, θ_4, θ_6 are so small numerically compared with θ_2, that the equation is approximately a Mathieu type. From Fig. 11 the point θ_0, θ_2 lies in a stable region between a_1, b_2, so there would have been justification for replacing $2r$ by $2r+1$ in (1) §6.11 in accordance with (4) $1°$ §4.70. Moreover, an approximate value of $\mu = i\beta$ may be calculated from (4) §4.74. Using only three terms, we find that $\mu \simeq \pm 0.0713i$ (10-inch slide-rule). The iso-β curve $\beta = 0.0713$ lying just above a_1 in Fig. 11 is an approximation to that for Hill's equation with the θ in §6.13.

6.40. Example. We shall determine μ for the equation [44]

$$\frac{d^2y}{dt^2} + 2\kappa\frac{dy}{dt} + [a' - 2q\,\psi(\omega t)]y = 0. \tag{1}$$

By §4.83 the substitution $y = e^{-\kappa t}u(t)$ leads to the equation

$$\frac{d^2u}{dt^2} + [a - 2q\,\psi(\omega t)]u = 0, \tag{2}$$

with $a = (a' - \kappa^2)$. For $\psi(\omega t)$ we choose the saw-tooth function represented graphically in Fig. 14. It has period $2\pi/\omega$, and the Fourier expansion is

$$\psi(\omega t) = \frac{2}{\pi}\sum_{n=1}^{\infty}(-1)^{n-1}\frac{\sin n\omega t}{n}. \tag{3}$$

We see that $\int_{-\pi/\omega}^{\pi/\omega}\psi(\omega t)\,dt = 0$, and that $|\psi(\omega t)|_{\max}^{\min} = 1$. We consider the interval $-\pi/\omega < t < \pi/\omega$, where the function is defined to be

$$\psi(\omega t) = \omega t/\pi. \tag{4}$$

For this interval *alone*, (2) may be written

$$\frac{d^2u}{dt^2} + a\left(1 - \frac{2q\omega}{a\pi}t\right)u = 0. \tag{5}$$

Writing $\tau = (1-\gamma_0 t)$, where $\gamma_0 = 2q\omega/a\pi$, (5) transforms to

$$\frac{d^2u}{d\tau^2} + b^3\tau u = 0, \tag{6}$$

with $b^3 = a^3\pi^2/4q^2\omega^2$. By aid of example 46, p. 38, reference [203] we find two linearly independent solutions of (6) to be

$$u_1 = \tau^{\frac{1}{2}}J_{\frac{1}{3}}(\alpha\tau^{\frac{3}{2}}) \quad \text{and} \quad u_2 = \tau^{\frac{1}{2}}Y_{\frac{1}{3}}(\alpha\tau^{\frac{3}{2}}), \tag{7}$$

where $\alpha = \pi a^{\frac{3}{2}}/3\omega q$. Although these solutions are valid for the interval $-\pi/\omega < t < \pi/\omega$ only, they enable us to determine μ by aid of (9) § 4.152. We now proceed to obtain the various components in that formula.

$$\frac{du_1}{d\tau} = \tau^{\frac{1}{2}}\frac{d}{d\tau}(\alpha\tau^{\frac{3}{2}})J_{\frac{1}{3}}'(\alpha\tau^{\frac{3}{2}}) + \tfrac{1}{2}\tau^{-\frac{1}{2}}J_{\frac{1}{3}}(\alpha\tau^{\frac{3}{2}})$$

$$= \tfrac{3}{2}\alpha\tau J_{\frac{1}{3}}'(\alpha\tau^{\frac{3}{2}}) + \tfrac{1}{2}\tau^{-\frac{1}{2}}J_{\frac{1}{3}}(\alpha\tau^{\frac{3}{2}}). \tag{8}$$

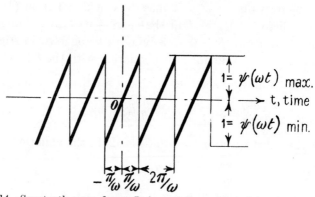

FIG. 14. Saw-tooth wave form. It is periodic and has finite discontinuities indicated by the thin vertical lines.

Using the recurrence relation

$$J_\nu'(z) = -\frac{\nu}{z}J_\nu(z) + J_{\nu-1}(z) \tag{9}$$

in (8) leads to

$$\frac{du_1}{d\tau} = \tfrac{3}{2}\alpha\tau J_{-\frac{2}{3}}(\alpha\tau^{\frac{3}{2}}). \tag{10}$$

Then

$$\frac{du_1}{dt} = \frac{du_1}{d\tau}\frac{d\tau}{dt} = -a^{\frac{1}{2}}\tau J_{-\frac{2}{3}}(\alpha\tau^{\frac{3}{2}}). \tag{11}$$

Similarly

$$\frac{du_2(\omega t)}{dt} = -a^{\frac{1}{2}}\tau Y_{-\frac{2}{3}}(\alpha\tau^{\frac{3}{2}}). \tag{12}$$

6.41. Values of the various functions at $t = \mp\pi/\omega$. Writing $2q/a = \gamma$ in the formulae in § 6.40, we obtain the following results:

$$u_1(\mp\pi) = (1\pm\gamma)^{\frac{1}{2}}J_{\frac{1}{3}}[\alpha(1\pm\gamma)^{\frac{3}{2}}], \quad u_1'(\mp\pi) = -a^{\frac{1}{2}}(1\pm\gamma)J_{-\frac{2}{3}}[\alpha(1\pm\gamma)^{\frac{3}{2}}];$$
$$\tag{1}$$

$$u_2(\mp\pi) = (1\pm\gamma)^{\frac{1}{2}}Y_{\frac{1}{3}}[\alpha(1\pm\gamma)^{\frac{3}{2}}], \quad u_2'(\mp\pi) = -a^{\frac{1}{2}}(1\pm\gamma)Y_{-\frac{2}{3}}[\alpha(1\pm\gamma)^{\frac{3}{2}}].$$
$$\tag{2}$$

The Wronskian for the Bessel functions of argument $\alpha(1\pm\gamma)^{\frac{1}{2}}$ is [202, p. 156, ex. 61 a]

$$\alpha(1\pm\gamma)^{\frac{1}{2}}[J_{\frac{1}{3}}Y'_{\frac{1}{3}}-J'_{\frac{1}{3}}Y_{\frac{1}{3}}] = 2/\pi. \tag{3}$$

Using (9) § 6.40 for $J'_{\frac{1}{3}}$ and $Y'_{\frac{1}{3}}$ in (3) gives

$$\alpha(1\pm\gamma)^{\frac{1}{2}}[J_{\frac{1}{3}}Y_{-\frac{2}{3}}-J_{-\frac{2}{3}}Y_{\frac{1}{3}}] = 2/\pi. \tag{4}$$

By (1) § 2.191, $u_1u'_2-u_2u'_1 \equiv c^2$, the argument in this case being $\mp\pi$. Substituting from (1), (2) into this identity yields

$$-a^{\frac{1}{2}}(1\pm\gamma)^{\frac{1}{2}}[J_{\frac{1}{3}}Y_{-\frac{2}{3}}-J_{-\frac{2}{3}}Y_{\frac{1}{3}}] = c^2 \tag{5}$$

and from (4), (5) it follows that

$$2c^2 = -4a^{\frac{1}{2}}/\pi\alpha. \tag{6}$$

6.42. Evaluation of μ. We have now found expressions for all the components in formula (9) § 4.152. Substituting from (1), (2), (6) § 6.41 therein, and writing $w_1 = \alpha(1+\gamma)^{\frac{1}{2}}$, $w_2 = \alpha(1-\gamma)^{\frac{1}{2}}$, we obtain after a little reduction

$$\cosh 2\mu\pi = \tfrac{1}{4}\pi\alpha(1-\gamma^2)^{\frac{1}{2}}\{(1-\gamma)^{\frac{1}{2}}[J_{-\frac{2}{3}}(w_2)Y_{\frac{1}{3}}(w_1)-J_{\frac{1}{3}}(w_1)Y_{-\frac{2}{3}}(w_2)]+$$
$$+(1+\gamma)^{\frac{1}{2}}[J_{-\frac{2}{3}}(w_1)Y_{\frac{1}{3}}(w_2)-J_{\frac{1}{3}}(w_2)Y_{-\frac{2}{3}}(w_1)]\}. \tag{1}$$

If the values of w_1, w_2 are large enough, (1) may be simplified by using the dominant terms in the asymptotic expansions of the Bessel functions. Then [202, pp. 160, 161]

$$J_{-\frac{2}{3}}(w) \sim \left(\frac{2}{\pi w}\right)^{\frac{1}{2}}\cos(w-\tfrac{1}{4}\pi+\tfrac{1}{3}\pi), \qquad J_{\frac{1}{3}}(w) \sim \left(\frac{2}{\pi w}\right)^{\frac{1}{2}}\cos(w-\tfrac{1}{4}\pi-\tfrac{1}{6}\pi);$$
$$\tag{2}$$

$$Y_{-\frac{2}{3}}(w) \sim \left(\frac{2}{\pi w}\right)^{\frac{1}{2}}\sin(w-\tfrac{1}{4}\pi+\tfrac{1}{3}\pi), \qquad Y_{\frac{1}{3}}(w) \sim \left(\frac{2}{\pi w}\right)^{\frac{1}{2}}\sin(w-\tfrac{1}{4}\pi-\tfrac{1}{6}\pi);$$
$$\tag{3}$$

the part omitted in each case being $O(1/w^{\frac{3}{2}})$. Substituting these into (1), after some reduction we find that

$$\cosh 2\mu\pi = \{\gamma/(1-\gamma^2)^{\frac{1}{2}}[(1+\gamma)^{\frac{1}{2}}-(1-\gamma)^{\frac{1}{2}}]\}\cos(w_1-w_2). \tag{4}$$

Since stability of the solutions of (1) § 6.40 depends upon the factor $e^{(\mu-\kappa)t}$ (see § 4.83), this subject may be investigated using (4). The circuit of Fig. 23 D is examined in this respect in [44], which may be consulted. Stability conditions for various mechanical and electrical devices are discussed in a number of the technological papers cited on pp. 373–81, and to these the technical reader is referred.

6.50. Stability of solutions. In § 4.60 we discussed this matter for the equation $y'' + (a - 2q\cos 2z)y = 0$, use being made of Fig. 8 B. It can be shown that, when $\psi(\omega z)$ is assigned, the (a, q)-plane for the equation $y'' + [a - 2q\psi(\omega z)]y = 0$ may be divided into stable and unstable regions after the manner of Fig. 8. The stable (unstable) regions lie between characteristic curves for solutions of integral order having period π and 2π† (π and π, or 2π and 2π). The stability diagram is symmetrical about the a-axis, provided $\psi(\omega z)$ is symmetrical about the origin, and is periodic with $\int_0^{2\pi} \psi(\omega z)\, dz = 0$. Characteristic curves for coexistent solutions of fractional order having period $2s\pi$, $s \geqslant 2$, and corresponding to the iso-β curves of Fig. 11, may be drawn in the stable regions of the plane. Here μ is imaginary, but in the unstable regions it is either real‡ or complex, according to the form of solution assumed (see § 4.70). Solutions of period π or 2π do not coexist (unless $q = 0$), and the second solutions corresponding thereto are probably non-periodic (like the Mathieu case), although a proof of these statements has not been published.

The asymptotic nature of the stability diagram has been discussed at some length in reference [171], which should be consulted for information on this topic. Amongst other matters it is shown that in the region corresponding to that below curve a_0 in Fig. 8 B, μ is real and the solutions unstable—as in the Mathieu case. This arises mainly from the fact that $|a| > 2q$ and a is negative. In the regions corresponding to those above the characteristic a_0,

$$a \sim -2q|\psi(\omega z)|_{\max} + O(q^{\frac{1}{2}}) \quad (a, q \text{ on right of } a\text{-axis}) \tag{1}$$

and $$a \sim -2|q|\,|\psi(\omega z)|_{\min} + O|q|^{\frac{1}{2}} \quad (\quad ,, \quad \text{left} \quad ,, \quad). \tag{2}$$

If, as contemplated hitherto, $|\psi(\omega z)|_{\substack{\max \\ \min}} = 1$, (12) § 12.21 is reproduced.

† Provided ψ has period π. If ψ has period 2π, the boundaries correspond to solutions with periods 2π, 4π. Reference [82] may be consulted in connexion with stability for small values of the θ in (2) § 6.10.

‡ In this case iso-μ curves may be plotted as in Fig. 11.

VII

NON-PERIODIC SECOND SOLUTIONS CORRESPONDING TO ce_m, se_m, Ce_m, Se_m

7.10. Non-periodicity of solution. If the first solution has period π or 2π, it may be shown that any second linearly independent solution cannot have either period. We now illustrate this by a particular case [84]:

THEOREM: If a be assigned for $ce_{2n}(z, q)$, the odd second solution cannot have period π when $q \neq 0$.

Proof. Suppose the second solution is the odd function

$$\sum_{r=0}^{\infty} c_{2r+2} \sin(2r+2)z,$$

which has period π. By (1) §3.10 we have the recurrence formula for the coefficients in the $ce_{2n}(z, q)$ series, namely,

$$(a-4)A_2 - q(A_4 + 2A_0) = 0. \tag{1}$$

If the assumed second solution is substituted in Mathieu's equation, we obtain the relation

$$(a-4)c_2 - qc_4 = 0. \tag{2}$$

Multiplying (1) by c_2, (2) by A_2, and subtracting leads to

$$A_2 c_4 - A_4 c_2 = \begin{vmatrix} A_2 & A_4 \\ c_2 & c_4 \end{vmatrix} = 2A_0 c_2. \tag{3}$$

When $r \geqslant 2$ the recurrence relations are, respectively,

$$(a-4r^2)A_{2r} = q(A_{2r+2} + A_{2r-2}), \tag{4}$$

and

$$(a-4r^2)c_{2r} = q(c_{2r+2} + c_{2r-2}). \tag{5}$$

Dividing (4) by (5) yields

$$A_{2r} c_{2r+2} - A_{2r+2} c_{2r} = A_{2r-2} c_{2r} - A_{2r} c_{2r-2}, \tag{6}$$

so [84]

$$\begin{vmatrix} A_{2r} & A_{2r+2} \\ c_{2r} & c_{2r+2} \end{vmatrix} = \begin{vmatrix} A_{2r-2} & A_{2r} \\ c_{2r-2} & c_{2r} \end{vmatrix} = \dots = \begin{vmatrix} A_2 & A_4 \\ c_2 & c_4 \end{vmatrix} = 2A_0 c_2. \tag{7}$$

For convergence of the series representing each of the two solutions, we must have $A_{2r} \to 0$, $c_{2r} \to 0$ as $r \to +\infty$. It follows that each determinant in (7) does likewise, so $A_0 c_2 = 0$. But $A_0 \neq 0$, save in the case $q = 0$, $n > 0$, so $c_2 = 0$. Hence all the c are zero, and a second solution having period π does not exist. The same conclusion may be reached for a solution of period 2π. When the period is $2s\pi$, $s \geqslant 2$, it may be inferred from §§ 2.16, 4.16 that the two solutions of Mathieu's equation coexist, and have the same period. This may be established by a method similar to that used above. Since the period cannot be a sub-multiple of π, it follows that the second solution corresponding to $ce_{2n}(z,q)$ is non-periodic. The cases of ce_{2n+1}, se_m may be argued in like manner. Since $Ce_m(z,q)$, $Se_m(z,q)$ are derived from $ce_m(z,q)$, $se_m(z,q)$, respectively, by writing iz for z, the same conclusion may be reached here. The periods are, of course, πi and $2\pi i$. It may be remarked that a general treatment of the periodicity of the solutions of Mathieu's equation is given in [150], to which reference should be made. A different approach to the non-periodicity aspect will be found in [71, 89, 126].

7.20. Relationship between first and second solutions. The following analysis is applicable when the first solution has period π, 2π, and the second is non-periodic. It does not hold when both solutions are periodic with period $2s\pi$, $s \geqslant 2$.

Choose $ce_{2n}(z,q)$ as the first solution with period π, even in z. Then we denote the second non-periodic solution, odd in z, by $fe_{2n}(z,q)$. If $(\pi+z)$ be written for z in the differential equation, it is unchanged, so $fe_{2n}(\pi+z)$ is also a solution. Thus we may write

$$fe_{2n}(\pi+z) = \gamma\, ce_{2n}(z) + \delta\, fe_{2n}(z), \qquad (1)$$

where γ, δ are constants, and the presence of q is presumed. Again, taking $(\pi+z)$ for z in (1) gives

$$fe_{2n}(2\pi+z) = \gamma\, ce_{2n}(z) + \delta\, fe_{2n}(\pi+z), \qquad (2)$$

since $ce_{2n}(z)$ has period π.

Substituting for the last member of (2) from (1) leads to

$$fe_{2n}(2\pi+z) = \gamma(1+\delta)ce_{2n}(z) + \delta^2 fe_{2n}(z). \qquad (3)$$

Replacing z in (3) by $(z-\pi)$, we get

$$fe_{2n}(\pi+z) = \gamma(1+\delta)ce_{2n}(z) - \delta^2 fe_{2n}(\pi-z), \qquad (4)$$

the negative sign arising from fe_{2n} being odd in z. Putting $-z$ for z in (1) and substituting in the third member of (4) leads to an alternative version of (1), namely,

$$fe_{2n}(\pi+z) = \gamma(1+\delta-\delta^2)ce_{2n}(z) + \delta^3 fe_{2n}(z). \qquad (5)$$

For the identity of (1), (5) we must have

$$\gamma = \gamma(1+\delta-\delta^2) \quad \text{and} \quad \delta = \delta^3 \quad \text{simultaneously.} \qquad (6)$$

Now $fe_{2n}(z)$ is non-periodic, so by (1) neither γ nor δ can vanish. Thus $\delta = 1$. Inserting this in (1) yields

$$fe_{2n}(\pi+z) = \gamma\, ce_{2n}(z)+fe_{2n}(z), \qquad (7)$$

and since γ is independent of z, it follows that

$$fe_{2n}(\pi+z)-fe_{2n}(z) = \gamma\, ce_{2n}(z), \qquad (8)$$

a periodic function having period π.† Thus $fe_{2n}(z)$ must satisfy (8). In addition, when $q = 0$ it must reduce to $\sin 2nz$, for $ce_{2n}(z)$ then reduces to $\cos 2nz$, and these are two independent solutions of $y''+ay = 0$, $a = 4n^2$.

If $f_{2n}(z,q)$ is a function periodic in z, with period π, and we write

$$fe_{2n}(z,q) = C_{2n}(q)z\, ce_{2n}(z,q)+f_{2n}(z,q), \qquad (9)$$

(8) is satisfied provided $\gamma = \pi C_{2n}(q)$.‡ Also, if $C_{2n}(q) \to 0$§ and $f_{2n}(z,q) \to \sin 2nz$ as $q \to 0$, (9) fulfils the conditions for a second non-periodic$^\Phi$ solution of Mathieu's equation.

7.21. The function $f_{2n}(z,q)$ and its normalization. The second member of (9) § 7.20 is odd in z, so $f_{2n}(z,q)$ must be odd in order that $fe_{2n}(z,q)$ may also be odd.

First normalization rule, based upon § 2.11. We take the function

$$f_{2n}(z,q) = \sin 2nz+ \sum_{r=1}^{\infty} q^r S_r(z), \qquad (1)$$

where $S_r(z)$ are odd continuous functions of z, the coefficient of $\sin 2nz$ is unity for *all* q, and $f_{2n}(z,q) \to \sin 2nz$ as $q \to 0$.

Second normalization rule based upon § 2.21. Here we take

$$f_{2n}(z,q) = \sum_{r=0}^{\infty} \bar{f}_{2r+2}^{(2n)} \sin(2r+2)z = C_{2n}(q) \sum_{r=0}^{\infty} f_{2r+2}^{(2n)} \sin(2r+2)z, \qquad (2)$$

where $\bar{f}_{2r+2}^{(2n)} = C_{2n}(q)f_{2r+2}^{(2n)}$. In § 7.41 it is shown that as $q \to 0$, $\bar{f}_{2n}^{(2n)} \to 1$ while $\bar{f}_{2r+2}^{(2n)} \to 0$, $r \neq n-1$. This is true if we adopt the rule that

$$C_{2n}^2(q) \sum_{r=0}^{\infty} [f_{2r+2}^{(2n)}]^2 = \sum_{r=0}^{\infty} [\bar{f}_{2r+2}^{(2n)}]^2 = 1. \qquad (3)$$

Then, as $q \to 0$, $\bar{f}_{2n}^{(2n)} = C_{2n}(q)f_{2n}^{(2n)} \to 1,$ $\qquad (4)$

and since $\bar{f}_{2r+2}^{(2n)} \to 0$, $r \neq n-1$,

$$f_{2n}(z,q) \to \sin 2nz \qquad (5)$$

---

† When the order of the function is $(2n+1)$, ce_{2n+1} has period 2π. Hence 2π must then be written for π throughout.

‡ See §§ 7.30–7.32 regarding $C_{2n}(q)$.

§ As shown in § 7.31, it is convenient to make $C_0(q) = 1$. $^\Phi$ $q \neq 0$.

as required. Now the $f_{2r+2}^{(2n)}$ may be calculated by the method given in §7.53. Then taking the positive root

$$C_{2n}(q) = 1 \Big/ \Big[\sum_{r=0}^{\infty} \{f_{2r+2}^{(2n)}\}^2 \Big]^{\frac{1}{2}}. \tag{6}$$

7.22. Definitions of the second solutions. By aid of §§ 7.20, 7.21 we define as follows:

$$\mathrm{fe}_{2n}(z,q) = C_{2n}(q)z\,\mathrm{ce}_{2n}(z,q) + f_{2n}(z,q) \qquad (a_{2n}), \tag{1}$$

$$\mathrm{fe}_{2n+1}(z,q) = C_{2n+1}(q)z\,\mathrm{ce}_{2n+1}(z,q) + f_{2n+1}(z,q) \quad (a_{2n+1}), \tag{2}$$

$$\mathrm{ge}_{2n+1}(z,q) = S_{2n+1}(q)z\,\mathrm{se}_{2n+1}(z,q) + g_{2n+1}(z,q) \quad (b_{2n+1}), \tag{3}$$

$$\mathrm{ge}_{2n+2}(z,q) = S_{2n+2}(q)z\,\mathrm{se}_{2n+2}(z,q) + g_{2n+2}(z,q) \quad (b_{2n+2}). \tag{4}$$

The series for $f_m(z,q)$, $g_m(z,q)$ are given below.

Function	First normalization in §7.21	Second normalization in §7.21	
$f_{2n}(z,q)$	$\sin 2nz + \sum_{r=1}^{\infty} q^r S_r(z)$	$C_{2n}(q) \sum_{r=0}^{\infty} f_{2r+2}^{(2n)} \sin(2r+2)z$	(1 a)
$f_{2n+1}(z,q)$	$\sin(2n+1)z + \sum_{r=1}^{\infty} q^r \overline{S}_r(z)$	$C_{2n+1}(q) \sum_{r=0}^{\infty} f_{2r+1}^{(2n+1)} \sin(2r+1)z$	(2 a)
$g_{2n+1}(z,q)$	$\cos(2n+1)z + \sum_{r=1}^{\infty} q^r \overline{C}_r(z)$	$S_{2n+1}(q) \sum_{r=0}^{\infty} g_{2r+1}^{(2n+1)} \cos(2r+1)z$	(3 a)
$g_{2n+2}(z,q)$	$\cos(2n+2)z + \sum_{r=1}^{\infty} q^r C_r(z)$	$S_{2n+2}(q) \sum_{r=0}^{\infty} g_{2r}^{(2n+2)} \cos 2rz$	(4 a)

As $q \to 0$,

$$C_m(q)f_m^{(m)} = \bar{f}_m^{(m)} \to 1, \qquad C_m(q) \to 0, \qquad f_m(z,q) \to \sin mz; \tag{5}$$

$$S_m(q)g_m^{(m)} = \bar{g}_m^{(m)} \to 1, \qquad S_m(q) \to 0, \qquad g_m(z,q) \to \cos mz. \tag{6}$$

The second normalization is merely (1) § 2.21 applied to $f_m(z,q)$, $g_m(z,q)$, so we get

$$C_{2n}^2 \sum_{r=0}^{\infty} f_{2r+2}^2 = C_{2n+1}^2 \sum_{r=0}^{\infty} f_{2r+1}^2 = S_{2n+1}^2 \sum_{r=0}^{\infty} g_{2r+1}^2$$

$$= S_{2n+2}^2 \Big[2g_0^2 + \sum_{r=1}^{\infty} g_{2r}^2 \Big] = 1. \tag{7}$$

The f, g are single-valued continuous functions of q.

$f_m(z,q)$, $g_m(z,q)$ are periodic, having period π, 2π, according as m is even or odd. The second solution comprises a non-periodic part involving the first solution, and a periodic part with the same period as the latter. By virtue of the factor z in the first part, the functions (1)–(4) tend to $\pm\infty$ with z. In accordance with (a) § 4.14 these solutions are unstable. Thus, if (a,q) is upon a boundary line a_m, b_m

in Figs. 8, 11, the first solution is stable, the second unstable. If (a, q) is not upon a_m, b_m, both solutions are either (a) stable,† (b) unstable in $-\infty < z < \infty$.

When q is positive, and a is a characteristic number for a function of integral order, the complete solution of Mathieu's equation is

$$y(z) = A \, \mathrm{ce}_m(z, q) + B \, \mathrm{fe}_m(z, q) \quad (a = a_m), \tag{8}$$

or
$$y(z) = \bar{A} \, \mathrm{se}_m(z, q) + \bar{B} \, \mathrm{ge}_m(z, q) \quad (a = b_m). \tag{9}$$

Either (8) or (9) constitutes a fundamental system of solutions.

7.30. Determination of $C_m(q)$, $S_m(q)$, $f_m(z, q)$, $g_m(z, q)$ **with first normalization in § 7.21.** There are at least five methods of approach, of which we select one.‡ We exemplify this by using the function

$$\mathrm{fe}_1(z, q) = C_1(q) z \, \mathrm{ce}_1(z, q) + f_1(z, q), \tag{1}$$

which corresponds to the first solution $\mathrm{ce}_1(z, q)$ having period 2π. $f_1(z, q)$ is the second member of .(2 a) § 7.22 with $n = 0$. Substituting (1) into

$$y'' + (a - 2q \cos 2z) y = 0 \tag{2}$$

we get

$$C_1(q) z [\mathrm{ce}_1'' + (a - 2q \cos 2z) \mathrm{ce}_1] + f_1'' + 2C_1(q) \mathrm{ce}_1' + (a - 2q \cos 2z) f_1 = 0. \tag{3}$$

Since ce_1 is a solution of (2) for $a = a_1$, the [ ] vanishes leaving

$$f_1'' + 2C_1(q) \mathrm{ce}_1' + (a - 2q \cos 2z) f_1 = 0. \tag{4}$$

By hypothesis $C_1(0) = 0$, so we assume $C_1(q) = \sum_{r=1}^{\infty} \alpha_r q^r$. Substituting this and $f_1(z, q) = \sin z + \sum_{r=1}^{\infty} q^r \bar{S}_r(z)$ into (4), we obtain, with the aid of results in § 2.13,

$$f_1'' = -\sin z + q \bar{S}_1'' + q^2 \bar{S}_2'' + q^3 \bar{S}_3'' + \dots,$$

$$2C_1 \mathrm{ce}_1' = -2 \left[\sin z - \frac{3}{8} q \sin 3z + \frac{1}{64} q^2 \left(-3 \sin 3z + \frac{5}{3} \sin 5 \right) z - \dots \right] \times$$
$$\times [\alpha_1 q + \alpha_2 q^2 + \alpha_3 q^3 + \dots],$$

$$a f_1 = [\sin z + q \bar{S}_1 + q^2 \bar{S}_2 + \dots] \left[1 + q - \frac{1}{8} q^2 - \frac{1}{64} q^3 - \frac{1}{1536} q^4 + \dots \right],$$

$$-2q f_1 \cos 2z = -2q [\tfrac{1}{2}(-\sin z + \sin 3z) + \cos 2z (q \bar{S}_1 + q^2 \bar{S}_2 + q^3 \bar{S}_3 + \dots)].$$

---

† The period is then $2s\pi$, $s \geqslant 2$, or infinity (see § 4.71). An infinite period implies a non-periodic bounded function.   ‡ Another is given in § 10.75.

Equating the coefficient of q^r to zero yields

q^0: $\qquad\qquad -\sin z + \sin z = 0$,   identically;

q: $\qquad\qquad \bar{S}_1'' + \bar{S}_1 - 2\alpha_1 \sin z + 2\sin z - \sin 3z = 0$.

Now the particular integral corresponding to $\sin z$ is $-\tfrac{1}{2}z \cos z$, which is non-periodic. Since $f_1(z, q)$ is to be periodic with period 2π, the coefficient of $\sin z$ must vanish, so $\alpha_1 = 1$. Thus

$$\bar{S}_1'' + \bar{S}_1 = \sin 3z, \quad \text{giving } \bar{S}_1 = -\frac{1}{8}\sin 3z.$$

q^2: $\quad \bar{S}_2'' + \bar{S}_2 - 2\alpha_2 \sin z + \frac{3}{4}\alpha_1 \sin 3z - \frac{1}{8}\sin z + \bar{S}_1 - 2\bar{S}_1 \cos 2z = 0,$

so $\qquad\qquad \bar{S}_2'' + \bar{S}_2 - 2\alpha_2 \sin z + \frac{5}{8}\sin 3z + \frac{1}{8}\sin 5z = 0.$

To avoid a non-periodic term, $\alpha_2 = 0$, so

$$\bar{S}_2'' + \bar{S}_2 = -\left(\frac{5}{8}\sin 3z + \frac{1}{8}\sin 5z\right),$$

giving $\qquad\qquad \bar{S}_2 = \frac{5}{64}\sin 3z + \frac{1}{192}\sin 5z.$

q^3: $\quad \bar{S}_3'' + \bar{S}_3 - 2\alpha_3 \sin z + \frac{\alpha_1}{32}\left(3 \sin 3z - \frac{5}{3}\sin 5z\right) - \frac{1}{64}\sin z -$

$$-\frac{1}{8}\bar{S}_1 + \bar{S}_2 - 2\bar{S}_2 \cos 2z = 0,$$

so

$$\bar{S}_3'' + \bar{S}_3 - \left(2\alpha_3 + \frac{3}{32}\right)\sin z + \frac{35}{192}\sin 3z - \frac{1}{8}\sin 5z - \frac{1}{192}\sin 7z = 0.$$

As before the coefficient of $\sin z$ must vanish, so $\alpha_3 = -3/64$, and

$$\bar{S}_3'' + \bar{S}_3 = -\frac{35}{192}\sin 3z + \frac{1}{8}\sin 5z + \frac{1}{192}\sin 7z,$$

giving $\qquad \bar{S}_3 = \frac{35}{1536}\sin 3z - \frac{1}{192}\sin 5z - \frac{1}{9216}\sin 7z,$

and so on. Thus

$$C_1(q) = \sum_{r=1}^{\infty} \alpha_r q^r = q - \frac{3}{64}q^3 - \frac{3}{256}q^4 + \frac{31}{36864}q^5 + O(q^6), \qquad (5)$$

and

$$f_1(z, q) = \sin z - \frac{1}{8}q \sin 3z + \frac{1}{64}q^2\left(5 \sin 3z + \frac{1}{3}\sin 5z\right) -$$

$$-\frac{1}{512}q^3\left(-\frac{35}{3}\sin 3z + \frac{8}{3}\sin 5z + \frac{1}{18}\sin 7z\right) + \dots. \qquad (6)$$

Finally the series representation of the second solution, corresponding to $ce_1(z,q)$, using the first normalization rule in § 7.21 is

$$fe_1(z,q) = \left[q - \frac{3}{64}q^3 - \frac{3}{256}q^4 + \frac{31}{36864}q^5 + O(q^6)\right]z\,ce_1(z,q) +$$

$$+ \left[\sin z - \frac{1}{8}q\sin 3z + \frac{1}{64}q^2\left(5\sin 3z + \frac{1}{3}\sin 5z\right) - \right.$$

$$-\frac{1}{512}q^3\left(-\frac{35}{3}\sin 3z + \frac{8}{3}\sin 5z + \frac{1}{18}\sin 7z\right) +$$

$$\left. + \frac{1}{4096}q^4\left(-\frac{17}{3}\sin 3z - \frac{343}{54}\sin 5z + \frac{61}{108}\sin 7z + \frac{1}{180}\sin 9z\right) - ...\right].$$

$$(7)$$

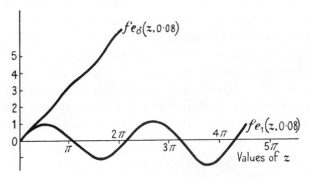

Fig. 15. Graphs of $fe_0(z,q)$, $fe_1(z,q)$, $q = 0.08$.

By virtue of the first member on the r.h.s. $fe_1(z,q)$ is non-periodic, unless there are values of $q \neq 0$ for which $C_1(q)$ vanishes. When $q \to 0$ in (7), $fe_1(z,q) \to \sin z$. Also

$$fe_1(2\pi+z) - fe_1(z) = C_1(q)2\pi\,ce_1(z,q), \text{ a function with period } 2\pi, \quad (8)$$

so the conditions in § 7.20 are satisfied (see footnote respecting odd-order functions).

The graphs of $fe_0(z, 0.08)$, $fe_1(z, 0.08)$ are depicted in Fig. 15.

7.31. $C_m(q)$, $S_m(q)$ for first normalization in § 7.21. The following were obtained by procedure different from that in § 7.30 [80]:

fe_0 $\qquad$ $C_0(q) = 1$ $\quad$ (by convention),† $\hfill (1)$

fe_1 $\qquad$ $C_1(q) = q - \frac{3}{64}q^3 - \frac{3}{256}q^4 + \frac{31}{36864}q^5 + O(q^6),$ $\hfill (2)$

† When $a = q = 0$, Mathieu's equation becomes $y'' = 0$. Thus $y = c_1 z + c_2$, where $ce_0(z, 0) = 1/\sqrt{2} = c_2$, and $fe_0(z, 0) = C_0(q)z\,ce_0(z, 0) = C_0(q)z/\sqrt{2}$. If we take $C_0(q) = 1$, $c_1 = 1/\sqrt{2}$, and $y = (1/\sqrt{2})(z+1)$.

fe$_2$
$$C_2(q) = \frac{1}{8}q^2 - \frac{17}{1152}q^4 + O(q^6), \tag{3}$$

fe$_3$
$$C_3(q) = \frac{1}{192}q^3 + O(q^4); \tag{4}$$

ge$_1$
$$S_1(q) = q - \frac{3}{64}q^3 + \frac{3}{256}q^4 + \frac{31}{36864}q^5 + O(q^6), \tag{5}$$

ge$_2$
$$S_2(q) = \frac{1}{8}q^2 + \frac{53}{6912}q^4 + O(q^6), \tag{6}$$

ge$_3$
$$S_3(q) = \frac{1}{192}q^3 + O(q^4). \tag{7}$$

7.32. $C_m(q)$, $S_m(q)$ for second normalization in § 7.21, when $q \to 0$. By § 7.41, $\bar{f}_m^{(m)}$, $\bar{g}_m^{(m)}$, the respective coefficients of $\sin mz$, $\cos mz$ in the periodic part of the series for fe$_m(z,q)$, ge$_m(z,q)$, tend to unity as $q \to 0$, the other coefficients tending to zero. By (1 a)–(4 a) § 7.22 the coefficient of $\sin mz$, $\cos mz$ is unity for all q, and the remainder tend to zero with q. Hence when $q \to 0$, $C_m(q)$, $S_m(q)$ for the second normalization are the limiting forms of these functions in the first normalization. Retaining only the terms of lowest order in § 7.31 gives

$$C_0(q) = 1; \qquad C_1(q) = S_1(q) = q; \qquad C_2(q) = S_2(q) = \frac{1}{8}q^2;$$

$$C_3(q) = S_3(q) = \frac{1}{192}q^3. \tag{1}$$

Accordingly these are the forms of the various functions as $q \to 0$. To illustrate this, the values of $C_1(1)$ and $C_3(1)$ were computed by the method of § 7.54 using (7) § 7.22. The results were

$$C_1(1) \simeq 0{\cdot}9526, \tag{2}$$

$$C_3(1) \simeq 0{\cdot}00513 \simeq 1/195. \tag{3}$$

These data indicate that $C_1(1) \to 1$, and $C_3(1) \to 1/192$.

7.40. Recurrence relations for $f_s^{(m)}$, $g_s^{(m)}$. If (1) § 7.22 is substituted in series form into (2) § 7.30 and the coefficient of $\sin(2r+2)z$ equated to zero for $r = 0, 1, 2, \ldots$, we obtain the two recurrence relations (omitting superscripts on the f)

fe$_{2n}(z,q)$:
$$(a-4)f_2 - qf_4 = 4A_2^{(2n)} \tag{1}$$

and $\quad (a-4r^2)f_{2r} - q(f_{2r+2} + f_{2r-2}) = 4rA_{2r}^{(2n)} \quad (r \geqslant 2). \tag{2}$

Similar procedure using (2)–(4) § 7.22 leads to the following:

$fe_{2n+1}(z,q)$:
$$(a-1+q)f_1-qf_3 = 2A_1^{(2n+1)}, \tag{3}$$

$$[a-(2r+1)^2]f_{2r+1}-q(f_{2r+3}+f_{2r-1}) = 2(2r+1)A_{2r+1}^{(2n+1)} \quad (r \geqslant 1). \tag{4}$$

$ge_{2n+1}(z,q)$:
$$(a-1-q)g_1-qg_3 = -2B_1^{(2n+1)}, \tag{5}$$

$$[a-(2r+1)^2]g_{2r+1}-q(g_{2r+3}+g_{2r-1}) = -2(2r+1)B_{2r+1}^{(2n+1)} \quad (r \geqslant 1). \tag{6}$$

$ge_{2n+2}(z,q)$:
$$ag_0-qg_2 = 0, \tag{7}$$

$$(a-4)g_2-q(g_4+2g_0) = -4B_2^{(2n+2)}, \tag{8}$$

$$(a-4r^2)g_{2r}-q(g_{2r+2}+g_{2r-2}) = -4rB_{2r}^{(2n+2)} \quad (r \geqslant 2). \tag{9}$$

7.41. Behaviour of $\bar{f}_m$, $\bar{g}_m$ as $q \to 0$. By § 3.32, $A_m^{(m)} \to 1$, $B_m^{(m)} \to 1$, and the remaining A, $B \to 0$ as $q \to 0$. We shall now demonstrate that $\bar{f}_m$, $\bar{g}_m$ have similar properties. We take the particular case of $fe_3(z,q)$. By §§ 2.151, 3.32, 3.33, 7.31, we have

$$a = 9+\tfrac{1}{16}q^2+\tfrac{1}{64}q^3+..., \qquad A_1^{(3)} = O(q), \qquad A_3^{(3)} \to 1,$$
$$A_5^{(3)} = O(q), \qquad C_3(q) = O(q^3), \quad \text{when } q \to 0. \tag{1}$$

Since $f_{2r+1} = \bar{f}_{2r+1}/C_3(q)$, (3), (4) § 7.40 may be written

$$(a-1+q)\bar{f}_1-q\bar{f}_3 = 2C_3(q)A_1^{(3)}, \tag{2}$$

$$[a-(2r+1)^2]\bar{f}_{2r+1}-q(\bar{f}_{2r+3}+\bar{f}_{2r-1}) = 2(2r+1)C_3(q)A_{2r+1}^{(3)} \quad (r \geqslant 1). \tag{3}$$

Substituting for a, A, from (1) into (2) gives

$$(8+q+\tfrac{1}{16}q^2+...)\bar{f}_1-q\bar{f}_3 = O(q^4). \tag{4}$$

Now assume that $\bar{f}_3$ tends to a constant value as $q \to 0$. Then

$$\bar{f}_1 \to q\bar{f}_3/(8+q) \simeq \tfrac{1}{8}q(1-\tfrac{1}{8}q)\bar{f}_3 \to 0. \tag{5}$$

Substituting from (1) into (3) with $r = 1$, 2, we get

$$(\tfrac{1}{16}q^2+\tfrac{1}{64}q^3+...)\bar{f}_3-q(\bar{f}_5+\bar{f}_1) \simeq 6C_3(q) \tag{6}$$

and

$$(\tfrac{1}{16}q^2+\tfrac{1}{64}q^3+...-16)\bar{f}_5-q(\bar{f}_7+\bar{f}_3) = O(q^4). \tag{7}$$

Since $\bar{f}_3 \to$ a constant as $q \to 0$, it follows that $\bar{f}_5 \to 0$. Similarly this result may be derived for all the $\bar{f}$ of higher order than 5. Neglecting $\bar{f}_7$ in (7), we obtain

$$\bar{f}_5 \simeq -\tfrac{1}{16}q\bar{f}_3. \tag{8}$$

Substituting from (5), (8) into (6) yields

$$(\tfrac{1}{16}q^2+\tfrac{1}{64}q^3+...+\tfrac{1}{16}q^2-\tfrac{1}{8}q^2+\tfrac{1}{64}q^3)\bar{f}_3 \simeq 6C_3(q). \tag{9}$$

Hence as $q \to 0$,
$$C_3(q) \to \bar{f}_3 q^3/192. \tag{10}$$

This result is compatible with (4) § 7.31, provided $\bar{f}_3 \to 1$ as $q \to 0$, so the assumption above (5) has been justified.

By similar analysis it may be shown that $\bar{f}_m^{(m)}$ and $\bar{g}_m^{(m)} \to 1$, while the remaining $\bar{f}, \bar{g} \to 0$ as $q \to 0$. This latter result is independent of the normalization, which must be compatible with it. The two normalizations in § 7.21 fulfil this requirement.

7.42. Behaviour of f_p, g_p, as $q \to 0$. Since $f_{2r+1}^{(3)} = \bar{f}_{2r+1}^{(3)}/C_3(q)$, we get by aid of (4) § 7.31

$$f_{2r+1} \to 192\bar{f}_{2r+1}/q^3. \tag{1}$$

From § 7.41, when $q \to 0$, it may be deduced that $\bar{f}_1$, $\bar{f}_5$ are $O(q)$, $\bar{f}_7 = O(q^2)$, $\bar{f}_9 = O(q^3)$, and so on. Since $\bar{f}_3 \to 1$, it follows from (1) that $f_1, f_3, f_5, f_7 \to \infty$, but this is inconsequential. Also by analysis of the type in § 7.41 it may be shown that $C_m(q)$, $S_m(q)$ are $O(q^m)$. Hence when $q = 0$, if $m = \left.\begin{matrix} 2n \\ 2n+1 \end{matrix}\right\}$ all f, g of order lower than m, and $\left.\begin{matrix} 2n-1 \\ 2n \end{matrix}\right\}$ of order higher than m are infinite. Thus, including $f_m^{(m)}$, $g_m^{(m)}$, there are $\left.\begin{matrix} 3n \\ 3n+1 \end{matrix}\right\}$ coefficients in the series which become infinite. As before, this is inconsequential.

7.50. Theory underlying computation of f_p, g_p. The recurrence relation (4) § 7.40 is a complete linear difference equation of the second order. Let ϕ_{2r+1}, ψ_{2r+1} be independent solutions of

$$[a-(2r+1)^2]c_{2r+1}-q(c_{2r+3}+c_{2r-1}) = 0, \tag{1}$$

and f_{2r+1} be a particular solution of (4) § 7.40. Then the general solution of the latter is

$$u_{2r+1} = f_{2r+1}+\delta\phi_{2r+1}+\epsilon\psi_{2r+1}, \tag{2}$$

where δ, ϵ are arbitrary constants. As shown in § 3.21, one solution of (1) tends to zero, the other to infinity as $r \to +\infty$. Now the A in the series for $ce_{2n+1}(z,q)$ satisfy a relation of the form (1), and they tend to zero as $r \to +\infty$. Hence we may replace $\delta\phi_{2r+1}$ by θA_{2r+1}, θ being a constant to be determined. For convergence of the series containing f_{2r+1} we must have $f_{2r+1} \to 0$ as $r \to +\infty$. Then from (2)

$$w_{2r+1} = (u_{2r+1}-\epsilon\psi_{2r+1}) = f_{2r+1}+\theta A_{2r+1} \to 0 \quad \text{as } r \to +\infty. \tag{3}$$

Now choose a value of $r = s$, which is such that: (1) $|A_{2r+1}|$ decreases rapidly with increase in r, (2) f_{2r+3}, say, vanishes to an adequate number of decimal places, (3) $|w_{2r-1}| \gg |w_{2r+3}|$. Since ϵ is arbitrary,† let it be such that when $r = s$, $w_{2r+1} = 0$. Then for $r < s$,

$$f_{2r+1} = w_{2r+1} - \theta A_{2r+1}^{(2n+1)}. \tag{4}$$

The value of θ depends for given a, q, m upon the value of s. Since f_{2r+1}, expressed to a limited number of decimal places, is independent of s (if large enough), it follows that w_{2r+1} is dependent upon s. Now $w_{2r+1} = u_{2r+1} - \epsilon \psi_{2r+1}$, so ϵ varies with s, as we should expect.

7.51. Calculation of the w in § 7.50. The w satisfy (4) § 7.40, so with $r = s$, we put $w_{2s+1} = 0$, and neglect w_{2s+3}. Using tabular values of the A [52, 95], we calculate

$$w_{2s-1} = -2(2s+1)A_{2s+1}^{(2n+1)}q^{-1}. \tag{1}$$

Also with $r = s$ and $(r-1)$ for r, since $w_{2s+1} = 0$, (4) § 7.40 gives

$$[a - (2r-1)^2]w_{2r-1} - qw_{2r-3} = 2(2r-1)A_{2r-1}^{(2n+1)}. \tag{2}$$

Since w_{2r-1} is known from (1), w_{2r-3} may be calculated from (2). Again with $(r-2)$ for r in (4) § 7.40, w_{2r-5} may be calculated using the values of w_{2r-1}, w_{2r-3}. Proceeding in this way we ultimately reach $r = 1$. Then

$$(a-9)w_3 - q(w_1 + w_5) = 6A_3^{(2n+1)}, \tag{3}$$

from which w_1 may be calculated, since w_3, w_5 are known.

7.52. Determination of θ in (4) § 7.50. Substituting from this equation into (3) § 7.40 gives

$$(a-1+q)(w_1 - \theta A_1) - q(w_3 - \theta A_3) = 2A_1^{(2n+1)}. \tag{1}$$

Also by (2) § 3.10

$$qA_3 = (a-1-q)A_1. \tag{2}$$

Then from (1), (2) we obtain

$$\theta = \frac{1}{2A_1}\left[\left(\frac{a-1+q}{q}\right)w_1 - w_3\right] - \frac{1}{q}. \tag{3}$$

Since the values of all quantities on the r.h.s. of (3) are known from § 7.51, θ may be calculated. Then the f_{2r+1} may be computed using (4) § 7.50.

7.53. Calculation of the f_{2r+1} in fe$_1(z, 8)$. Here $q = 8$, $a = -0.43594\ 36013\ 20_9$. We divide (4) § 7.40 throughout by q, and substitute w for f, since w_{2r+1} is a solution. Then

$$q^{-1}[a - (2r+1)^2]w_{2r+1} - (w_{2r+3} + w_{2r-1}) = 2(2r+1)A_{2r+1}^{(1)}q^{-1}. \tag{1}$$

---

† Its value need not be known.

We now choose s to conform with the conditions specified below (3) §7.50. Usually several trial s will be required at this stage,

TABLE 8. *Numerical data for evaluation of* $f^{(1)}_{2r+1}$ *in* $\mathrm{fe}_1(z, 8)$

$$s = 7, \quad w_{15} = 0$$

r	$2r+1$	$\dfrac{(2r+1)^2 - a}{q}$	$(-1)^r A^{(1)}_{2r+1}$	$(-1)^r 2(2r+1) A^{(1)}_{2r+1}/q$
0	1	$0\cdot 17949\ldots$	$0\cdot 62641\ 79353_1$	$0\cdot 15660\ 44838_3$
1	3	$1\cdot 17949\ldots$	$0\cdot 73885\ 55385_6$	$0\cdot 55414\ 16539_2$
2	5	$3\cdot 17949\ldots$	$0\cdot 24505\ 69636_1$	$0\cdot 30632\ 12045_1$
3	7	$6\cdot 17949\ldots$	$0\cdot 04030\ 13496_2$	$0\cdot 07052\ 73618_3$
4	9	$10\cdot 17949\ldots$	$..398\ 49422_5$	$..896\ 61200_7$
5	11	$15\cdot 17949\ldots$	$...26\ 33419_3$	$...72\ 41903_0$
6	13	$21\cdot 17949\ldots$	$....1\ 24547_0$	$....4\ 04777_9$
7	15	$28\cdot 17949\ldots$	$......\ .4424_1$	$.....\ 16590_4$
8	17	$36\cdot 17949\ldots$	$......\ ..122_4$	$......\ ..520_2$
9	19	$45\cdot 17949\ldots$	$......\ ....2_7$	$......\ ...12_8$

r	$(-1)^r w_{2r+1}$	$(-1)^r \theta A^{(1)}_{2r+1}$	$\begin{array}{c}(-1)^{r+1}f^{(1)}_{2r+1}\\ =[w_{2r+1}-\theta A^{(1)}_{2r+1}](-1)^{r+1}\end{array}$
0	$1\cdot 54597\ 72_{56}$	$1\cdot 07865\ 75_{42}$	$\overline{0}\cdot 46731\ 97_{14}$
1	$1\cdot 04543\ 43_{31}$	$1\cdot 27226\ 89_{67}$	$0\cdot 22683\ 46_{36}$
2	$0\cdot 24124\ 68_{21}$	$0\cdot 42197\ 47_{35}$	$0\cdot 18072\ 79_{14}$
3	$0\cdot 02792\ 94_{41}$	$0\cdot 06939\ 67_{27}$	$0\cdot 04146\ 72_{86}$
4	$..187\ 03_{23}$	$..686\ 18_{53}$	$..499\ 15_{30}$
5	$....7\ 56_{15}$	$...45\ 34_{60}$	$...37\ 78_{45}$
6	$.....\ 16_{59}$	$....2\ 14_{46}$	$....1\ 97_{87}$
7	zero	$.....\ .7_{62}$	$.....\ .7_{62}$
8			
9			

e.g. $r = 8, 9$ in Table 8. With $r = s$ in (1), we put $w_{2s+1} = 0$, neglect w_{2s+3}, and obtain

$$w_{2s-1} = -2(2s+1)A^{(1)}_{2s+1}q^{-1}. \tag{2}$$

Choosing $r = s = 7$, $A_{15} = -4\cdot 424_1 \times 10^{-7}$, and (2) gives

$$w_{13} = 30 \times 4\cdot 424_1 \times 10^{-7}/8 = 1\cdot 6590_4 \times 10^{-6}. \tag{3}$$

Taking $r = 6$ in (1), $A_{13} = 1\cdot 24547_0 \times 10^{-5}$, so with $w_{15} = 0$, by hypothesis, we get

$$-\tfrac{1}{8}(169\cdot 43594\ldots)1\cdot 6590_4 \times 10^{-6} - w_{11} = \tfrac{26}{8} \times 1\cdot 24547_0 \times 10^{-5},$$

giving

$$w_{11} = -7\cdot 56_{15} \times 10^{-5}. \tag{4}$$

Taking $r = 5$, $A_{11} = -2\cdot 63341\ 9_3 \times 10^{-4}$, and using w_{13}, w_{11} in (1), we find that

$$w_9 = 1\cdot 8703_{23} \times 10^{-3}. \tag{5}$$

Proceeding in this way we obtain the values in column 6, Table 8.
Using (3) § 7.52 yields

$$\theta = 1{\cdot}72194\ 54961. \tag{6}$$

Next we calculate $\theta A^{(1)}_{2r+1}$ and get column 7. Finally subtraction of
the corresponding values in column 7 from those in column 6 yields
the $f^{(1)}_{2r+1}$.

Check that conditions in § 7.50 are satisfied.

(1) The $|A_{2r+1}|$ decrease rapidly with increase in $r \geqslant 3$; see column
4, Table 8.

(2) With $r = 7$, f_{17} vanishes to seven decimal places, which is
adequate here.

(3) Writing $(r+1)$ for r in (1), we get

$$[a-(2r+3)^2]w_{2r+3}-q(w_{2r+5}+w_{2r+1}) = 2(2r+3)A^{(1)}_{2r+3}. \tag{7}$$

$w_{15} = 0$, by hypothesis, while for $r = 7$, $(2r+3)^2 \gg |a|$, so (7) becomes
approximately

$$w_{2r+3}+qw_{2r+5}/(2r+3)^2 = -2A^{(1)}_{2r+3}/(2r+3). \tag{8}$$

For $r \geqslant 3$, the data in column 6, Table 8, show that the w decrease
rapidly with increase in r.[†] Then $|w_{17}| > |w_{19}|$, so in (8) the term
in w_{2r+5} may be neglected. Hence

$$w_{17} \simeq -2A_{17}/17 = -2 \times 1{\cdot}22_4 \times 10^{-8}/17$$
$$\simeq -1{\cdot}44 \times 10^{-9}. \tag{9}$$

Thus $\qquad |w_{13}/w_{17}| \simeq 1{\cdot}659 \times 10^{-6}/1{\cdot}44 \times 10^{-9} \simeq 1{\cdot}15 \times 10^3. \tag{10}$

We have shown, therefore, that the imposed conditions are satisfied.
It is of interest to remark that in a second set of calculations with
$w_{19} = 0$, $\theta \simeq 1{\cdot}946$, which exceeds the value at (6) above, while for
a given $r \leqslant 6$, w exceeds that in Table 8. This is in accordance with
§ 7.50. The $f^{(1)}_{2r+1}$ are in agreement to the eighth decimal place,
$r = 0$ to 7.

7.54. Normalization. We use the second normalization rule in
§ 7.21. Then from the values of f_{2r+1} in Table 8

$$\sum_{r=0}^{\infty} f^2_{2r+1} = 0{\cdot}30424\ 88_4. \tag{1}$$

Substituting in (7) § 7.22, we obtain

$$C_1(q) = 1/(0{\cdot}30424\ 88_4)^{\frac{1}{2}}$$
$$= 1{\cdot}81294\ 87_8. \tag{2}$$

[†] Since $w_{15} = 0$, it might be preferable to say that $|w_{2r+3}/w_{2r+1}|$ decreases rapidly
with increase in r, the case of $r = 7$ being omitted.

Multiplying the figures in column 8, Table 8, by (2) yields column 3, Table 9. Then

$$\mathrm{fe}_1(z, 8) = (1 \cdot 812...)z\,\mathrm{ce}_1(z, 8) + \sum_{r=0}^{\infty} \bar{f}_{2r+1}^{(1)} \sin(2r+1)z. \tag{3}$$

TABLE 9

r	$2r+1$	$\bar{f}_{2r+1}^{(1)} = C_1(q)f_{2r+1}^{(1)}$
0	1	$0 \cdot 84722\ 67_0$
1	3	$0 \cdot 41123\ 95_7$
2	5	$\bar{0} \cdot 32765\ 04_5$
3	7	$0 \cdot 07517\ 80_7$
4	9	$\bar{0} \cdot 00904\ 93_9$
5	11	$0 \cdot 00068\ 50_2$
6	13	$\bar{0} \cdot 00003\ 58_7$
7	15	$0 \cdot 00000\ 13_8$

7.55. Formulae for calculating f_{2n}, g_{2n+1}, g_{2n+2}. These may be derived by analysis similar to that in § 7.50, and we get:

$\mathrm{fe}_{2n}(z, q)$:

$$f_{2r}^{(2n)} = w_{2r} - \theta A_{2r}^{(2n)}, \tag{1}$$

$$\theta = -\frac{1}{2A_0}\left[\left(\frac{4-a}{q}\right)w_2 + w_4\right] - \frac{2a}{q^2}. \tag{2}$$

$\mathrm{ge}_{2n+1}(z, q)$:

$$g_{2r+1}^{(2n+1)} = w_{2r+1} - \theta B_{2r+1}^{(2n+1)}, \tag{3}$$

$$\theta = -\frac{1}{2B_1}\left[\left(\frac{a-1-q}{q}\right)w_1 - w_3\right] - \frac{1}{q}. \tag{4}$$

$\mathrm{ge}_{2n+2}(z, q)$:

$$g_{2r+2}^{(2n+2)} = w_{2r+2} - \theta B_{2r+2}^{(2n+2)}, \tag{5}$$

$$\theta = \frac{1}{B_2}\left(w_2 - \frac{a}{q}w_0\right). \tag{6}$$

The procedure in calculating the f, g is identical in form with that in §§ 7.53, 7.54, and the normalization rule at (7) § 7.22 is used to determine $C_m(q)$, $S_m(q)$.

7.60. Second solutions corresponding to $\mathrm{ce}_m(z, -q), \mathrm{se}_m(z, -q)$. These are derived by writing $(\tfrac{1}{2}\pi - z)$ for z in (1)–(4) § 7.22. Thus, with the aid of (2)–(5) § 2.18, we obtain

$\mathrm{fe}_{2n}(z, -q)$

$$= (-1)^{n+1}\mathrm{fe}_{2n}(\tfrac{1}{2}\pi - z, q) \quad (a_{2n}) \tag{1}$$

$$= -C_{2n}(q)\left[(\tfrac{1}{2}\pi - z)\mathrm{ce}_{2n}(z, -q) + (-1)^n \sum_{r=0}^{\infty}(-1)^r f_{2r+2}^{(2n)} \sin(2r+2)z\right], \tag{2}$$

$$fe_{2n+1}(z, -q)$$
$$= (-1)^n ge_{2n+1}(\tfrac{1}{2}\pi - z, q) \quad (b_{2n+1}) \tag{3}$$
$$= S_{2n+1}(q)\Big[(\tfrac{1}{2}\pi - z)ce_{2n+1}(z, -q) + (-1)^n \sum_{r=0}^{\infty} (-1)^r g_{2r+1}^{(2n+1)} \sin(2r+1)z\Big]; \tag{4}$$

$$ge_{2n+1}(z, -q)$$
$$= (-1)^n fe_{2n+1}(\tfrac{1}{2}\pi - z, q) \quad (a_{2n+1}) \tag{5}$$
$$= C_{2n+1}(q)\Big[(\tfrac{1}{2}\pi - z)se_{2n+1}(z, -q) + (-1)^n \sum_{r=0}^{\infty} (-1)^r f_{2r+1}^{(2n+1)} \cos(2r+1)z\Big], \tag{6}$$

$$ge_{2n+2}(z, -q)$$
$$= (-1)^n ge_{2n+2}(\tfrac{1}{2}\pi - z, q) \quad (b_{2n+2}) \tag{7}$$
$$= S_{2n+2}(q)\Big[(\tfrac{1}{2}\pi - z)se_{2n+2}(z, -q) + (-1)^n \sum_{r=0}^{\infty} (-1)^r g_{2r}^{(2n)} \cos 2rz\Big]. \tag{8}$$

Then by § 7.22, when $q \to 0$,
$$fe_m(z, -q) \to +\sin mz, \qquad ge_m(z, -q) \to +\cos mz,$$
the multipliers $(-1)^n$ ensuring the conventional positive signs. Since $ce_m(z, -q) \to +\cos mz$ and $se_m(z, -q) \to +\sin mz$, we obtain the two solutions of $y'' + m^2 y = 0$, which is the degenerate form of Mathieu's equation when $q = 0$.

The complete solution of $y'' + (a + 2q \cos 2z)y = 0$ for q positive, i.e. q negative in the standard form, is obtained from (8), (9) § 7.22 by writing $-q$ for q, the characteristic numbers being those above and in § 2.18.

7.61. Second solutions corresponding to $Ce_m(z, q)$, $Se_m(z, q)$. These are solutions of $y'' - (a - 2q \cosh 2z)y = 0$, corresponding to $a = a_m$, $a = b_m$ respectively. They are derived from (1)–(4) § 7.22 by writing iz for z. Thus for the second normalization of § 7.21, with the aid of (2)–(5) § 2.30, we get:

$$Fe_{2n}(z, q) = -i\, fe_{2n}(zi, q)$$
$$= C_{2n}(q)z\, Ce_{2n}(z, q) + F_{2n}(z, q) \quad (a_{2n}), \tag{1}$$

$$Fe_{2n+1}(z, q) = -i\, fe_{2n+1}(zi, q)$$
$$= C_{2n+1}(q)z\, Ce_{2n+1}(z, q) + F_{2n+1}(z, q) \quad (a_{2n+1}); \tag{2}$$

$$Ge_{2n+1}(z, q) = ge_{2n+1}(zi, q)$$
$$= -S_{2n+1}(q)z\, Se_{2n+1}(z, q) + G_{2n+1}(z, q) \quad (b_{2n+1}), \tag{3}$$

$$Ge_{2n+2}(z, q) = ge_{2n+2}(zi, q)$$
$$= -S_{2n+2}(q)z\, Se_{2n+2}(z, q) + G_{2n+2}(z, q) \quad (b_{2n+2}). \tag{4}$$

By writing iz for z in the third members of (1 a)–(4 a) § 7.22, we obtain

$$F_{2n}(z,q) = C_{2n}(q) \sum_{r=0}^{\infty} f_{2r+2}^{(2n)} \sinh(2r+2)z, \tag{1 a}$$

$$F_{2n+1}(z,q) = C_{2n+1}(q) \sum_{r=0}^{\infty} f_{2r+1}^{(2n+1)} \sinh(2r+1)z; \tag{2 a}$$

$$G_{2n+1}(z,q) = S_{2n+1}(q) \sum_{r=0}^{\infty} g_{2r+1}^{(2n+1)} \cosh(2r+1)z, \tag{3 a}$$

$$G_{2n+2}(z,q) = S_{2n+2}(q) \sum_{r=0}^{\infty} g_{2r}^{(2n+2)} \cosh 2rz. \tag{4 a}$$

By § 7.22, when $q \to 0$, $\mathrm{Fe}_m(z,q) \to +\sinh mz$, $\mathrm{Ge}_m(z,q) \to +\cosh mz$. The complete solution of the differential equation for q positive is

$$y(z) = A\,\mathrm{Ce}_m(z,q) + B\,\mathrm{Fe}_m(z,q) \quad (a_m) \tag{5}$$

or
$$y(z) = \bar{A}\,\mathrm{Se}_m(z,q) + \bar{B}\,\mathrm{Ge}_m(z,q) \quad (b_m), \tag{6}$$

according as the characteristic number is a_m or b_m. Either (5) or (6) constitutes a fundamental system of solutions for the modified Mathieu functions of integral order.

7.62. Second solutions corresponding to $\mathrm{Ce}_m(z, -q)$, $\mathrm{Se}_m(z, -q)$. These are solutions of $y'' - (a + 2q \cosh 2z)y = 0$. They are derived from (1)–(4) § 7.61 by writing $(\tfrac{1}{2}\pi i + z)$ for z, since this alters the sign of q in the equation in § 7.61. Thus from (1) § 7.61 we have

$(-1)^n \mathrm{Fe}_{2n}(\tfrac{1}{2}\pi i + z, q)$

$$= C_{2n}(q)\Big[(\tfrac{1}{2}\pi i + z)\mathrm{Ce}_{2n}(z, -q) + (-1)^n \sum_{r=0}^{\infty} (-1)^{r+1} f_{2r+2}^{(2n)} \sinh(2r+2)z\Big].\dagger \tag{1}$$

Now, if z is real, the r.h.s. represents a complex function, but it is expedient that the function defined should be real. Since $\mathrm{Ce}_{2n}(z, -q)$ is a first solution of the differential equation, there is no need to retain $\tfrac{1}{2}\pi i\,\mathrm{Ce}_{2n}(z, -q)$. Accordingly we adopt the following definitions:

$\mathrm{Fe}_{2n}(z, -q)$

$$= C_{2n}(q)\Big[z\,\mathrm{Ce}_{2n}(z, -q) + (-1)^n \sum_{r=0}^{\infty} (-1)^{r+1} f_{2r+2}^{(2n)} \sinh(2r+2)z\Big] \quad (a_{2n}), \tag{2}$$

† This result is obtained also, if we take $-i\,\mathrm{fe}_{2n}(iz, -q)$, using (1) § 7.60.

$\mathrm{Fe}_{2n+1}(z, -q)$

$$= -S_{2n+1}(q)\Big[z\,\mathrm{Ce}_{2n+1}(z, -q)+(-1)^{n+1}\sum_{r=0}^{\infty}(-1)^r g_{2r+1}^{(2n+1)}\sinh(2r+1)z\Big]$$

$$(b_{2n+1});\quad (3)$$

$\mathrm{Ge}_{2n+1}(z, -q)$

$$= C_{2n+1}(q)\Big[z\,\mathrm{Se}_{2n+1}(z, -q)+(-1)^n\sum_{r=0}^{\infty}(-1)^r f_{2r+1}^{(2n+1)}\cosh(2r+1)z\Big]$$

$$(a_{2n+1}),\quad (4)$$

$\mathrm{Ge}_{2n+2}(z, -q)$

$$= -S_{2n+2}(q)\Big[z\,\mathrm{Se}_{2n+2}(z, -q)+(-1)^n\sum_{r=0}^{\infty}(-1)^r g_{2r}^{(2n+2)}\cosh 2rz\Big]$$

$$(b_{2n+2}).\quad (5)$$

By § 7.22, when $q \to 0$,

$$\mathrm{Fe}_m(z, -q) \to +\sinh mz, \qquad \mathrm{Ge}_m(z, -q) \to +\cosh mz,$$

these being solutions of $y'' - m^2 y = 0$, the degenerate form of the modified Mathieu equation when $q = 0$. As in § 7.60 the multipliers $(-1)^n$ ensure the conventional positive signs. The complete solution of $y'' - (a + 2q\cosh 2z)y = 0$ for q positive, i.e. q negative in the standard form, is obtained by writing $-q$ for q in (5), (6) § 7.61, the characteristic numbers being those above and in § 2.31.

SOLUTIONS IN SERIES OF BESSEL FUNCTIONS

8.10. First solution of $y'' - (a - 2q\cosh 2z)y = 0$, $q > 0$. Let $u = 2k\cosh z$, $k^2 = q > 0$, and the equation becomes [52]

$$(u^2 - 4k^2)y'' + uy' + (u^2 - p^2)y = 0, \tag{1}$$

with $p^2 = (a + 2k^2)$. Assume a solution

$$y = \sum_{r=0}^{\infty} (-1)^r c_{2r} J_{2r}(u), \tag{2}$$

and substitute it into (1); then we get

$$\sum_{r=0}^{\infty} (-1)^r c_{2r}[(u^2 - 4k^2)J_{2r}'' + uJ_{2r}' + (u^2 - p^2)J_{2r}] = 0. \tag{3}$$

From Bessel's equation

$$u^2 J_{2r}'' + uJ_{2r}' + u^2 J_{2r} = 4r^2 J_{2r}, \tag{4}$$

and by recurrence relations

$$4J_{2r}'' = J_{2r-2} - 2J_{2r} + J_{2r+2}. \tag{5}$$

Substituting (4), (5) into (3) leads to

$$\sum_{r=0}^{\infty} (-1)^r c_{2r}[(4r^2 - a)J_{2r} - k^2(J_{2r-2} + J_{2r+2})] = 0, \tag{6}$$

since $2k^2 - p^2 = -a$. Equating coefficients of J_{2r} to zero ($r = 0, 1, 2,...$), we obtain

J_0 $ac_0 - k^2 c_2 = 0,$ (7)

J_2 $(a - 4)c_2 - k^2(c_4 + 2c_0) = 0,$ (8)

J_{2r} $(a - 4r^2)c_{2r} - k^2(c_{2r+2} + c_{2r-2}) = 0$ $(r \geqslant 2).$ (9)

Now (9) is a linear difference equation of the second order, and it has two independent solutions, so the complete solution takes the form

$$u_{2r} = \gamma c_{2r} + \delta d_{2r}, \tag{10}$$

where γ, δ are arbitrary constants. When $r \to +\infty$, $c_{2r} \to 0$, while by § 3.21 $|d_{2r}| \to \infty$ in such a way that $|v_{2r+2}| \sim 4(r+1)^2 q^{-1}$. Thus by $2°$ § 8.50, (2) would diverge, so the solution d_{2r} is inadmissible, i.e. $\delta = 0$.† Since (7)–(9) are identical in form with the recurrence relations (1) § 3.10 for the A in

$$\mathrm{Ce}_{2n}(z, q) = \sum_{r=0}^{\infty} A_{2r}^{(2n)} \cosh 2rz \quad (a_{2n}), \tag{11}$$

† See § 3.21.

it follows that c_{2r} is a constant multiple of $A_{2r}^{(2n)}$. Hence

$$K \sum_{r=0}^{\infty} (-1)^r A_{2r}^{(2n)} J_{2r}(2k \cosh z) \tag{12}$$

is a solution of $y'' - (a - 2q \cosh 2z)y = 0$. Now both (11), (12) are even functions of z with period πi and they satisfy this equation for the same (a, q). Thus one is a constant multiple of the other. Accordingly

$$\mathrm{Ce}_{2n}(z, q) = K \sum_{r=0}^{\infty} (-1)^r A_{2r}^{(2n)} J_{2r}(2k \cosh z). \tag{13}$$

By 2° §8.50 this series is absolutely and uniformly convergent in any finite part of the z-plane. Putting $z = \frac{1}{2}\pi i$ gives

$$K = \mathrm{ce}_{2n}(\tfrac{1}{2}\pi, q)/A_0^{(2n)}, \tag{14}$$

since all the B.F. vanish except when $r = 0$, giving $J_0(0) = 1$. Hence from (13), (14) it follows that

$$\mathrm{Ce}_{2n}(z, q) = \frac{\mathrm{ce}_{2n}(\tfrac{1}{2}\pi, q)}{A_0^{(2n)}} \sum_{r=0}^{\infty} (-1)^r A_{2r}^{(2n)} J_{2r}(2k \cosh z) \quad (a_{2n}). \tag{15}$$

By taking $u = 2k \sinh z$ in the differential equation and proceeding as shown above, we derive the solution

$$K_1 \sum_{r=0}^{\infty} A_{2r}^{(2n)} J_{2r}(2k \sinh z). \tag{16}$$

This is even with period πi, and is also a constant multiple of $\mathrm{Ce}_{2n}(z, q)$. With $z = 0$, $K_1 = \mathrm{ce}_{2n}(0, q)/A_0^{(2n)}$, so

$$\mathrm{Ce}_{2n}(z, q) = \frac{\mathrm{ce}_{2n}(0, q)}{A_0^{(2n)}} \sum_{r=0}^{\infty} A_{2r}^{(2n)} J_{2r}(2k \sinh z) \quad (a_{2n}). \tag{17}$$

Thus (15), (17) are alternative forms of the first solution.

The multipliers K pertaining to various functions in the sections which follow are derived in Chapter X.

8.11. The second solution. Since the recurrence relations for the Bessel functions Y_{2r} are identical in form with those for J_{2r}, and both functions satisfy the same differential equation, it follows from (15), (17) §8.10 that the function defined by

$$\mathrm{Fey}_{2n}(z, q) = \frac{\mathrm{ce}_{2n}(\tfrac{1}{2}\pi, q)}{A_0^{(2n)}} \sum_{r=0}^{\infty} (-1)^r A_{2r}^{(2n)} Y_{2r}(2k \cosh z) \quad (|\cosh z| > 1) \tag{1}†$$

$$= \frac{\mathrm{ce}_{2n}(0, q)}{A_0^{(2n)}} \sum_{r=0}^{\infty} A_{2r}^{(2n)} Y_{2r}(2k \sinh z) \quad \left(\begin{matrix} |\sinh z| > 1 \\ R(z) > 0 \end{matrix}\right) \tag{2}$$

† The y in Fey signifies the Y-Bessel function.

is an independent solution for $a = a_{2n}$. The restrictions indicated on the right are necessary for absolute and uniform convergence, and are obtained in 3° § 8.50. Actually, although both˙ series are non-uniformly convergent as $|\cosh z|$ or $|\sinh z| \to 1$, they converge when these arguments are unity, but the rate of convergence is dead slow! Solutions in B.F. products are free from these disadvantages (see § 13.61).

Using the well-known expansion for the Y functions in (1), (2), we find that

$$\mathrm{Fey}_{2n}(z, q) = \frac{2}{\pi}\left[\gamma + \log\left(k\,\frac{\cosh z}{\sinh z}\right)\right]\mathrm{Ce}_{2n}(z, q) + \text{two double summations.}$$

(3)

γ being Euler's constant. The first member on the r.h.s. may be written

$$\frac{2}{\pi}[\gamma + \log k + \log\tfrac{1}{2}(1 \pm e^{-2z}) + z]\mathrm{Ce}_{2n}(z, q),$$

(4)

from which it is clear that neither (1) nor (2) is periodic in z. In Chapter XIII we shall obtain a relationship between $\mathrm{Fey}_{2n}(z, q)$ and the alternative second solution $\mathrm{Fe}_{2n}(z, q)$ of Chapter VII. It is not possible to do this using the series (1), (2), since the non-uniform convergence of (1) and the divergence of (2) at the origin renders term-by-term differentiation invalid.† This applies to kindred functions in succeeding sections.

The complete solution of the equation, corresponding to $a = a_{2n}$, is

$$y = A\,\mathrm{Ce}_{2n}(z, q) + B\,\mathrm{Fey}_{2n}(z, q),$$

(5)

where A, B are arbitrary constants. This constitutes a fundamental system.

8.12. The solutions $\mathrm{Ce}_{2n+1}(z, q)$, $\mathrm{Fey}_{2n+1}(z, q)$. By analysis similar to that in § 8.10, we obtain (1), (3) below:

$\mathrm{Ce}_{2n+1}(z, q)$

$$= -\frac{\mathrm{ce}'_{2n+1}(\tfrac{1}{2}\pi, q)}{kA_1^{(2n+1)}} \sum_{r=0}^{\infty} (-1)^r A_{2r+1}^{(2n+1)} J_{2r+1}(2k\cosh z) \quad (a_{2n+1}) \quad (1)$$

$$= \frac{\mathrm{ce}_{2n+1}(0, q)}{kA_1^{(2n+1)}} \coth z \sum_{r=0}^{\infty} (2r+1)A_{2r+1}^{(2n+1)} J_{2r+1}(2k\sinh z); \quad (2)$$

† The result of so doing to (1) gives $\mathrm{Fey}'_{2n}(0, q) = 0$, which is untrue by virtue of (9) § 13.31.

$\mathrm{Fey}_{2n+1}(z, q)$

$$= -\frac{\mathrm{ce}'_{2n+1}(\tfrac{1}{2}\pi, q)}{kA_1^{(2n+1)}} \sum_{r=0}^{\infty} (-1)^r A_{2r+1}^{(2n+1)} Y_{2r+1}(2k \cosh z) \tag{3}$$

$$= \frac{\mathrm{ce}_{2n+1}(0, q)}{kA_1^{(2n+1)}} \coth z \sum_{r=0}^{\infty} (2r+1) A_{2r+1}^{(2n+1)} Y_{2r+1}(2k \sinh z). \tag{4}$$

The restrictions at (1), (2) § 8.11 apply to (3), (4) respectively.

To derive (2), (4), we observe that $\mathrm{Ce}_{2n+1}(z, q)$ is an even function of z, whereas $J_{2r+1}(2k \sinh z)$ is an odd one. If we multiply the latter by the odd function $\coth z$ the product function is even. Assuming that $y = \coth z\, w(u)$, with $u = 2k \sinh z$, and proceeding as in § 8.10 leads to the series solutions (2), (4). By virtue of the logarithmic term in the expansion of Y_{2r+1}, these solutions are non-periodic, but (1), (2) have period $2\pi i$. The complete solution takes the same form as (5) § 8.11.

8.13. The solutions $\mathrm{Se}_m(z, q)$, $\mathrm{Gey}_m(z, q)$. As before we assume a Bessel series with argument $u = 2k \cosh z$, namely,

$$w(u) = \sum_{r=0}^{\infty} (-1)^r c_{2r+1} J_{2r+1}(u), \tag{1}$$

this being an even function of z. But $\mathrm{Se}_{2n+1}(z, q)$ is odd in z, so we take the odd function

$$y = \tanh z\, w(u) \tag{2}$$

and substitute it in the differential equation. Then the transformed equation is [52]

$$(u^2 - 4k^2) w'' + uw' + (u^2 - p^2) w + 8k^2 \frac{d}{du}(w/u) = 0. \tag{3}$$

Proceeding as in § 8.10, we find that

$$c_{2r+1} = K_1(2r+1) B_{2r+1}^{(2n+1)}, \tag{4}$$

K_1 being a constant multiplier. Hence

$$\tanh z\, w(u) = \tanh z \sum_{r=0}^{\infty} (-1)^r (2r+1) B_{2r+1}^{(2n+1)} J_{2r+1}(2k \cosh z) \tag{5}$$

is a first solution of $y'' - (a - 2q \cosh 2z) y$ corresponding to the characteristic number $a = b_{2n+1}$. By analysis of the type in § 8.10 we obtain $\mathrm{Se}_{2n+1}(z, q)$

$$= \frac{\mathrm{se}_{2n+1}(\tfrac{1}{2}\pi, q)}{kB_1^{(2n+1)}} \tanh z \sum_{r=0}^{\infty} (-1)^r (2r+1) B_{2r+1}^{(2n+1)} J_{2r+1}(2k \cosh z) \quad (b_{2n+1}) \tag{6}$$

$$= \frac{\mathrm{se}'_{2n+1}(0, q)}{kB_1^{(2n+1)}} \sum_{r=0}^{\infty} B_{2r+1}^{(2n+1)} J_{2r+1}(2k \sinh z). \tag{7}$$

These representations both have period $2\pi i$. Since $\sinh z$ is odd in z, (7) was obtained by substituting (1) with $u = 2k \sinh z$ in the differential equation.

The remaining solutions derived as shown above and in previous sections are

$\mathrm{Gey}_{2n+1}(z, q)$

$$= \frac{\mathrm{se}_{2n+1}(\tfrac{1}{2}\pi, q)}{k B_1^{(2n+1)}} \tanh z \sum_{r=0}^{\infty} (-1)^r (2r+1) B_{2r+1}^{(2n+1)} Y_{2r+1}(2k \cosh z) \quad (b_{2n+1})$$

$$(8)$$

$$= \frac{\mathrm{se}_{2n+1}'(0, q)}{k B_1^{(2n+1)}} \sum_{r=0}^{\infty} B_{2r+1}^{(2n+1)} Y_{2r+1}(2k \sinh z). \tag{9}$$

These are the second solutions corresponding to (6), (7). By virtue of the logarithmic term in the expansion of the Y function, (8), (9) are non-periodic. Attention is drawn to the restrictions and comments in § 8.11.

$\mathrm{Se}_{2n+2}(z, q)$

$$= -\frac{\mathrm{se}_{2n+2}'(\tfrac{1}{2}\pi, q)}{k^2 B_2^{(2n+2)}} \tanh z \sum_{r=0}^{\infty} (-1)^r (2r+2) B_{2r+2}^{(2n+2)} J_{2r+2}(2k \cosh z) \quad (b_{2n+2})$$

$$(10)$$

$$= \frac{\mathrm{se}_{2n+2}'(0, q)}{k^2 B_2^{(2n+2)}} \coth z \sum_{r=0}^{\infty} (2r+2) B_{2r+2}^{(2n+2)} J_{2r+2}(2k \sinh z). \tag{11}$$

The B.F. in (10), (11) being of even order are both even in z, but the hyperbolic multipliers are both odd. Hence the representations are odd in z, also they have period πi.

The second solutions (apart from $\mathrm{Ge}_m(z, q)$ in Chapter VII) corresponding to (10), (11) are

$\mathrm{Gey}_{2n+2}(z, q)$

$$= -\frac{\mathrm{se}_{2n+2}'(\tfrac{1}{2}\pi, q)}{k^2 B_2^{(2n+2)}} \tanh z \sum_{r=0}^{\infty} (-1)^r (2r+2) B_{2r+2}^{(2n+2)} Y_{2r+2}(2k \cosh z) \quad (b_{2n+2})$$

$$(12)$$

$$= \frac{\mathrm{se}_{2n+2}'(0, q)}{k^2 B_2^{(2n+2)}} \coth z \sum_{r=0}^{\infty} (2r+2) B_{2r+2}^{(2n+2)} Y_{2r+2}(2k \sinh z). \tag{13}$$

See remarks below (9) above. The complete solution takes the form

$$y = A \, \mathrm{Se}_m(z, q) + B \, \mathrm{Gey}_m(z, q). \tag{14}$$

8.14. The solutions $\mathrm{Fek}_m(z, q)$, $\mathrm{Gek}_m(z, q)$. These are derived from §§ 8.11–8.13 by expressing the Y functions in the series for

$\mathrm{Fey}_m(z,q)$, $\mathrm{Gey}_m(z,q)$ in terms of the J- and K-Bessel functions. Thus

$$K_\nu(u) = \tfrac{1}{2}\pi e^{\frac{1}{2}\pi(\nu+1)i} H_\nu^{(1)}(iu), \tag{1}$$

so

$$Y_\nu(u) = iJ_\nu(u) - \frac{2}{\pi} e^{-\frac{1}{2}\pi\nu i} K_\nu(-iu). \tag{2}$$

Writing $\nu = 2r$, and applying (2) to (1) § 8.11 yields

$$\mathrm{Fey}_{2n}(z,q) = \frac{\mathrm{ce}_{2n}(\tfrac{1}{2}\pi,q)}{A_0^{(2n)}} \times$$

$$\times \left[i \sum_{r=0}^{\infty} (-1)^r A_{2r}^{(2n)} J_{2r}(2k\cosh z) - \frac{2}{\pi} \sum_{r=0}^{\infty} A_{2r}^{(2n)} K_{2r}(-2ik\cosh z) \right]$$

$$(k > 0,\ |\cosh z| > 1) \quad (a_{2n}) \tag{3}$$

$$= i\,\mathrm{Ce}_{2n}(z,q) - 2\mathrm{Fek}_{2n}(z,q), \tag{4}$$

where we adopt the definition

$$\mathrm{Fek}_{2n}(z,q) = \frac{\mathrm{ce}_{2n}(\tfrac{1}{2}\pi,q)}{\pi A_0^{(2n)}} \sum_{r=0}^{\infty} A_{2r}^{(2n)} K_{2r}(-2ik\cosh z) \quad (a_{2n}). \tag{5}$$

In like manner (2) § 8.11 yields

$$\mathrm{Fek}_{2n}(z,q) = \frac{\mathrm{ce}_{2n}(0,q)}{\pi A_0^{(2n)}} \sum_{r=0}^{\infty} (-1)^r A_{2r}^{(2n)} K_{2r}(-2ik\sinh z). \tag{6}$$

Since $\mathrm{Fey}_{2n}(z,q)$, $\mathrm{Ce}_{2n}(z,q)$ are real if z is real, it follows from (4) that $\mathrm{Fek}_{2n}(z,q)$ is complex. The restrictions at (1), (2) § 8.11 apply here, and convergence is considered in § 8.50. By virtue of the logarithmic term in the series for the K function, (5), (6) are non-periodic in z. These remarks apply also to the remaining functions given below:

$$\mathrm{Fey}_{2n+1}(z,q) = i[\mathrm{Ce}_{2n+1}(z,q) + 2\,\mathrm{Fek}_{2n+1}(z,q)], \tag{7}$$

with

$$\mathrm{Fek}_{2n+1}(z,q)$$

$$= -\frac{\mathrm{ce}_{2n+1}'(\tfrac{1}{2}\pi,q)}{\pi k A_1^{(2n+1)}} \sum_{r=0}^{\infty} A_{2r+1}^{(2n+1)} K_{2r+1}(-2ik\cosh z) \quad (a_{2n+1}) \tag{8}$$

$$= \frac{\mathrm{ce}_{2n+1}(0,q)}{\pi k A_1^{(2n+1)}} \coth z \sum_{r=0}^{\infty} (-1)^r (2r+1) A_{2r+1}^{(2n+1)} K_{2r+1}(-2ik\sinh z). \tag{9}$$

$$\mathrm{Gey}_{2n+1}(z,q) = i[\mathrm{Se}_{2n+1}(z,q) + 2\,\mathrm{Gek}_{2n+1}(z,q)], \tag{10}$$

with

$$\mathrm{Gek}_{2n+1}(z,q)$$

$$= \frac{\mathrm{se}_{2n+1}(\tfrac{1}{2}\pi,q)}{\pi k B_1^{(2n+1)}} \tanh z \sum_{r=0}^{\infty} (2r+1)B_{2r+1}^{(2n+1)}K_{2r+1}(-2ik\cosh z) \quad (b_{2n+1})$$

$$\tag{11}$$

$$= \frac{\mathrm{se}_{2n+1}'(0,q)}{\pi k B_1^{(2n+1)}} \sum_{r=0}^{\infty} (-1)^r B_{2r+1}^{(2n+1)}K_{2r+1}(-2ik\sinh z). \tag{12}$$

$$\mathrm{Gey}_{2n+2}(z,q) = i\,\mathrm{Se}_{2n+2}(z,q) - 2\,\mathrm{Gek}_{2n+2}(z,q), \tag{13}$$

with

$$\mathrm{Gek}_{2n+2}(z,q)$$

$$= \frac{\mathrm{se}_{2n+2}'(\tfrac{1}{2}\pi,q)}{\pi k^2 B_2^{(2n+2)}} \tanh z \sum_{r=0}^{\infty} (2r+2)B_{2r+2}^{(2n+2)}K_{2r+2}(-2ik\cosh z) \quad (b_{2n+2})$$

$$\tag{14}$$

$$= -\frac{\mathrm{se}_{2n+2}'(0,q)}{\pi k^2 B_2^{(2n+2)}} \coth z \sum_{r=0}^{\infty} (-1)^r(2r+2)B_{2r+2}^{(2n+2)}K_{2r+2}(-2ik\sinh z).$$

$$\tag{15}$$

If desired the K functions may be expressed in terms of Hankel functions by aid of (1).

The complete solutions given at (5) § 8.11, (14) § 8.13 may sometimes be unsuitable. However, in any complete solution of that type it is permissible to substitute Fek_m for Fey_m, and Gek_m for Gey_m, by virtue of (4), (7), (10), (13).

8.20. First solution of $y'' + (a - 2q\cos 2z)y = 0.$

By writing $-iz$ for z in the series for Ce_m, Se_m in §§ 8.10, 8.12, 8.13 we obtain

$$\mathrm{ce}_{2n}(z,q) = \frac{\mathrm{ce}_{2n}(\tfrac{1}{2}\pi,q)}{A_0^{(2n)}} \sum_{r=0}^{\infty} (-1)^r A_{2r}^{(2n)}J_{2r}(2k\cos z) \quad (a_{2n}) \tag{1}$$

$$= \frac{\mathrm{ce}_{2n}(0,q)}{A_0^{(2n)}} \sum_{r=0}^{\infty} (-1)^r A_{2r}^{(2n)}I_{2r}(2k\sin z), \tag{2}$$

$$\mathrm{ce}_{2n+1}(z,q) = -\frac{\mathrm{ce}_{2n+1}'(\tfrac{1}{2}\pi,q)}{kA_1^{(2n+1)}} \sum_{r=0}^{\infty} (-1)^r A_{2r+1}^{(2n+1)}J_{2r+1}(2k\cos z) \quad (a_{2n+1}) \tag{3}$$

$$= \frac{\mathrm{ce}_{2n+1}(0,q)}{kA_1^{(2n+1)}} \cot z \sum_{r=0}^{\infty} (-1)^r(2r+1)A_{2r+1}^{(2n+1)}I_{2r+1}(2k\sin z), \tag{4}$$

$$\mathrm{se}_{2n+1}(z,q) = \frac{\mathrm{se}_{2n+1}(\tfrac{1}{2}\pi,q)}{kB_1^{(2n+1)}} \tan z \sum_{r=0}^{\infty} (-1)^r(2r+1)B_{2r+1}^{(2n+1)}J_{2r+1}(2k\cos z)$$

$$(b_{2n+1}) \quad (5)$$

$$= \frac{\mathrm{se}_{2n+1}'(0,q)}{kB_1^{(2n+1)}} \sum_{r=0}^{\infty} (-1)^r B_{2r+1}^{(2n+1)}I_{2r+1}(2k\sin z), \tag{6}$$

$$se_{2n+2}(z,q) = -\frac{se'_{2n+2}(\tfrac{1}{2}\pi,q)}{k^2 B_2^{(2n+2)}} \tan z \sum_{r=0}^{\infty} (-1)^r(2r+2)B_{2r+2}^{(2n+2)}J_{2r+2}(2k\cos z)$$
$$(b_{2n+2}) \quad (7)$$

$$= \frac{se'_{2n+2}(0,q)}{k^2 B_2^{(2n+2)}} \cot z \sum_{r=0}^{\infty} (-1)^r(2r+2)B_{2r+2}^{(2n+2)}I_{2r+2}(2k\sin z). \quad (8)$$

8.30. Solutions of $y''-(a+2q\cosh 2z)y = 0$, $q > 0$. If we write $(\tfrac{1}{2}\pi i+z)$ for z in $y''-(a-2q\cosh 2z)y = 0$, it takes the above form, i.e. the sign of q is changed. Making this change of variable in series derived in § 8.10 et seq. leads to the following representations:†

$$Ce_{2n}(z,-q) = (-1)^n Ce_{2n}(\tfrac{1}{2}\pi i+z,q) \quad (a_{2n}) \quad\quad (1)$$

$$= (-1)^n \frac{ce_{2n}(\tfrac{1}{2}\pi,q)}{A_0^{(2n)}} \sum_{r=0}^{\infty} A_{2r}^{(2n)}I_{2r}(2k\sinh z) \quad\quad (2)$$

$$= (-1)^n \frac{ce_{2n}(0,q)}{A_0^{(2n)}} \sum_{r=0}^{\infty} (-1)^r A_{2r}^{(2n)}I_{2r}(2k\cosh z). \quad\quad (3)$$

The multiplier $(-1)^n$ is needed by virtue of that in § 2.31.

$$Fey_{2n}(z,-q) = (-1)^n Fey_{2n}(\tfrac{1}{2}\pi i+z,q) \quad (a_{2n}) \quad\quad (4)$$

$$= (-1)^n \frac{ce_{2n}(\tfrac{1}{2}\pi,q)}{A_0^{2n}} \sum_{r=0}^{\infty} (-1)^r A_{2r}^{(2n)}Y_{2r}(2ik\sinh z) \quad\quad (5)$$

$$= (-1)^n \frac{ce_{2n}(0,q)}{A_0^{(2n)}} \sum_{r=0}^{\infty} A_{2r}^{(2n)}Y_{2r}(2ik\cosh z). \quad\quad (6)$$

$$Fek_{2n}(z,-q) = (-1)^n Fek_{2n}(\tfrac{1}{2}\pi i+z,q) \quad\quad (7)$$

$$= (-1)^n \frac{ce_{2n}(\tfrac{1}{2}\pi,q)}{\pi A_0^{(2n)}} \sum_{r=0}^{\infty} A_{2r}^{(2n)}K_{2r}(2k\sinh z) \quad\quad (8)$$

$$= (-1)^n \frac{ce_{2n}(0,q)}{\pi A_0^{(2n)}} \sum_{r=0}^{\infty} (-1)^r A_{2r}^{(2n)}K_{2r}(2k\cosh z). \quad\quad (9)$$

$$Fey_{2n}(z,-q) = i\,Ce_{2n}(z,-q) - 2\,Fek_{2n}(z,-q). \quad\quad (10)$$

$$Ce_{2n+1}(z,-q)$$
$$= (-1)^{n+1}i\,Se_{2n+1}(\tfrac{1}{2}\pi i+z,q) \quad (b_{2n+1}) \quad\quad (11)$$

$$= (-1)^n \frac{se_{2n+1}(\tfrac{1}{2}\pi,q)}{kB_1^{(2n+1)}} \coth z \sum_{r=0}^{\infty} (2r+1)B_{2r+1}^{(2n+1)}I_{2r+1}(2k\sinh z) \quad (12)$$

$$= (-1)^n \frac{se'_{2n+1}(0,q)}{kB_1^{(2n+1)}} \sum_{r=0}^{\infty} (-1)^r B_{2r+1}^{(2n+1)}I_{2r+1}(2k\cosh z). \quad\quad (13)$$

† Formulae 2, 3, 9, 12, 13, 19, 22, 23, 29, 32, 33, 39 are given in reference [6] without the multipliers external to the Σ. The method of derivation differs from that used here.

$\mathrm{Fey}_{2n+1}(z,-q)$

$$= (-1)^{n+1}i\,\mathrm{Gey}_{2n+1}(\tfrac{1}{2}\pi i + z, q) \quad (b_{2n+1}) \tag{14}$$

$$= (-1)^{n+1}i\frac{\mathrm{se}_{2n+1}(\tfrac{1}{2}\pi, q)}{kB_1^{(2n+1)}}\coth z \sum_{r=0}^{\infty}(-1)^r(2r+1)B_{2r+1}^{(2n+1)}Y_{2r+1}(2ik\sinh z) \tag{15}$$

$$= (-1)^{n+1}i\frac{\mathrm{se}_{2n+1}'(0, q)}{kB_1^{(2n+1)}}\sum_{r=0}^{\infty}B_{2r+1}^{(2n+1)}Y_{2r+1}(2ik\cosh z). \tag{16}$$

$\mathrm{Fek}_{2n+1}(z,-q)$

$$= (-1)^n\,\mathrm{Gek}_{2n+1}(\tfrac{1}{2}\pi i + z, q) \tag{17}$$

$$= (-1)^n\frac{\mathrm{se}_{2n+1}(\tfrac{1}{2}\pi, q)}{\pi kB_1^{(2n+1)}}\coth z\sum_{r=0}^{\infty}(2r+1)B_{2r+1}^{(2n+1)}K_{2r+1}(2k\sinh z) \tag{18}$$

$$= (-1)^n\frac{\mathrm{se}_{2n+1}'(0, q)}{\pi kB_1^{(2n+1)}}\sum_{r=0}^{\infty}(-1)^rB_{2r+1}^{(2n+1)}K_{2r+1}(2k\cosh z). \tag{19}$$

$$\mathrm{Fey}_{2n+1}(z,-q) = i\,\mathrm{Ce}_{2n+1}(z,-q) + 2\,\mathrm{Fek}_{2n+1}(z,-q). \tag{20}$$

$\mathrm{Se}_{2n+1}(z,-q)$

$$= (-1)^{n+1}i\,\mathrm{Ce}_{2n+1}(\tfrac{1}{2}\pi i + z, q) \quad (a_{2n+1}) \tag{21}$$

$$= (-1)^{n+1}\frac{\mathrm{ce}_{2n+1}'(\tfrac{1}{2}\pi, q)}{kA_1^{(2n+1)}}\sum_{r=0}^{\infty}A_{2r+1}^{(2n+1)}I_{2r+1}(2k\sinh z) \tag{22}$$

$$= (-1)^n\frac{\mathrm{ce}_{2n+1}(0, q)}{kA_1^{(2n+1)}}\tanh z\sum_{r=0}^{\infty}(-1)^r(2r+1)A_{2r+1}^{(2n+1)}I_{2r+1}(2k\cosh z). \tag{23}$$

$\mathrm{Gey}_{2n+1}(z,-q)$

$$= (-1)^{n+1}i\,\mathrm{Fey}_{2n+1}(\tfrac{1}{2}\pi i + z, q) \quad (a_{2n+1}) \tag{24}$$

$$= (-1)^n i\frac{\mathrm{ce}_{2n+1}'(\tfrac{1}{2}\pi, q)}{kA_1^{(2n+1)}}\sum_{r=0}^{\infty}(-1)^rA_{2r+1}^{(2n+1)}Y_{2r+1}(2ik\sinh z) \tag{25}$$

$$= (-1)^{n+1}i\frac{\mathrm{ce}_{2n+1}(0, q)}{kA_1^{(2n+1)}}\tanh z\sum_{r=0}^{\infty}(2r+1)A_{2r+1}^{(2n+1)}Y_{2r+1}(2ik\cosh z). \tag{26}$$

$\mathrm{Gek}_{2n+1}(z,-q)$

$$= (-1)^n\,\mathrm{Fek}_{2n+1}(\tfrac{1}{2}\pi i + z, q) \tag{27}$$

$$= (-1)^{n+1}\frac{\mathrm{ce}_{2n+1}'(\tfrac{1}{2}\pi, q)}{\pi kA_1^{(2n+1)}}\sum_{r=0}^{\infty}A_{2r+1}^{(2n+1)}K_{2r+1}(2k\sinh z) \tag{28}$$

$$= (-1)^n\frac{\mathrm{ce}_{2n+1}(0, q)}{\pi kA_1^{(2n+1)}}\tanh z\sum_{r=0}^{\infty}(-1)^r(2r+1)A_{2r+1}^{(2n+1)}K_{2r+1}(2k\cosh z). \tag{29}$$

$$\mathrm{Gey}_{2n+1}(z,-q) = i\,\mathrm{Se}_{2n+1}(z,-q) + 2\,\mathrm{Gek}_{2n+1}(z,-q). \tag{30}$$

$\mathrm{Se}_{2n+2}(z, -q)$

$$= (-1)^{n+1}\mathrm{Se}_{2n+2}(\tfrac{1}{2}\pi i + z, q) \quad (b_{2n+2}) \tag{31}$$

$$= (-1)^{n+1}\frac{\mathrm{se}'_{2n+2}(\tfrac{1}{2}\pi, q)}{k^2 B_2^{(2n+2)}}\coth z \sum_{r=0}^{\infty}(2r+2)B_{2r+2}^{(2n+2)}I_{2r+2}(2k\sinh z) \tag{32}$$

$$= (-1)^{n}\frac{\mathrm{se}'_{2n+2}(0, q)}{k^2 B_2^{(2n+2)}}\tanh z \sum_{r=0}^{\infty}(-1)^r(2r+2)B_{2r+2}^{(2n+2)}I_{2r+2}(2k\cosh z). \tag{33}$$

$\mathrm{Gey}_{2n+2}(z, -q)$

$$= (-1)^{n+1}\mathrm{Gey}_{2n+2}(\tfrac{1}{2}\pi i + z, q) \quad (b_{2n+2}) \tag{34}$$

$$= (-1)^{n}\frac{\mathrm{se}'_{2n+2}(\tfrac{1}{2}\pi, q)}{k^2 B_2^{(2n+2)}}\coth z \sum_{r=0}^{\infty}(-1)^r(2r+2)B_{2r+2}^{(2n+2)}Y_{2r+2}(2ik\sinh z) \tag{35}$$

$$= (-1)^{n+1}\frac{\mathrm{se}'_{2n+2}(0, q)}{k^2 B_2^{(2n+2)}}\tanh z \sum_{r=0}^{\infty}(2r+2)B_{2r+2}^{(2n+2)}Y_{2r+2}(2ik\cosh z). \tag{36}$$

$\mathrm{Gek}_{2n+2}(z, -q)$

$$= (-1)^{n+1}\mathrm{Gek}_{2n+2}(\tfrac{1}{2}\pi i + z, q) \tag{37}$$

$$= (-1)^{n+1}\frac{\mathrm{se}'_{2n+2}(\tfrac{1}{2}\pi, q)}{\pi k^2 B_2^{(2n+2)}}\coth z \sum_{r=0}^{\infty}(2r+2)B_{2r+2}^{(2n+2)}K_{2r+2}(2k\sinh z) \tag{38}$$

$$= (-1)^{n}\frac{\mathrm{se}'_{2n+2}(0, q)}{\pi k^2 B_2^{(2n+2)}}\tanh z \sum_{r=0}^{\infty}(-1)^r(2r+2)B_{2r+2}^{(2n+2)}K_{2r+2}(2k\cosh z). \tag{39}$$

$$\mathrm{Gey}_{2n+2}(z, -q) = i\,\mathrm{Se}_{2n+2}(z, -q) - 2\,\mathrm{Gek}_{2n+2}(z, -q). \tag{40}$$

The functions involving the Y-Bessel function are complex, but those involving the K-Bessel function are real, if z is real.

8.40. First solution of $y'' + (a + 2q\cos 2z)y = 0, q > 0$. This may be derived by writing $-iz$ for z in the first solution of

$$y'' - (a + 2q\cosh 2z)y = 0$$

given in §8.30, or by putting $(\tfrac{1}{2}\pi - z)$ for z in the first solution of $y'' + (a - 2q\cos 2z)y = 0$ given in §8.20. Thus we find that

$$\mathrm{ce}_{2n}(z, -q) = (-1)^n\,\mathrm{ce}_{2n}(\tfrac{1}{2}\pi - z, q) = (-1)^n\,\mathrm{Ce}_{2n}(-iz, q) \quad (a_{2n}) \tag{1}$$

$$= (-1)^n\frac{\mathrm{ce}_{2n}(\tfrac{1}{2}\pi, q)}{A_0^{(2n)}} \sum_{r=0}^{\infty}(-1)^r A_{2r}^{(2n)}J_{2r}(2k\sin z) \tag{2}$$

$$= (-1)^n\frac{\mathrm{ce}_{2n}(0, q)}{A_0^{(2n)}} \sum_{r=0}^{\infty}(-1)^r A_{2r}^{(2n)}I_{2r}(2k\cos z). \tag{3}$$

$\mathrm{ce}_{2n+1}(z, -q)$

$$= (-1)^n \mathrm{se}_{2n+1}(\tfrac{1}{2}\pi - z, q) \quad (b_{2n+1}) \tag{4}$$

$$= (-1)^n \frac{\mathrm{se}_{2n+1}(\tfrac{1}{2}\pi, q)}{k B_1^{(2n+1)}} \cot z \sum_{r=0}^{\infty} (-1)^r (2r+1) B_{2r+1}^{(2n+1)} J_{2r+1}(2k \sin z) \tag{5}$$

$$= (-1)^n \frac{\mathrm{se}_{2n+1}(0, q)}{k B_1^{(2n+1)}} \sum_{r=0}^{\infty} (-1)^r B_{2r+1}^{(2n+1)} I_{2r+1}(2k \cos z). \tag{6}$$

$\mathrm{se}_{2n+1}(z, -q)$

$$= (-1)^n \mathrm{ce}_{2n+1}(\tfrac{1}{2}\pi - z, q) \quad (a_{2n+1}) \tag{7}$$

$$= (-1)^{n+1} \frac{\mathrm{ce}'_{2n+1}(\tfrac{1}{2}\pi, q)}{k A_1^{(2n+1)}} \sum_{r=0}^{\infty} (-1)^r A_{2r+1}^{(2n+1)} J_{2r+1}(2k \sin z) \tag{8}$$

$$= (-1)^n \frac{\mathrm{ce}_{2n+1}(0, q)}{k A_1^{(2n+1)}} \tan z \sum_{r=0}^{\infty} (-1)^r (2r+1) A_{2r+1}^{(2n+1)} I_{2r+1}(2k \cos z). \tag{9}$$

$\mathrm{se}_{2n+2}(z, -q)$

$$= (-1)^n \mathrm{se}_{2n+2}(\tfrac{1}{2}\pi - z, q) \quad (b_{2n+2}) \tag{10}$$

$$= (-1)^{n+1} \frac{\mathrm{se}'_{2n+2}(\tfrac{1}{2}\pi, q)}{k^2 B_2^{(2n+2)}} \cot z \sum_{r=0}^{\infty} (-1)^r (2r+2) B_{2r+2}^{(2n+2)} J_{2r+2}(2k \sin z) \tag{11}$$

$$= (-1)^n \frac{\mathrm{se}'_{2n+2}(0, q)}{k^2 B_2^{(2n+2)}} \tan z \sum_{r=0}^{\infty} (-1)^r (2r+2) B_{2r+2}^{(2n+2)} I_{2r+2}(2k \cos z). \tag{12}$$

8.50. Convergence of solutions.

1°. *Formulae asymptotic in m.* To discuss convergence we require formulae for the various Bessel functions, valid when m, the order of the function, is very large and positive, and far exceeds the argument $|u|$. Then the first terms in the ordinary expansions of $J_m(u)$, $I_m(u)$ predominate, and we may write

$$J_m(u) \sim I_m(u) \sim \frac{1}{m!}\left(\frac{u}{2}\right)^m. \tag{1}$$

Similarly we have

$$Y_m(u) \sim -\frac{2}{\pi} K_m(u) \sim -\frac{1}{\pi}(m-1)!\left(\frac{2}{u}\right)^m. \tag{2}$$

From (1), (2) we infer that under the above condition

$$|Y_m(u)| \gg |J_m(u)| \quad \text{and} \quad |K_m(u)| \gg |I_m(u)|. \tag{3}$$

2°. *Series involving J and I functions.* If $2r \gg |2k \cosh z|$, (1) 1° gives, with r extremely large,

$$J_{2r}(2k \cosh z) \sim \frac{1}{(2r)!}(k \cosh z)^{2r}. \tag{1}$$

When r is large enough, by (4) § 3.21

$$|A_{2r+2}^{(2n)}/A_{2r}^{(2n)}| \simeq |k^2|/4(r+1)^2. \tag{2}$$

Thus, taking the ratio of the moduli of the $(r+1)$th and rth terms in (15) § 8.10, we get

$$\left|\frac{A_{2r+2}J_{2r+2}(2k\cosh z)}{A_{2r}J_{2r}(2k\cosh z)}\right| \to \frac{|k^4||\cosh z|^2}{16(r+1)^4} \to 0 \quad \text{as } r \to +\infty, \tag{3}$$

if z is finite but unrestricted. Hence the series is absolutely convergent. By applying the 'M' test, it may be proved to converge uniformly in any closed region of the z-plane, or in any closed interval, z real. These conclusions are applicable to all series in this chapter which involve the J and I functions.

3°. *Series involving Y and K functions.* We consider (1) § 8.11. Then (2) 1° gives

$$Y_{2r}(2k\cosh z) \sim -(2r-1)!/\pi(k\cosh z)^{2r} \tag{1}$$

and, therefore, by aid of (2) 2°,

$$\left|\frac{A_{2r+2}Y_{2r+2}(2k\cosh z)}{A_{2r}Y_{2r}(2k\cosh z)}\right| \simeq \frac{|k^2|(2r+1)2r}{4(r+1)^2|k^2||\cosh z|^2} \to 1/|\cosh z|^2 \tag{2}$$

as $r \to +\infty$. If $|\cosh z| > 1$, the series is absolutely convergent, and the 'M' test shows that it is uniformly convergent. As $z \to 0$ the convergence becomes non-uniform. The series converges at the origin, but the rate of convergence is very slow. If $|\cosh z| < 1$, z is imaginary, $|\cos z| < 1$, and the series diverges.

When the argument of the Y function is $2k\sinh z$, the third member of (2) is $1/|\sinh z|^2$. Hence the series is absolutely and uniformly convergent for $|\sinh z| > 1$; for $|\sinh z| = 1$ it converges non-uniformly, but when $|\sinh z| < 1$ it diverges. Thus (1) § 8.11 represents $\text{Fey}_{2n}(z, q)$ up to and including the origin, whereas (2) § 8.11 holds up to $|\sinh z| = 1$ only, so $z = \log_e(1+2^{\frac{1}{2}})$. Owing to the logarithmic term in the expansions of the Y and K functions of integral order, the additional restriction that $R(z) > 0$ must be imposed when the argument is $2k\sinh z$. Despite non-uniformity of convergence, as shown in § 13.60, the function $\text{Fey}_{2n}(z, q)$ is continuous, but its derivative at $z = 0$ cannot be obtained from either (1), (2) § 8.11 by term-by-term differentiation. These conclusions apply to all series in this chapter involving Y or K functions.

WAVE EQUATION IN ELLIPTICAL COORDINATES: ORTHOGONALITY THEOREM

9.10. The two-dimensional wave equation. In two-dimensional problems associated with sinusoidal wave motion, the displacement ζ, or its equivalent, at any point (x, y), must satisfy the wave equation, namely,

$$\frac{\partial^2 \zeta}{\partial x^2} + \frac{\partial^2 \zeta}{\partial y^2} + k_1^2 \zeta = 0, \tag{1}$$

where k_1 is a constant dependent upon the properties of the medium, and the pulsatance of the disturbance therein. In problems pertaining to a rectangular boundary, e.g. a rectangular membrane, (1) is solved in the form given, subject to the particular boundary conditions imposed. If the boundary is circular or elliptical in shape, it is expedient, prior to solution, to transform (1) to either polar or elliptical coordinates, as the case may be.

9.11. Elliptical coordinates. We write $x + iy = h \cosh(\xi + i\eta)$, so that, equating real and imaginary parts, $x = h \cosh \xi \cos \eta$, $y = h \sinh \xi \sin \eta$. Thus

$$\frac{x^2}{h^2 \cosh^2 \xi} + \frac{y^2}{h^2 \sinh^2 \xi} = \cos^2 \eta + \sin^2 \eta = 1, \tag{1}$$

and

$$\frac{x^2}{h^2 \cos^2 \eta} - \frac{y^2}{h^2 \sin^2 \eta} = \cosh^2 \xi - \sinh^2 \xi = 1. \tag{2}$$

Then (1) represents a family of confocal ellipses with major axes $2h \cosh \xi$, minor axes $2h \sinh \xi$, the common foci being the points $x = \pm h$, $y = 0$. Also (2) represents a family of confocal hyperbolas with the same foci, as illustrated in Fig. 16 A. The two families of conics intersect orthogonally, and each intersection corresponds to a point defined by the coordinates $x = h \cosh \xi \cos \eta$, $y = h \sinh \xi \sin \eta$. The angle η varies from 0 to 2π in passing once round an ellipse, while if we consider a stretched elastic membrane clamped between two similar elliptical rings, ξ varies from zero along the line of foci to ξ_0 at the rings.

At the extremities of the major axis of any confocal ellipse (Fig. 16 A), $\eta = 0, \pi, y = 0$, and $x = \pm h \cosh \xi = \pm a$. At the ends of the minor axis, $\eta = \frac{1}{2}\pi, \frac{3}{2}\pi, x = 0$, and $y = \pm h \sinh \xi = \pm b$. If e is the eccentricity of the ellipse, $h = ae$, so $\cosh \xi = e^{-1}$, and when $e \to 1$, $\xi \to 0$, while $a \to h$. Thus a long elliptical cylinder degenerates to a ribbon of equal length, whose width is $2h$, i.e. the interfocal

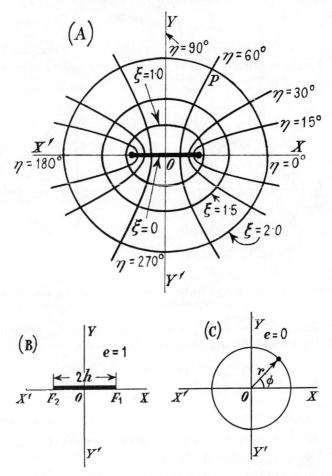

FIG. 16. (A) Orthogonally intersecting confocal ellipses and hyperbolas for elliptical coordinates. P has elliptical coordinates $\xi = 2$, $\eta = \frac{1}{3}\pi$ (60°), and cartesian coordinates $x = h\cosh 2 \cos \frac{1}{3}\pi$, $y = h\sinh 2 \sin \frac{1}{3}\pi$.

(B) Degenerate form of ellipse when $e = 1$. As $e \to 1$, $a \to h$, $b \to 0$ and the ellipse $\to$ the interfocal line of length $2h$.

(C) Degenerate form of ellipse, when eccentricity $e = 0$. The foci coalesce at the centre of a circle radius r, equal to the semi-major axis. The original hyperbola through P (see A) is now radii making $\phi = \pm\frac{1}{3}\pi$ with $X'OX$.

distance (see Fig. 16 B). With a constant, if $e \to 0$, $\xi \to \infty$, and the ellipse tends to a circle of radius a. Since $h = ae$, $h \to 0$, the foci tend to coalesce at the origin, and $h\cosh\xi \to h\sinh\xi \to a$. If h be constant, as $a \to \infty$, $\xi \to \infty$, and $e \to 0$, so that the confocal ellipses tend to become concentric circles. Now (2) may be written

$$\frac{x^2}{\cos^2\eta} - \frac{y^2}{\sin^2\eta} = h^2. \tag{3}$$

As $h \to 0$, $y/x \to \pm\tan\eta$, so $\eta \to \phi$, $\cos\eta \to \cos\phi$, the confocal hyperbolas ultimately become radii of the circle and make angles ϕ with the X-axis, as in Fig. 16 c.

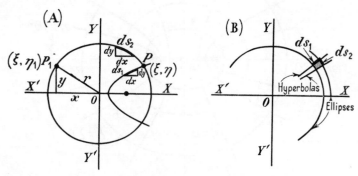

FIG. 17. (A) Hyperbolic (ds_1), elliptic (ds_2) arc length, and radius vector r. (B) Area $(ds_1\,ds_2)$ enclosed by two contiguous pairs of orthogonally intersecting confocal ellipses and hyperbolas.

9.12. Arc lengths ds_1, ds_2, and radius vector r. Referring to Fig. 17, the hyperbolic and elliptic arc lengths are, respectively,

$$ds_1 = [(\partial x/\partial\xi)^2 + (\partial y/\partial\xi)^2]^{\frac{1}{2}}\,d\xi \tag{1}$$

and

$$ds_2 = [(\partial x/\partial\eta)^2 + (\partial y/\partial\eta)^2]^{\frac{1}{2}}\,d\eta. \tag{2}$$

Now

$$\partial x/\partial\xi = h\sinh\xi\cos\eta, \qquad \partial y/\partial\xi = h\cosh\xi\sin\eta,$$

$$\partial x/\partial\eta = -h\cosh\xi\sin\eta, \qquad \partial y/\partial\eta = h\sinh\xi\cos\eta,$$

so each bracketed member in (1), (2) is

$$l_1 = h[\cosh^2\xi\sin^2\eta + \sinh^2\xi\cos^2\eta]^{\frac{1}{2}} = h(\cosh^2\xi - \cos^2\eta)^{\frac{1}{2}} \tag{3}$$

$$= \frac{h}{2^{\frac{1}{2}}}(\cosh 2\xi - \cos 2\eta)^{\frac{1}{2}}. \tag{4}$$

Hence from (1)–(3) we obtain

$$ds_1 = l_1\,d\xi \quad \text{and} \quad ds_2 = l_1\,d\eta. \tag{5}$$

Since ds_1 is along the direction of the normal to the ellipse, we may write

$$dn = l_1\,d\xi. \tag{6}$$

The distance of any point (x, y) from the origin, expressed in elliptical coordinates, is

$$r = (x^2+y^2)^{\frac{1}{2}} = h[\cosh^2\xi\cos^2\eta+\sinh^2\xi\sin^2\eta]^{\frac{1}{2}} = h(\cosh^2\xi-\sin^2\eta)^{\frac{1}{2}} \tag{7}$$

$$= \frac{h}{2^{\frac{1}{2}}}(\cosh 2\xi+\cos 2\eta)^{\frac{1}{2}}. \tag{8}$$

When ξ is large enough, $\cosh\xi \sim \sinh\xi \sim \frac{1}{2}e^\xi$, so by (3), (7) with h constant, $l_1 \sim h\cosh\xi \sim h\sinh\xi \sim r$ the radius vector. Hence we may write

$$ds_1 \sim r\,d\xi \sim dr; \quad ds_2 \sim r\,d\eta; \quad ds_1 ds_2 \sim r\,dr d\eta. \tag{9}$$

9.20. Transformation of (1) § 9.10 to elliptical coordinates.
Write $z = x+iy = h\cosh(\xi+i\eta)$, $\bar{z} = x-iy = h\cosh(\xi-i\eta)$, then $z\bar{z} = x^2+y^2$, and

$$\frac{4\partial^2 z\bar{z}}{\partial z \partial\bar{z}} = \left(\frac{\partial^2}{\partial x^2}+\frac{\partial^2}{\partial y^2}\right)z\bar{z}. \tag{1}$$

Putting $\zeta = \xi+i\eta$, $\bar{\zeta} = \xi-i\eta$, we get $z = h\cosh\zeta$, $\bar{z} = h\cosh\bar{\zeta}$, and $\zeta\bar{\zeta} = \xi^2+\eta^2$. Thus

$$\frac{\partial\zeta}{\partial z} = \frac{1}{h\sinh\zeta}, \quad \frac{\partial\bar{\zeta}}{\partial\bar{z}} = \frac{1}{h\sinh\bar{\zeta}}, \quad \frac{4\partial^2\zeta\bar{\zeta}}{\partial\zeta\partial\bar{\zeta}} = \left(\frac{\partial^2}{\partial\xi^2}+\frac{\partial^2}{\partial\eta^2}\right)\zeta\bar{\zeta},$$

so

$$\frac{\partial}{\partial z} = \frac{1}{h\sinh\zeta}\frac{\partial}{\partial\zeta}, \quad \frac{\partial}{\partial\bar{z}} = \frac{1}{h\sinh\bar{\zeta}}\frac{\partial}{\partial\bar{\zeta}}, \quad \text{and} \quad \frac{4\partial^2}{\partial\zeta\partial\bar{\zeta}} = \frac{\partial^2}{\partial\xi^2}+\frac{\partial^2}{\partial\eta^2}.$$

Hence

$$\frac{4\partial^2}{\partial z\partial\bar{z}} = \frac{\partial^2}{\partial x^2}+\frac{\partial^2}{\partial y^2} = \frac{4}{h^2\sinh\zeta\sinh\bar{\zeta}}\frac{\partial^2}{\partial\zeta\partial\bar{\zeta}}, \tag{2}$$

or

$$\frac{\partial^2}{\partial x^2}+\frac{\partial^2}{\partial y^2} = \frac{2}{h^2(\cosh 2\xi-\cos 2\eta)}\left(\frac{\partial^2}{\partial\xi^2}+\frac{\partial^2}{\partial\eta^2}\right). \tag{3}$$

Applying (3) to (1) § 9.10 leads to the equation

$$\frac{\partial^2\zeta}{\partial\xi^2}+\frac{\partial^2\zeta}{\partial\eta^2}+2k^2(\cosh 2\xi-\cos 2\eta)\zeta = 0, \tag{4}$$

with $2k = k_1 h$. Then (4) is the two-dimensional wave equation (1) § 9.10 expressed in elliptical coordinates.

9.21. Solution of (4) § 9.20. Let the desired form of solution be $\zeta(\xi, \eta) = \psi(\xi)\phi(\eta)$, where ψ is a function of ξ alone, and ϕ a function of η alone. Then we obtain

$$\phi\frac{d^2\psi}{d\xi^2}+\psi\frac{d^2\phi}{d\eta^2}+2k^2(\cosh 2\xi-\cos 2\eta)\psi\phi = 0. \tag{1}$$

Dividing throughout by $\psi\phi$ and rearranging leads to

$$\frac{1}{\psi}\frac{d^2\psi}{d\xi^2} + 2k^2\cosh 2\xi = -\frac{1}{\phi}\frac{d^2\phi}{d\eta^2} + 2k^2\cos 2\eta. \tag{2}$$

Since the l.h.s. is independent of η, and the r.h.s. of ξ, each side must be a constant, say a. Accordingly we obtain the two ordinary equations

$$\frac{d^2\phi}{d\eta^2} + (a - 2k^2\cos 2\eta)\phi = 0 \tag{3}$$

and

$$\frac{d^2\psi}{d\xi^2} - (a - 2k^2\cosh 2\xi)\psi = 0, \tag{4}$$

where a is the separation constant.† Then (3), (4) are the canonical forms with which we have dealt hitherto, and the above analysis illustrates the genesis of the equations which bear Mathieu's name. If in (3) we write $\pm i\xi$ for η, it is transformed into (4), while the latter is transformed into (3) if $\pm i\eta$ be written for ξ.

9.30. Integral order solutions of (1) § 9.21. A solution comprises the product of any two functions which are solutions of (3), (4) § 9.21, respectively, *for the same values of a and q*. Since a may have *any* value, the number of solutions is unlimited. In practical applications the appropriate solutions are usually given by ordinary and modified Mathieu functions of *integral order*, i.e. solutions of (3), (4) § 9.21 corresponding to $a = a_m$, b_m. The solutions

TABLE 10. *Solutions of* (1) § 9.21 *when a has values for Mathieu functions of integral order.* $q > 0$

$\zeta = \psi_m(\xi)\phi_m(\eta)$ for $a = a_m$	Property	$\zeta = \psi_m(\xi)\phi_m(\eta)$ for $a = b_m$	Property
$\mathrm{Ce}_m(\xi, q)\mathrm{ce}_m(\eta, q)$	Period π or 2π in η, m even or odd; Period πi or $2\pi i$ in ξ, m even or odd	$\mathrm{Se}_m(\xi, q)\mathrm{se}_m(\eta, q)$	
$\mathrm{Fe}_m(\xi, q)\mathrm{ce}_m(\eta, q)$	Period π or 2π in η, m even or odd; Non-periodic in ξ	$\mathrm{Ge}_m(\xi, q)\mathrm{se}_m(\eta, q)$	As in column 2.
$\mathrm{Ce}_m(\xi, q)\mathrm{fe}_m(\eta, q)$	Non-periodic in η; Period πi or $2\pi i$ in ξ, m even or odd	$\mathrm{Se}_m(\xi, q)\mathrm{ge}_m(\eta, q)$	
$\mathrm{Fe}_m(\xi, q)\mathrm{fe}_m(\eta, q)$ $m = 0, 1, 2,...$	Non-periodic in η, ξ	$\mathrm{Ge}_m(\xi, q)\mathrm{ge}_m(\eta, q)$ $m = 1, 2, 3,...$	

† This must not be confused with the semi-major axis of the ellipse.

$\phi(\eta) = \mathrm{ce}_m(\eta, q)$ or $\mathrm{se}_m(\eta, q)$ with a, q real are important by virtue of their periodicity in π, 2π, and single-valuedness. Various product pairs, including second solutions of (3), (4) § 9.21, i.e. ordinary and modified Mathieu functions of the second kind, are set out in Table 10.

When $q < 0$, the solutions in Table 10 are valid provided the definitions of the various functions in Chapters II, VII are used.

Alternative solutions. As shown in Chapter VIII, there are alternative second solutions of equation (4) § 9.21. These are set out in Table 11. (See Chapter XIII also.)

TABLE 11. *Alternative second solutions of* (1) § 9.21

Solution	Alternative solution	Defined at	Solution	Alternative solution	Defined at
$\mathrm{Fe}_m(\xi, q)$	$\mathrm{Fey}_m(\xi, q)$ $\mathrm{Fek}_m(\xi, q)$	§§ 8.11, 8.12 § 8.14	$\mathrm{Fe}_m(\xi, -q)$	$\mathrm{Fey}_m(\xi, -q)$ $\mathrm{Fek}_m(\xi, -q)$	§ 8.30 ,,
$\mathrm{Ge}_m(\xi, q)$	$\mathrm{Gey}_m(\xi, q)$ $\mathrm{Gek}_m(\xi, q)$	§ 8.13 § 8.14	$\mathrm{Ge}_m(\xi, -q)$	$\mathrm{Gey}_m(\xi, -q)$ $\mathrm{Gek}_m(\xi, -q)$	,, ,,

9.31. Solutions of (1) § 9.21 of real fractional order. When (a, q) lies on an iso-β curve in Fig. 11 the order of the solution is $\nu = m+\beta$, $0 < \beta < 1$, and the solutions of (3), (4) § 9.21 coexist for $a = a_{m+\beta}$. Then the solutions of (1) § 9.21 are as shown in Table 12. Definitions of the various functions are given in §§ 4.71, 4.76.

TABLE 12. *Solutions of* (1) § 9.21 *when* $a = a_{m+\beta}$ *for Mathieu functions of real fractional order* $\nu = m+\beta$, *and* q *is positive*

$\zeta = \psi_\nu(\xi)\phi_\nu(\eta)$ for $a = a_\nu$	Property of solutions
$\mathrm{Ce}_\nu(\xi, q)\mathrm{ce}_\nu(\eta, q)$ $\mathrm{Se}_\nu(\xi, q)\mathrm{ce}_\nu(\eta, q)$ $\mathrm{Ce}_\nu(\xi, q)\mathrm{se}_\nu(\eta, q)$ $\mathrm{Se}_\nu(\xi, q)\mathrm{se}_\nu(\eta, q)$	If β is a rational fraction p/s in its lowest terms, $0 < p/s < 1$, all solutions in η have period $2s\pi$, and in ξ have period $2s\pi i$. If β is irrational, all solutions are non-periodic in η, ξ.

When q is negative Table 12 is applicable provided appropriate definitions of the functions are used, e.g. in § 4.71. We omit consideration of solutions when (a, q) lies in an unstable region of Figs. 8, 11.

9.40. Orthogonality theorem [135]. Let $q_{n,m}$ be such that for n a positive integer and $\xi = \xi_0$, $\psi_n(\xi_0, q_{n,m}) = 0$,† where ψ_n is a solution of (4) § 9.21. Then if a, q are real, the point $(a_{n,m}, q_{n,m})$ lies on

† $q_{n,m}$ is a parametric zero of ψ_n: see §§ 12.40, 12.41.

the characteristic curve for the function $\phi_n(\eta, q)$, the latter being an integral-order solution of (3) §9.21. For instance, the curve a_2 in Fig. 8 corresponds to $\mathrm{ce}_2(\eta, q)$ and also to $\mathrm{Ce}_2(\xi, q)$. It follows that we may write

$$\frac{d^2\phi_n}{d\eta^2} + (a_{n,m} - 2q_{n,m}\cos 2\eta)\phi_n = 0 \tag{1}$$

and

$$\frac{d^2\psi_n}{d\xi^2} - (a_{n,m} - 2q_{n,m}\cosh 2\xi)\psi_n = 0. \tag{2}$$

Put $\zeta_{n,m} = \psi_n\phi_n$, then for $(a_{n,m}, q_{n,m})$ we have

$$\frac{\partial^2\zeta_{n,m}}{\partial\xi^2} + \frac{\partial^2\zeta_{n,m}}{\partial\eta^2} + 2q_{n,m}(\cosh 2\xi - \cos 2\eta)\zeta_{n,m} = 0. \tag{3}$$

Also for $(a_{p,r}, q_{p,r})$

$$\frac{\partial^2\zeta_{p,r}}{\partial\xi^2} + \frac{\partial^2\zeta_{p,r}}{\partial\eta^2} + 2q_{p,r}(\cosh 2\xi - \cos 2\eta)\zeta_{p,r} = 0. \tag{4}$$

Multiplying (3) by $\zeta_{p,r}$, (4) by $\zeta_{n,m}$, and subtracting the second from the first we obtain

$$\frac{\partial}{\partial\xi}\left[\zeta_{p,r}\frac{\partial\zeta_{n,m}}{\partial\xi} - \zeta_{n,m}\frac{\partial\zeta_{p,r}}{\partial\xi}\right] + \frac{\partial}{\partial\eta}\left[\zeta_{p,r}\frac{\partial\zeta_{n,m}}{\partial\eta} - \zeta_{n,m}\frac{\partial\zeta_{p,r}}{\partial\eta}\right] +$$
$$+ 2(q_{n,m} - q_{p,r})(\cosh 2\xi - \cos 2\eta)\zeta_{n,m}\zeta_{p,r} = 0. \tag{5}$$

Integrating (5) with respect to ξ from 0 to ξ_0, and to η from 0 to 2π, we get

$$\int_0^{2\pi}\left[\zeta_{p,r}\frac{\partial\zeta_{n,m}}{\partial\xi} - \zeta_{n,m}\frac{\partial\zeta_{p,r}}{\partial\xi}\right]_0^{\xi_0}d\eta + \int_0^{\xi_0}\left[\zeta_{p,r}\frac{\partial\zeta_{n,m}}{\partial\eta} - \zeta_{n,m}\frac{\partial\zeta_{p,r}}{\partial\eta}\right]_0^{2\pi}d\xi +$$
$$+ 2(q_{n,m} - q_{p,r})\int_0^{\xi_0}\int_0^{2\pi}(\cosh 2\xi - \cos 2\eta)\zeta_{n,m}\zeta_{p,r}\,d\xi d\eta = 0. \tag{6}$$

If $\zeta_{n,m} = \mathrm{Ce}_{n,m}\,\mathrm{ce}_{n,m}$ or $\mathrm{Se}_{n,m}\,\mathrm{se}_{n,m}$, $\zeta_{p,r} = \mathrm{Ce}_{p,r}\,\mathrm{ce}_{p,r}$ or $\mathrm{Se}_{p,r}\,\mathrm{se}_{p,r}$, the first integrand in (6) vanishes at $\xi = 0, \xi_0$, while the second vanishes by virtue of its periodicity in η. Hence it follows that the last integral is zero if $p \neq n$, i.e.

$$\int_0^{\xi_0}\int_0^{2\pi}(\cosh 2\xi - \cos 2\eta)\zeta_{n,m}\zeta_{p,r}\,d\xi d\eta = 0. \tag{7}$$

This holds also if $p = n$, $r \neq m$. If $p = n$ and $r = m$, the double integral does not vanish. Then we have

$$\int_0^{\xi_0} \int_0^{2\pi} \left. \begin{matrix} \mathrm{Ce}_{n,m}^2(\xi)\mathrm{ce}_{n,m}^2(\eta) \\ \mathrm{Se}_{n,m}^2(\xi)\mathrm{se}_{n,m}^2(\eta) \end{matrix} \right\} (\cosh 2\xi - \cos 2\eta) \, d\xi d\eta \neq 0. \tag{8}$$

It may be remarked that if $\phi_n = \mathrm{ce}_{n,m}$ or $\mathrm{se}_{n,m}$, these functions do not satisfy the *usual* orthogonal relations (§ 2.19) since $\mathrm{ce}_{n,m}$, $\mathrm{ce}_{p,r}$ have different q values, as also have $\mathrm{se}_{n,m}$, $\mathrm{se}_{p,r}$, $n \neq p$, $m \neq r$.

The η integrals in (8) may be evaluated by aid of the following formulae:

$$\frac{1}{\pi} \int_0^{2\pi} \mathrm{ce}_{2n}^2(\eta)\cos 2\eta \, d\eta = A_0^{(2n)}A_2^{(2n)} + \sum_{r=0}^{\infty} A_{2r}^{(2n)}A_{2r+2}^{(2n)} = \Theta_{2n}, \tag{9}$$

$$\frac{1}{\pi} \int_0^{2\pi} \mathrm{ce}_{2n+1}^2(\eta)\cos 2\eta \, d\eta = \tfrac{1}{2}[A_1^{(2n+1)}]^2 + \sum_{r=0}^{\infty} A_{2r+1}^{(2n+1)}A_{2r+3}^{(2n+1)} = \Theta_{2n+1}, \tag{10}$$

$$\frac{1}{\pi} \int_0^{2\pi} \mathrm{se}_{2n+1}^2(\eta)\cos 2\eta \, d\eta = -\tfrac{1}{2}[B_1^{(2n+1)}]^2 + \sum_{r=0}^{\infty} B_{2r+1}^{(2n+1)}B_{2r+3}^{(2n+1)} = \Psi_{2n+1}, \tag{11}$$

$$\frac{1}{\pi} \int_0^{2\pi} \mathrm{se}_{2n+2}^2(\eta)\cos 2\eta \, d\eta = \sum_{r=0}^{\infty} B_{2r+2}^{(2n+2)}B_{2r+4}^{(2n+2)} = \Psi_{2n+2}. \tag{12}$$

Those parts of the ξ integrals involving $\cosh 2\xi$ may be expressed in terms of derivatives by aid of (7) § 14.21.

INTEGRAL EQUATIONS AND RELATIONS

10.10. Definition. The equation

$$y(z) = \lambda \int_a^b \chi(u,z)y(u)\,du, \qquad (1)$$

in which $\chi(u,z)$ is a known function of the variables u, z, and λ a particular constant, is called a homogeneous linear integral equation for the unknown function $y(u)$. $\chi(u,z)$ is termed the nucleus or kernel, and it is symmetrical if $\chi(u,z) = \chi(z,u)$, e.g. $e^{-uz} = e^{-zu}$. The equation has a continuous solution only for a discrete set of values of λ. These are called the characteristic values of the nucleus. The nuclei with which we shall deal herein are continuous and symmetrical in u, z, except in § 10.30 et seq.

THEOREM. Let

1°. $\phi(u)$, $\phi'(u)$, $\phi''(u)$ be continuous with period π or 2π, such that $\phi'' + (a - 2k^2 \cos 2u)\phi = 0$;

2°. $\chi(u,z)$, $\chi'_{u,z}$, $\chi''_{u,z}$ be continuous in u, z, such that

$$(a) \quad [\phi\chi'_u - \phi'_u\chi]_{u=0}^{u=2\pi} = 0,$$

$$(b) \quad \frac{\partial^2\chi}{\partial u^2} - \frac{\partial^2\chi}{\partial z^2} - 2k^2(\cos 2u - \cos 2z)\chi = 0,\dagger$$

then

$$y(z) = \lambda \int_0^{2\pi} \chi(u,z)\phi(u)\,du \qquad (1)$$

satisfies Mathieu's equation.

Proof. By (1)

$$\frac{d^2y}{dz^2} + (a - 2k^2\cos 2z)y = \lambda \int_0^{2\pi} \left[\frac{\partial^2\chi}{\partial z^2} - (2k^2\cos 2z)\chi\right]\phi\,du + \lambda a \int_0^{2\pi}\chi\phi\,du \qquad (2)$$

$$= \lambda \int_0^{2\pi} \frac{\partial^2\chi}{\partial u^2}\phi\,du + \lambda \int_0^{2\pi}(a - 2k^2\cos 2u)\chi\phi\,du \qquad (3)$$

---

† This is the wave equation $\dfrac{\partial^2\chi}{\partial u^2} + \dfrac{\partial^2\chi}{\partial z^2} + 2k^2(\cosh 2u - \cos 2z)\chi = 0$ expressed in the modified elliptical coordinates $x = h\cos u\cos z$, $y = ih\sin u\sin z$, i.e. iu is written for u.

by $2^\circ (b)$. Now

$$\int_0^{2\pi} \phi \frac{\partial^2 \chi}{\partial u^2} \, du = \int_0^{2\pi} \phi \, d(\chi_u') = [\phi \chi_u']_0^{2\pi} - \int_0^{2\pi} \phi' \, d\chi \tag{4}$$

$$= [\phi \chi_u' - \phi_u' \chi]_0^{2\pi} + \int_0^{2\pi} \phi'' \chi \, du. \tag{5}$$

By hypothesis [ ] vanishes, so

$$\int_0^{2\pi} \phi \frac{\partial^2 \chi}{\partial u^2} \, du = \int_0^{2\pi} \frac{\partial^2 \phi}{\partial u^2} \chi \, du. \tag{6}$$

Substituting from (6) into the r.h.s. of (3) leads to

$$\frac{d^2 y}{dz^2} + (a - 2k^2 \cos 2z)y = \lambda \int_0^{2\pi} \left[\frac{d^2 \phi}{du^2} + (a - 2k^2 \cos 2u)\phi \right] \chi \, du$$

$$= 0, \quad \text{by hypothesis.} \tag{7}$$

Hence $y(z)$ satisfies Mathieu's equation.

If $\chi(u, z)$ is periodic in u, z, with period π, 2π, $y(u)$ has the same period as $\phi(u)$, so $\phi(u) = \lambda_0 y(u)$. Accordingly we have the homogeneous linear integral equation of the first kind for the periodic functions $ce_m(z, q)$, $se_m(z, q)$, namely,

$$y(z) = \lambda_0 \int_0^{2\pi} \chi(u, z)y(u) \, du. \tag{8}$$

If $[\phi \chi_u' - \phi_u' \chi]_0^\pi = 0$, the upper limit in (8) may be π.

The theorem is valid for $Ce_m(z, q)$, $Se_m(z, q)$ if for z we write iz in (1), so that y satisfies $y'' - (a - 2k^2 \cosh 2z)y = 0$.

10.11. The eight primary nuclei for $ce_m(z, q)$, $se_m(z, q)$. We commence with the wave equation

$$\frac{\partial^2 \chi}{\partial x^2} + \frac{\partial^2 \chi}{\partial y^2} + k_1^2 \chi = 0, \tag{1}$$

where $k_1 h = 2k$. By substitution we confirm that simple solutions are: $\chi = e^{ik_1 x}$, $e^{ik_1 y}$, $ye^{ik_1 x}$, and $xe^{ik_1 y}$. The real and imaginary parts of these functions are separate solutions, so we obtain the eight given in Table 13.

TABLE 13

Solutions of (1)	
$\cos k_1 x$	$\cos k_1 y$
$\sin k_1 x$	$x \cos k_1 y$
$\sin k_1 y$	$y \cos k_1 x$
$y \sin k_1 x$	$x \sin k_1 y$

In modified elliptical coordinates, $x = h \cos u \cos z$, $y = ih \sin u \sin z$, and by §9.20, (1) may be transformed to

$$\frac{\partial^2 \chi}{\partial u^2} - \frac{\partial^2 \chi}{\partial z^2} - 2k^2(\cos 2u - \cos 2z)\chi = 0, \qquad (2)$$

which is (b) 2° §10.10. Substituting for x, y from above in Table 13 and omitting the multiplier i, we obtain eight primary solutions of (2). These are the eight primary nuclei $\chi(u, z)$, and they may be used in (8) §10.10 with the upper limit π. They are set out in Table 14.

TABLE 14. *The eight primary nuclei for* $ce_m(z, q)$, $se_m(z, q)$, $q > 0$

	$\chi(u, z) = $ *nucleus of* (8) § 10.10, *and a solution of* (2)					$y(z)$
1	$\cos(2k \cos u \cos z)$	λ_{2n}	1′	$\cosh(2k \sin u \sin z)$	λ'_{2n}	$ce_{2n}(z, q)$
2	$\sin(2k \cos u \cos z)$	λ_{2n+1}	2′	$\cos u \cos z \times$ $\times \cosh(2k \sin u \sin z)$	λ'_{2n+1}	$ce_{2n+1}(z, q)$
3	$\sinh(2k \sin u \sin z)$	μ_{2n+1}	3′	$\sin u \sin z \times$ $\times \cos(2k \cos u \cos z)$	μ'_{2n+1}	$se_{2n+1}(z, q)$
4	$\sin u \sin z \times$ $\times \sin(2k \cos u \cos z)$	μ_{2n+2}	4′	$\cos u \cos z \times$ $\times \sinh(2k \sin u \sin z)$	μ'_{2n+2}	$se_{2n+2}(z, q)$

Each nucleus in Table 14 is symmetrical and periodic in u, z. (1), (4) have period π, while (2), (3) have period 2π. The functions $y(z)$ are allocated to their respective nuclei by considering periodicity, evenness, and oddness. Since $ce_m(z, q)$, $se_m(z, q)$ satisfy a homogeneous linear integral equation with a symmetrical nucleus, it follows that they are orthogonal [215] (see also § 2.19).

We have now to derive the characteristic values λ_m, μ_m corresponding to various nuclei. This may be effected by aid of Bessel series for the Mathieu functions, as shown hereafter.

10.12. Bessel function expansions. Inserting nucleus 1 Table 14, § 10.11 and $ce_{2n}(u, q)$ in (8) § 10.10, with limits 0, π, we get

$$ce_{2n}(z, q) = \lambda_{2n} \int_0^\pi \cos(2k \cos u \cos z)ce_{2n}(u)\, du \qquad (a_{2n}). \qquad (1)$$

Substituting the expansions of the circular [202, p. 43] and Mathieu functions, (1) becomes

$$\mathrm{ce}_{2n}(z,q) = \lambda_{2n} \int_0^\pi \left[J_0(2k\cos z) + 2\sum_{r=1}^\infty (-1)^r J_{2r}(2k\cos z)\cos 2ru \right] \times$$
$$\times \sum_{s=0}^\infty A_{2s}^{(2n)} \cos 2su \, du. \quad (2)$$

Consider any r in the first Σ. By virtue of orthogonality of the circular functions, all integrals vanish save when $r = s$. Thus we get

$$(-1)^r 2\lambda_{2n} J_{2r}(2k\cos z) A_{2r}^{(2n)} \int_0^\pi \cos^2 2ru \, du$$
$$= (-1)^r \lambda_{2n} \pi A_{2r}^{(2n)} J_{2r}(2k\cos z). \quad (3)$$

Hence the expansion of the Mathieu function in B.F. is

$$\mathrm{ce}_{2n}(z,q) = \lambda_{2n} \pi \sum_{r=0}^\infty (-1)^r A_{2r}^{(2n)} J_{2r}(2k\cos z). \quad (4)$$

By $2°$ § 8.50, the r.h.s. of (4) is absolutely and uniformly convergent in any closed rectangle of the z-plane, k^2 real > 0. Since the r.h.s. represents $\mathrm{ce}_{2n}(z,q)$, it and also (1) is a solution of

$$y'' + (a - 2q\cos 2z)y = 0,$$

$q > 0$, $a = a_{2n}$. This remark applies as well to the integral equations and their expansions for $\mathrm{ce}_{2n+1}(z,q)$, $\mathrm{se}_m(z,q)$, with $q > 0$, $a = a_{2n+1}$, b_m, respectively, given in later sections.

Determination of λ_{2n}. In (4) put $z = \frac{1}{2}\pi$, then $\cos z = 0$, and all the J vanish except $J_0(0) = 1$. Therefore

$$\lambda_{2n} = \mathrm{ce}_{2n}(\tfrac{1}{2}\pi, q)/\pi A_0^{(2n)} = \sum_{r=0}^\infty (-1)^r A_{2r}^{(2n)}/\pi A_0^{(2n)}, \quad (5)$$

so λ_{2n} is a function of q. Using the tabular values of the A, we have for $n = 2$, $q = 8$,

$$\mathrm{ce}_4(\tfrac{1}{2}\pi, 8) \simeq \sum_{r=0}^8 (-1)^r A_{2r}^{(4)} = 0\cdot24703\ 39 - 0\cdot59450\ 88 +$$
$$+ 0\cdot63941\ 57 + 0\cdot33453\ 00 + 0\cdot06089\ 34 + 0\cdot00607\ 17 +$$
$$+ 0\cdot00039\ 05 + 0\cdot00001\ 77 + 0\cdot00000\ 06$$
$$= 0\cdot69384\ 47.† \quad (6)$$

Hence by (5), (6) we get

$$\lambda_4 = 0\cdot69384\ 47/\pi \times 0\cdot24703\ 39 = 0\cdot89275... \quad (7)$$

when $q = 8$.

† This may be obtained from [95] to five decimal places.

10.13. Exponential nucleus. We shall now demonstrate that

$$\mathrm{ce}_{2n}(z, q) = \lambda_{2n} \int_0^{\pi} e^{2ik\cos u \cos z}\, \mathrm{ce}_{2n}(u)\, du \quad (a_{2n}). \tag{1}$$

To do so, we merely need to prove that its imaginary part vanishes, since by (1) § 10.12 its real part represents $\mathrm{ce}_{2n}(z, q)$. Then

$$\text{Imag. part} = \lambda_{2n} \int_0^{\pi} 2 \sum_{m=0}^{\infty} (-1)^m J_{2m+1}(2k\cos z)\cos(2m+1)u\; \mathrm{ce}_{2n}(u)\, du, \tag{2}$$

and this vanishes by virtue of the orthogonality of the circular functions. In the same way it may be shown that integral equations in the sections below can have exponential nuclei. Either the real or the imaginary part of the integral vanishes, as the case may be.

10.14. Bessel series for $\mathrm{ce}_{2n+1}(z, q)$. Using this function and nucleus 2, Table 14, § 10.11 in (8) § 10.10, a repetition of the analysis in § 10.12 yields

$$\mathrm{ce}_{2n+1}(z, q) = \lambda_{2n+1} \pi \sum_{r=0}^{\infty} (-1)^r A_{2r+1}^{(2n+1)} J_{2r+1}(2k\cos z) \quad (a_{2n+1}). \tag{1}$$

By 2° § 8.50 this series is absolutely and uniformly convergent in any closed rectangle of the z-plane, k^2 real > 0, as also is its first derivative. Consequently term-by-term differentiation is permissible, so

$$\mathrm{ce}'_{2n+1}(z, q) = -\lambda_{2n+1}\, 2\pi k \sin z \times$$

$$\times \sum_{r=0}^{\infty} (-1)^r A_{2r+1}^{(2n+1)}[d\, J_{2r+1}(2k\cos z)/d(2k\cos z)]. \tag{2}$$

Now $J'_m(u) = \frac{1}{2}[J_{m-1}(u) - J_{m+1}(u)]$, and since $J_p(0) = 0$ if $p \neq 0$, when $z = \frac{1}{2}\pi$, the only non-zero term is $\frac{1}{2}J_0(0) = \frac{1}{2}$. Thus

$$\mathrm{ce}'_{2n+1}(\tfrac{1}{2}\pi, q) = -\pi k A_1^{(2n+1)} \lambda_{2n+1}, \tag{3}$$

so

$$\lambda_{2n+1} = -\mathrm{ce}'_{2n+1}(\tfrac{1}{2}\pi, q)/\pi k A_1^{(2n+1)} = \sum_{r=0}^{\infty} (-1)^r (2r+1) A_{2r+1}^{(2n+1)}/\pi k A_1^{(2n+1)}. \tag{4}$$

10.15. Additional expansions. Using nuclei 1′, 3 from Table 14 § 10.11 and proceeding as in §§ 10.12, 10.14, we find that

$$\mathrm{ce}_{2n}(z, q) = \lambda'_{2n} \pi \sum_{r=0}^{\infty} (-1)^r A_{2r}^{(2n)} I_{2r}(2k\sin z) \quad (a_{2n}), \tag{1}$$

with
$$\lambda'_{2n} = \frac{1}{\pi A_0^{(2n)}} \sum_{r=0}^{\infty} A_{2r}^{(2n)} = \frac{ce_{2n}(0,q)}{\pi A_0^{(2n)}}; \qquad (2)$$

$$se_{2n+1}(z,q) = \mu_{2n+1} \pi \sum_{r=0}^{\infty} (-1)^r B_{2r+1}^{(2n+1)} I_{2r+1}(2k \sin z) \qquad (3)$$

with
$$\mu_{2n+1} = \frac{1}{\pi k B_1^{(2n+1)}} \sum_{r=0}^{\infty} (2r+1) B_{2r+1}^{(2n+1)} = \frac{se'_{2n+1}(0,q)}{\pi k B_1^{(2n+1)}}. \qquad (4)$$

10.16. Determination of μ_{2n+2}, λ'_{2n+1}, μ'_{2n+1}, μ'_{2n+2}. If we select μ_{2n+2}, the integral equation, using nucleus 4, Table 14, is

$$se_{2n+2}(z,q) = \mu_{2n+2} \int_0^{\pi} \sin u \sin z \sin(2k \cos u \cos z) \times$$
$$\times se_{2n+2}(u,q)\, du \quad (b_{2n+2}) \quad (1)$$

$$= 2\mu_{2n+2} \int_0^{\pi} \sin u \sin z \sum_{r=0}^{\infty} (-1)^r J_{2r+1}(2k \cos z)\cos(2r+1)u \times$$
$$\times \sum_{s=0}^{\infty} B_{2s+2}^{(2n+2)} \sin(2s+2)u\, du \quad (2)$$

$$= \mu_{2n+2} \int_0^{\pi} \sin z \sum_{r=0}^{\infty} (-1)^r J_{2r+1}(2k \cos z)\cos(2r+1)u \times$$
$$\times \sum_{s=0}^{\infty} B_{2s+2}^{(2n+2)}[\cos(2s+1)u - \cos(2s+3)u]\, du \quad (3)$$

$$= \mu_{2n+2} \tfrac{1}{2}\pi \sin z \times$$
$$\times \sum_{r=0}^{\infty} (-1)^r B_{2r+2}^{(2n+2)}[J_{2r+1}(2k \cos z) + J_{2r+3}(2k \cos z)]. \quad (4)$$

Now $\left(\dfrac{2r+2}{u}\right) J_{2r+2}(u) = \tfrac{1}{2}[J_{2r+1}(u) + J_{2r+3}(u)]$, so (4) takes the form

$$se_{2n+2}(z,q) = \mu_{2n+2} \frac{\pi \tan z}{2k} \sum_{r=0}^{\infty} (-1)^r (2r+2) B_{2r+2}^{(2n+2)} J_{2r+2}(2k \cos z). \quad (5)$$

This series and its first derivative is absolutely and uniformly convergent for all finite values of z, k^2 real > 0. Thus term-by-term differentiation with respect to z is valid and we get

$$se'_{2n+2}(z,q) = \mu_{2n+2} \frac{\pi}{2k} \Bigg[\sum_{r=0}^{\infty} (-1)^r (2r+2) B_{2r+2}^{(2n+2)}\{\sec^2 z\, J_{2r+2}(2k \cos z) -$$
$$- k \tan z \sin z [J_{2r+1}(2k \cos z) - J_{2r+3}(2k \cos z)]\} \Bigg]. \quad (6)$$

As $z \to \frac{1}{2}\pi$ all terms vanish except $\sec^2 z\, J_2(2k\cos z) \to \frac{1}{2}k^2$ and $-k\tan z\sin z\, J_1(2k\cos z) \to -k^2$. Hence

$$\mathrm{se}'_{2n+2}(\tfrac{1}{2}\pi, q) = -\mu_{2n+2}\frac{\pi}{2}kB_2^{(2n+2)}, \tag{7}$$

so

$$\mu_{2n+2} = -2\,\mathrm{se}'_{2n+2}(\tfrac{1}{2}\pi, q)/\pi k B_2^{(2n+2)} \tag{8}$$

$$= \frac{2}{\pi k B_2^{(2n+2)}}\sum_{r=0}^{\infty}(-1)^r(2r+2)B_{2r+2}^{(2n+2)}. \tag{9}$$

For the remaining nuclei in Table 14 § 10.11, we obtain

$$\mathrm{ce}_{2n+1}(z, q) = \lambda'_{2n+1}\frac{\pi\cot z}{2k}\times$$

$$\times\sum_{r=0}^{\infty}(-1)^r(2r+1)A_{2r+1}^{(2n+1)}I_{2r+1}(2k\sin z)\quad(a_{2n+1}),\tag{10}$$

with

$$\lambda'_{2n+1} = \frac{2\,\mathrm{ce}_{2n+1}(0, q)}{\pi A_1^{(2n+1)}} = \frac{2}{\pi A_1^{(2n+1)}}\sum_{r=0}^{\infty}A_{2r+1}^{(2n+1)}.\tag{11}$$

$$\mathrm{se}_{2n+1}(z, q) = \mu'_{2n+1}\frac{\pi\tan z}{2k}\times$$

$$\times\sum_{r=0}^{\infty}(-1)^r(2r+1)B_{2r+1}^{(2n+1)}J_{2r+1}(2k\cos z)\quad(b_{2n+1}),\tag{12}$$

with

$$\mu'_{2n+1} = \frac{2\,\mathrm{se}_{2n+1}(\tfrac{1}{2}\pi, q)}{\pi B_1^{(2n+1)}} = \frac{2}{\pi B_1^{(2n+1)}}\sum_{r=0}^{\infty}(-1)^r B_{2r+1}^{(2n+1)}.\tag{13}$$

$$\mathrm{se}_{2n+2}(z, q) = \mu'_{2n+2}\frac{\pi\cot z}{2k}\times$$

$$\times\sum_{r=0}^{\infty}(-1)^r(2r+2)B_{2r+2}^{(2n+2)}I_{2r+2}(2k\sin z)\quad(b_{2n+2}),\tag{14}$$

with

$$\mu'_{2n+2} = \frac{2\,\mathrm{se}'_{2n+2}(0, q)}{\pi k B_2^{(2n+2)}} = \frac{2}{\pi k B_2^{(2n+2)}}\sum_{r=0}^{\infty}(2r+2)B_{2r+2}^{(2n+2)}.\tag{15}$$

By 2^0 § 8.50 all series in § 10.15 and the present section are absolutely and uniformly convergent in any closed rectangle of the z-plane, $k^2 = q$ real > 0.

The characteristic values in Table 15 are expressed in terms of the coefficients in the series for the corresponding Mathieu functions. By § 3.21 the sigma terms are absolutely convergent in $0 \leqslant q \leqslant q_0$. By § 3.25 the A, B are continuous functions of q, and by § 3.30 $A_0^{(2n)}$, $A_1^{(2n+1)}$, $B_1^{(2n+1)}$, $B_2^{(2n+2)}$ have no zeros in $q > 0$, but tend to zero monotonically as $q \to +\infty$. λ_0, $\lambda'_0 \to 1/\pi$ and λ'_1, $\mu'_1 \to 2/\pi$ as $q \to 0$, and are continuous in $0 \leqslant q \leqslant q_0$. For $n > 0$, λ_{2n}, λ'_{2n}, λ'_{2n+1}, μ'_{2n+1},

TABLE 15. *Characteristic values for the nuclei in Table* 14

$\lambda_{2n} = \dfrac{\text{ce}_{2n}(\frac{1}{2}\pi, q)}{\pi A_0^{(2n)}}$	$\lambda'_{2n} = \dfrac{\text{ce}_{2n}(0, q)}{\pi A_0^{(2n)}}$	$\text{ce}_{2n}(z, q)$
$= \dfrac{\displaystyle\sum_{r=0}^{\infty} (-1)^r A_{2r}^{(2n)}}{\pi A_0^{(2n)}}$	$= \dfrac{\displaystyle\sum_{r=0}^{\infty} A_{2r}^{(2n)}}{\pi A_0^{(2n)}}$	
$\lambda_{2n+1} = -\dfrac{\text{ce}'_{2n+1}(\frac{1}{2}\pi, q)}{\pi k A_1^{(2n+1)}}$	$\lambda'_{2n+1} = \dfrac{2\,\text{ce}_{2n+1}(0, q)}{\pi A_1^{(2n+1)}}$	$\text{ce}_{2n+1}(z, q)$
$= \dfrac{\displaystyle\sum_{r=0}^{\infty} (-1)^r(2r+1)A_{2r+1}^{(2n+1)}}{\pi k A_1^{(2n+1)}}$	$= \dfrac{2\displaystyle\sum_{r=0}^{\infty} A_{2r+1}^{(2n+1)}}{\pi A_1^{(2n+1)}}$	
$\mu_{2n+1} = \dfrac{\text{se}'_{2n+1}(0, q)}{\pi k B_1^{(2n+1)}}$	$\mu'_{2n+1} = \dfrac{2\,\text{se}_{2n+1}(\frac{1}{2}\pi, q)}{\pi B_1^{(2n+1)}}$	$\text{se}_{2n+1}(z, q)$
$= \dfrac{\displaystyle\sum_{r=0}^{\infty} (2r+1)B_{2r+1}^{(2n+1)}}{\pi k B_1^{(2n+1)}}$	$= \dfrac{2\displaystyle\sum_{r=0}^{\infty} (-1)^r B_{2r+1}^{(2n+1)}}{\pi B_1^{(2n+1)}}$	
$\mu_{2n+2} = -\dfrac{2\,\text{se}'_{2n+2}(\frac{1}{2}\pi, q)}{\pi k B_2^{(2n+2)}}$	$\mu'_{2n+2} = \dfrac{2\,\text{se}'_{2n+2}(0, q)}{\pi k B_2^{(2n+2)}}$	$\text{se}_{2n+2}(z, q)$
$= -\dfrac{2\displaystyle\sum_{r=0}^{\infty} (-1)^r(2r+2)B_{2r+2}^{(2n+2)}}{\pi k B_2^{(2n+2)}}$	$= \dfrac{2\displaystyle\sum_{r=0}^{\infty} (2r+2)B_{2r+2}^{(2n+2)}}{\pi k B_2^{(2n+2)}}$	

and for $n \geqslant 0$, λ_{2n+1}, μ_{2n+1}, μ_{2n+2}, μ'_{2n+2} are continuous, $0 < q \leqslant q_0$. The discontinuity in each of the first set at $q = 0$ is due to vanishing of the coefficient in the denominator. That in each of the second set arises from the factor $k^{-1} = q^{-\frac{1}{2}}$, and for $n > 0$ to vanishing of the coefficient in the denominator. The form of the latter may be derived from the general result (9) § 3.33. Thus as $q \to 0$, we obtain

$$A_0^{(2n)} \simeq q^n/2^{2n-1}(2n)!; \qquad B_2^{(2n+2)} \simeq (n+1)q^n/2^{2n}(2n+1)!; \quad (16)$$

$$A_1^{(2n+1)} \simeq B_1^{(2n+1)} \simeq q^n/2^{2n}(2n)! \qquad (17)$$

The reciprocal of each coefficient has an infinity of order n at $q = 0$.

TABLE 16. *Illustrating behaviour of characteristic values as*
$q \to 0$

Characteristic value	Behaviour as $q \to 0$	Characteristic value	Behaviour as $q \to 0$
λ_{2n}	$\to \infty, n > 0$	λ'_{2n}	$\to \infty, n > 0$
λ_{2n+1}	$\to \infty$	λ'_{2n+1}	$\to \infty, n > 0$
μ_{2n+1}	$\to \infty$	μ'_{2n+1}	$\to \infty, n > 0$
μ_{2n+2}	$\to \infty$	μ'_{2n+2}	$\to \infty$

10.17. Theorem on integral relations. If $y(u)$ is a Mathieu function of period π or 2π; $\chi(u,z)$ the corresponding nucleus for the integral equation; $\xi_u'(u,z) = \chi(u,z)$, so that $\xi(u,z) = \int^u \chi(u,z)\,du$ and $[y(u)\xi(u,z)]_{u=0}^{u=\pi} = 0$, then

$$y(z) = -\lambda \int_0^\pi \left[\int^u \chi(u,z)\,du \right] y'(u)\,du. \tag{1}$$

Proof. Substituting for χ into (8) §10.10, we get

$$y(z)/\lambda = \int_0^\pi \xi_u'(u,z)y(u)\,du = \int_0^\pi y(u)\,d[\xi(u,z)]_u \tag{2}$$

$$= [y(u)\xi(u,z)]_{u=0}^{u=\pi} - \int_0^\pi \xi(u,z)y'(u)\,du, \tag{3}$$

so

$$y(z) = -\lambda \int_0^\pi \left[\int^u \chi(u,z)\,du \right] y'(u)\,du, \tag{4}$$

since the first member on the r.h.s. of (3) vanishes, by hypothesis.

10.18. Example. To illustrate the application of (4) §10.17, we take nucleus 4 in Table 14 §10.11, namely,

$$\chi(u,z) = \sin u \sin z \sin(2k \cos u \cos z)$$

with $y(u) = \mathrm{se}_{2n+2}(u,q)$. Then

$$\xi(u,z) = \int^u \chi(u,z)\,du = -\frac{\tan z}{2k} \int^u \sin(2k \cos u \cos z)\,d(2k \cos u \cos z) \tag{1}$$

$$= \frac{\tan z}{2k} \cos(2k \cos u \cos z). \tag{2}$$

But $[y(u)\xi(u,z)]_{u=0}^{u=\pi} = 0$, so

$$\cot z\, \mathrm{se}_{2n+2}(z,q)$$

$$= -\frac{\lambda}{2k} \int_0^\pi \cos(2k \cos u \cos z)\mathrm{se}_{2n+2}'(u)\,du \tag{3}$$

$$= -\frac{\lambda}{2k} \int_0^\pi \left[J_0(2k \cos z) + 2\sum_{r=0}^\infty (-1)^{r+1} J_{2r+2}(2k \cos z)\cos(2r+2)u \right] \times$$

$$\times \sum_{s=0}^\infty (2s+2)B_{2s+2}^{(2n+2)} \cos(2s+2)u\,du \tag{4}$$

$$= \frac{\pi\lambda}{2k} \sum_{r=0}^\infty (-1)^r (2r+2)B_{2r+2}^{(2n+2)} J_{2r+2}(2k \cos z). \tag{5}$$

Comparison with (5) § 10.16 shows that $\lambda = \mu_{2n+2}$, so from (3) and (1) § 10.16 we get

$$2k \int_0^\pi \sin u \cos z \sin(2k \cos u \cos z) \mathrm{se}_{2n+2}(u, q) \, du$$

$$= - \int_0^\pi \cos(2k \cos u \cos z) \mathrm{se}'_{2n+2}(u, q) \, du. \quad (6)$$

The integral relations given below may be derived by analysis akin to that above.

$$\tan z \, \mathrm{ce}_{2n+1}(z, q) = -\frac{\lambda'_{2n+1}}{2k} \int_0^\pi \sinh(2k \sin u \sin z) \mathrm{ce}'_{2n+1}(u, q) \, du, \quad (7)$$

$$\cot z \, \mathrm{se}_{2n+1}(z, q) = \frac{\mu'_{2n+1}}{2k} \int_0^\pi \sin(2k \cos u \cos z) \mathrm{se}'_{2n+1}(u, q) \, du, \quad (8)$$

$$\tan z \, \mathrm{se}_{2n+2}(z, q) = -\frac{\mu'_{2n+2}}{2k} \int_0^\pi \cosh(2k \sin u \sin z) \mathrm{se}'_{2n+2}(u, q) \, du. \quad (9)$$

10.19. Formulae for $\mathrm{ce}_m(z, -q)$, $\mathrm{se}_m(z, -q)$. These functions are solutions of the equation $y'' + (a + 2q \cos 2z)y = 0$. Thus the required formulae may be derived from those in preceding sections by aid of § 2.18. The values of q and k remain as before, i.e. $q > 0$.

10.20. Integral relations for $\mathrm{Ce}_m(z, q)$, $\mathrm{Se}_m(z, q)$. These are derived by applying the relationships in (2)–(5) § 2.30 to the integral equations for $\mathrm{ce}_m(z, q)$, $\mathrm{se}_m(z, q)$ in § 10.12 et seq. Thus

$\mathrm{Ce}_{2n}(z, q)$

$$= \frac{\mathrm{ce}_{2n}(\frac{1}{2}\pi, q)}{\pi A_0^{(2n)}} \int_0^\pi \cos(2k \cos u \cosh z) \mathrm{ce}_{2n}(u, q) \, du \quad (1)$$

$$= \frac{\mathrm{ce}_{2n}(0, q)}{\pi A_0^{(2n)}} \int_0^\pi \cos(2k \sin u \sinh z) \mathrm{ce}_{2n}(u, q) \, du; \quad (2)$$

$\mathrm{Ce}_{2n+1}(z, q)$

$$= -\frac{\mathrm{ce}'_{2n+1}(\frac{1}{2}\pi, q)}{\pi k A_1^{(2n+1)}} \int_0^\pi \sin(2k \cos u \cosh z) \mathrm{ce}_{2n+1}(u, q) \, du \quad (3)$$

$$= \frac{2 \mathrm{ce}_{2n+1}(0, q)}{\pi A_1^{(2n+1)}} \int_0^\pi \cos u \cosh z \cos(2k \sin u \sinh z) \mathrm{ce}_{2n+1}(u, q) \, du; \quad (4)$$

$\mathrm{Se}_{2n+1}(z, q)$

$$= \frac{2 \, \mathrm{se}_{2n+1}(\frac{1}{2}\pi, q)}{\pi B_1^{(2n+1)}} \int_0^\pi \sin u \sinh z \cos(2k \cos u \cosh z) \mathrm{se}_{2n+1}(u, q) \, du \quad (5)$$

$$= \frac{\mathrm{se}'_{2n+1}(0, q)}{\pi k B_1^{(2n+1)}} \int_0^\pi \sin(2k \sin u \sinh z) \mathrm{se}_{2n+1}(u, q) \, du; \quad (6)$$

$\mathrm{Se}_{2n+2}(z, q)$

$$= -\frac{2 \, \mathrm{se}'_{2n+2}(\frac{1}{2}\pi, q)}{\pi k B_2^{(2n+2)}} \int_0^\pi \sin u \sinh z \sin(2k \cos u \cosh z) \mathrm{se}_{2n+2}(u, q) \, du \quad (7)$$

$$= \frac{2 \, \mathrm{se}'_{2n+2}(0, q)}{\pi k B_2^{(2n+2)}} \int_0^\pi \cos u \cosh z \sin(2k \sin u \sinh z) \mathrm{se}_{2n+2}(u, q) \, du. \quad (8)$$

The evaluations of (1)–(8) are given at (15), (17) § 8.10; (1), (2) § 8.12; (6), (7), (10), (11) § 8.13, respectively. From § 10.18 and Table 15 § 10.16 additional relations in which ce'_{2n+1}, se'_{2n+1}, se'_{2n+2} appear under the integral sign may be written down. All the above representations of the modified Mathieu functions are first solutions of (1) § 2.30, provided a has its proper value.

10.21. Integral relations for $\mathrm{Ce}_m(z, -q)$, $\mathrm{Se}_m(z, -q)$. These may be derived from (1)–(8) § 10.20 by applying the definitions (1), (11), (21), (31), § 8.30. Thus

$\mathrm{Ce}_{2n}(z, -q)$

$$= \frac{(-1)^n \, \mathrm{ce}_{2n}(\frac{1}{2}\pi, q)}{\pi A_0^{(2n)}} \int_0^\pi \cosh(2k \cos u \sinh z) \mathrm{ce}_{2n}(u, q) \, du \quad (1)$$

$$= \frac{(-1)^n \, \mathrm{ce}_{2n}(0, q)}{\pi A_0^{(2n)}} \int_0^\pi \cosh(2k \sin u \cosh z) \mathrm{ce}_{2n}(u, q) \, du; \quad (2)$$

$\mathrm{Ce}_{2n+1}(z, -q)$

$$= \frac{(-1)^n \, 2 \, \mathrm{se}_{2n+1}(\frac{1}{2}\pi, q)}{\pi B_1^{(2n+1)}} \int_0^\pi \sin u \cosh z \cosh(2k \cos u \sinh z) \mathrm{se}_{2n+1}(u, q) \, du \quad (3)$$

$$= \frac{(-1)^n \, \mathrm{se}'_{2n+1}(0, q)}{\pi k B_1^{(2n+1)}} \int_0^\pi \sinh(2k \sin u \cosh z) \mathrm{se}_{2n+1}(u, q) \, du; \quad (4)$$

$\mathrm{Se}_{2n+1}(z, -q)$

$$= \frac{(-1)^{n+1} \mathrm{ce}'_{2n+1}(\frac{1}{2}\pi, q)}{\pi k A_1^{(2n+1)}} \int_0^\pi \sinh(2k \cos u \sinh z) \mathrm{ce}_{2n+1}(u, q)\, du \qquad (5)$$

$$= \frac{(-1)^n 2\, \mathrm{ce}_{2n+1}(0, q)}{\pi A_1^{(2n+1)}} \int_0^\pi \cos u \sinh z \cosh(2k \sin u \cosh z) \mathrm{ce}_{2n+1}(u, q)\, du; \qquad (6)$$

$\mathrm{Se}_{2n+2}(z, -q)$

$$= \frac{(-1)^{n+1} 2\, \mathrm{se}'_{2n+2}(\frac{1}{2}\pi, q)}{\pi k B_2^{(2n+2)}} \int_0^\pi \sin u \cosh z \sinh(2k \cos u \sinh z) \mathrm{se}_{2n+2}(u, q)\, du \qquad (7)$$

$$= \frac{(-1)^n 2\, \mathrm{se}'_{2n+2}(0, q)}{\pi k B_2^{(2n+2)}} \int_0^\pi \cos u \sinh z \sinh(2k \sin u \cosh z) \mathrm{se}_{2n+2}(u, q)\, du. \qquad (8)$$

The evaluations of (1)–(8) are given at (2), (3), (12), (13), (22), (23), (32), (33) § 8.30. All the representations of the modified Mathieu functions are first solutions of (1) § 2.31, provided a has its proper value.

10.30. Bessel-circular function nuclei. Hitherto our nuclei have been limited to circular and hyperbolic functions. But the wave equation admits of a plurality of solutions, and other nuclei may, therefore, be derived. Any solution expressed in *modified* elliptical coordinates, which satisfies conditions (a), (b), $2°$ § 10.10, may be used as a nucleus for the integral (1) § 10.10.†

We commence by transforming

$$\frac{\partial^2 \chi}{\partial x^2} + \frac{\partial^2 \chi}{\partial y^2} + k_1^2 \chi = 0, \qquad (1)$$

to cylindrical polar coordinates, where $x = r \cos \alpha$, $y = r \sin \alpha$. By established procedure we obtain

$$\frac{\partial^2 \chi}{\partial r^2} + \frac{1}{r}\frac{\partial \chi}{\partial r} + \frac{1}{r^2}\frac{\partial^2 \chi}{\partial \alpha^2} + k_1^2 \chi = 0. \qquad (2)$$

Writing $\chi = U(r)V(\alpha)$ and using analysis akin to that in § 9.21 yields the two ordinary equations

$$\frac{d^2 U}{dr^2} + \frac{1}{r}\frac{dU}{dr} + \left(k_1^2 - \frac{\nu^2}{r^2}\right)U = 0, \qquad (3)$$

and

$$\frac{d^2 V}{d\alpha^2} + \nu^2 V = 0, \qquad (4)$$

† Provided the integral converges.

ν^2 being the separation constant. The formal solutions of (3), (4) are, respectively, $J_\nu(k_1 r)$, $Y_\nu(k_1 r)$; and $\cos \nu\alpha$, $\sin \nu\alpha$. Thus if $J_\nu(k_1 r)\cos \nu\alpha$, $J_\nu(k_1 r)\sin \nu\alpha$, $Y_\nu(k_1 r)\cos \nu\alpha$, $Y_\nu(k_1 r)\sin \nu\alpha$ are expressed in *modified* elliptical coordinates, we get the sets of B.F. nuclei in Table 17. Each nucleus satisfies conditions (a), (b), 2° § 10.10 and the integral (1) § 10.10 converges if due regard is paid to the phase and modulus of z.

TABLE 17. *Bessel-circular function nuclei:* k^2 real > 0

Nucleus $\chi(r,\alpha) = U(r)V(\alpha)$ $(m = 0, 1, 2,...)$	$\phi(u)$	$y(z)$	$y(iz)$	Remarks
1 $J_{2m}(k_1 r)\genfrac{}{}{0pt}{}{\cos}{\sin}(2m\alpha)$	$\genfrac{}{}{0pt}{}{\mathrm{ce}}{\mathrm{se}_{2n}}(u,q)$	$\genfrac{}{}{0pt}{}{\mathrm{ce}}{\mathrm{se}_{2n}}(z,q)$	$\genfrac{}{}{0pt}{}{\mathrm{Ce}}{\mathrm{Se}_{2n}}(z,q)$	$r = h[\frac{1}{2}(\cos 2u + \cos 2z)]^{\frac{1}{2}}$ for $y(z)$; χ in 1, 2, are then periodic and symmetrical in u, z: period π, 2π, respectively. In (3), (4) replace $\cos 2z$ by $\cosh 2z$, $R(z) > 0$. χ in 3, 4, are non-periodic, as also are Fey, Gey (see § 8.11). The nuclei for $y(iz)$ are skew-symmetrical in u, z.
2 $J_{2m+1}(k_1 r)\genfrac{}{}{0pt}{}{\cos}{\sin}(2m+1)\alpha$	$\genfrac{}{}{0pt}{}{\mathrm{ce}}{\mathrm{se}_{2n+1}}(u,q)$	$\genfrac{}{}{0pt}{}{\mathrm{ce}}{\mathrm{se}_{2n+1}}(z,q)$	$\genfrac{}{}{0pt}{}{\mathrm{Ce}}{\mathrm{Se}_{2n+1}}(z,q)$	
3 $Y_{2m}(k_1 r)\genfrac{}{}{0pt}{}{\cos}{\sin}(2m\alpha)$	$\genfrac{}{}{0pt}{}{\mathrm{ce}}{\mathrm{se}_{2n}}(u,q)$	—	$\genfrac{}{}{0pt}{}{\mathrm{Fey}}{\mathrm{Gey}_{2n}}(z,q)$	
4 $Y_{2m+1}(k_1 r)\genfrac{}{}{0pt}{}{\cos}{\sin}(2m+1)\alpha$	$\genfrac{}{}{0pt}{}{\mathrm{ce}}{\mathrm{se}_{2n+1}}(u,q)$	—	$\genfrac{}{}{0pt}{}{\mathrm{Fey}}{\mathrm{Gey}_{2n+1}}(z,q)$	

Formula for r. $r = (x^2 + y^2)^{\frac{1}{2}}$ with

$$x = h \cos u \cos z, \qquad y = ih \sin u \sin z,$$

the modified elliptical coordinates. Thus

$$r = h[\tfrac{1}{2}(\cos 2u + \cos 2z)]^{\frac{1}{2}} \tag{5}$$

and, since $k_1 h = 2k$,

$$k_1 r = k[2(\cos 2u + \cos 2z)]^{\frac{1}{2}}. \tag{6}$$

Y_p has a singularity at the origin, and since $k_1 r$ has zeros when $\cos 2u = -\cos 2z$, (6) cannot be used as the argument of the Y function if z is real. Writing iz for z, $R(z) > 0$, there are no zeros (u real), so we obtain the argument for the J, Y functions used in the nuclei for the modified Mathieu functions in column 5, Table 17, i.e.

$$k_1 r = k[2(\cos 2u + \cosh 2z)]^{\frac{1}{2}}. \tag{7}$$

Formulae for $\cos p\alpha$, $\sin p\alpha$. From above,

$$\cos \alpha = x/r = \cos u \cos z/[\tfrac{1}{2}(\cos 2u + \cos 2z)]^{\frac{1}{2}} \tag{8}$$

and

$$\sin \alpha = y/r = i \sin u \sin z/[\tfrac{1}{2}(\cos 2u + \cos 2z)]^{\frac{1}{2}}. \tag{9}$$

Then by de Moivre's theorem

$$(\cos p\alpha + i \sin p\alpha) = (\cos \alpha + i \sin \alpha)^p, \tag{10}$$

so $\cos p\alpha$, $\sin p\alpha$ are obtained by equating real and imaginary parts in (10), and substituting from (8), (9). The remarks in column 6, Table 17, may now be confirmed.

10.31. Hankel-circular function nuclei: k^2 **real** > 0. By (4) § 8.14

$$\text{Fek}_{2n}(z,q) = \tfrac{1}{2}[i\,\text{Ce}_{2n}(z,q) - \text{Fey}_{2n}(z,q)] \quad (a_{2n}), \tag{1}$$

so by Table 17, § 10.30 we see that the nucleus for $\text{Fek}_{2n}(z,q)$ is

$$\tfrac{1}{2}[iJ_{2m}(k_1 r) - Y_{2m}(k_1 r)]\cos 2m\alpha = \tfrac{1}{2}iH^{(1)}_{2m}(k_1 r)\cos 2m\alpha, \tag{2}$$

in which $k_1 r$ is given by (7) § 10.30, with $R(z) > 0$. Other nuclei are set out in Table 18.

TABLE 18. *Hankel-circular function nuclei: k^2 real > 0*

	Nucleus $\chi(r, \alpha)$ $(m = 0, 1, 2, \ldots)$	$\phi(u)$ in (1) § 10.10	$y(z)$ in (1) § 10.10
1	$H^{(1)}_{2m}(k_1 r){\cos \atop \sin}(2m\alpha)$	${\text{ce} \atop \text{se}}_{2n}(u, q)$	${\text{Fek} \atop \text{Gek}}_{2n}(z, q)$
2	$H^{(1)}_{2m+1}(k_1 r){\cos \atop \sin}(2m+1)\alpha$	${\text{ce} \atop \text{se}}_{2n+1}(u, q)$	${\text{Fek} \atop \text{Gek}}_{2n+1}(z, q)$

The Hankel function may be expressed in terms of the K-Bessel function by the relationship (1) § 8.14.

10.32. Nuclei for k^2 **real** < 0. Here we write $-k_1^2$ for k_1^2 in (3) § 10.30: (4) § 10.30 is unchanged. The formal solutions of (3) § 10.30 are now the modified B.F. $I_\nu(k_1 r)$ and $K_\nu(k_1 r)$. Hence we have the nuclei $I_\nu(k_1 r)\cos \nu\alpha$, $I_\nu(k_1 r)\sin \nu\alpha$, $K_\nu(k_1 r)\cos \nu\alpha$, and $K_\nu(k_1 r)\sin \nu\alpha$. $Y_\nu(ik_1 r)$ is also a solution of (3) § 10.30, so $Y_\nu(ik_1 r)\cos \nu\alpha$ and $Y_\nu(ik_1 r)\sin \nu\alpha$ may be used as alternative nuclei. The nuclei are set out in Table 19.

TABLE 19. *Bessel-circular function nuclei: k^2 real < 0*

	Nucleus $\chi(r, \alpha)$ $(m = 0, 1, 2, \ldots)$	$\phi(u)$	$y(z)$	$y(iz)$	Remarks
1	$I_{2m}(k_1 r){\cos \atop \sin}(2m\alpha)$	${\text{ce} \atop \text{se}}_{2n}(u, -q)$	${\text{ce} \atop \text{se}}_{2n}(z, -q)$	${\text{Ce} \atop \text{Se}}_{2n}(z, -q)$	Those in Table 17 apply here, *mu-tatis mutandis*.
2	$I_{2m+1}(k_1 r){\cos \atop \sin}(2m+1)\alpha$	${\text{ce} \atop \text{se}}_{2n+1}(u, -q)$	${\text{ce} \atop \text{se}}_{2n+1}(z, -q)$	${\text{Ce} \atop \text{Se}}_{2n+1}(z, -q)$	If $Y(ik_1 r)$ is used in (3), (4), Fey,
3	$K_{2m}(k_1 r){\cos \atop \sin}(2m\alpha)$	${\text{ce} \atop \text{se}}_{2n}(u, -q)$	—	${\text{Fek} \atop \text{Gek}}_{2n}(z, -q)$	Gey are obtained for $y(iz)$.
4	$K_{2m+1}(k_1 r){\cos \atop \sin}(2m+1)\alpha$	${\text{ce} \atop \text{se}}_{2n+1}(u, -q)$	—	${\text{Fek} \atop \text{Gek}}_{2n+1}(z, -q)$	

10.33. Integral equation for $\text{ce}_{2n}(z,q)$ with Bessel nucleus. In 1, Table 17 put $m = 0$, $\phi(u) = \text{ce}_{2n}(u,q)$, and insert χ, ϕ in (8) §10.10 with upper limit π. Then

$$\text{ce}_{2n}(z,q) = \varphi_{2n} \int_0^\pi J_0\{k[2(\cos 2u + \cos 2z)]^{\frac{1}{2}}\}\text{ce}_{2n}(u,q)\,du. \tag{1}$$

To determine φ_{2n}, let $z = 0$, then from (1)

$$\text{ce}_{2n}(0,q) = \varphi_{2n} \int_0^\pi J_0(2k\cos u) \sum_{r=0}^\infty A_{2r}^{(2n)} \cos 2ru\,du. \tag{2}$$

Now by (2) §10.34, with $z = 0$,

$$\int_0^\pi J_0(2k\cos u)\cos 2ru\,du$$

$$= \int_0^\pi \left[J_0^2(k) + 2\sum_{m=1}^\infty (-1)^m J_m^2(k)\cos 2mu \right]\cos 2ru\,du \tag{3}$$

$$= (-1)^r \pi J_r^2(k). \tag{4}$$

Hence from (2), (4) we obtain

$$\varphi_{2n} = \text{ce}_{2n}(0,q) \bigg/ \pi \sum_{r=0}^\infty (-1)^r A_{2r}^{(2n)} J_r^2(k). \tag{5}$$

An alternative expression for φ_{2n} may be derived as follows: Insert the value of λ_{2n} from (5) §10.12 into (4) §10.12 and integrate both sides of the latter with respect to z from 0 to π. Then

$$\int_0^\pi \sum_{r=0}^\infty A_{2r}^{(2n)} \cos 2rz\,dz = \pi A_0^{(2n)}$$

$$= \frac{\text{ce}_{2n}(\tfrac{1}{2}\pi,q)}{A_0^{(2n)}} \int_0^\pi \sum_{r=0}^\infty (-1)^r A_{2r}^{(2n)} J_{2r}(2k\cos z)\,dz \tag{6}$$

$$= \frac{\text{ce}_{2n}(\tfrac{1}{2}\pi,q)}{A_0^{(2n)}}\left[\pi \sum_{r=0}^\infty (-1)^r A_{2r}^{(2n)} J_r^2(k) \right], \tag{7}$$

since $\int_0^\pi J_{2r}(2k\cos z)\,dz = \pi J_r^2(k)$. Thus from (7) we get

$$\sum_{r=0}^\infty (-1)^r A_{2r}^{(2n)} J_r^2(k) = [A_0^{(2n)}]^2 / \text{ce}_{2n}(\tfrac{1}{2}\pi,q). \tag{8}$$

Substituting the r.h.s. of (8) in the denominator of (5) leads to

$$\varphi_{2n} = \text{ce}_{2n}(0,q)\text{ce}_{2n}(\tfrac{1}{2}\pi,q) / \pi[A_0^{(2n)}]^2. \tag{9}$$

10.34. Expansions of Mathieu functions in Bessel function products. We apply the addition theorem

$$J_0[(v_1'^2+v_2'^2+2v_1'v_2'\cos 2u)^{\frac{1}{2}}] = \sum_{m=0}^{\infty} (-1)^m \epsilon_m J_m(v_1')J_m(v_2')\cos 2mu, \quad (1)$$

where $\epsilon_0 = 1$, $\epsilon_m = 2$ for $m \geqslant 1$. Let $v_1' = ke^{iz}$, $v_2' = ke^{-iz}$, and (1) gives

$$J_0\{k[2(\cos 2u+\cos 2z)]^{\frac{1}{2}}\} = \sum_{m=0}^{\infty} (-1)^m \epsilon_m J_m(ke^{-iz})J_m(ke^{iz})\cos 2mu. \quad (2)$$

Substituting from (2) into (1) § 10.33 we obtain

$$\text{ce}_{2n}(z,q)$$
$$= \varphi_{2n} \sum_{r=0}^{\infty} \sum_{m=0}^{\infty} (-1)^m A_{2r}^{(2n)} \epsilon_m J_m(ke^{-iz})J_m(ke^{iz}) \int_0^{\pi} \cos 2ru \cos 2mu \, du, \quad (3)$$

term-by-term integration being permissible, since the series before and after integration are absolutely and uniformly convergent. Now

$$\int_0^{\pi} \cos 2ru \cos 2mu \, du = \left.\begin{array}{ll} \pi & (m = r = 0), \\ 0 & (m \neq r > 0), \\ \tfrac{1}{2}\pi & (m = r > 0). \end{array}\right\} \quad (4)$$

Hence (3) becomes

$$\text{ce}_{2n}(z,q) = \varphi_{2n} \pi \sum_{r=0}^{\infty} (-1)^r A_{2r}^{(2n)} J_r(ke^{-iz}) J_r(ke^{iz}), \quad (5)$$

so this series satisfies $y''+(a-2k^2\cos 2z)y = 0$, $k^2 > 0$. When $z = 0$, (5) gives

$$\varphi_{2n} = \text{ce}_{2n}(0,q)\Big/\pi \sum_{r=0}^{\infty} (-1)^r A_{2r}^{(2n)} J_r^2(k), \quad (6)$$

as at (5) § 10.33.

If in (5) we write iz for z, this being permissible by § 13.60, then

$$\text{Ce}_{2n}(z,q) = \varphi_{2n} \pi \sum_{r=0}^{\infty} (-1)^r A_{2r}^{(2n)} J_r(ke^{-z}) J_r(ke^{z}), \quad (7)$$

so the r.h.s. satisfies $y''-(a-2k^2\cosh 2z)y = 0$, $k^2 > 0$.

Substituting $(\tfrac{1}{2}\pi-z)$ for z in (5) leads to

$$\text{ce}_{2n}(z,-q) = (-1)^n\varphi_{2n} \pi \sum_{r=0}^{\infty} (-1)^r A_{2r}^{(2n)} I_r(ke^{-iz}) I_r(ke^{iz}), \quad (8)$$

so the r.h.s. satisfies $y''+(a+2k^2\cos 2z)y = 0$, $k^2 > 0$.

Putting iz for z in (8), or $(\tfrac{1}{2}\pi i+z)$ for z in (7), yields

$$\text{Ce}_{2n}(z,-q) = (-1)^n\varphi_{2n} \pi \sum_{r=0}^{\infty} (-1)^r A_{2r}^{(2n)} I_r(ke^{-z}) I_r(ke^{z}), \quad (9)$$

so the r.h.s. satisfies $y''-(a+2k^2\cosh 2z)y = 0$, $k^2 > 0$. The multiplier $(-1)^n$ is used in accordance with the definitions in §§ 2.18, 2.31.

10.35. Integral relation for $Se_{2n+1}(z,q)$ **with Bessel nucleus.**
In (2) Table 17, if we put $m = 0$, iz for z, take $\phi(u) = se_{2n+1}(u,q)$, (8) § 10.10 gives, with the aid of (4) § 2.30,

$$Se_{2n+1}(z,q) = \varphi_{2n+1} \int_0^{2\pi} J_1(k_1 r)\sin\alpha \sum_{s=0}^{\infty} B_{2s+1}^{(2n+1)}\sin(2s+1)u \, du, \quad (1)$$

where $k_1 r = k[2(\cos 2u + \cosh 2z)]^{\frac{1}{2}} = k(e^{2z}+e^{-2z}+2\cos 2u)^{\frac{1}{2}}$. Now if $\mathfrak{C}$ is a cylinder function, then [214, (4), p. 365]

$$\frac{\mathfrak{C}_\nu(\varpi)}{\varpi^\nu} = 2^\nu\Gamma(\nu) \sum_{m=0}^{\infty} (-1)^m(m+\nu)\frac{J_{m+\nu}(v_1)\mathfrak{C}_{m+\nu}(v_2)C_m^\nu(\cos 2u)}{v_1^\nu v_2^\nu}, \quad (2)$$

with $\varpi^2 = v_1^2+v_2^2+2v_1 v_2 \cos 2u$, $|v_1| < |v_2|$, while $C_m^\nu(\cos 2u)$ is the coefficient of α_1^m in the expansion of $(1-2\alpha_1\cos 2u+\alpha_1^2)^{-\nu}$ in ascending powers of α_1. Thus

$$C_m^\nu(\cos 2u) = \sum_{s=0}^{\leq\frac{1}{2}m} (-1)^s \frac{2^{m-2s}\Gamma(\nu+m-s)\cos^{m-2s}2u}{(m-2s)!\,s!\,\Gamma(\nu)} \quad (3)$$

and in particular

$$\sin u \, C_m^1(\cos 2u) = \sin(2m+2)u/2\cos u = (-1)^m \sum_{p=0}^{m}(-1)^p\sin(2p+1)u, \quad (4)$$

the third member being obtained by expressing the second in exponentials and expanding. Also from (5), (9) § 10.30 with $-iz$ for z

$$\sin\alpha = y/r = h\sinh z\sin u/r = 2k\sinh z\sin u/k_1 r. \quad (5)$$

Writing J for $\mathfrak{C}$, $v_1 = ke^{-z}$, $v_2 = ke^z$, $\nu = 1$ in (2), and using (4), (5), we obtain

$$J_1(k_1 r)\sin\alpha = \frac{4}{k}\sinh z \sum_{m=0}^{\infty}(m+1)w_{m+1}\sum_{p=0}^{m}(-1)^p\sin(2p+1)u, \quad (6)$$

with $$w_{m+1} = J_{m+1}(v_1)J_{m+1}(v_2).$$

Hence from (1), (6)

$$Se_{2n+1}(z,q) = \varphi_{2n+1}\frac{4}{k}\sinh z \sum_{m=0}^{\infty}w_{m+1}(m+1)\times$$

$$\times \int_0^{2\pi}\sum_{p=0}^{m}(-1)^p\sin(2p+1)u\sum_{s=0}^{\infty}B_{2s+1}^{(2n+1)}\sin(2s+1)u \, du. \quad (7)$$

Since $\displaystyle\int_0^{2\pi} \sin(2m{+}1)u\sin(2s{+}1)u\,du = \left.\begin{matrix} 0\ (m \neq s) \\ \pi\ (m = s \geqslant 0) \end{matrix}\right\}$, the value of $(m{+}1)$ times the integral in (7) is found to be

$$\pi\bar{B}_{2m+1} = \pi(m{+}1)[B_1{-}B_3{+}B_5{-}...{+}(-1)^m B_{2m+1}]. \tag{8}$$

Hence by (7), (8)

$$\mathrm{Se}_{2n+1}(z,q) = \varphi_{2n+1}\frac{4\pi\sinh z}{k}\sum_{m=0}^{\infty} \bar{B}_{2m+1}\,w_{m+1}. \tag{9}$$

10.36. Alternative form of (9) § 10.35. By applying the formula

$$J_\nu(v) = \frac{2(\nu{+}1)}{v}J_{\nu+1}(v){-}J_{\nu+2}(v), \tag{1}$$

to $\qquad W_\nu = J_\nu(v_1)J_{\nu+1}(v_2){-}J_{\nu+1}(v_1)J_\nu(v_2), \tag{2}$

and writing $w_{\nu+1} = J_{\nu+1}(v_1)J_{\nu+1}(v_2)$, we obtain the recurrence relation

$$W_\nu = \frac{4}{k}(\nu{+}1)\sinh z\,.\,w_{\nu+1}{+}W_{\nu+1}. \tag{3}$$

Applying (3) to its r.h.s. repeatedly and writing m for ν yields

$$W_m = \frac{4}{k}\sinh z[(m{+}1)w_{m+1}{+}(m{+}2)w_{m+2}{+}(m{+}3)w_{m+3}{+}...]. \tag{4}$$

Accordingly we have

$$\sum_{m=0}^{\infty} (-1)^m B_{2m+1}^{(2n+1)}W_m$$

$$= \frac{4}{k}\sinh z[B_1(w_1{+}2w_2{+}3w_3{+}...){-}$$

$$\qquad {-}B_3(2w_2{+}3w_3{+}...){+}B_5(3w_3{+}4w_4{+}...){-}...] \tag{5}$$

$$= \frac{4}{k}\sinh z\sum_{m=0}^{\infty} (m{+}1)[B_1{-}B_3{+}B_5{-}...{+}(-1)^m B_{2m+1}]w_{m+1} \tag{6}$$

$$= \frac{4}{k}\sinh z\sum_{m=0}^{\infty} \bar{B}_{2m+1}\,w_{m+1}. \tag{7}$$

Hence from (9) § 10.35 and (7) above, we obtain

$$\mathrm{Se}_{2n+1}(z,q) = \varphi_{2n+1}\,\pi\sum_{r=0}^{\infty} (-1)^r B_{2r+1}^{(2n+1)}[J_r(v_1)J_{r+1}(v_2){-}J_{r+1}(v_1)J_r(v_2)]. \tag{8}$$

10.37. Determination of φ_{2n+1}. When $z \to +\infty$, the asymptotic form of $\mathrm{Se}_{2n+1}(z, q)$ is, by (8) § 10.36,

$$\mathrm{Se}_{2n+1}(z, q) \sim -\varphi_{2n+1} \pi B_1 (2/\pi v_2)^{\frac{1}{2}} \cos(v_2 + \tfrac{1}{4}\pi). \tag{1}$$

Comparing this with (5) § 11.10, we see that

$$\varphi_{2n+1} = s_{2n+1}/\pi B_1. \tag{2}$$

With this value of φ_{2n+1} in (8) § 10.36, (5) § 13.11 is reproduced.

10.38. Integral relations for $\mathrm{Fey}_{2n}(z, q)$, $\mathrm{Gey}_{2n+1}(z, q)$. From Table 17 we get

$$\mathrm{Fey}_{2n}(z, q) = \bar{\varphi}_{2n} \int_0^{2\pi} Y_0\{k[2(\cos 2u + \cosh 2z)]^{\frac{1}{2}}\} \mathrm{ce}_{2n}(u, q) \, du. \tag{1}$$

By § 10.34 and (2) § 10.35 we see that the value of the integral may be obtained from the r.h.s. of (7) § 10.34, if $Y_r(ke^z)$ be written for $J_r(ke^z)$. Thus

$$\mathrm{Fey}_{2n}(z, q) = \bar{\varphi}_{2n} \, 2\pi \sum_{r=0}^{\infty} (-1)^r A_{2r}^{(2n)} J_r(ke^{-z}) Y_r(ke^z). \tag{2}$$

If we let $z \to +\infty$ and equate the asymptotic form of the r.h.s. to (9) § 11.10, we find that

$$\bar{\varphi}_{2n} = \mathrm{ce}_{2n}(0, q) \mathrm{ce}_{2n}(\tfrac{1}{2}\pi, q)/2\pi A_0^2. \tag{3}$$

With this value of $\bar{\varphi}_{2n}$, (2) gives the B.F. product series for $\mathrm{Fey}_{2n}(z, q)$ at (1) § 13.20.

Again, from Table 17 we get

$$\mathrm{Gey}_{2n+1}(z, q) = \bar{\varphi}_{2n+1} \int_0^{2\pi} Y_1\{k[2(\cos 2u + \cosh 2z)]^{\frac{1}{2}}\} \sin \alpha \, \mathrm{se}_{2n+1}(u, q) \, du; \tag{4}$$

and from (2) § 10.35 we see that the analysis for the present case is the same as that in §§ 10.35, 10.36, provided $Y_m(ke^z)$ be written for $J_m(ke^z)$. Then by (8) § 10.36

$$\mathrm{Gey}_{2n+1}(z, q) = \bar{\varphi}_{2n+1} \pi \sum_{r=0}^{\infty} (-1)^r B_{2r+1}^{(2n+1)} [J_r(v_1) Y_{r+1}(v_2) - J_{r+1}(v_1) Y_r(v_2)]. \tag{5}$$

If we determine $\bar{\varphi}_{2n+1}$ as indicated above, the expansion (8) § 13.20 is reproduced. Moreover, we have here a method of obtaining the B.F. product series representations of the modified Mathieu functions of the first and second kinds, which is an alternative to that given in Chapter XIII.

10.40. Integral relations for Fek_m, Ce_m, Fey_m, Gek_m, Se_m, Gey_m, $q > 0$, **with infinite upper limit.** We commence with the formula

$$K_{2r}(z) = \int_0^\infty e^{-z\cosh u} \cosh 2ru\, du. \tag{1}$$

This integral converges uniformly with respect to z if $R(z) \geqslant x$, $x > 0$. Under this condition, if $-2ik\cosh z$ be written for z, we get

$$\sum_{r=0}^\infty A_{2r}^{(2n)} K_{2r}(-2ik\cosh z) = \int_0^\infty \sum_{r=0}^\infty e^{2ik\cosh z\cosh u} A_{2r}^{(2n)} \cosh 2ru\, du \tag{2}$$

$$= \int_0^\infty e^{2ik\cosh z\cosh u} \text{Ce}_{2n}(u,q)\, du. \tag{3}$$

If z and k are real, the above restriction may be removed, since the real and imaginary parts of (3) are absolutely and uniformly convergent by §10.42. Then by (5) §8.14 and (3) above we have the integral relationship

$$\text{Fek}_{2n}(z,q) = \frac{\text{ce}_{2n}(\tfrac{1}{2}\pi, q)}{\pi A_0^{(2n)}} \int_0^\infty e^{2ik\cosh z\cosh u} \text{Ce}_{2n}(u,q)\, du. \tag{4}$$

Applying (4) §8.14 to (4), on equating real and imaginary parts, we obtain

$$\text{Ce}_{2n}(z,q) = \frac{2\,\text{ce}_{2n}(\tfrac{1}{2}\pi, q)}{\pi A_0^{(2n)}} \int_0^\infty \sin(2k\cosh z\cosh u)\text{Ce}_{2n}(u,q)\, du \tag{5}$$

and

$$\text{Fey}_{2n}(z,q) = -\frac{2\,\text{ce}_{2n}(\tfrac{1}{2}\pi, q)}{\pi A_0^{(2n)}} \int_0^\infty \cos(2k\cosh z\cosh u)\text{Ce}_{2n}(u,q)\, du. \tag{6}$$

Similar analysis leads to the following:

$$\text{Fek}_{2n+1}(z,q) = -\frac{\text{ce}_{2n+1}'(\tfrac{1}{2}\pi, q)}{k\pi A_1^{(2n+1)}} \int_0^\infty e^{2ik\cosh z\cosh u} \text{Ce}_{2n+1}(u,q)\, du, \tag{7}$$

$$\text{Ce}_{2n+1}(z,q) = \frac{2\,\text{ce}_{2n+1}'(\tfrac{1}{2}\pi, q)}{k\pi A_1^{(2n+1)}} \int_0^\infty \cos(2k\cosh z\cosh u)\text{Ce}_{2n+1}(u,q)\, du, \tag{8}$$

and

$$\text{Fey}_{2n+1}(z,q) = \frac{2\,\text{ce}_{2n+1}'(\tfrac{1}{2}\pi, q)}{k\pi A_1^{(2n+1)}} \int_0^\infty \sin(2k\cosh z\cosh u)\text{Ce}_{2n+1}(u,q)\, du. \tag{9}$$

To derive integral relations for Gek_m, Se_m, Gey_m we commence with the integral relationship [132]

$$\nu K_\nu(z) = z \int_0^\infty e^{-z \cosh u} \sinh u \sinh \nu u \, du = \tfrac{1}{2}\pi\nu e^{\frac{1}{2}\pi(\nu+1)i} H_\nu^{(1)}(zi), \quad (10)$$

$R(z) > 0$. Then by aid of formulae in § 8.14 we find that

$\mathrm{Gek}_{2n+1}(z,q)$

$$= -\frac{2i\,\mathrm{se}_{2n+1}(\tfrac{1}{2}\pi,q)}{\pi B_1^{(2n+1)}} \int_0^\infty e^{2ik\cosh z \cosh u} \sinh z \sinh u \, \mathrm{Se}_{2n+1}(u,q) \, du,$$

$$\quad (11)$$

$\mathrm{Se}_{2n+1}(z,q)$

$$= -\frac{4\,\mathrm{se}_{2n+1}(\tfrac{1}{2}\pi,q)}{\pi B_1^{(2n+1)}} \int_0^\infty \sin(2k\cosh z \cosh u)\sinh z \sinh u \, \mathrm{Se}_{2n+1}(u,q) \, du,$$

$$\quad (12)$$

$\mathrm{Gey}_{2n+1}(z,q)$

$$= \frac{4\,\mathrm{se}_{2n+1}(\tfrac{1}{2}\pi,q)}{\pi B_1^{(2n+1)}} \int_0^\infty \cos(2k\cosh z \cosh u)\sinh z \sinh u \, \mathrm{Se}_{2n+1}(u,q) \, du,$$

$$\quad (13)$$

$\mathrm{Gek}_{2n+2}(z,q)$

$$= -\frac{2i\,\mathrm{se}_{2n+2}'(\tfrac{1}{2}\pi,q)}{k\pi B_2^{(2n+2)}} \int_0^\infty e^{2ik\cosh z \cosh u} \sinh z \sinh u \, \mathrm{Se}_{2n+2}(u,q) \, du,$$

$$\quad (14)$$

$\mathrm{Se}_{2n+2}(z,q)$

$$= -\frac{4\,\mathrm{se}_{2n+2}'(\tfrac{1}{2}\pi,q)}{k\pi B_2^{(2n+2)}} \int_0^\infty \cos(2k\cosh z \cosh u)\sinh z \sinh u \, \mathrm{Se}_{2n+2}(u,q) \, du,$$

$$\quad (15)$$

$\mathrm{Gey}_{2n+2}(z,q)$

$$= -\frac{4\,\mathrm{se}_{2n+2}'(\tfrac{1}{2}\pi,q)}{k\pi B_2^{(2n+2)}} \int_0^\infty \sin(2k\cosh z \cosh u)\sinh z \sinh u \, \mathrm{Se}_{2n+2}(u,q) \, du.$$

$$\quad (16)$$

Relations (11)–(16) may also be expressed as follows:

$\mathrm{Gek}_{2n+1}(z,q)$

$$= \frac{\mathrm{se}_{2n+1}(\tfrac{1}{2}\pi,q)}{k\pi B_1^{(2n+1)}} \tanh z \int_0^\infty e^{2ik\cosh z \cosh u} \mathrm{Se}_{2n+1}'(u,q) \, du, \quad (17)$$

$\mathrm{Se}_{2n+1}(z,q)$

$$= -\frac{2\,\mathrm{se}_{2n+1}(\tfrac{1}{2}\pi,q)}{k\pi B_1^{(2n+1)}} \tanh z \int_0^\infty \cos(2k\cosh z \cosh u)\mathrm{Se}_{2n+1}'(u,q) \, du, \quad (18)$$

$\text{Gey}_{2n+1}(z, q)$

$$= -\frac{2\,\text{se}_{2n+1}(\frac{1}{2}\pi, q)}{k\pi B_1^{(2n+1)}} \tanh z \int_0^\infty \sin(2k\cosh z \cosh u)\text{Se}'_{2n+1}(u, q)\, du, \quad (19)$$

$\text{Gek}_{2n+2}(z, q)$

$$= \frac{\text{se}'_{2n+2}(\frac{1}{2}\pi, q)}{k^2\pi B_2^{(2n+2)}} \tanh z \int_0^\infty e^{2ik\cosh z \cosh u}\,\text{Se}'_{2n+2}(u, q)\, du, \quad (20)$$

$\text{Se}_{2n+2}(z, q)$

$$= \frac{2\,\text{se}'_{2n+2}(\frac{1}{2}\pi, q)}{k^2\pi B_2^{(2n+2)}} \tanh z \int_0^\infty \sin(2k\cosh z \cosh u)\text{Se}'_{2n+2}(u, q)\, du, \quad (21)$$

$\text{Gey}_{2n+2}(z, q)$

$$= -\frac{2\,\text{se}'_{2n+2}(\frac{1}{2}\pi, q)}{k^2\pi B_2^{(2n+2)}} \tanh z \int_0^\infty \cos(2k\cosh z \cosh u)\text{Se}'_{2n+2}(u, q)\, du. \quad (22)$$

On integrating by parts and using the result that

$$\text{Se}_m(0) = \text{Se}_m(\infty) = 0,$$

(17)–(22) reduce to (11)–(16), respectively.

(4), (7), (11), (14), (17), (20) converge if $k\cosh z$ is complex, provided that its imaginary part is greater than zero. The arguments of the circular functions in the integrals obtained by separation into real and imaginary parts must be real. The nuclei in the integral equations (5), (8), (12), (15) are symmetrical in u and z. §§ 10.42–10.45 are based on $k > 0, z$ real: $z \geqslant 0$ in (4)–(9), $z > 0$ in (11)–(22).

10.41. Integral relations for $\text{Fek}_m(z, -q)$, $\text{Gek}_m(z, -q)$. These are obtained by applying (7), etc., § 8.40 to (4), (7), (11), (14) § 10.40. For example, if $R(z) > 0$,

$$\text{Fek}_{2n}(z, -q) = \frac{(-1)^n\,\text{ce}_{2n}(\frac{1}{2}\pi, q)}{\pi A_0^{(2n)}} \int_0^\infty e^{-2k\sinh z \cosh u}\text{Ce}_{2n}(u, q)\, du. \quad (1)$$

The remaining relations may be obtained by the reader. There are, however, alternative relations for these functions, which we shall now give. Applying (1) § 10.40 to (9), (19) § 8.30, we obtain

$$\text{Fek}_{2n}(z, -q) = \frac{\text{ce}_{2n}(0, q)}{\pi A_0^{(2n)}} \int_0^\infty e^{-2k\cosh z \cosh u}\text{Ce}_{2n}(u, -q)\, du. \quad (2)$$

It should be noticed that for Ce_{2n}, $q > 0$ in (1) and < 0 in (2).

$$\mathrm{Fek}_{2n+1}(z, -q) = \frac{se'_{2n+1}(0, q)}{k\pi B_1^{(2n+1)}} \int_0^\infty e^{-2k\cosh z \cosh u} Ce_{2n+1}(u, -q)\, du.$$

(3)

Similarly from (10) § 10.40 and (29), (39) § 8.30 we find that if $z > 0$

$$\mathrm{Gek}_{2n+1}(z, -q)$$

$$= \frac{2\, ce_{2n+1}(0, q)}{\pi A_1^{(2n+1)}} \int_0^\infty e^{-2k\cosh z \cosh u} \sinh z \sinh u\, Se_{2n+1}(u, -q)\, du, \quad (4)$$

$$\mathrm{Gek}_{2n+2}(z, -q)$$

$$= \frac{2\, se'_{2n+2}(0, q)}{k\pi B_2^{(2n+2)}} \int_0^\infty e^{-2k\cosh z \cosh u} \sinh z \sinh u\, Se_{2n+2}(u, -q)\, du. \quad (5)$$

If $(\tfrac{1}{2}\pi i + z)$ be written for z in the integrals in § 10.40 corresponding to Ce_m, Fey_m, Se_m, Gey_m, they diverge.

10.42. Convergence of integrals (4)–(9) § 10.40.

In that section functions are defined by infinite integrals whose properties we shall now investigate. Constant multipliers will be omitted for brevity. We exemplify using (6) § 10.40. Both members of the integrand are continuous in $0 \leqslant u \leqslant u_0$, however large u_0 may be, the continuity of the first member holding in any closed interval of z real. Thus $\int_0^{u_0}$ exists, so we consider $\int_{u_0}^\infty$ with u_0 extremely large. Then by (2) § 11.10 the asymptotic form of $Ce_{2n}(u) \propto x^{-\frac{1}{2}}\sin(x + \tfrac{1}{4}\pi)$, where $x = 2k\cosh u$, $du \simeq dx/x$. With these substitutions the integral for consideration is

$$I = \int_{x_0}^\infty \cos(x \cosh z)\sin(x + \tfrac{1}{4}\pi)x^{-\frac{3}{2}}\, dx.$$

(1)

Since $|\cos(x\cosh z)\sin(x + \tfrac{1}{4}\pi)| \leqslant 1$ if z is real, we get

$$I \leqslant \int_{x_0}^\infty x^{-\frac{3}{2}}\, dx = 2x_0^{-\frac{1}{2}},$$

(2)

so the original integral converges absolutely. Further, the convergence is independent of z in any closed interval $0 \leqslant z \leqslant z_2$, so (6) § 10.40 is absolutely and uniformly convergent therein. Consequently it represents a continuous function in the interval. In § 13.60

it is demonstrated that the series for $\mathrm{Fey}_{2n}(z,q)$—the function represented by (6) § 10.40—is uniformly convergent in $z_1 \leqslant z \leqslant z_2$, and so represents a continuous function therein. The convergence of (4), (7) § 10.40 follows from that of their real and imaginary parts.

10.43. Differentiation under the integral sign. This is valid provided the resulting integral is uniformly convergent. To exemplify, we differentiate (6) § 10.40 with respect to z, and obtain (omitting the external multiplier)

$$\sinh z \int_0^\infty 2k \cosh u \sin(2k \cosh z \cosh u)\mathrm{Ce}_{2n}(u,q)\,du. \tag{1}$$

Thus we consider the integral

$$I = \sinh z \int_{x_0}^\infty \sin(x \cosh z)\sin(x+\tfrac{1}{4}\pi)x^{-\frac{1}{2}}\,dx \tag{2}$$

$$= \tfrac{1}{2}\sinh z \int_{l \to +\infty}^{l}{}_{x_0} \{-\cos[x(\cosh z+1)+\tfrac{1}{4}\pi]+$$
$$+\cos[x(\cosh z-1)-\tfrac{1}{4}\pi]\}x^{-\frac{1}{2}}\,dx. \tag{3}$$

Now $-\cos[\ \ ]$ oscillates between finite limits for any z in $z_1 \leqslant z \leqslant z_2$ as $l \to +\infty$, while $x^{-\frac{1}{2}} \to 0$ monotonically. Hence by a known theorem† the integral converges uniformly with respect to z in the interval. It vanishes at $z = 0$, owing to the factor $\sinh z$.

In the second integral of (3) write

$$x(\cosh z-1) = y, \qquad dx = dy/(\cosh z-1),$$

and we get

$$I_2 = \frac{\tfrac{1}{2}\sinh z}{(\cosh z-1)^{\frac{1}{2}}} \int_{y_0}^{y} \cos(y-\tfrac{1}{4}\pi)y^{-\frac{1}{2}}\,dy, \tag{4}$$

the upper limit being $y = x(\cosh z-1)$, $x \to +\infty$, and the lower limit

$$y_0 = x_0(\cosh z-1).$$

From what precedes it is clear that, excluding the region of $z = 0$, (4) is uniformly convergent in any closed interval $z_1 \leqslant z \leqslant z_2$. When $z \to 0$, the external factor tends to $1/\sqrt{2}$, the upper limit $y \to \tfrac{1}{2}xz^2$, and $y_0 \to \tfrac{1}{2}x_0 z^2$. Thus as $z \to 0$, $y_0 \to 0$, but $y \to 0$ or ∞ according to the way $z \to 0$, i.e. it is not *unique*. Hence (1) is uniformly convergent in $0 < z_1 \leqslant z \leqslant z_2$. Accordingly $\mathrm{Fey}'_{2n}(z,q)$, as defined

† See Bromwich, *Theory of Infinite Series.*

by the integral, is continuous in $z > 0$. A second differentiation under the integral sign is not permissible, since the resulting integral is oscillatory and diverges owing to presence of the factor $x^{\frac{1}{2}}$ in the integrand. The preceding conclusions apply equally to (5), (8), (9) § 10.40.

10.44. Convergence of integrals (11)–(16) § 10.40. The investigation follows on the lines of that in the preceding section. In all cases we get an integral akin to (3) § 10.43, so the integrals are uniformly convergent in $z_1 \leqslant z \leqslant z_2$. Thus they represent continuous functions. These integrals cannot be differentiated under the sign, since the resulting integrals diverge. As in § 10.43, z_1 real > 0.

10.45. Convergence of integrals in § 10.41. The analytical procedure is similar to that in §§ 10.42, 10.43. Thus for (2) § 10.41 we consider

$$\int_{x_0}^{\infty} e^{-x \cosh z}(x^{-\frac{1}{2}}e^x)\, dx/x = \int_{x_0}^{\infty} e^{-x(\cosh z - 1)}x^{-\frac{3}{2}}\, dx \tag{1}$$

with $x = 2k \cosh u$. It is obvious that (1) is absolutely and uniformly convergent in $0 \leqslant z \leqslant z_2$, so $\mathrm{Fek}_{2n}(z, -q)$, as defined by (2) § 10.41, is a continuous function of z. Differentiating (2) § 10.41 under the integral sign with respect to z leads to a consideration of

$$\int_{x_0}^{\infty} e^{-x(\cosh z - 1)}x^{-\frac{1}{2}}\, dx. \tag{2}$$

This is seen to be absolutely and uniformly convergent in $z_1 \leqslant z \leqslant z_2$, so long as the neighbourhood of $z = 0$ is excluded. It diverges if $z = 0$. These conclusions apply equally to (3) § 10.41. In the case of (4), (5) § 10.41, integrals of type (2) above are involved, so the preceding conclusion applies. These latter integrals can be differentiated under the sign, except in the neighbourhood of $z = 0$.

10.50. Integral equations for $\mathrm{ce}_m(z, q)$, $\mathrm{se}_m(z, q)$ with nucleus $e^{2ik(\cosh \xi \cos \eta \cos \theta + \sinh \xi \sin \eta \sin \theta)}$. It is readily confirmed by substitution that [183]

$$\zeta = \int_0^{2\pi} e^{ik_1(x \cos \theta + y \sin \theta)}f(\theta)\, d\theta, \tag{1}$$

$f(\theta)$ being an arbitrary differentiable function of θ, is a solution of

$$\frac{\partial^2 \zeta}{\partial x^2} + \frac{\partial^2 \zeta}{\partial y^2} + k_1^2 \zeta = 0. \tag{2}$$

Introducing elliptical coordinates (Chap. IX), and taking

$$4k^2 = k_1^2 h^2 > 0,$$

(1), (2) become, respectively,

$$\zeta = \int_0^{2\pi} e^{2ikw} f(\theta) \, d\theta, \tag{3}$$

and

$$\frac{\partial^2 \zeta}{\partial \xi^2} + \frac{\partial^2 \zeta}{\partial \eta^2} + 2k^2(\cosh 2\xi - \cos 2\eta)\zeta = 0, \tag{4}$$

with $w = \cosh \xi \cos \eta \cos \theta + \sinh \xi \sin \eta \sin \theta$. The physical interpretation of (3), (4) deserves to be mentioned. (4) is the equation for propagation of 'elliptical' waves, and (3) is a solution thereof. Now e^{2ikw} represents a system of omnidirectional plane waves, since θ varies from 0 to 2π. Hence we may visualize 'elliptical' waves as being synthesized from 'plane' waves moving in all directions (θ) and properly coordinated in amplitude and phase $[f(\theta)]$.

As a suitable solution of (4) we take $\zeta = f_1(\xi)f_2(\eta)$, where f_1, f_2 are solutions of

$$\frac{d^2 f_1}{d\xi^2} - (a - 2k^2 \cosh 2\xi)f_1 = 0 \tag{5}$$

and

$$\frac{d^2 f_2}{d\eta^2} + (a - 2k^2 \cos 2\eta)f_2 = 0, \tag{6}$$

respectively.

The next step is to define $f(\theta)$, so that (3) is a solution of (6) with ζ written for f_2. From (3)

$$\frac{d^2 \zeta}{d\eta^2} = - \int_0^{2\pi} [4k^2(\sinh \xi \cos \eta \sin \theta - \cosh \xi \sin \eta \cos \theta)^2 +$$

$$+ 2ik(\cosh \xi \cos \eta \cos \theta + \sinh \xi \sin \eta \sin \theta)]e^{2ikw} f(\theta) \, d\theta. \tag{7}$$

Now

$$(\sinh \xi \cos \eta \sin \theta - \cosh \xi \sin \eta \cos \theta)^2$$

$$= (\sinh \xi \sin \eta \cos \theta - \cosh \xi \cos \eta \sin \theta)^2 - \tfrac{1}{2}(\cos 2\eta - \cos 2\theta). \tag{8}$$

Substituting from (8) into (7) gives

$$\frac{d^2 \zeta}{d\eta^2} = \int_0^{2\pi} f(\theta)\left[2k^2(\cos 2\eta - \cos 2\theta) + \frac{\partial^2}{\partial \theta^2}\right]e^{2ikw} \, d\theta. \tag{9}$$

Then by (3), (9)

$$\frac{d^2\zeta}{d\eta^2} + (a - 2k^2\cos 2\eta)\zeta = \int_0^{2\pi} f(\theta)\left[a - 2k^2\cos 2\theta + \frac{\partial^2}{\partial\theta^2}\right]e^{2ikw}\,d\theta. \quad (10)$$

But

$$f(\theta)\frac{\partial^2}{\partial\theta^2}(e^{2ikw}) = \frac{\partial}{\partial\theta}\left[f(\theta)\frac{\partial}{\partial\theta}(e^{2ikw})\right] - \frac{\partial f(\theta)}{\partial\theta}\frac{\partial}{\partial\theta}(e^{2ikw})$$

$$= \frac{\partial}{\partial\theta}\left[f(\theta)\frac{\partial}{\partial\theta}(e^{2ikw}) - \frac{\partial f(\theta)}{\partial\theta}e^{2ikw}\right] + \frac{\partial^2 f}{\partial\theta^2}e^{2ikw}. \quad (11)$$

Substituting from (11) into (10) leads to

$$\frac{d^2\zeta}{d\eta^2} + (a - 2k^2\cos 2\eta)\zeta = \int_0^{2\pi}[f''(\theta) + (a - 2k^2\cos 2\theta)f(\theta)]e^{2ikw}\,d\theta\ +$$

$$+ \left[f(\theta)\frac{\partial}{\partial\theta}(e^{2ikw}) - \frac{\partial f(\theta)}{\partial\theta}e^{2ikw}\right]_0^{2\pi} \quad (12)$$

If $f(\theta)$ satisfies (6), the first [ ] in (12) vanishes, while if $f(\theta)$ has period π, 2π, the second [ ] vanishes at the limits. Under these conditions ζ satisfies (6) as required, so $f(\theta)$ must be a multiple of $\mathrm{ce}_m(\theta, q)$, $\mathrm{se}_m(\theta, q)$. Also with the same a, q in (5), (6) it follows that $f_1(\xi, q) \propto \mathrm{Ce}_m(\xi, q)$ or $\mathrm{Se}_m(\xi, q)$, and $f_2(\eta, q) \propto \mathrm{ce}_m(\eta, q)$ or $\mathrm{se}_m(\eta, q)$. Thus (3) yields the integral equations

$$\mathrm{Ce}_m(\xi)\mathrm{ce}_m(\eta) = \rho_m \int_0^{2\pi} e^{2ikw}\,\mathrm{ce}_m(\theta)\,d\theta \quad (13)$$

and

$$\mathrm{Se}_m(\xi)\mathrm{se}_m(\eta) = \sigma_m \int_0^{2\pi} e^{2ikw}\,\mathrm{se}_m(\theta)\,d\theta. \quad (14)$$

ρ_m, σ_m are the characteristic values of the nucleus e^{2ikw}.

10.51. Evaluation of (13), (14) § 10.50. We commence by writing

$$2kw = 2k(x_1\cos\theta + y_1\sin\theta) = z_1\cos(\theta - \alpha), \quad (1)$$

where

$$x_1 = x/h = \cosh\xi\cos\eta, \qquad y_1 = y/h = \sinh\xi\sin\eta,$$

$$z_1 = 2k(\cosh^2\xi\cos^2\eta + \sinh^2\xi\sin^2\eta)^{\frac{1}{2}} = 2k(\cosh^2\xi - \sin^2\eta)^{\frac{1}{2}} = k_1 r,$$

and $\alpha = \tan^{-1}(y_1/x_1)$, or $\tan\alpha = \tanh\xi\tan\eta$. Next we use the expansion [202, p. 43]

$$e^{i[z_1\cos(\theta-\alpha)]} = J_0(z_1) + 2\sum_{p=1}^{\infty} i^p\cos p(\theta - \alpha)J_p(z_1), \quad (2)$$

together with that of $ce_{2n}(\theta)$, in the integrand of (13) § 10.50, thereby obtaining

$$Ce_{2n}(\xi)ce_{2n}(\eta) = \rho_{2n} \int_0^{2\pi} \left[J_0(z_1) + 2\sum_{p=1}^{\infty} i^p \cos p(\theta-\alpha)J_p(z_1) \right] \times$$

$$\times \sum_{r=0}^{\infty} A_{2r}^{(2n)} \cos 2r\theta \, d\theta. \quad (3)$$

Now

$$\int_0^{2\pi} \left[J_0(z_1) + 2\sum_{p=1}^{\infty} i^p \cos p(\theta-\alpha)J_p(z_1) \right] \cos 2r\theta \, d\theta = 2\pi i^{2r} \cos 2r\alpha \, J_{2r}(z_1),$$
$$(4)$$

the other integrals vanishing by virtue of orthogonality of the circular functions. Also, the series concerned are absolutely and uniformly convergent. Hence by (3), (4) we obtain the result

$$Ce_{2n}(\xi)ce_{2n}(\eta) = 2\pi\rho_{2n} \sum_{r=0}^{\infty} (-1)^r A_{2r}^{(2n)} \cos 2r\alpha \, J_{2r}(z_1), \quad (5)$$

this series being absolutely and uniformly convergent. Since the r.h.s. of (3) when evaluated is real, it follows that the imaginary part vanishes, so

$$\int_0^{2\pi} \sin[z_1 \cos(\theta-\alpha)]ce_{2n}(\theta) \, d\theta = 0. \quad (6)$$

To evaluate ρ_{2n} in (5), put $\eta = 0$, then $\alpha = 0$ and $z_1 = 2k\cosh\xi$, giving

$$Ce_{2n}(\xi)ce_{2n}(0) = 2\pi\rho_{2n} \sum_{r=0}^{\infty} (-1)^r A_{2r}^{(2n)} J_{2r}(2k\cosh\xi). \quad (7)$$

Thus from (7) above and (15) § 8.10,

$$\rho_{2n} = ce_{2n}(0,q)ce_{2n}(\tfrac{1}{2}\pi,q)/2\pi A_0^{(2n)} = p_{2n}/2\pi. \quad (8)$$

Using (8) in (13) § 10.50, and remembering that the imaginary part vanishes by (6), we get the integral equation for $ce_{2n}(\eta,q)$, namely,

$$Ce_{2n}(\xi)ce_{2n}(\eta) = \rho_{2n} \int_0^{2\pi} \cos[z_1 \cos(\theta-\alpha)]ce_{2n}(\theta) \, d\theta \quad (9)$$

$$= p_{2n} \sum_{r=0}^{\infty} (-1)^r A_{2r}^{(2n)} \cos 2r\alpha \, J_{2r}(z_1). \quad (10)$$

10.52. The remaining integral equations. Analysis similar to that in § 10.51, using the multipliers p_m, s_m defined in Appendix I, leads to the following:

$$\rho_{2n+1} = p_{2n+1}/2\pi, \quad (1)\dagger$$

† When used in (13), (14) § 10.50, ρ_{2n+1}, σ_{2n+1} must be multiplied by $-i$, since the l.h.s. are real.

$$\mathrm{Ce}_{2n+1}(\xi)\mathrm{ce}_{2n+1}(\eta) = p_{2n+1} \int_0^{2\pi} \sin[z_1 \cos(\theta-\alpha)]\mathrm{ce}_{2n+1}(\theta)\, d\theta \tag{2}$$

$$= -p_{2n+1} \sum_{r=0}^{\infty} (-1)^r A_{2r+1}^{(2n+1)} \cos(2r+1)\alpha\, J_{2r+1}(z_1), \tag{3}$$

$$\int_0^{2\pi} \cos[z_1 \cos(\theta-\alpha)]\mathrm{ce}_{2n+1}(\theta)\, d\theta = 0. \tag{4}$$

$$\sigma_{2n+1} = s_{2n+1}/2\pi, \tag{5}$$

$$\mathrm{Se}_{2n+1}(\xi)\mathrm{se}_{2n+1}(\eta) = \sigma_{2n+1} \int_0^{2\pi} \sin[z_1 \cos(\theta-\alpha)]\mathrm{se}_{2n+1}(\theta)\, d\theta \tag{6}$$

$$= s_{2n+1} \sum_{r=0}^{\infty} (-1)^r B_{2r+1}^{(2n+1)} \sin(2r+1)\alpha\, J_{2r+1}(z_1), \tag{7}$$

$$\int_0^{2\pi} \cos[z_1 \cos(\theta-\alpha)]\mathrm{se}_{2n+1}(\theta)\, d\theta = 0. \tag{8}$$

$$\sigma_{2n+2} = s_{2n+2}/2\pi, \tag{9}$$

$$\mathrm{Se}_{2n+2}(\xi)\mathrm{se}_{2n+2}(\eta) = \sigma_{2n+2} \int_0^{2\pi} \cos[z_1 \cos(\theta-\alpha)]\mathrm{se}_{2n+2}(\theta)\, d\theta \tag{10}$$

$$= -s_{2n+2} \sum_{r=0}^{\infty} (-1)^r B_{2r+2}^{(2n+2)} \sin(2r+2)\alpha\, J_{2r+2}(z_1), \tag{11}$$

$$\int_0^{2\pi} \sin[z_1 \cos(\theta-\alpha)]\mathrm{se}_{2n+2}(\theta)\, d\theta = 0. \tag{12}$$

By analysis similar to that in § 8.50 it may be shown that the series herein and in § 10.51 are absolutely and uniformly convergent in any finite region of the z-plane.

10.53. Expansions of $\genfrac{}{}{0pt}{}{\cos}{\sin}\{2k(\cosh\xi\cos\eta\cos\theta + \sinh\xi\sin\eta\sin\theta)\}$, $k^2 > 0$. Assume that

$$\cos[z_1 \cos(\theta-\alpha)]$$

$$= \sum_{m=0}^{\infty} [C_{2m}(\eta)\mathrm{Ce}_{2m}(\xi)\mathrm{ce}_{2m}(\theta) + S_{2m+2}(\eta)\mathrm{Se}_{2m+2}(\xi)\mathrm{se}_{2m+2}(\theta)]. \tag{1}$$

Multiply both sides by $\mathrm{ce}_{2n}(\theta)$, integrate with respect to θ from 0 to 2π, and we get

$$\int_0^{2\pi} \cos[z_1 \cos(\theta-\alpha)]\mathrm{ce}_{2n}(\theta)\, d\theta = \pi C_{2n}(\eta)\mathrm{Ce}_{2n}(\xi), \tag{2}$$

the other integrals vanishing by virtue of orthogonality (§ 2.19). From (2) above, (8), (9) § 10.51, it follows that

$$C_{2n}(\eta) = 2\,\mathrm{ce}_{2n}(\eta)/p_{2n}. \tag{3}$$

Multiplying both sides of (1) by $\mathrm{se}_{2n+2}(\theta)$ and proceeding as before, we get

$$S_{2n+2}(\eta) = 2\,\mathrm{se}_{2n+2}(\eta)/s_{2n+2}. \tag{4}$$

Substituting (3), (4) into (1) yields the expansion

$$\cos\{2k(\cosh\xi\cos\eta\cos\theta + \sinh\xi\sin\eta\sin\theta)\}$$

$$= 2\sum_{n=0}^{\infty}\left[\frac{\mathrm{Ce}_{2n}(\xi)\mathrm{ce}_{2n}(\eta)\mathrm{ce}_{2n}(\theta)}{p_{2n}} + \frac{\mathrm{Se}_{2n+2}(\xi)\mathrm{se}_{2n+2}(\eta)\mathrm{se}_{2n+2}(\theta)}{s_{2n+2}}\right]. \tag{5}$$

By similar analysis we find that

$$\sin\{2k(\cosh\xi\cos\eta\cos\theta + \sinh\xi\sin\eta\sin\theta)\}$$

$$= 2\sum_{n=0}^{\infty}\left[\frac{\mathrm{Ce}_{2n+1}(\xi)\mathrm{ce}_{2n+1}(\eta)\mathrm{ce}_{2n+1}(\theta)}{p_{2n+1}} + \frac{\mathrm{Se}_{2n+1}(\xi)\mathrm{se}_{2n+1}(\eta)\mathrm{se}_{2n+1}(\theta)}{s_{2n+1}}\right]. \tag{6}$$

In (5), (6) write $i\xi$ for ξ, then, referring to § 10.60, the r.h.s. of (5) above reduces to the form (7) for $\theta = 0$, and to (8) for $\theta = \frac{1}{2}\pi$, while (6) above reduces to the form (9) for $\theta = 0$, and to (10) for $\theta = \frac{1}{2}\pi$. Accordingly we obtain the expansion

$$e^{iz_1\cos(\theta-\alpha)}$$

$$= e^{ik_1(x\cos\theta+y\sin\theta)} = \cos\{k_1(x\cos\theta+y\sin\theta)\} + i\sin\{k_1(x\cos\theta+y\sin\theta)\}$$

$$= 2\sum_{n=0}^{\infty}\left[\frac{1}{p_{2n}}\mathrm{Ce}_{2n}(\xi)\mathrm{ce}_{2n}(\eta)\mathrm{ce}_{2n}(\theta) + \frac{1}{s_{2n+2}}\mathrm{Se}_{2n+2}(\xi)\mathrm{se}_{2n+2}(\eta)\mathrm{se}_{2n+2}(\theta) + \right.$$

$$+ i\left\{\frac{1}{p_{2n+1}}\mathrm{Ce}_{2n+1}(\xi)\mathrm{ce}_{2n+1}(\eta)\mathrm{ce}_{2n+1}(\theta) + \right.$$

$$\left.\left. + \frac{1}{s_{2n+1}}\mathrm{Se}_{2n+1}(\xi)\mathrm{se}_{2n+1}(\eta)\mathrm{se}_{2n+1}(\theta)\right\}\right]. \tag{7}$$

When the fundamental ellipse tends to a circle, it may be shown, by aid of Appendix I, that with $\theta = 0$, $\frac{1}{2}\pi$, (5), (6) degenerate to well-known expansions in B.F.

10.60. Expansions of nuclei in characteristic functions, $q > 0$.
If in (2) § 10.11 we put $\chi = R(u)S(z)$, and proceed as in § 9.21, we obtain the two ordinary equations

$$\frac{d^2R}{du^2} + (a - 2q\cos 2u)R = 0 \tag{1}$$

and
$$\frac{d^2 S}{dz^2} + (a - 2q \cos 2z)S = 0. \tag{2}$$

For a *given value of q*, if $a = a_m$, the products of the first solutions of (1), (2) are $\chi_{mc} = c_m \operatorname{ce}_m(u)\operatorname{ce}_m(z)$, while if $a = b_m$ we have

$$\chi_{ms} = s_m \operatorname{se}_m(u)\operatorname{se}_m(z),$$

c_m and s_m being arbitrary constants, m taking positive integral values. Hence we may write

$$\chi = \sum_{m=0}^{\infty} c_m \operatorname{ce}_m(u)\operatorname{ce}_m(z) + \sum_{m=1}^{\infty} s_m \operatorname{se}_m(u)\operatorname{se}_m(z). \tag{3}$$

Now $\chi = e^{2ik \cos u \cos z}$ and $e^{-2k \sin u \sin z}$ are also solutions of (2) § 10.11. It appears, then, that these composite integral function solutions may be expressed in infinite series of periodic Mathieu functions. The real part of the first, being even in u, z, is the nucleus for $\operatorname{ce}_{2n}(z,q)$. Now the second series on the r.h.s. of (3) is odd in u, z, while $\operatorname{ce}_{2n}(z,q)$ has period π. Let us assume, then, that

$$\cos(2k \cos u \cos z) = \sum_{s=0}^{\infty} c_{2s} \operatorname{ce}_{2s}(u)\operatorname{ce}_{2s}(z), \tag{4}$$

the r.h.s. of which is even in u, z and admits the period π in both variables. To determine c_{2s} multiply both sides of (4) by $\operatorname{ce}_{2n}(u)$ and integrate with respect to u from 0 to π. Then

$$\int_0^{\pi} \cos(2k \cos u \cos z)\operatorname{ce}_{2n}(u)\,du = c_{2n} \operatorname{ce}_{2n}(z) \int_0^{\pi} \operatorname{ce}_{2n}^2(u)\,du, \tag{5}$$

all other terms on the r.h.s. vanishing by virtue of orthogonality (§ 2.19). Hence by (5) above and (1) § 10.12,

$$\operatorname{ce}_{2n}(z)/\lambda_{2n} = \tfrac{1}{2}\pi c_{2n} \operatorname{ce}_{2n}(z),$$

so, using (5) § 10.12,

$$c_{2n} = 2/\pi\lambda_{2n} = 2A_0^{(2n)}/\operatorname{ce}_{2n}(\tfrac{1}{2}\pi, q). \tag{6}$$

Consequently from (4), (6) we obtain

$$\cos(2k \cos u \cos z) = 2 \sum_{n=0}^{\infty} \frac{A_0^{(2n)}}{\operatorname{ce}_{2n}(\tfrac{1}{2}\pi, q)} \operatorname{ce}_{2n}(u)\operatorname{ce}_{2n}(z), \tag{7}$$

which is the expansion of the nucleus for $\operatorname{ce}_{2n}(z,q)$ in terms of the functions themselves. The seven remaining primary nuclei in

Table 14 (p. 180) may be expanded in a similar way, and the results are given below [97]:

$$\cosh(2k \sin u \sin z) = 2 \sum_{n=0}^{\infty} \frac{A_0^{(2n)}}{\mathrm{ce}_{2n}(0)}\, \mathrm{ce}_{2n}(u)\mathrm{ce}_{2n}(z), \tag{8}$$

$$\sin(2k \cos u \cos z) = -2k \sum_{n=0}^{\infty} \frac{A_1^{(2n+1)}}{\mathrm{ce}'_{2n+1}(\tfrac{1}{2}\pi)}\, \mathrm{ce}_{2n+1}(u)\mathrm{ce}_{2n+1}(z), \tag{9}$$

$$\sinh(2k \sin u \sin z) = 2k \sum_{n=0}^{\infty} \frac{B_1^{(2n+1)}}{\mathrm{se}'_{2n+1}(0)}\, \mathrm{se}_{2n+1}(u)\mathrm{se}_{2n+1}(z), \tag{10}$$

$$\cos u \cos z \cosh(2k \sin u \sin z) = \sum_{n=0}^{\infty} \frac{A_1^{(2n+1)}}{\mathrm{ce}_{2n+1}(0)}\, \mathrm{ce}_{2n+1}(u)\mathrm{ce}_{2n+1}(z), \tag{11}$$

$$\sin u \sin z \cos(2k \cos u \cos z) = \sum_{n=0}^{\infty} \frac{B_1^{(2n+1)}}{\mathrm{se}_{2n+1}(\tfrac{1}{2}\pi)}\, \mathrm{se}_{2n+1}(u)\mathrm{se}_{2n+1}(z), \tag{12}$$

$$\sin u \sin z \sin(2k \cos u \cos z) = -k \sum_{n=0}^{\infty} \frac{B_2^{(2n+2)}}{\mathrm{se}'_{2n+2}(\tfrac{1}{2}\pi)}\, \mathrm{se}_{2n+2}(u)\mathrm{se}_{2n+2}(z), \tag{13}$$

$$\cos u \cos z \sinh(2k \sin u \sin z) = k \sum_{n=0}^{\infty} \frac{B_2^{(2n+2)}}{\mathrm{se}'_{2n+2}(0)}\, \mathrm{se}_{2n+2}(u)\mathrm{se}_{2n+2}(z). \tag{14}$$

By writing iz for z in the above relationships, series are obtained in terms of Mathieu and modified Mathieu functions. For z real, convergence of the series follows from the fact that the A, $B \to 0$ as $n \to +\infty$ (see § 3.35).

10.61. Results deducible from § 10.60. Writing $u = \tfrac{1}{2}\pi$ in (7) § 10.60 yields

$$1 = 2 \sum_{n=0}^{\infty} A_0^{(2n)}\mathrm{ce}_{2n}(z). \tag{1}$$

Assuming the r.h.s. of (9) § 10.60 and its first derivative are uniformly convergent with respect to u, by differentiating and substituting $u = \tfrac{1}{2}\pi$ we get

$$\cos z = \sum_{n=0}^{\infty} A_1^{(2n+1)}\mathrm{ce}_{2n+1}(z). \tag{2}$$

In a similar way we find that

$$\sin z = \sum_{n=0}^{\infty} B_1^{(2n+1)}\mathrm{se}_{2n+1}(z), \tag{3}$$

$$\sin 2z = \sum_{n=0}^{\infty} B_2^{(2n+2)}\mathrm{se}_{2n+2}(z). \tag{4}$$

Inserting the expansion of $\mathrm{ce}_{2n}(z)$ in (1) gives

$$1 = 2 \sum_{n=0}^{\infty} A_0^{(2n)} \sum_{r=0}^{\infty} A_{2r}^{(2n)} \cos 2rz. \tag{5}$$

Since the l.h.s. is independent of z, equating constant terms, i.e. $r = 0$, yields

$$1 = 2 \sum_{n=0}^{\infty} [A_0^{(2n)}]^2. \tag{6}$$

Equating the coefficient of $\cos 2rz$ to zero leads to

$$\sum_{n=0}^{\infty} A_0^{(2n)} A_{2r}^{(2n)} = 0 \quad (r \neq 0). \tag{7}$$

Similarly we deduce that

$$\sum_{n=0}^{\infty} [A_1^{(2n+1)}]^2 = \sum_{n=0}^{\infty} [B_1^{(2n+1)}]^2 = \sum_{n=0}^{\infty} [B_2^{(2n+2)}]^2 = 1. \tag{8}$$

Using the orthogonal properties of the functions the following expansions may be obtained:

$$\cos 2rz = \sum_{n=0}^{\infty} A_{2r}^{(2n)} \, \mathrm{ce}_{2n}(z), \tag{9}$$

$$\cos(2r+1)z = \sum_{n=0}^{\infty} A_{2r+1}^{(2n+1)} \, \mathrm{ce}_{2n+1}(z), \tag{10}$$

$$\sin(2r+1)z = \sum_{n=0}^{\infty} B_{2r+1}^{(2n+1)} \, \mathrm{se}_{2n+1}(z), \tag{11}$$

$$\sin(2r+2)z = \sum_{n=0}^{\infty} B_{2r+2}^{(2n+2)} \, \mathrm{se}_{2n+2}(z), \tag{12}$$

$$\sum_{\substack{n=0 \\ r>0}}^{\infty} [A_{2r}^{(2n)}]^2 = \sum_{n=0}^{\infty} [A_{2r+1}^{(2n+1)}]^2 = \sum_{n=0}^{\infty} [B_{2r+1}^{(2n+1)}]^2 = \sum_{n=0}^{\infty} [B_{2r+2}^{(2n+2)}]^2 = 1, \tag{13}$$

$$\sum_{n=0}^{\infty} [A_{2r}^{(2n)} A_{2s}^{(2n)}] = \sum_{n=0}^{\infty} [A_{2r+1}^{(2n+1)} A_{2s+1}^{(2n+1)}] = \sum_{n=0}^{\infty} [B_{2r+1}^{(2n+1)} B_{2s+1}^{(2n+1)}]$$

$$= \sum_{n=0}^{\infty} [B_{2r+2}^{(2n+2)} B_{2s+2}^{(2n+2)}] = 0 \quad (14)$$

provided $r \neq s$. Additional relationships between the functions of integral order will be found in reference [97].

10.62. Additional expansions. Assuming uniform convergence of the series in § 10.60, numerous results may be deduced by differentiating or by integrating term by term. Two examples involving B.F. will suffice to illustrate this point. Integrate both sides of (7) § 10.60 with respect to u from 0 to π, and we get

$$1^{\circ}. \qquad J_0(2k \cos z) = 2 \sum_{n=0}^{\infty} [A_0^{(2n)}]^2 \, \mathrm{ce}_{2n}(z, q) / \mathrm{ce}_{2n}(\tfrac{1}{2}\pi, q). \tag{1}$$

If $z = 0$, $$J_0(2k) = 2 \sum_{n=0}^{\infty} [A_0^{(2n)}]^2 \, \mathrm{ce}_{2n}(0, q)/\mathrm{ce}_{2n}(\tfrac{1}{2}\pi, q);$$ (2)

while for $z = \tfrac{1}{2}\pi$ $$1 = 2 \sum_{n=0}^{\infty} [A_0^{(2n)}]^2,$$ (3)

as at (6) § 10.61.

2°. Multiplying both sides of (7) § 10.60 by $\cos 2mu$ and integrating as before leads to

$$J_{2m}(2k \cos z) = \sum_{n=0}^{\infty} A_0^{(2n)} A_{2m}^{(2n)} \, \mathrm{ce}_{2n}(z, q)/\mathrm{ce}_{2n}(\tfrac{1}{2}\pi, q) \quad (m > 0). \quad (4)$$

Rigorous proofs of the validity of results in §§ 10.53, 10.60, 10.61, and a demonstration that, under conditions similar to those for the Fourier case, a function of period π, 2π may be expanded in a series of Mathieu functions of integral order, are beyond the scope of the text. For functions having period $2s\pi$, $s \geqslant 2$, the Mathieu functions of order $2n+\beta$, $2n+1+\beta$, $\beta = p/s$, $0 < \beta < 1$, would be needed (see §§ 2.20, 4.71).

10.70. Integral equations of the second kind. We commence with the equation

$$\frac{d^2y}{du^2} + [a - 2q\,\psi(\omega u)]y = 0, \quad (1)$$

where $\psi(\omega u)$ has the same properties as in (1) § 6.10.

Multiplying throughout by $\sin \nu u$, $\nu^2 = a$, gives

$$\sin \nu u \, y'' + a \sin \nu u \, y = 2q\,\psi(\omega u)\sin \nu u \, y, \quad (2)$$

so $$\int_0^z \sin \nu u \, dy' + a \int_0^z \sin \nu u \, y \, du = 2q \int_0^z \psi(\omega u)\sin \nu u \, y \, du. \quad (3)$$

Thus

$$[y' \sin \nu u]_0^z - \nu \int_0^z \cos \nu u \, dy + a \int_0^z \sin \nu u \, y \, du = 2q \int_0^z \psi(\omega u)\sin \nu u \, y \, du, \quad (4)$$

and ultimately, since $a = \nu^2$, we get

$$y'(z)\sin \nu z - \nu y(z)\cos \nu z = -\nu y(0) + 2q \int_0^z \psi(\omega u)\sin \nu u \, y \, du. \quad (5)$$

If in (2) $\sin \nu u$ is replaced by $\cos \nu u$, the equation corresponding to (5) is

$$y'(z)\cos \nu u + \nu y(z)\sin \nu z = y'(0) + 2q \int_0^z \psi(\omega u)\cos \nu u \, y \, du. \quad (6)$$

Multiplying (5) by $\cos \nu z/\nu$, (6) by $\sin \nu z/\nu$, and subtracting the first from the second, yields the integral equation

$$y(z) = y(0)\cos \nu z + \frac{y'(0)\sin \nu z}{\nu} + \frac{2q}{\nu} \int_0^z \sin \nu(z-u)\psi(\omega u)y(u) \, du. \quad (7)$$

Hence we are led to two solutions of (1), in the form of the integral equations of the second kind with variable upper limits, namely,

$$y_1(z) = y_1(0)\cos \nu z + \frac{y_1'(0)\sin \nu z}{\nu} + \frac{2q}{\nu} \int_0^z \sin \nu(z-u)\psi(\omega u)y_1(u) \, du, \quad (8)$$

and

$$y_2(z) = y_2(0)\cos \nu z + \frac{y_2'(0)\sin \nu z}{\nu} + \frac{2q}{\nu} \int_0^z \sin \nu(z-u)\psi(\omega u)y_2(u) \, du. \quad (9)$$

If we specify the initial conditions, as in § 4.10, to be

$$y_1(0) = 1, \qquad y_1'(0) = 0,$$
$$y_2(0) = 0, \qquad y_2'(0) = 1,$$

(8), (9) give

$$y_1(z) = \cos \nu z + \frac{2q}{\nu} \int_0^z \sin \nu(z-u)\psi(\omega u)y_1(u) \, du \quad (10)$$

and

$$y_2(z) = \frac{\sin \nu z}{\nu} + \frac{2q}{\nu} \int_0^z \sin \nu(z-u)\psi(\omega u)y_2(u) \, du, \quad (11)$$

respectively. For Mathieu's equation $\psi(\omega u) = \cos 2u$.

10.71. Integral equations for $y'' - (a - 2q \cosh 2z)y = 0$**.** Using the procedure in § 10.70 but with $\sinh \nu u$, $\cosh \nu u$ for $\sin \nu u$, and $\cos \nu u$, respectively, we get

$$y(z) = y(0)\cosh \nu z + \frac{y'(0)\sinh \nu z}{\nu} - \frac{2q}{\nu} \int_0^z \sinh \nu(z-u)\cosh 2u \, y(u) \, du. \quad (1)$$

For the initial conditions in § 10.70, (1) yields

$$y_1(z) = \cosh \nu z - \frac{2q}{\nu} \int_0^z \sinh \nu(z-u)\cosh 2u \, y_1(u) \, du \quad (z \text{ finite}) \quad (2)$$

and

$$y_2(z) = \frac{\sinh \nu z}{\nu} - \frac{2q}{\nu} \int_0^z \sinh \nu(z-u)\cosh 2u \, y_2(u) \, du \quad (z \text{ finite}), \quad (3)$$

where $y_1(z)$, $y_2(z)$ are, respectively, even and odd solutions of the above differential equation.

10.72. Solution of (10), (11) § 10.70. Write $p = 2q/\nu$, and assume that
$$y_1(z) = \cos \nu z + pc_1(z) + p^2 c_2(z) + p^3 c_3(z) + \cdots, \qquad (1)$$
the c being continuous functions of z. Substituting (1) into (10) § 10.70 we get

$$pc_1(z) + p^2 c_2(z) + \cdots$$
$$= p \int_0^z \sin \nu(z-u)\psi(\omega u)[\cos \nu u + pc_1(u) + p^2 c_2(u) + \cdots]\, du. \qquad (2)$$

Equating the coefficients of p on each side of (2), we have

$$c_1(z) = \int_0^z \sin \nu(z-u)\cos \nu u\, \psi(\omega u)\, du$$
$$= \tfrac{1}{2} \int_0^z [\sin \nu(z-2u) + \sin \nu z]\psi(\omega u)\, du$$
$$= \tfrac{1}{2}\sin \nu z \int_0^z \psi(\omega u)\, du + \tfrac{1}{2} \int_0^z \sin \nu(z-2u)\psi(\omega u)\, du. \qquad (3)$$

This is now substituted for $c_1(u)$ into the r.h.s. of (2) and $c_2(z)$ obtained by equating the coefficients of p^2 on each side. If p and $p|\psi(\omega u)|$ are small enough, a first approximation is given by

$$y_1(z) \simeq \cos \nu z + (q/\nu)\left[\sin \nu z \int_0^z \psi(\omega u)\, du + \int_0^z \sin \nu(z-2u)\psi(\omega u)\, du\right], \qquad (4)$$

the omitted part being $O(1/\nu^2)$. Similarly for (11) § 10.70, we find that

$$y_2(z) \simeq \frac{\sin \nu z}{\nu} - (q/\nu^2)\left[\cos \nu z \int_0^z \psi(\omega u)\, du - \int_0^z \cos \nu(z-2u)\psi(\omega u)\, du\right], \qquad (5)$$

the omitted part being $O(1/\nu^3)$.

10.73. Alternative forms of (7) § 10.70. This may be written

$$y(z) = C_\nu \cos \nu z + S_\nu \sin \nu z + \frac{2q}{\nu} \int_0^z \sin \nu(z-u)\psi(\omega u)y(u)\, du, \qquad (1)$$

where $C_\nu = y(0)$, $S_\nu = y'(0)/\nu$. Now let $a = m^2 + \lambda^2$, m being an integer, then (1) § 10.70 becomes either

$$\frac{d^2 y}{dz^2} + [m^2 - \{-\lambda^2 + 2q\,\psi(\omega z)\}]y = 0 \qquad (2)$$

or

$$\frac{d^2 y}{dz^2} + [\lambda^2 - \{2q\,\psi(\omega z) - m^2\}]y = 0. \qquad (3)$$

Since (1) is an integral equation for (1) § 10.70, it follows that the integral equations of the second kind for (2), (3) are, respectively,

$$y(z) = C_m \cos mz + S_m \sin mz + \frac{1}{m} \int_0^z \sin m(z-u)[2q\,\psi(\omega u) - \lambda^2]y(u)\,du, \tag{4}$$

$$y(z) = C_\lambda \cos \lambda z + S_\lambda \sin \lambda z + \frac{1}{\lambda} \int_0^z \sin \lambda(z-u)[2q\,\psi(\omega u) - m^2]y(u)\,du. \tag{5}$$

Alternatively, if we take $a = \alpha_1^2 + \alpha_2^2$, by varying either α_1 or α_2, keeping a constant, we can write down an infinite number of integral equations. The C, S are functions of q.

10.74. Integro-differential equations for
$$y'' + 2\kappa y' + [a - 2q\,\psi(\omega z)]y = 0.$$

The integro-differential equations corresponding to (1), (4), (5) §10.73 are, respectively,

$$y(z) = \bar{C}_\nu \cos \nu z + \bar{S}_\nu \sin \nu z + \frac{1}{\nu} \int_0^z \sin \nu(z-u)\left[2q\,\psi(\omega u) - 2\kappa\frac{d}{du}\right]y(u)\,du, \tag{1}$$

$$y(z) = \bar{C}_m \cos mz + \bar{S}_m \sin mz +$$
$$+ \frac{1}{m} \int_0^z \sin m(z-u)\left[2q\,\psi(\omega u) - \lambda^2 - 2\kappa\frac{d}{du}\right]y(u)\,du, \tag{2}$$

and

$$y(z) = \bar{C}_\lambda \cos \lambda z + \bar{S}_\lambda \sin \lambda z +$$
$$+ \frac{1}{\lambda} \int_0^z \sin \lambda(z-u)\left[2q\,\psi(\omega u) - m^2 - 2\kappa\frac{d}{du}\right]y(u)\,du. \tag{3}$$

The $\bar{C}$, $\bar{S}$ are functions of q.

10.75. Second solution of Mathieu's equation using (4) § 10.73.
The integral equation may be split up into the two parts, namely,

$$y_1(z) = C_m \cos mz + \frac{1}{m} \int_0^z \sin m(z-u)(2q\cos 2u - \lambda^2)y_1(u)\,du \tag{1}$$

and

$$y_2(z) = S_m \sin mz + \frac{1}{m} \int_0^z \sin m(z-u)(2q\cos 2u - \lambda^2)y_2(u)\,du. \tag{2}$$

Let a be the characteristic number for $\mathrm{ce}_2(z,q)$, then we have to determine $y_2(z)$ from (2). For $\mathrm{ce}_2(z,q)$, by (5) §2.151

$$a = 4 + \frac{5}{12}q^2 - \frac{763}{13824}q^4 + \cdots; \tag{3}$$

so with $m = 2$, $\qquad \lambda^2 = \frac{5}{12}q^2 - \frac{763}{13824}q^4 + \cdots. \tag{4}$

Assume that

$$y_2(u) = s_0(u) + qs_1(u) + q^2 s_2(u) + \cdots, \tag{5}$$

$$S_2(q) = 1 + \beta_1 q + \beta_2 q^2 + \beta_3 q^3 + \cdots. \tag{6}$$

Substituting (4), (5), (6) into (2) gives

$$s_0(z) + qs_1(z) + q^2 s_2(z) + q^3 s_3(z) + \cdots = (1 + \beta_1 q + \beta_2 q^2 + \beta_3 q^3 + \cdots)\sin 2z +$$

$$+ \int_0^z \sin 2(z-u)\left[q\cos 2u - \frac{5}{24}q^2 + \frac{763}{27648}q^4 - \cdots \right] \times$$

$$\times [s_0(u) + qs_1(u) + q^2 s_2(u) + \cdots]\, du. \tag{7}$$

Equating like powers of q on both sides of (7) leads to

$$q^0 \qquad s_0(z) = \sin 2z, \tag{8}$$

$$q \qquad s_1(z) = \beta_1 \sin 2z + \int_0^z \sin 2(z-u)\cos 2u\, s_0(u)\, du$$

$$= \beta_1 \sin 2z + \tfrac{1}{2} \int_0^z \sin 2(z-u)\sin 4u\, du$$

$$= (\beta_1 + \tfrac{1}{6})\sin 2z - \tfrac{1}{12}\sin 4z. \tag{9}$$

If for the sake of illustration we adopt the normalization of §2.11, the coefficient of $\sin 2z$ is unity for all q. Thus in $s_1(z)$, $s_2(z),\ldots$ the coefficient of $\sin 2z$ must vanish, so

$$\beta_1 = -\tfrac{1}{6} \quad \text{and} \quad s_1(z) = -\tfrac{1}{12}\sin 4z; \tag{10}$$

$$q^2 \quad s_2(z) = \beta_2 \sin 2z + \int_0^z \sin 2(z-u)\left[\cos 2u\, s_1(u) - \frac{5}{24}s_0(u)\right] du$$

$$= \beta_2 \sin 2z - \int_0^z \sin 2(z-u)\left[\frac{1}{12}\cos 2u \sin 4u + \frac{5}{24}\sin 2u\right] du$$

$$= \left(\beta_2 - \frac{9}{128}\right)\sin 2z + \frac{1}{8}z\cos 2z + \frac{1}{384}\sin 6z. \tag{11}$$

Thus $\qquad \beta_2 = \dfrac{9}{128}$ and $s_2(z) = \dfrac{1}{8}z\cos 2z + \dfrac{1}{384}\sin 6z.$ (12)

$$q^3 \quad s_3(z) = \left(\beta_3 - \frac{619}{34560}\right)\sin 2z -$$

$$-\left[-\frac{1}{32}z + \frac{1}{96}z\cos 4z - \frac{53}{13824}\sin 4z + \frac{1}{23040}\sin 8z\right],$$

giving $\qquad\qquad\qquad \beta_3 = \dfrac{619}{34560},$

and

$$s_3(z) = -\left[-\frac{1}{32}z + \frac{1}{96}z\cos 4z - \frac{53}{13824}\sin 4z + \frac{1}{23040}\sin 8z\right], \quad (13)$$

and so on. Then

$$y_2(z) = \sum_{r=0}^{\infty} q^r s_r(z) = \sin 2z - \frac{1}{12}q\sin 4z + q^2\left(\frac{1}{8}z\cos 2z + \frac{1}{384}\sin 6z\right) -$$

$$-q^3\left(-\frac{1}{32}z + \frac{1}{96}z\cos 4z - \frac{53}{13824}\sin 4z + \frac{1}{23040}\sin 8z\right) + \dots \quad (14)$$

Thus

$$y_2(z) = \mathrm{fe}_2(z,q) = \frac{1}{8}q^2\left(1 - \frac{17}{144}q^2 - \dots\right)z\,\mathrm{ce}_2(z,q) + \sin 2z - \frac{1}{12}q\sin 4z +$$

$$+ \frac{1}{384}q^2\sin 6z - \frac{1}{512}q^3\left(-\frac{53}{27}\sin 4z + \frac{1}{45}\sin 8z\right) + \dots \quad (15)$$

$$= \left(1 - \frac{1}{6}q + \frac{9}{128}q^2 + \frac{619}{34560}q^3 - \dots\right)\sin 2z +$$

$$+ \int_0^z \sin 2(z-u)\left[q\cos 2u - \frac{5}{24}q^2 + \frac{763}{27648}q^4 - \dots\right]\mathrm{fe}_2(u,q)\,du. \quad (16)$$

A similar treatment of equation (1) would yield the series for $\mathrm{ce}_2(z,q)$, the first solution of Mathieu's equation with $a = a_2$, as given at (3) §2.150. In general, if $y_1(z) = \mathrm{ce}_m(z,q)$ and the q series for a is unknown, write

$$a = m^2 + \alpha_1 q + \alpha_2 q^2 + \alpha_3 q^3 + \dots, \quad (17)$$

make the coefficient of $\cos mz$ unity, and determine $\alpha_1, \alpha_2, \dots$ so that all terms in the expansion are periodic in π or 2π, according as m is even or odd (see § 2.13 et seq.). To obtain $\mathrm{se}_m(z,q)$, treat (2) in this way. $\mathrm{ge}_m(z,q)$ can be obtained by analysis similar to that from (3)–(15).

10.76. Integral equations for $y_1(z)y_2(z)$. Let $y_1(z)$, $y_2(z)$ be independent solutions of

$$y'' + (a - 2q\cos 2u)y = 0, \tag{1}$$

for the same a, q. Then writing $\xi(u) = (2q\cos 2u - a)$, we have

$$y_1'' - \xi(u)y_1 = 0 \tag{2}$$

and

$$y_2'' - \xi(u)y_2 = 0. \tag{3}$$

Multiplying (2) by y_2', (3) by y_1', adding and integrating with respect to u from 0 to z, gives

$$\int_0^z (y_1'' y_2' + y_1' y_2'')\, du = \int_0^z (y_1' y_2 + y_2' y_1)\xi(u)\, du, \tag{4}$$

so

$$\int_0^z d(y_1' y_2') = \int_0^z \xi(u)\, d(y_1 y_2). \tag{5}$$

Hence by partial integration of the r.h.s. of (5) we find that

$$y_1'(z)y_2'(z) = y_1'(0)y_2'(0) - y_1(0)y_2(0)\xi(0) +$$

$$+ y_1(z)y_2(z)\xi(z) + 4q\int_0^z y_1(u)y_2(u)\sin 2u\, du. \tag{6}$$

If the initial conditions are $y_1(0) = y_2'(0) = 1$, $y_1'(0) = y_2(0) = 0$, the first two members on the r.h.s. of (6) vanish, and we obtain

$$y_1'(z)y_2'(z) = y_1(z)y_2(z)\xi(z) + 4q\int_0^z y_1(u)y_2(u)\sin 2u\, du. \tag{7}$$

Results similar to (6), (7) may be obtained in connexion with Hill's equation.

For the equation $y'' - (a - 2q\cosh 2u)y = 0$, with

$$\chi(u) = (2q\cosh 2u - a)$$

we get

$$y_1'(z)y_2'(z) = y_1'(0)y_2'(0) + y_1(0)y_2(0)\chi(0) -$$

$$- y_1(z)y_2(z)\chi(z) + 4q\int_0^z y_1(u)y_2(u)\sinh 2u\, du. \tag{8}$$

10.77. Differential equation satisfied by $w(z) = y_1(z)y_2(z)$. Mathieu's equation may be written

$$y'' - \xi y = 0, \tag{1}$$

where $\xi = (2q\cos 2z - a)$. Differentiating (1) gives $y''' - \xi y' - \xi' y = 0$, so

$$y_1''' - \xi y_1' - \xi' y_1 = 0 \tag{2}$$

and

$$y_2''' - \xi y_2' - \xi' y_2 = 0. \tag{3}$$

Multiplying (2) by y_2, (3) by y_1, and adding leads to the equation

$$y_1'''y_2+y_2'''y_1-2\xi'y_1y_2-\xi(y_1y_2'+y_2y_1') = 0. \tag{4}$$

From (1) we have

$$(y_1''-\xi y_1)y_2' = 0 \tag{5}$$

and

$$(y_2''-\xi y_2)y_1' = 0, \tag{6}$$

so by addition

$$y_1''y_2'+y_2''y_1' = \xi(y_1y_2'+y_2y_1') = \xi w'. \tag{7}$$

Also

$$w''' = y_1'''y_2+y_2'''y_1+3(y_1''y_2'+y_2''y_1'). \tag{8}$$

Hence from (4), (7), (8) the equation sought is

$$w'''-4\xi w'-2\xi'w = 0. \tag{9}$$

This result applies to Hill's equation (1) § 6.10, provided

$$\xi = [2q\,\psi(\omega z)-a].$$

The complete solution of (9) with three arbitrary constants is

$$w = Ay_1^2+By_1y_2+Cy_2^2. \tag{10}$$

ASYMPTOTIC FORMULAE

11.10. Approximations. The modified Mathieu functions lend themselves readily to the derivation of approximate asymptotic formulae when $R(z)$ is large and positive. If k and z are such that $2k\cosh z \simeq ke^z = v$, this being appreciably greater than the order of the function, the dominant term in the asymptotic expansion of $J_{2r}(2k\cosh z)$ is [203, p. 81]

$$(2/\pi v)^{\frac{1}{2}}\cos(v-\tfrac{1}{4}\pi-r\pi) = (-1)^r(2/\pi v)^{\frac{1}{2}}\sin(v+\tfrac{1}{4}\pi). \tag{1}$$

Substituting (1) in (15) § 8.10 and using the multipliers p_m, s_m in Appendix I, § 3, leads to the approximate result

$$\mathrm{Ce}_{2n}(z,q) \sim p_{2n}(2/\pi v)^{\frac{1}{2}}\sin(v+\tfrac{1}{4}\pi) \quad (a_{2n}). \tag{2}$$

Writing

$$J_{2r+1}(2k\cosh z) \sim (2/\pi v)^{\frac{1}{2}}\cos\{v-\tfrac{1}{4}\pi-\tfrac{1}{2}(2r+1)\pi\}$$

$$= (-1)^{r+1}(2/\pi v)^{\frac{1}{2}}\cos(v+\tfrac{1}{4}\pi) \tag{3}$$

in (1) § 8.12 leads to

$$\mathrm{Ce}_{2n+1}(z,q) \sim -p_{2n+1}(2/\pi v)^{\frac{1}{2}}\cos(v+\tfrac{1}{4}\pi) \quad (a_{2n+1}). \tag{4}$$

The same result follows from (2) § 8.12, while (6), (7) § 8.13 give with

$$\tanh z \simeq \coth z \simeq 1, \qquad 2k\sinh z \simeq 2k\cosh z \simeq ke^z,$$

$$\mathrm{Se}_{2n+1}(z,q) \sim -s_{2n+1}(2/\pi v)^{\frac{1}{2}}\cos(v+\tfrac{1}{4}\pi) \quad (b_{2n+1}). \tag{5}$$

From (4), (5) when $R(z) > 0$ is large enough, it follows that

$$\mathrm{Ce}_{2n+1}(z,q) \sim (p_{2n+1}/s_{2n+1})\mathrm{Se}_{2n+1}(z,q). \tag{6}$$

From (10), (11) § 8.13 we derive

$$\mathrm{Se}_{2n+2}(z,q) \sim s_{2n+2}(2/\pi v)^{\frac{1}{2}}\sin(v+\tfrac{1}{4}\pi) \quad (b_{2n+2}), \tag{7}$$

and so by (2), (7), when $R(z) > 0$ is large enough, we may write

$$\mathrm{Ce}_{2n+2}(z,q) \sim (p_{2n+2}/s_{2n+2})\mathrm{Se}_{2n+2}(z,q). \tag{8}$$

As z (large and real) increases, all the above functions, and those at (9)–(12), alternate† with ever-increasing rapidity, but decreasing amplitudes. When $z \to +\infty$ they all tend to zero exponentially.

The second solutions corresponding to the first given above are defined in §§ 8.11–8.13. Using the multipliers in Appendix I and

---

† An alternating function is one which oscillates and has real zeros.

proceeding as at (1)–(4), we obtain the following approximate asymptotic representations:

$$\text{Fey}_{2n}(z,q) \sim -p_{2n}\left(\frac{2}{\pi v}\right)^{\frac{1}{2}}\cos(v+\tfrac{1}{4}\pi) \qquad (a_{2n}), \tag{9}$$

$$\text{Fey}_{2n+1}(z,q) \sim -p_{2n+1}\left(\frac{2}{\pi v}\right)^{\frac{1}{2}}\sin(v+\tfrac{1}{4}\pi) \qquad (a_{2n+1}), \tag{10}$$

$$\text{Gey}_{2n+1}(z,q) \sim -s_{2n+1}\left(\frac{2}{\pi v}\right)^{\frac{1}{2}}\sin(v+\tfrac{1}{4}\pi) \qquad (b_{2n+1}), \tag{11}$$

$$\text{Gey}_{2n+2}(z,q) \sim -s_{2n+2}\left(\frac{2}{\pi v}\right)^{\frac{1}{2}}\cos(v+\tfrac{1}{4}\pi) \qquad (b_{2n+2}). \tag{12}$$

The dominant term in the asymptotic formula for $\text{Fey}_{2n+2}(z,q)$ is a constant multiple of that of Gey_{2n+2}, the constant being p_{2n+2}/s_{2n+2}. A similar remark applies to (10), (11). These formulae are valid if $R(v) \to +\infty$ with v, so $-\tfrac{1}{2}\pi < \text{phase } z < \tfrac{1}{2}\pi$.

11.11. Approximate formulae for $\text{Me}_m^{(1),(2)}(z,q)$, $\text{Ne}_m^{(1),(2)}(z,q)$, $\text{Fek}_m(z,q)$, $\text{Gek}_m(z,q)$. Using the dominant term in the asymptotic expansions of the Hankel functions in § 13.40,† if $|v| \gg n$ we get:

$$\text{Me}_{2n}^{(1),(2)}(z,q) \sim p_{2n}\left(\frac{2}{\pi v}\right)^{\frac{1}{2}}e^{\pm i(v-\frac{1}{4}\pi)} \qquad (a_{2n}), \tag{1}$$

$$\text{Me}_{2n+1}^{(1),(2)}(z,q) \sim p_{2n+1}\left(\frac{2}{\pi v}\right)^{\frac{1}{2}}e^{\pm i(v-\frac{3}{4}\pi)} \qquad (a_{2n+1}), \tag{2}$$

$$\text{Ne}_{2n+1}^{(1),(2)}(z,q) \sim s_{2n+1}\left(\frac{2}{\pi v}\right)^{\frac{1}{2}}e^{\pm i(v-\frac{3}{4}\pi)} \qquad (b_{2n+1}), \tag{3}$$

$$\text{Ne}_{2n+2}^{(1),(2)}(z,q) \sim s_{2n+2}\left(\frac{2}{\pi v}\right)^{\frac{1}{2}}e^{\pm i(v-\frac{1}{4}\pi)} \qquad (b_{2n+2}). \tag{4}$$

Note that (1) is a constant multiple of (4), and (2) of (3).

Applying the relationships in § 13.41 to (1)–(4), formulae for $\text{Fek}_m(z,q)$, $\text{Gek}_m(z,q)$ are derived immediately. As $z \to +\infty$ the first function tends to a constant multiple of the second, for any m.

11.12. Formulae for $q < 0$. Using the formulae in § 8.30 and proceeding as in § 11.10, we obtain the following:

$$\text{Ce}_{2n}(z,-q) \sim p'_{2n}\, e^v/(2\pi v)^{\frac{1}{2}} \qquad (a_{2n}), \tag{1}$$

$$\text{Ce}_{2n+1}(z,-q) \sim s'_{2n+1}\, e^v/(2\pi v)^{\frac{1}{2}} \qquad (b_{2n+1}), \tag{2}$$

$$\text{Se}_{2n+1}(z,-q) \sim p'_{2n+1}\, e^v/(2\pi v)^{\frac{1}{2}} \qquad (a_{2n+1}), \tag{3}$$

$$\text{Se}_{2n+2}(z,-q) \sim s'_{2n+2}\, e^v/(2\pi v)^{\frac{1}{2}} \qquad (b_{2n+2}). \tag{4}$$

† Or the formulae in § 11.10, substituted into (1), (2) § 13.40.

These functions are constant multiples of one another, and each tends to $+\infty$ monotonically as $z \to +\infty$.

The formulae for $\mathrm{Fek}_{2n}(z, -q)$, $\mathrm{Fek}_{2n+1}(z, -q)$, $\mathrm{Gek}_{2n+1}(z, -q)$, $\mathrm{Gek}_{2n+2}(z, -q)$ are obtained from (1)–(4), respectively, on replacing e^v by e^{-v}. Each function tends to zero monotonically as $z \to +\infty$.

All formulae given hitherto in this chapter depend upon z being large enough for the Bessel functions in §§ 8.10–8.30 to be represented (approximately) by the dominant terms in their asymptotic expansions. We shall now remove this restriction on z, and establish what may be regarded as accurate asymptotic expansions.

11.20. Accurate asymptotic expansions in z. We commence with the modified Mathieu equation

$$y'' - (a - 2k^2 \cosh 2z)y = 0. \tag{1}$$

If in (1) we write $x = -ike^z = -iv$, it becomes [37]

$$\frac{d^2y}{dx^2} + \frac{1}{x}\frac{dy}{dx} - \left(1 + \frac{a}{x^2} + \frac{k^4}{x^4}\right)y = 0. \tag{2}$$

A second transformation is effected by putting $y = we^{-x}$, and we now get

$$\frac{d^2w}{dx^2} - \left(2 - \frac{1}{x}\right)\frac{dw}{dx} - \left(\frac{1}{x} + \frac{a}{x^2} + \frac{k^4}{x^4}\right)w = 0. \tag{3}$$

To solve (3) assume that $w = \sum_{r=0}^{\infty}(-1)^r c_r x^{-r-\frac{1}{2}}$, with $c_0 = 1$. Inserting this in (3) and equating coefficients of like powers of x to zero, we obtain the recurrence relations

$$8c_1 + (4a - 1) = 0, \tag{4}$$

$$16c_2 + (4a - 9)c_1 = 0, \tag{5}$$

and $\qquad 2(r+1)c_{r+1} + [a - (r + \tfrac{1}{2})^2]c_r + k^4 c_{r-2} = 0 \quad (r \geqslant 2). \tag{6}$

From (4)–(6) we find the expressions for the c to be as follows [103]:

$$c_1 = -\frac{(4a - 1^2)}{8}, \qquad c_2 = \frac{(4a - 1^2)(4a - 3^2)}{2! \, 8^2}, \tag{7}$$

$$c_3 = -\frac{(4a - 1^2)(4a - 3^2)(4a - 5^2)}{3! \, 8^3} - \frac{1}{3!}k^4, \tag{8}$$

$$c_4 = \frac{(4a - 1^2)(4a - 3^2)(4a - 5^2)(4a - 7^2)}{4! \, 8^4} + \frac{k^4}{2 \cdot 4!}(4a - 13), \tag{9}$$

and so on. It should be noted that, (1) the dominant term and the two which follow are independent of k, (2) the first member of each

c is identical with that in the asymptotic series for $J_\nu(v)$ when $a = \nu^2$, i.e. the degenerate form of the c when $k \to 0$. If x remains constant meanwhile, equation (2) reduces to the standard form for the B.F. $J_\nu(v)$ and $Y_\nu(v)$. Frequently the terms involving k in (8), (9) are small numerically, compared with the earlier terms in the series, and may be neglected, but this point should always be checked. The solution of (2), with $x = -iv$, is

$$y = we^{-x} = \frac{e^{iv}}{(-iv)^{\frac{1}{2}}} \sum_{r=0}^{\infty} (-1)^r c_r(-iv)^{-r} = \frac{e^{i(v+\frac{1}{4}\pi)}}{v^{\frac{1}{2}}} \sum_{r=0}^{\infty} c_r(iv)^{-r} \qquad (10)$$

$$= \frac{e^{i(v+\frac{1}{4}\pi)}}{v^{\frac{1}{2}}}[(1 - c_2 v^{-2} + c_4 v^{-4} - \ldots) - i(c_1 v^{-1} - c_3 v^{-3} + \ldots)] \tag{11}$$

$$= \frac{e^{i(v+\frac{1}{4}\pi)}}{v^{\frac{1}{2}}}[P - iQ], \tag{12}$$

where
$$P = 1 - c_2 v^{-2} + c_4 v^{-4} - \ldots \tag{13}$$
and
$$Q = c_1 v^{-1} - c_3 v^{-3} + c_5 v^{-5} - \ldots. \tag{14}$$

The real and imaginary parts of (12) are linearly independent solutions of (1), so we have the two solutions

$$y_1(z) = v^{-\frac{1}{2}}[P\cos(v + \tfrac{1}{4}\pi) + Q\sin(v + \tfrac{1}{4}\pi)] \tag{15}$$
and
$$y_2(z) = v^{-\frac{1}{2}}[P\sin(v + \tfrac{1}{4}\pi) - Q\cos(v + \tfrac{1}{4}\pi)]. \tag{16}$$

When $z \to +\infty$, we may write

$$y_1(z) \sim v^{-\frac{1}{2}}\cos(v + \tfrac{1}{4}\pi) \tag{17}$$
and
$$y_2(z) \sim v^{-\frac{1}{2}}\sin(v + \tfrac{1}{4}\pi), \tag{18}$$

these being the dominant terms in the asymptotic expansions (15), (16) respectively.

11.21. Asymptotic expansions for Ce_m, Se_m, Fey_m, Gey_m, $q > 0$. If (18) § 11.20 is multiplied by $p_{2n}(2/\pi)^{\frac{1}{2}}$, we obtain (2) § 11.10, the dominant term in the asymptotic formula for $\mathrm{Ce}_{2n}(z, q)$. Hence using (16) § 11.20 we infer that

$$\mathrm{Ce}_{2n}(z, q) \sim p_{2n}(2/\pi v)^{\frac{1}{2}}[P_{2n}^{(a)}\sin(v + \tfrac{1}{4}\pi) - Q_{2n}^{(a)}\cos(v + \tfrac{1}{4}\pi)] \quad (a_{2n}). \tag{1}$$

The subscript $2n$ and the superscript (a) signify that a_{2n} is to be used for a in the formulae for the c in (7)–(9) § 11.20.

If (17) § 11.20 is multiplied by $-p_{2n}(2/\pi)^{\frac{1}{2}}$, we obtain (9) § 11.10, the dominant term in the asymptotic formula for $\mathrm{Fey}_{2n}(z, q)$. Hence using (15) § 11.20 we infer that

$$\mathrm{Fey}_{2n}(z, q) \sim -p_{2n}(2/\pi v)^{\frac{1}{2}}[P_{2n}^{(a)}\cos(v + \tfrac{1}{4}\pi) + Q_{2n}^{(a)}\sin(v + \tfrac{1}{4}\pi)] \quad (a_{2n}). \tag{2}$$

Writing

$$R_{2n}^{(a)} = \left(\frac{2}{\pi v}\right)^{\frac{1}{2}} [P_{2n}^{(a)} \sin(v+\tfrac{1}{4}\pi) - Q_{2n}^{(a)} \cos(v+\tfrac{1}{4}\pi)] \quad (a_{2n}), \tag{3}$$

$$S_{2n}^{(a)} = \left(\frac{2}{\pi v}\right)^{\frac{1}{2}} [P_{2n}^{(a)} \cos(v+\tfrac{1}{4}\pi) + Q_{2n}^{(a)} \sin(v+\tfrac{1}{4}\pi)] \quad (a_{2n}), \tag{4}$$

and proceeding as shown above, we arrive at the following:

$$\mathrm{Ce}_{2n+1}(z,q) \sim -p_{2n+1} S_{2n+1}^{(a)} \quad (a_{2n+1}), \tag{5}$$

$$\mathrm{Se}_{2n+1}(z,q) \sim -s_{2n+1} S_{2n+1}^{(b)} \quad (b_{2n+1}), \tag{6}$$

$$\mathrm{Se}_{2n+2}(z,q) \sim +s_{2n+2} R_{2n+2}^{(b)} \quad (b_{2n+2}), \tag{7}$$

$$\mathrm{Fey}_{2n+1}(z,q) \sim -p_{2n+1} R_{2n+1}^{(a)} \quad (a_{2n+1}), \tag{8}$$

$$\mathrm{Gey}_{2n+1}(z,q) \sim -s_{2n+1} R_{2n+1}^{(b)} \quad (b_{2n+1}), \tag{9}$$

$$\mathrm{Gey}_{2n+2}(z,q) \sim -s_{2n+2} S_{2n+2}^{(b)} \quad (b_{2n+2}). \tag{10}$$

In the series for $R_m^{(a),(b)}$, $S_m^{(a),(b)}$ the c in § 11.20 are obtained using the characteristic numbers given at the r.h.s.

The asymptotic expansions for $\mathrm{Me}_m^{(1),(2)}(z,q)$, $\mathrm{Ne}_m^{(1),(2)}(z,q)$ may be written down immediately by aid of (1), (2) § 13.40 and the appropriate formulae above. Then by means of § 13.41 the asymptotic expansions for $\mathrm{Fek}_m(z,q)$, $\mathrm{Gek}_m(z,q)$ may be derived. The phase range in the above formulae is $-\tfrac{1}{2}\pi < \text{phase } z < \tfrac{1}{2}\pi$.

11.22. Degeneration of expansions in § 11.21 to those for $J_m(k_1 r)$, $Y_m(k_1 r)$. By Appendix I when $z \to +\infty$, $k \to 0$, $a \to 4n^2$, then $ke^z \to k_1 r$ and

$$\mathrm{Ce}_{2n}(z,q) \to p_{2n}' J_{2n}(k_1 r). \tag{1}$$

As $k \to 0$, the series $P_{2n}^{(a)}$, $Q_{2n}^{(a)}$ degenerate to those in the asymptotic expansion of $J_{2n}(k_1 r)$, excluding the factors

$$(2/\pi k_1 r)^{\frac{1}{2}} \, {\cos \atop \sin}(k_1 r - \tfrac{1}{4}\pi - n\pi)$$

[see reference 202, p. 158]. In a similar way, under the above conditions, the asymptotic expansion of $\mathrm{Fey}_{2n}(z,q)$ degenerates to p_{2n}' times that of $Y_{2n}(k_1 r)$, and so on.

11.23. Accurate asymptotic expansions for $q < 0$. These are derived by applying the definitions at (1), (4),... § 8.30 to the expansions for $q > 0$ in § 11.21. Thus from (1) § 8.30 and (1) § 11.21 we obtain

$$\mathrm{Ce}_{2n}(z,-q) \sim \frac{p_{2n}'}{(2\pi v)^{\frac{1}{2}}} \left[e^v \sum_{r=0}^{\infty} c_r v^{-r} - i e^{-v} \sum_{r=0}^{\infty} (-1)^r c_r v^{-r} \right] \quad (a_{2n}), \tag{1}$$

the c being those in § 11.20 with $a = a_{2n}$, $c_0 = 1$. Since

$$\mathrm{Ce}_{2n}(z, -q) = \sum_{r=0}^{\infty} (-1)^r A_{2r}^{(2n)} \cosh 2rz,$$

it is a real function if z is real. The imaginary part of (1) must *then* be omitted. This remark applies also to (3)–(5) below. The phase-range for formulae in this section is $-\frac{1}{2}\pi < $ phase $z < \frac{1}{2}\pi$. Under the conditions stated in § 11.22

$$\mathrm{Ce}_{2n}(z, -q) \to p'_{2n} I_{2n}(k_1 r), \tag{2}$$

and the part in [ ] in (1) degenerates to the series which occur in the asymptotic formula for $I_{2n}(k_1 r)$.

For the other functions we obtain

$$\mathrm{Ce}_{2n+1}(z, -q) \sim \frac{s'_{2n+1}}{(2\pi v)^{\frac{1}{2}}} \left[e^v \sum_{r=0}^{\infty} c_r v^{-r} + i e^{-v} \sum_{r=0}^{\infty} (-1)^r c_r v^{-r} \right] \quad (b_{2n+1}), \ (3)$$

the c being those in § 11.20 with $a = b_{2n+1}$.

$$\mathrm{Se}_{2n+1}(z, -q) \sim \frac{p'_{2n+1}}{(2\pi v)^{\frac{1}{2}}} [\text{as at (3) but } a = a_{2n+1}] \quad (a_{2n+1}), \tag{4}$$

$$\mathrm{Se}_{2n+2}(z, -q) \sim \frac{s'_{2n+2}}{(2\pi v)^{\frac{1}{2}}} [\text{as at (1) but } a = b_{2n+2}] \quad (b_{2n+2}). \tag{5}$$

Each of the four functions above tends to $+\infty$ monotonically as $z \to +\infty$.

$$\mathrm{Fey}_{2n}(z, -q) \sim \frac{p'_{2n}}{(2\pi v)^{\frac{1}{2}}} i \, [\text{as at (3) but } a = a_{2n}] \quad (a_{2n}), \tag{6}$$

$$\mathrm{Fey}_{2n+1}(z, -q) \sim \frac{s'_{2n+1}}{(2\pi v)^{\frac{1}{2}}} i \, [\text{as at (1) but } a = b_{2n+1}] \quad (b_{2n+1}), \tag{7}$$

$$\mathrm{Gey}_{2n+1}(z, -q) \sim \frac{p'_{2n+1}}{(2\pi v)^{\frac{1}{2}}} i \, [\text{as at (1) but } a = a_{2n+1}] \quad (a_{2n+1}), \tag{8}$$

$$\mathrm{Gey}_{2n+2}(z, -q) \sim \frac{s'_{2n+2}}{(2\pi v)^{\frac{1}{2}}} i \, [\text{as at (3) but } a = b_{2n+2}] \quad (b_{2n+2}). \tag{9}$$

Each of the four functions in (6)–(9) tends to $+i\infty$ monotonically as $z \to +\infty$.

Applying the relationship (10) § 8.30 to the expansions (1), (6) above, yields

$$\mathrm{Fek}_{2n}(z, -q) \sim \frac{p'_{2n}}{(2\pi v)^{\frac{1}{2}}} e^{-v} \sum_{r=0}^{\infty} (-1)^r c_r v^{-r} \quad (a_{2n}), \tag{10}$$

the c being those in § 11.20 with $a = a_{2n}$, $c_0 = 1$. The formulae for $\mathrm{Fek}_{2n+1}(z, -q)$, $\mathrm{Gek}_{2n+1}(z, -q)$, $\mathrm{Gek}_{2n+2}(z, -q)$ are obtained from

(10) on replacing p'_{2n} by s'_{2n+1}, p'_{2n+1}, s'_{2n+2}, respectively, and using the c corresponding to the characteristic numbers b_{2n+1}, a_{2n+1}, b_{2n+2}. These functions tend to zero monotonically as $z \to +\infty$.

When the conditions in § 11.22 are satisfied,

$$\frac{1}{(2\pi v)^{\frac{1}{2}}} e^{-v} \sum_{r=0}^{\infty} (-1)^r c_r v^{-r} \to \frac{1}{\pi} K_{2n}(k_1 r), \tag{11}$$

i.e. $1/\pi$ times the asymptotic expansion of the K-Bessel function. The degenerate forms of the four asymptotic expansions above are then constant multiples of each other. Formulae for $\mathrm{Me}_m^{(1),(2)}(z, -q)$, $\mathrm{Ne}^{(1),(2)}(z, -q)$ may be derived from (10) and kindred formulae, by aid of the relationships in § 13.41.

11.30. Alternative asymptotic expansions in z, with argument $2k \cosh z$. Previously the argument has been $v = ke^z$, but it may sometimes be expedient to use $u = 2k \cosh z$, so we shall develop the appropriate asymptotic series.

The functions $\mathrm{Ce}_m(z, q)$, $\mathrm{Fey}_m(z, q)$, $q > 0$. Let $x = -2ik \cosh z$ in (1) § 11.20 and we get

$$(x^2 + 4k^2)y'' + xy' - (x^2 + p^2)y = 0, \tag{1}$$

where $p^2 = (a + 2k^2)$. Writing $y = we^{-x}$ in (1) transforms it to

$$(x^2 + 4k^2)w'' - (2x^2 - x + 8k^2)w' - (x - p_1^2)w = 0, \tag{2}$$

with $p_1^2 = (2k^2 - a)$. As in § 11.20 we now assume that

$$w = \sum_{r=0}^{\infty} (-1)^r d_r x^{-r-\frac{1}{2}}, \tag{3}$$

with $d_0 = 1$.

Inserting (3) in (2) and equating coefficients of like powers of x to zero, we obtain the relations [52]

$$d_1 = \tfrac{1}{2}(p_1^2 + \tfrac{1}{4}), \tag{4}$$

$$d_2 = \tfrac{1}{8}(p_1^2 + \tfrac{1}{4})(p_1^2 + \tfrac{9}{4}) - k^2, \tag{5}$$

$$2(r+1)d_{r+1} = [p_1^2 + \tfrac{1}{4}(2r+1)^2]d_r - 4k^2(2r-1)d_{r-1} + \\ + k^2(2r-1)(2r-3)d_{r-2} \quad (r \geqslant 2). \tag{6}$$

By expressing (4), (5) in a slightly different way, they are readily compared with (7) §11.20. Thus

$$d_1 = -\frac{(4a - 1^2 - 8k^2)}{8} = -\frac{(4a - 1^2)}{8} + k^2, \tag{7}$$

$$d_2 = \frac{(4a - 1^2)(4a - 3^2)}{2! \, 8^2} - \tfrac{1}{2}k^2(a + \tfrac{3}{4} - k^2). \tag{8}$$

Writing
$$T = 1 - d_2 u^{-2} + d_4 u^{-4} - \dots, \tag{9}$$
$$U = d_1 u^{-1} - d_3 u^{-3} + d_5 u^{-5} - \dots, \tag{10}$$

by aid of §§ 11.10, 11.21 we obtain

$$\text{Ce}_{2n}(z, q) \sim p_{2n}\left(\frac{2}{\pi u}\right)^{\frac{1}{2}}[T_{2n}^{(a)}\sin(u + \tfrac{1}{4}\pi) - U_{2n}^{(a)}\cos(u + \tfrac{1}{4}\pi)]$$
$$(a_{2n}), \tag{11}$$

$$\text{Ce}_{2n+1}(z, q) \sim -p_{2n+1}\left(\frac{2}{\pi u}\right)^{\frac{1}{2}}[T_{2n+1}^{(a)}\cos(u + \tfrac{1}{4}\pi) + U_{2n+1}^{(a)}\sin(u + \tfrac{1}{4}\pi)]$$
$$(a_{2n+1}), \tag{12}$$

$$\text{Fey}_{2n}(z, q) \sim -p_{2n}\left(\frac{2}{\pi u}\right)^{\frac{1}{2}}[\text{as at (12) but with } 2n \text{ for } 2n+1]$$
$$(a_{2n}), \tag{13}$$

$$\text{Fey}_{2n+1}(z, q) \sim -p_{2n+1}\left(\frac{2}{\pi u}\right)^{\frac{1}{2}}[\text{as at (11) but with } 2n+1 \text{ for } 2n]$$
$$(a_{2n+1}). \tag{14}$$

The phase range of (11)–(14) is $-\tfrac{1}{2}\pi < \text{phase } z < \tfrac{1}{2}\pi$.

When $k \to 0$, the parts $(2/\pi u)^{\frac{1}{2}}[\quad]$ in (11)–(14) degenerate to the asymptotic expansions for the Bessel functions $J_{2n}(u)$, $J_{2n+1}(u)$, $Y_{2n}(u)$, $Y_{2n+1}(u)$, respectively (see § 11.22).

11.31. Formulae for $q < 0$. To obtain these use definitions (1), (11), etc. § 8.30 in (11)–(14) § 11.30. Then $u = 2k\cosh z$ becomes $2ik\sinh z$, and the required expansions are found if in (1), (3), (6), (7) § 11.23 we write $2k\sinh z$ for v and d_r for c_r.

11.32. The functions $\text{Se}_m(z, q)$, $\text{Gey}_m(z, q), q > 0$. First we derive the differential equation for $\chi(z) = y(z)/\sinh z$ by writing
$$y(z) = \chi(z)\sinh z$$
in (1) § 11.20.

It transforms to
$$\frac{d^2\chi}{dz^2} + 2\coth z\frac{d\chi}{dz} + (4k^2\cosh^2 z + 1 - p^2)\chi = 0, \tag{1}$$

where $p^2 = a + 2k^2$. The solution of (1) is, therefore, $y/\sinh z$, where y may be $\text{Se}_m(z, q)$, $\text{Gey}_m(z, q)$. Now write $x = -2ik\cosh z$ and (1) becomes [52]
$$(x^2 + 4k^2)\frac{d^2\chi}{dx^2} + 3x\frac{d\chi}{dx} - (p^2 + x^2 - 1)\chi = 0. \tag{2}$$

If in (2) we substitute $\chi = we^{-x}$, we obtain
$$(x^2 + 4k^2)w'' - (2x^2 - 3x + 8k^2)w' - (3x - p_1^2 - 1)w = 0, \tag{3}$$
with $p_1^2 = (2k^2 - a)$.

To solve (3) assume that

$$w = \sum_{r=0}^{\infty} (-1)^r e_r\, x^{-r-\frac{3}{4}}. \tag{4}$$

Inserting (4) into (3) and equating coefficients of like powers of x to zero, we obtain [52]

$$e_1 = \tfrac{1}{2}(p_1^2+\tfrac{1}{4}), \tag{5}$$

$$e_2 = \tfrac{1}{8}(p_1^2+\tfrac{1}{4})(p_1^2+\tfrac{9}{4})-3k^2, \tag{6}$$

$$2(r+1)e_{r+1} = [(p_1^2+1)+\tfrac{1}{4}(2r+3)(2r-1)]e_r - $$
$$-4k^2(2r+1)e_{r-1}+k^2(4r^2-1)e_{r-2} \quad (r \geqslant 2). \tag{7}$$

Then using the procedure in §11.20 with $u = 2k\cosh z$,

$$V = 1-e_2 u^{-2}+e_4 u^{-4}-\dots \tag{8}$$

and
$$W = e_1 u^{-1}-e_3 u^{-3}+e_5 u^{-5}-\dots, \tag{9}$$

we obtain the asymptotic expansions

$$\mathrm{Se}_{2n+1}(z,q) \sim -s_{2n+1}\tanh z \left(\frac{2}{\pi u}\right)^{\frac{1}{2}} \times$$
$$\times [V^{(b)}_{2n+1}\cos(u+\tfrac{1}{4}\pi)+W^{(b)}_{2n+1}\sin(u+\tfrac{1}{4}\pi)] \quad (b_{2n+1}), \tag{10}$$

$$\mathrm{Se}_{2n+2}(z,q) \sim s_{2n+2}\tanh z \left(\frac{2}{\pi u}\right)^{\frac{1}{2}} \times$$
$$\times [V^{(b)}_{2n+2}\sin(u+\tfrac{1}{4}\pi)-W^{(b)}_{2n+2}\cos(u+\tfrac{1}{4}\pi)] \quad (b_{2n+2}), \tag{11}$$

$$\mathrm{Gey}_{2n+1}(z,q) \sim -s_{2n+1}\tanh z \left(\frac{2}{\pi u}\right)^{\frac{1}{2}} \times$$
$$\times [\text{as at (11) but } 2n+1 \text{ for } 2n+2] \quad (b_{2n+1}), \tag{12}$$

$$\mathrm{Gey}_{2n+2}(z,q) \sim -s_{2n+2}\tanh z \left(\frac{2}{\pi u}\right)^{\frac{1}{2}} \times$$
$$\times [\text{as at (10) but } 2n+2 \text{ for } 2n+1] \quad (b_{2n+2}). \tag{13}$$

The phase range of (10)–(13) is $-\tfrac{1}{2}\pi < \text{phase } z < \tfrac{1}{2}\pi$.

When $k \to 0$, the parts $(2/\pi u)^{\frac{1}{2}}[\quad]$ in (10)–(13) degenerate to the asymptotic expansions for the Bessel functions $J_{2n+1}(u)$, $J_{2n+2}(u)$, $Y_{2n+1}(u)$, $Y_{2n+2}(u)$, respectively (see §11.22).

11.33. Formulae for $q < 0$. Write $2k \sinh z$ for v, e_r for c_r in (4), (5), (8), (9) §11.23 and multiply by $\coth z$. The expansions so obtained are identical with those found by applying the definitions (21), (31), (24), (34) §8.30, respectively, to (10)–(13) §11.32.

11.34. Formulae for $\mathrm{Fek}_m(z, -q)$, $\mathrm{Gek}_m(z, -q)$. These may be obtained from the asymptotic expansions for $\mathrm{Ce}_m(z, -q)$, $\mathrm{Fey}_m(z, -q)$, $\mathrm{Se}_m(z, -q)$, $\mathrm{Gey}_m(z, -q)$ and application of formulae (10), (20), (30), (40) § 8.30.

11.40. Asymptotic formulae for $\mathrm{ce}_m(z, q)$, $\mathrm{se}_m(z, q)$ **when** q **is large and positive** [52]. From (12) § 12.21 we see that when q is very large and positive, $a \sim -2q + O(q^{\frac{1}{2}})$, so we shall assume that

$$a = -2q + \alpha q^{\frac{1}{2}} + \alpha_0 + \alpha_1 q^{-\frac{1}{2}} + \alpha_2 q^{-1} + \alpha_3 q^{-\frac{3}{2}} + ..., \tag{1}$$

where $\alpha, \alpha_0, \alpha_1, ...$ are constants dependent upon the function and its order. Putting this series for a in the standard Mathieu equation for ce_m, se_m gives

$$y'' - (4q\cos^2 z)y + (\alpha q^{\frac{1}{2}} + \alpha_0 + \alpha_1 q^{-\frac{1}{2}} + \alpha_2 q^{-1} + ...)y = 0. \tag{2}$$

To solve this equation we assume that [73, 101]

$$y = e^{q^{\frac{1}{2}}\chi(z)}\zeta(z)[1 + q^{-\frac{1}{2}}f_1(z) + q^{-1}f_2(z) + ...]. \tag{3}$$

Substituting (3) into (2) and equating coefficients of q, $q^{\frac{1}{2}}$, q^0, $q^{-\frac{1}{2}}$, q^{-1} to zero yields the equations

$$[\chi']^2 = 4\cos^2 z, \tag{4}$$

$$2\chi'\zeta' + (\alpha + \chi'')\zeta = 0, \tag{5}$$

$$\zeta'' + (\alpha_0 + 2\chi'f_1')\zeta = 0, \tag{6}$$

$$f_1\zeta'' + 2f_1'\zeta' + (f_1'' + 2\chi'f_2' + \alpha_0 f_1 + \alpha_1)\zeta = 0, \tag{7}$$

$$f_2\zeta'' + 2f_2'\zeta' + (f_2'' + 2\chi'f_3' + \alpha_0 f_2 + \alpha_1 f_1 + \alpha_2)\zeta = 0. \tag{8}$$

Solving (4), (5) we obtain

$$\left.\begin{array}{l}\chi = \pm 2\sin z + \text{a constant} \\ \text{and} \qquad \zeta = \text{a constant}/(\cos z)^{\frac{1}{2}}\{\tan(\frac{1}{2}z + \frac{1}{4}\pi)\}^{\pm\alpha/4}.\end{array}\right\} \tag{9}$$

Inserting (9) into (3) leads to the first approximations:

$$y_1 = e^{2k\sin z}/(\cos z)^{\frac{1}{2}}\{\tan(\tfrac{1}{2}z + \tfrac{1}{4}\pi)\}^{\alpha/4} \tag{10}$$

$$\text{and} \qquad y_2 = e^{-2k\sin z}\{\tan(\tfrac{1}{2}z + \tfrac{1}{4}\pi)\}^{\alpha/4}/(\cos z)^{\frac{1}{2}}. \tag{11}$$

These are formal approximate solutions of $y'' + (a - 2q\cos 2z)y = 0$, when q is large and positive.

A first approximation to (1) is

$$a + 2q \simeq \alpha q^{\frac{1}{2}}, \tag{12}$$

and from § 12.30 $\qquad a + 2q \sim 2(2p+1)q^{\frac{1}{2}}, \tag{13}$

where $p = 0$ for ce_0, se_1; $p = m$ for ce_m, se_{m+1}. Thus we take

$$\alpha = 2(2p+1). \tag{14}$$

If in addition we use the formulae

$$[\tan(\tfrac{1}{2}z+\tfrac{1}{4}\pi)]^{-\frac{1}{2}} = 2^{\frac{1}{2}}\cos(\tfrac{1}{2}z+\tfrac{1}{4}\pi)/\cos^{\frac{1}{2}}z, \tag{15}$$

$$[\tan(\tfrac{1}{2}z+\tfrac{1}{4}\pi)]^{\frac{1}{2}} = 2^{\frac{1}{2}}\sin(\tfrac{1}{2}z+\tfrac{1}{4}\pi)/\cos^{\frac{1}{2}}z, \tag{16}$$

(10), (11) may be expressed in the form

$$y_1 = 2^{p+\frac{1}{2}}e^{2k\sin z}[\cos(\tfrac{1}{2}z+\tfrac{1}{4}\pi)]^{2p+1}/(\cos z)^{p+1} \tag{17}$$

and $$y_2 = 2^{p+\frac{1}{2}}e^{-2k\sin z}[\sin(\tfrac{1}{2}z+\tfrac{1}{4}\pi)]^{2p+1}/(\cos z)^{p+1}. \tag{18}$$

Writing $-z$ for z in (18) gives (17), and vice versa.

11.41. Construction of asymptotic formulae for ce_m, se_m, q **large and positive [52].** First we remark that (17) § 11.40 has poles at $z = ...-\tfrac{5}{2}\pi, -\tfrac{1}{2}\pi, \tfrac{3}{2}\pi, \tfrac{7}{2}\pi,...$, and in general at $z = (4r+3)\tfrac{1}{2}\pi$, $r = -\infty$ to $+\infty$. Also (18) § 11.40 has poles at $z = \tfrac{1}{2}\pi(2r+1)$. Since ce_m, se_m are bounded functions, the variable z must be restricted to exclude the singularities of (17), (18) § 11.40.

Secondly, using the two latter formulae, the solutions of Mathieu's equation may be expressed by $y = \epsilon y_1 \pm \theta y_2$, where ϵ, θ are appropriate constants: for ce_0, se_1, $p = 0$, so bearing in mind the interchangeability of (17), (18) § 11.40, we choose $\epsilon = \theta = C_0 2^{-\frac{1}{2}}$. Thus we obtain

$$y = C_0[e^{2k\sin z}\cos(\tfrac{1}{2}z+\tfrac{1}{4}\pi)\pm e^{-2k\sin z}\sin(\tfrac{1}{2}z+\tfrac{1}{4}\pi)]/\cos z, \tag{1}$$

these being valid in $-\tfrac{1}{2}\pi < z < \tfrac{1}{2}\pi$ and $\tfrac{1}{2}\pi < z < \tfrac{3}{2}\pi$, thereby avoiding the singularities mentioned above. We have now to discriminate between these solutions to ascertain which represents ce_0 and which se_1. With the upper/lower sign (1) is even/odd in $-\tfrac{1}{2}\pi < z < \tfrac{1}{2}\pi$, and with the lower/upper sign it is even/odd in $\tfrac{1}{2}\pi < z < \tfrac{3}{2}\pi$. Hence we have deduced that when $q > 0$ is large enough,

$$\genfrac{}{}{0pt}{}{ce_0}{se_1}(z,q) \sim C_0[e^{2k\sin z}\cos(\tfrac{1}{2}z+\tfrac{1}{4}\pi)+e^{-2k\sin z}\sin(\tfrac{1}{2}z+\tfrac{1}{4}\pi)]/\cos z, \tag{2}$$

the open interval $-\tfrac{1}{2}\pi < z < \tfrac{1}{2}\pi$ pertaining to ce_0 and $\tfrac{1}{2}\pi < z < \tfrac{3}{2}\pi$ to se_1. Also

$$\genfrac{}{}{0pt}{}{ce_0}{se_1}(z,q) \sim C_0[e^{2k\sin z}\cos(\tfrac{1}{2}z+\tfrac{1}{4}\pi)-e^{-2k\sin z}\sin(\tfrac{1}{2}z+\tfrac{1}{4}\pi)]/\cos z, \tag{3}$$

the open interval $\tfrac{1}{2}\pi < z < \tfrac{3}{2}\pi$ for ce_0 and $-\tfrac{1}{2}\pi < z < \tfrac{1}{2}\pi$ for se_1.

An argument similar to that above enables the following to be derived:

$$\left. \begin{array}{l} \text{ce}_m \\ \text{se}_{m+1} \end{array} (z,q) \text{ in } -\tfrac{1}{2}\pi < z < \tfrac{1}{2}\pi \right\}$$

$$\sim \begin{array}{l} C_m \\ S_{m+1} \end{array} \{e^{2k\sin z}[\cos(\tfrac{1}{2}z+\tfrac{1}{4}\pi)]^{2m+1} \pm e^{-2k\sin z}[\sin(\tfrac{1}{2}z+\tfrac{1}{4}\pi)]^{2m+1}\}/\cos^{m+1}z. \tag{4}$$

For the interval $\tfrac{1}{2}\pi < z < \tfrac{3}{2}\pi$, alter the centre signs to $\mp$. The constants C, S are determined in § 11.42.

q large and negative. The formulae for this case may be derived from (2)–(4) by applying the relationships in § 2.18 and altering the range of z accordingly.

11.42. Formulae for $\text{Ce}_m(z,q)$, $\text{Se}_{m+1}(z,q)$, q large and positive.
If the method given in §§ 11.40, 11.41 is applied to (1) § 2.30, use being made of the fact that Ce is even and Se odd, the results obtained are those in § 11.41 with zi written for z. Thus

$$\text{Ce}_m(z,q) \sim 2^{\frac{1}{2}}C_m[e^{2ik\sinh z}(\cosh\tfrac{1}{2}z - i\sinh\tfrac{1}{2}z)^{2m+1} +$$
$$+ e^{-2ik\sinh z}(\cosh\tfrac{1}{2}z + i\sinh\tfrac{1}{2}z)^{2m+1}]/(2\cosh z)^{m+1}. \tag{1}$$

Putting $a = \cosh\tfrac{1}{2}z$, $b = \sinh\tfrac{1}{2}z$, $\theta = \tan^{-1}(b/a)$, (1) becomes

$$\text{Ce}_m(z,q) \sim \frac{[\tfrac{1}{2}(a^2+b^2)]^{m+\frac{1}{2}}C_m}{(\cosh z)^{m+1}}\{e^{i[2k\sinh z - (2m+1)\theta]} + e^{-i[2k\sinh z - (2m+1)\theta]}\}, \tag{2}$$

$$= \frac{C_m}{2^{m-\frac{1}{2}}\cosh^{\frac{1}{2}}z}\cos[2k\sinh z - (2m+1)\tan^{-1}(\tanh\tfrac{1}{2}z)]. \tag{3}$$

In the same way we find that

$$\text{Se}_{m+1}(z,q) \sim \frac{S_{m+1}}{2^{m-\frac{1}{2}}\cosh^{\frac{1}{2}}z}\sin[2k\sinh z - (2m+1)\tan^{-1}(\tanh\tfrac{1}{2}z)]. \tag{4}$$

The phase range of (3), (4) is $-\tfrac{1}{2}\pi < \text{phase } z < \tfrac{1}{2}\pi$. For z imaginary, formulae in §§ 11.41, 11.43 may be used.

When $z \to +\infty$, $\cosh z \to v/2k$, $2k\sinh z \to v$, $\tanh\tfrac{1}{2}z \to 1$, so that (3) degenerates to

$$\text{Ce}_m(z,q) \sim C_m \frac{(\pi k)^{\frac{1}{2}}}{2^{m-\frac{1}{2}}}\left(\frac{2}{\pi v}\right)^{\frac{1}{2}}\cos(v - \tfrac{1}{4}\pi - \tfrac{1}{2}m\pi). \tag{5}$$

Thus with $m = 2n$, $2n+1$ we get

$$\text{Ce}_{2n}(z,q) \sim C_{2n}(-1)^n \frac{(\pi k)^{\frac{1}{2}}}{2^{2n-\frac{1}{2}}}\left(\frac{2}{\pi v}\right)^{\frac{1}{2}}\sin(v + \tfrac{1}{4}\pi), \tag{6}$$

$$\text{Ce}_{2n+1}(z,q) \sim C_{2n+1}(-1)^{n+1}\frac{(\pi k)^{\frac{1}{2}}}{2^{2n+\frac{1}{2}}}\left(\frac{2}{\pi v}\right)^{\frac{1}{2}}\cos(v + \tfrac{1}{4}\pi). \tag{7}$$

From (4) we have

$$\mathrm{Se}_{m+1}(z,q) \sim S_{m+1}\frac{(\pi k)^{\frac{1}{2}}}{2^{m-\frac{1}{2}}}\left(\frac{2}{\pi v}\right)^{\frac{1}{2}}\sin(v-\tfrac{1}{4}\pi-\tfrac{1}{2}m\pi), \qquad (8)$$

so

$$\mathrm{Se}_{2n+1}(z,q) \sim S_{2n+1}(-1)^{n+1}\frac{(\pi k)^{\frac{1}{2}}}{2^{2n-\frac{1}{2}}}\left(\frac{2}{\pi v}\right)^{\frac{1}{2}}\cos(v+\tfrac{1}{4}\pi) \qquad (9)$$

and

$$\mathrm{Se}_{2n+2}(z,q) \sim S_{2n+2}(-1)^{n+1}\frac{(\pi k)^{\frac{1}{2}}}{2^{2n+\frac{1}{2}}}\left(\frac{2}{\pi v}\right)^{\frac{1}{2}}\sin(v+\tfrac{1}{4}\pi). \qquad (10)$$

The expressions for the C and S may now be written down on comparison with (2), (4), (5), (7) § 11.10, since as $z \to +\infty$ the corresponding formulae tend to equality. Thus we get [52]

$$C_{2n} = (-1)^n 2^{2n-\frac{1}{2}}\,\mathrm{ce}_{2n}(0)\mathrm{ce}_{2n}(\tfrac{1}{2}\pi)/A_0^{(2n)}(\pi k)^{\frac{1}{2}}, \qquad (11)$$

$$C_{2n+1} = (-1)^{n+1} 2^{2n+\frac{1}{2}}\,\mathrm{ce}_{2n+1}(0)\mathrm{ce}'_{2n+1}(\tfrac{1}{2}\pi)/kA_1^{(2n+1)}(\pi k)^{\frac{1}{2}}, \qquad (12)$$

$$S_{2n+1} = (-1)^n 2^{2n-\frac{1}{2}}\,\mathrm{se}'_{2n+1}(0)\mathrm{se}_{2n+1}(\tfrac{1}{2}\pi)/kB_1^{(2n+1)}(\pi k)^{\frac{1}{2}}, \qquad (13)$$

$$S_{2n+2} = (-1)^{n+1} 2^{2n+\frac{1}{2}}\,\mathrm{se}'_{2n+2}(0)\mathrm{se}'_{2n+2}(\tfrac{1}{2}\pi)/k^2 B_2^{(2n+2)}(\pi k)^{\frac{1}{2}}. \qquad (14)$$

q large and negative. The formulae for this case may be derived by applying (1), (11); (21), (31) § 8.30 to (3); (4) above, and taking the real part, when z is real.

11.43. Higher approximations [52]. (6) § 11.40 may be expressed in the form

$$f_1' = -[\alpha_0 + \zeta''/\zeta]/2\chi'. \qquad (1)$$

Substituting from (9) § 11.40 into (1) and taking $m_1 = (2m+1)$ gives

$$f_1(z) = \mp(\tfrac{1}{32})\big[\{[(m_1^2+3)\sin z \mp 4m_1]/\cos^2 z\} + \\ + (m_1^2+1+8\alpha_0)\log_e \tan(\tfrac{1}{2}z+\tfrac{1}{4}\pi)\big]. \qquad (2)$$

The additive constant of integration has been omitted, since it does not affect the ultimate result. Then the second approximations are

$$\left.\begin{matrix}\mathrm{ce}_m \\ \mathrm{se}_{m+1}\end{matrix}\right\}(z,q) \text{ in } -\tfrac{1}{2}\pi < z < \tfrac{1}{2}\pi$$

$$\sim K_m[y_1(1+{}_{-2}f_1 q^{-\frac{1}{2}}) \pm y_2(1+{}_2 f_1 q^{-\frac{1}{2}})]/2^{m+\frac{1}{2}}. \qquad (3)$$

For the interval $\tfrac{1}{2}\pi < z < \tfrac{3}{2}\pi$, alter the centre signs in (3) to $\mp$. y_1, y_2 are, respectively, (17), (18) § 11.40, while ${}_{-2}f_1$, ${}_2f_1$ represent f_1 in (2) with two negative or two positive signs. Since ce_m, se_{m+1} are periodic, (3) must not alter, save in sign, when $-z$ is written for z. Hence the logarithmic term must vanish, so

$$\alpha_0 = -(m_1^2+1)/8 = -(2m^2+2m+1)/4. \qquad (4)$$

Thus the second approximations for q large and positive are

$$\begin{matrix} ce_m \\ se_{m+1} \end{matrix} (z,q) \text{ in } -\tfrac{1}{2}\pi < z < \tfrac{1}{2}\pi \Big\}$$

$$\sim \begin{matrix} C_m \\ S_{m+1} \end{matrix} \Big\{ e^{2k\sin z}[\cos(\tfrac{1}{2}z+\tfrac{1}{4}\pi)]^{2m+1} \times$$

$$\times[1+\{(2m+1)-(m^2+m+1)\dot{\text{s}}\text{in}\,z\}/8k\cos^2 z]\pm$$

$$\pm e^{-2k\sin z}[\sin(\tfrac{1}{2}z+\tfrac{1}{4}\pi)]^{2m+1}\times$$

$$\times[1+\{(2m+1)+(m^2+m+1)\sin z\}/8k\cos^2 z]\Big\}/\cos^{m+1}z. \quad (5)$$

For the interval $\tfrac{1}{2}\pi < z < \tfrac{3}{2}\pi$, alter the centre signs to $\mp$. Remembering that the log term in (2) is zero, we see that $f_1(z)$ has singularities at $z = \tfrac{1}{2}\pi(2r+1)$, r any integer, and these are common to (5). Thus the formula is invalid in the neighbourhood of any of these points, so (5) must be restricted to the condition that $k\cos^2 z$ is large enough.

11.44. Asymptotic expansion for a [52, 92, 93].

If in § 11.43 the analysis is extended up to f_5, and at each stage the logarithmic term is made to vanish by equating its coefficient to zero, the values of the α in (1) § 11.40 are obtained in terms of m_1 and q. Then we get the following asymptotic expansion:

$$a \sim -2q+2m_1 q^{\frac{1}{2}}-(m_1^2+1)2^{-3}-(m_1^3+3m_1)q^{-\frac{1}{2}}2^{-7}-$$

$$-(5m_1^4+34m_1^2+9)q^{-1}2^{-12}-(33m_1^5+410m_1^3+405m_1)q^{-\frac{3}{2}}2^{-17}-$$

$$-(63m_1^6+1260m_1^4+2943m_1^2+486)q^{-2}2^{-20}-$$

$$-(527m_1^7+15617m_1^5+69001m_1^3+41607m_1)q^{-\frac{5}{2}}2^{-25}-..., \quad (1)$$

with $m_1 = (2p+1)$. $p = 0$ gives a_0, b_1; $p = 1$ gives a_1, b_2; and in general $p = m$ gives a_m, b_{m+1}. Since all the characteristic curves $a_{m+\beta}$ lying between a_m, b_{m+1} are mutually asymptotic when q is large enough, (1) gives $a_{m+\beta}$ for $p = m$. This will be clear from Figs. 8, 11. In references [92, 93] formula (1) is derived by a procedure different from that outlined above. Both methods involve some very heavy algebra.

When $q \to +\infty$, (1) may be written

$$a \sim -2q+2(2p+1)q^{\frac{1}{2}}, \quad (2)$$

so the form in § 12.30 is reproduced.

For p moderate, (1) gives accurate results for comparatively small values of q. For an assigned q, the accuracy decreases with increase in p. Thus to maintain accuracy to a definite number of decimal places (or units in the sth significant figure, whichever is preferred) q must increase with increase in p. We may say that (1) gives adequate accuracy, provided p^2/q is not too large. To illustrate the order of accuracy attained for various q, Table 20 is appended. When $q > 40$, formula (1) with $p = 0, 1$ gives a correct to the fifth decimal place at least. The accurate values were obtained from reference [52]. Additional information regarding the accuracy of (1) is given on p. 299 reference [93].

TABLE 20. *Data illustrating accuracy of formula* (1)

Values of q	$-a_0, -b_1$ from (1)	Accurate values		$-a_1, -b_2$ from (1)	Accurate values	
		$-a_0$	$-b_1$		$-a_1$	$-b_2$
8	10·60604	10·60672	10·60536	0·41144	0·43596	0·38936
16	24·25868	24·25868	24·25864	9·33456	9·35268	9·33412
40	67·64216	67·64216	67·64216	43·35228	43·35228	43·35228

In reference [56] asymptotic formulae are deduced for the difference between two characteristic numbers in a stable region of the (a, q) plane. There are also asymptotic formulae for a when the curves a_m, b_m are approached from an unstable region.

ZEROS OF THE MATHIEU AND MODIFIED MATHIEU FUNCTIONS OF INTEGRAL ORDER

12.10. Real zeros of $ce_m(z,q)$, $se_m(z,q)$. If q is fixed and $m \geqslant 1$, these functions vanish for certain real values of z. Consider the case $q = 0$ when the functions reduce to $\cos mz$, $\sin mz$, respectively. In the interval $0 \leqslant z < \pi$, the graphs of $\cos mz$, $\sin mz$ cross the z-axis m times, so each function has m real zeros in this interval. The case $m = 3$ is illustrated for $\cos 3z$ in Fig. 18 A, there being three zeros in $0 \leqslant z < \pi$. We shall now demonstrate that the number of zeros of $ce_3(z,q)$ in $q \geqslant 0$ remains constant [87].

Let q be increased from zero, and suppose that a fourth zero appeared. Its genesis would entail the curve of Fig. 18 A bending towards the z-axis as shown by the broken line. From the theory of equations, the existence of a minimum value above the z-axis would entail the occurrence of two conjugate complex zeros of the type $z_1 = \alpha+i\beta$, $z_2 = \alpha-i\beta$. Further increase in q would be accompanied by the minimum approaching and ultimately being tangential to the z-axis, thereby introducing a double zero, i.e. $z = \alpha$ *bis* (Fig. 18 B). For a greater q the minimum would occur below the axis, thereby entailing two different simple real zeros (Fig. 18 c).

If $z = \alpha$ were a double zero, we could write

$$ce_3(z,q) = (z-\alpha)^2 f(z) = y(z), \quad \text{say.} \tag{1}$$

Then
$$y'(z) = 2(z-\alpha)f(z)+(z-\alpha)^2 f'(z), \tag{2}$$

so
$$y'(\alpha) = 0. \tag{3}$$

Now $y''+(a-2q\cos 2z)y = 0$, and $y(\alpha) = 0$, by hypothesis, so $y''(\alpha) = 0$. Hence $y(\alpha) = y'(\alpha) = y''(\alpha) = 0$, so $y(z)$ must be a null function, i.e. $y(z) \equiv 0$. But $ce_3(z,q)$ is not a null function, so a double zero cannot occur. A similar argument may be used to show that the number of zeros cannot decrease. It follows that the number of zeros of $ce_3(z,q)$ in $0 \leqslant z < \pi$ is independent of q in $q \geqslant 0$. In general a discussion on the above basis leads to the conclusion that ce_m, se_m have m simple zeros in $0 \leqslant z < \pi$. se_m has a simple zero at the origin, so it has $(m-1)$ zeros in $0 < z < \pi$. When $q = 0$ the zeros are equally spaced, i.e. for the circular functions, but, as shown later, they tend to cluster about $z = \frac{1}{2}\pi$ as $q \to +\infty$, excepting that of se_m at the origin. This discussion shows that as the number of zeros in a given interval is independent of q, the graphs of ce_m, se_m are distorted versions of those of $\cos mz$, $\sin mz$ (see Figs. 1–4).

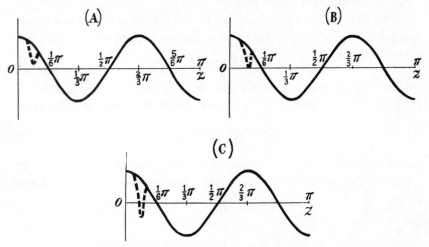

FIG. 18. Illustrating that the number of zeros of a Mathieu function (ce, se) in a given interval is independent of q. See § 12.10.

12.20. An inequality for a, q. We obtain this by aid of Sturm's first comparison theorem which is used for comparing Mathieu's equation with two forms derived therefrom. *First* we remark that integral-order solutions have rm zeros in the interval $0 \leqslant z < r\pi$, r being a positive integer > 0, e.g. ce_2, se_3 have 6, 9 zeros, respectively, in $0 \leqslant z < 3\pi$. *Secondly*, the first maximum of $(a-2q\cos 2z)$ occurs when $z = \frac{1}{2}\pi$ and has the value $(a+2q)$, so we consider the equation

$$y''+(a+2q)y = 0. \tag{1}$$

Its formal solutions are $\cos z(a+2q)^{\frac{1}{2}}$, $\sin z(a+2q)^{\frac{1}{2}}$, and in the interval $0 \leqslant z < r\pi$ both of these functions will have at least rm zeros, provided that

$$(a+2q)^{\frac{1}{2}} > \left(m-\frac{1}{2r}\right). \tag{2}$$

By Sturm's first comparison theorem the solutions of Mathieu's equation cannot have more zeros in $0 \leqslant z < r\pi$ than those in each solution of (1). Hence by (2), if ce_m, se_m each have rm zeros, it follows that

$$a > \left(m-\frac{1}{2r}\right)^2 - 2q. \tag{3}$$

But r is arbitrary, so we can make it tend to $+\infty$, thereby obtaining the inequality

$$a \geqslant m^2 - 2q, \tag{4}$$

$q \geqslant 0$, the equality sign being for $q = 0$.

Thirdly, the first minimum of $(a - 2q \cos 2z)$ occurs when $z = 0$ and has the value $(a - 2q)$. Proceeding as before, we consider the comparison equation

$$y'' + (a - 2q)y = 0, \tag{5}$$

whose formal solutions are $\cos z(a - 2q)^{\frac{1}{2}}$, $\sin z(a - 2q)^{\frac{1}{2}}$. In the interval $0 \leqslant z < r\pi$, the number of zeros will not exceed rm, provided that

$$(a - 2q)^{\frac{1}{2}} < \left(m + \frac{1}{2r}\right). \tag{6}$$

By the comparison theorem the solutions ce_m, se_m each have as many zeros as (but no more than) the solutions of (5) in $0 \leqslant z < r\pi$. Hence

$$(a - 2q) < \left(m + \frac{1}{2r}\right)^2 \tag{7}$$

or

$$a < \left(m + \frac{1}{2r}\right)^2 + 2q. \tag{8}$$

As before, let $r \to +\infty$, and we obtain the inequality

$$a \leqslant m^2 + 2q, \tag{9}$$

$q \geqslant 0$. Combining the inequalities (4), (9) we find that the characteristic numbers for ce_m, se_m satisfy

$$m^2 - 2q \leqslant a \leqslant m^2 + 2q, \tag{10}$$

for $q \geqslant 0$, the equality signs pertaining to $q = 0$. If $q < 0$, we have

$$m^2 - 2q \geqslant a \geqslant m^2 + 2q. \tag{11}$$

The analysis herein is based upon reference [87].

12.21. Form of a when q is large. Here and in the succeeding section it is expedient to use the equation

$$y'' + (a + 2q \cos 2z)y = 0, \tag{1}$$

where $q > 0$. From the expansion of $\cos 2z$ we get the inequality

$$1 - 2z^2 \leqslant \cos 2z \leqslant 1 - 2z^2 + 2z^4/3. \tag{2}$$

If in (1) we replace $\cos 2z$ by the first and third members of (2), we obtain the two comparison equations [91]

$$y'' + (a + 2q - 4qz^2)y = 0 \tag{3}$$

and

$$y'' + (a + 2q - 4qz^2 + \tfrac{4}{3}qz^4)y = 0. \tag{4}$$

Then by Sturm's first comparison theorem the odd or even solution of (1) has at least as many zeros, in a finite interval, as that of (3), but no more than that of (4). Writing $z = x/2q^{\frac{1}{4}}$ in (3), (4) yields

$$\frac{d^2y}{dx^2} + \left[\left(\frac{a+2q}{4q^{\frac{1}{2}}}\right) - \frac{1}{4}x^2\right]y = 0 \tag{5}$$

and

$$\frac{d^2y}{dx^2} + \left[\left(\frac{a+2q}{4q^{\frac{1}{2}}}\right) - \frac{1}{4}x^2 + \frac{x^4}{48q^{\frac{1}{2}}}\right]y = 0. \tag{6}$$

Now the interval of z to be considered is $0 \leqslant z < \pi$, and since the corresponding range of x is $0 \leqslant x < 2q^{\frac{1}{4}}\pi$, x can be made as large as we please by suitable choice of q.

Substituting $l+\frac{1}{2}$ for $(a+2q)/4q^{\frac{1}{2}}$ in (5) leads to the equation for the parabolic cylinder functions $D_l(x)$, i.e.

$$\frac{d^2y}{dx^2} + [(l+\tfrac{1}{2}) - \tfrac{1}{4}x^2]y = 0. \tag{7}$$

Using the notation of (5), it is known [140] that with s a positive integer, if

$$2s - \tfrac{1}{2} < \frac{a+2q}{4q^{\frac{1}{2}}} \leqslant 2s + \tfrac{3}{2}, \tag{8}$$

the odd solutions of (7) have s zeros in $0 < x < +\infty$, while if

$$2s - \tfrac{3}{2} < \frac{a+2q}{4q^{\frac{1}{2}}} \leqslant 2s + \tfrac{1}{2}, \tag{9}$$

its even solutions have s zeros in the same interval. Thus for *any* solution of (1) having a finite number of zeros in $0 \leqslant z < \pi$—and this includes periodic and non-periodic classes of solution—it follows that, as $q \to +\infty$,

$$\frac{a+2q}{4q^{\frac{1}{2}}} = O(1), \tag{10}$$

i.e. it is bounded. It can also be shown that as $q \to -\infty$,

$$\frac{a-2q}{4|q|^{\frac{1}{2}}} = O(1). \tag{11}$$

Finally, therefore, we obtain the form of a for $|q|$ large, namely [91],

$$a = -2|q| + O|q|^{\frac{1}{2}}. \tag{12}$$

12.22. Distribution of zeros as $q \to \infty$ **[91].** When $q \ggg x$ in (5), (6) § 12.21 the term in x^4 in the latter may be ignored. Then the two equations are the same, so their respective solutions have an equal number of zeros in a given interval of x. Now $z = x/2q^{\frac{1}{4}}$, so when

x is finite and q large enough, the solutions of (3), (4) § 12.21 have an equal number of zeros in a given interval. Also the solutions of (3) § 12.21 are non-alternating† if

$$(a+2q-4qz^2) < 0,$$

i.e. if
$$z^2 > (a+2q)/4q. \tag{1}$$

But from (12) § 12.21, with $q > 0$ in (1) § 12.21,

$$a = -2q+O(q^{\frac{1}{2}}),$$

so (1) takes the form

$$z^2 > O(q^{\frac{1}{2}})/4q = \lambda^2 q^{-\frac{3}{2}}, \tag{2}$$

λ being bounded and positive. Thus in the small interval

$$-\lambda q^{-\frac{3}{4}} < z < \lambda q^{-\frac{3}{4}}, \qquad a+2q-4qz^2 > 0,$$

so both solutions of (3) § 12.21 are alternating functions.‡ Moreover, they have the same number of zeros in the above interval. Hence, as $q \to +\infty$, any solution of (1) § 12.21 has a finite number of zeros in the interval $(-\lambda q^{-\frac{3}{4}}, \lambda q^{-\frac{3}{4}})$. Since $a = -2q+O(q^{\frac{1}{2}})$, we get

$$a+2q\cos 2z = 2q(\cos 2z-1)+O(q^{\frac{1}{2}}), \tag{3}$$

and in the two intervals $-\pi+\lambda q^{-\frac{3}{4}} < z < -\lambda q^{-\frac{3}{4}}$, $\lambda q^{-\frac{3}{4}} < z < \pi-\lambda q^{-\frac{3}{4}}$, neither of which includes the origin, (3) is negative. It follows that the solutions in these intervals do not alternate, and no more than one zero can occur in each. The above argument rests upon the hypothesis that q is large. Accordingly as $q \to +\infty$ the interval $(-\lambda q^{-\frac{3}{4}}, \lambda q^{-\frac{3}{4}}) \to 0$, and the zeros of (1) § 12.21 in the interval $-\frac{1}{2}\pi \leqslant z < \frac{1}{2}\pi$ congregate or condense on each side of the origin.

To obtain the result of letting $q \to +\infty$ for $ce_m(z,q)$, $se_m(z,q)$, we remark that $y''+(a+2q\cos 2z)y = 0$ takes the canonical form $y''+(a-2q\cos 2z)y = 0$ if $(\frac{1}{2}\pi+z)$ be written for z. Doing this with the above interval, we conclude that as $q \to +\infty$ the zeros of $ce_m(z,q)$, $se_m(z,q)$ in $0 \leqslant z < \pi$ condense about $\frac{1}{2}\pi$, with the exception of one, namely, the zero of $se_m(z,q)$ at the origin. The interval of condensation is $(\frac{1}{2}\pi-\lambda q^{-\frac{3}{4}}, \frac{1}{2}\pi+\lambda q^{-\frac{3}{4}})$. The condensation phenomenon is illustrated by the curves in Figs. 19 A, B, plotted from data in reference [96]. They are asymptotic to the line $\theta = 90° = \frac{1}{2}\pi^c$. The function $ce_0(z,q)$ has double zeros at $z = 0, \pi, 2\pi,...$ as $q \to +\infty$, i.e. the graph is tangential to the z-axis (see Fig. 3, $ce_0(z,8)$). It may be remarked that in $0 < z < \frac{1}{2}\pi$, $ce_{2n}(z,q)$, $ce_{2n+1}(z,q)$, $se_{2n+1}(z,q)$, $se_{2n+2}(z,q)$ each

---

† Oscillatory but devoid of real zeros, i.e. $f(z) \neq 0$.
‡ Oscillatory but having real zeros.

have n simple zeros. For this reason $se_{2n+2}(z,q)$ is used in preference to $se_{2n}(z,q)$ which has only $(n-1)$ zeros in the interval.

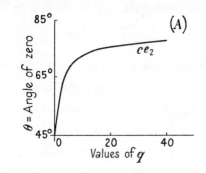

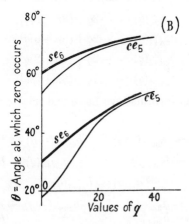

FIG. 19. Illustrating condensation of zeros at $\frac{1}{2}\pi$: (A) for $ce_2(z,q)$, (B) $ce_5(z,q)$, $se_6(z,q)$ as $q \to +\infty$. The curves are asymptotic to $\theta = \frac{1}{2}\pi$. ce_5, se_6 each have *two* zeros in $0 < z < \frac{1}{2}\pi$ (see Figs. 1, 4).

12.30. Approximate asymptotic formulae for a [91].

To obtain these we have to determine a value for $O(q^{\frac{1}{2}})$ in (12) § 12.21. Consider $ce_{2n}(z,-q)$, $ce_{2n+1}(z,-q)$, the even solutions of integral order of $y'' + (a + 2q\cos 2z)y = 0$. If $q > 0$ is large enough, by (9) § 12.21 we may write

$$\frac{a+2q}{4q^{\frac{1}{2}}} \sim 2s + \tfrac{1}{2}, \qquad (1)$$

the asymptotic sign referring to q. Transposing (1) and writing n for s gives the desired asymptotic formulae, namely,

$$a_{2n}(-q) \sim -2q + (8n+2)q^{\frac{1}{2}}, \qquad (2)$$

$$a_{2n+1}(-q) \sim -2q + (8n+2)q^{\frac{1}{2}}. \qquad (3)$$

If $q > 0$ is large enough, $se_{2n+1}(z, -q)$, $se_{2n+2}(z, -q)$ each have $(2n+1)$ zeros in the neighbourhood of the origin, the additional zero of se_{2n+2} occurring at $z = \frac{1}{2}\pi$. Since $se_m(z, -q)$ is odd in z, by (8) § 12.21 we get

$$\frac{a+2q}{4q^{\frac{1}{2}}} \sim 2s+\tfrac{3}{2}. \tag{4}$$

This leads to the asymptotic formulae

$$b_{2n+1}(-q) \sim -2q+(8n+6)q^{\frac{1}{2}}, \tag{5}$$

$$b_{2n+2}(-q) \sim -2q+(8n+6)q^{\frac{1}{2}}. \tag{6}$$

Formulae (2), (3), (5), (6) apply to the equation

$$y''+(a-2q\cos 2z)y = 0$$

when $q < 0$. For q positive it can be deduced that

$$a_{2n}(q) \sim -2q+(8n+2)q^{\frac{1}{2}}, \tag{7}$$

$$a_{2n+1}(q) \sim -2q+(8n+6)q^{\frac{1}{2}}, \tag{8}$$

$$b_{2n+1}(q) \sim -2q+(8n+2)q^{\frac{1}{2}}, \tag{9}$$

$$b_{2n+2}(q) \sim -2q+(8n+6)q^{\frac{1}{2}}. \tag{10}$$

From the preceding formulae we have the relationships, asymptotic in q (see Fig. 8),

$$a_{2n}(-q) \sim a_{2n+1}(-q), \qquad b_{2n+1}(-q) \sim b_{2n+2}(-q); \tag{11}$$

$$a_{2n}(q) \sim b_{2n+1}(q), \qquad a_{2n+1}(q) \sim b_{2n+2}(q),$$

or
$$a_m(q) \sim b_{m+1}(q); \tag{12}$$

$$a_{2n \atop 2n+1}(-q) \sim a_{2n \atop b_{2n+1}}(q), \qquad b_{2n+1 \atop 2n+2}(-q) \sim a_{2n+1 \atop b_{2n+2}}(q). \tag{13}$$

In the above formulae n is assumed to be finite.

12.31. Accuracy of formulae in § 12.30. This is illustrated for several cases by the data in Table 21.

TABLE 21

	$-a_0(q) \sim -b_1(q)$		$-a_2(q) \sim -b_3(q)$	
Values of q	*Value from* (7) § 12.30	*Accurate value*	*Value from* (7) § 12.30	*Accurate value*
80	142·12...	142·3671...	70·60...	73·9437...
160	294·71...	294·9453...	193·51...	196·8521...
1600	3120·00	3120·2508...	2800·00	2803·2779...

For $n = 0$ in (7), (9) § 12.30, i.e. for $ce_0(z, q)$, $se_1(z, q)$, the discrepancy occurs in the first decimal place, whereas with $n = 1$, i.e. $ce_2(z, q)$,

$\mathrm{se}_3(z, q)$, there is a difference of 3 in each of the digits. Thus for an assigned n the accuracy increases with increase in q, but for a given q it decreases with increase in n. The 'accurate' values were obtained from ref. [52], p. 325.

12.40. Zeros of $\mathrm{Ce}_m(z, q)$, $\mathrm{Se}_m(z, q)$, $\mathrm{Fey}_m(z, q)$, $\mathrm{Gey}_m(z, q)$, z **large and positive.** Reference to the approximate asymptotic formulae in § 11.10 shows that for any $k > 0$, each of these functions has an infinity of zeros. As z increases, the graphs of the functions oscillate about the z-axis with steadily decreasing amplitude. The zeros of $\mathrm{Ce}_{2n}(z, q)$, $\mathrm{Se}_{2n+2}(z, q)$, $\mathrm{Fey}_{2n+1}(z, q)$, $\mathrm{Gey}_{2n+1}(z, q)$ occur approximately when $\sin(v+\tfrac{1}{4}\pi)$ vanishes. Thus we have

$$v+\tfrac{1}{4}\pi \simeq r\pi \quad \text{or} \quad ke^z \simeq (r-\tfrac{1}{4})\pi, \tag{1}$$

so

$$z_r \simeq \log_e[(4r-1)\pi/4k]. \tag{2}$$

Now $v \gg 1$, so by (1) $r \gg 1$ but integral. From (2) it follows that, to the order of approximation contemplated, the zeros in z are independent of the order of the function.

By § 11.10 the zeros of $\mathrm{Ce}_{2n+1}(z, q)$, $\mathrm{Se}_{2n+1}(z, q)$, $\mathrm{Fey}_{2n}(z, q)$, $\mathrm{Gey}_{2n+2}(z, q)$ occur approximately when $\cos(v+\tfrac{1}{4}\pi)$ vanishes. Thus

$$z_r \simeq \log_e[(4r+1)\pi/4k]. \tag{3}$$

Parametric zeros, z large and positive. These are the values of q for which, with z assigned, the function vanishes. From (1) we get

$$q_r = k_r^2 \simeq (4r-1)^2\pi^2 e^{-2z}/16, \tag{4}$$

which gives the parametric zeros of the four functions prior to (1). From (3)

$$q_r = k_r^2 \simeq (4r+1)^2\pi^2 e^{-2z}/16, \tag{5}$$

which gives the parametric zeros of the four functions just above (3). These formulae are independent of the order of the function. As $z \to +\infty$, the interval between successive zeros tends to vanish, so they condense in the neighbourhood of $q = +0$.

12.41. More accurate formulae for parametric zeros of $\mathrm{Ce}_m(z, q)$, $\mathrm{Se}_m(z, q)$. These may be derived from (3), (4) § 11.42. From the former we get for $\mathrm{Ce}_{2n}(z, q)$

$$2k \sinh z \simeq (2r+1)\pi/2+(4n+1)\tan^{-1}(\tanh \tfrac{1}{2}z), \tag{1}$$

provided k is large enough. In problems on elliptical membranes and wave guides, $\cosh z_0 = e^{-1}$ at the bounding ellipse. Thus

$\sinh z_0 = e^{-1}(1-e^2)^{\frac{1}{2}}$, $\tanh \frac{1}{2}z_0 = [(1-e)/(1+e)]^{\frac{1}{2}}$. Substituting these in (1) leads to

$$\mathrm{Ce}_{2n}(z,q)$$
$$k_r^2 \simeq \{(r+\tfrac{1}{2})\pi + (4n+1)\tan^{-1}[(1-e)/(1+e)]^{\frac{1}{2}}\}^2 e^2/4(1-e^2). \quad (2)$$

For $\mathrm{Ce}_{2n+1}(z,q)$ write $(4n+3)$ for $(4n+1)$ in (2). Similarly (4) § 11.42 leads to

$$\mathrm{Se}_{2n+1}(z,q)$$
$$k_r^2 \simeq \{(r+1)\pi + (4n+1)\tan^{-1}[(1-e)/(1+e)]^{\frac{1}{2}}\}^2 e^2/4(1-e^2). \quad (3)$$

For $\mathrm{Se}_{2n+2}(z,q)$ write $(4n+3)$ for $(4n+1)$ in (3).

In these formulae r takes all integral values $\geqslant 1$. The accuracy improves with increase in r, also as $e \to 1$, i.e. as the ellipse becomes long and narrow, thereby increasing k_r.

12.42. Large zeros of $\mathrm{Ce}_m'(z,q)$, $\mathrm{Se}_m'(z,q)$. By differentiating the formulae in § 11.42 we find that the large zeros of Ce_m' are in close agreement with those of Se_{m+1}, and a similar remark applies to Se_m' and Ce_{m-1}. Accordingly the large zeros of $\mathrm{Ce}_{2n}'(z,q)$ are given by (3) § 12.41, while those of $\mathrm{Se}_{2n+1}'(z,q)$ are given by (2) § 12.41, and so on.

12.43. Large zeros of $J_m(z)$. By Appendix I as $e \to 0$, the ellipse tends to a circle, $\mathrm{Ce}_m(z,q) \to p_m' J_m(k_1 a)$, $\mathrm{Se}_m(z,q) \to s_m' J_m(k_1 a)$: also $k_1 h = 2k$, $h = ae$, so $k_1 a = 2ke^{-1}$. Thus (2), (3) § 12.41 degenerate to the well-known formulae for the large zeros of the Bessel functions, namely,

$$J_{2n}: \qquad k_1 a \simeq (r+\tfrac{1}{2})\pi + (4n+1)\pi/4 = (r+n+\tfrac{3}{4})\pi, \qquad (1)$$

$$J_{2n+1}: \qquad k_1 a \simeq (r+1)\pi + (4n+1)\pi/4 = (r+n+\tfrac{5}{4})\pi. \qquad (2)$$

XIII

SOLUTIONS IN BESSEL FUNCTION PRODUCT SERIES

13.10. Method of solution [36]. The equation whose solutions we require is

$$y'' - (a - 2q \cosh 2z)y = 0, \tag{1}$$

i.e. the modified Mathieu equation, which may be written in the form

$$y'' + [k^2(e^{2z} + e^{-2z}) - a]y = 0, \tag{2}$$

with $k^2 = q \neq 0$. Now

$$w_1 = J_r(ke^{-z}) \text{ satisfies } w_1'' + (k^2 e^{-2z} - r^2)w_1 = 0, \tag{3}$$

while $\quad w_2 = J_\rho(ke^z) \text{ satisfies } w_2'' + (k^2 e^{2z} - \rho^2)w_2 = 0, \tag{4}$

r integral, ρ integral or fractional. Multiplying (3) by w_2, (4) by w_1, and adding gives

$$w_1'' w_2 + w_2'' w_1 + [k^2(e^{2z} + e^{-2z}) - r^2 - \rho^2]w_1 w_2 = 0, \tag{5}$$

which is equivalent to

$$\frac{d^2}{dz^2}(w_1 w_2) + (2k^2 \cosh 2z - r^2 - \rho^2)w_1 w_2 = 2w_1' w_2'. \tag{6}$$

Writing $y = w_1 w_2$ and adding $-ay$ to both sides, (6) becomes

$$\frac{d^2 y}{dz^2} + (2k^2 \cosh 2z - a)y = -2k^2 J_r' J_\rho' + (r^2 + \rho^2 - a)J_r J_\rho. \tag{7}$$

By aid of recurrence relations we obtain

$$2J_r' J_\rho' = -\frac{2r\rho}{k^2} J_r J_\rho + J_{r-1} J_{\rho-1} + J_{r+1} J_{\rho+1}. \tag{8}$$

Substituting from (8) into the r.h.s. of (7) yields the equation

$$\frac{d^2 y}{dz^2} + (2k^2 \cosh 2z - a)y = [(r+\rho)^2 - a]J_r J_\rho - k^2(J_{r-1} J_{\rho-1} + J_{r+1} J_{\rho+1}). \tag{9}$$

Writing $\rho = r + \nu$, assume that

$$y = \sum_{r=-\infty}^{\infty} (-1)^r d_{2r} J_r(ke^{-z}) J_{r+\nu}(ke^z) \tag{10}$$

is a solution of (1). If $v_1 = ke^{-z}$, $v_2 = ke^z$, then we must have, by (9),

$$\sum_{r=-\infty}^{\infty} (-1)^r d_{2r}[\{(2r+\nu)^2 - a\}J_r(v_1)J_{r+\nu}(v_2) - $$
$$- k^2\{J_{r-1}(v_1)J_{r+\nu-1}(v_2) + J_{r+1}(v_1)J_{r+\nu+1}(v_2)\}] = 0. \tag{11}$$

In (11) the coefficient of $J_r(v_1)J_{r+\nu}(v_2)$ will vanish provided

$$d_{2r}[a-(2r+\nu)^2]-q(d_{2r+2}+d_{2r-2}) = 0. \tag{12}$$

Now $\qquad Ce_{2n+\nu}(z,q) = \sum_{r=-\infty}^{\infty} A_{2r}^{(2n+\nu)} \cosh(2r+\nu)z, \tag{13}$

satisfies (1), and the recurrence formula for the A is identical in form with (12). Hence for the same a, q, if $d_{2r} = K_{2n+\nu} A_{2r}^{(2n+\nu)}$, $K_{2n+\nu}$ being a constant, it follows that when $k \neq 0$,

$$y = K_{2n+\nu} \sum_{r=-\infty}^{\infty} (-1)^r A_{2r}^{(2n+\nu)} J_r(v_1) J_{r+\nu}(v_2) \tag{14}$$

is a solution of (1). Since (1) is unaltered if we change z to $-z$, then

$$y = K_{2n+\nu} \sum_{r=-\infty}^{\infty} (-1)^r A_{2r}^{(2n+\nu)} J_{r+\nu}(v_1) J_r(v_2) \tag{15}$$

is also a solution. Adding and subtracting (14), (15) yields the two series, even and odd in z,

$$K_{2n+\nu} \sum_{r=-\infty}^{\infty} (-1)^r A_{2r}^{(2n+\nu)} [J_r(v_1)J_{r+\nu}(v_2) \pm J_{r+\nu}(v_1)J_r(v_2)], \tag{16}$$

both of which satisfy (1). By analysis similar to that in § 13.60, we find that these series are absolutely and uniformly convergent in any closed region of the z-plane, *including $z = 0$*.

13.11. B.F. product series for $Ce_m(z,q)$, $Se_m(z,q)$. Write $\beta = \nu$, and apply (2) § 4.711 to (16) § 13.10 as $\beta \to 0$. Then the first series becomes

$$K_{2n} \sum_{r=0}^{\infty} (-1)^r A_{2r}^{(2n)} J_r(v_1) J_r(v_2) \quad (a_{2n}), \tag{1}$$

while the second series vanishes. Now (1) represents an even function of z with period πi, which is a solution of (1) § 13.10 for $a = a_{2n}$. Hence we infer that (1) is a constant multiple of $Ce_{2n}(z,q)$, to which (13) § 13.10 also reduces as $\nu \to 0$. We now determine K_{2n}. As $z \to +\infty$, all terms of (1) are negligible in comparison with the first, and this has the value

$$K_{2n} A_0^{(2n)}(2/\pi)v_2^{-\frac{1}{2}} \sin(v_2+\tfrac{1}{4}\pi), \tag{2}$$

when the dominant term of the asymptotic expansion for $J_0(v_2)$ is used [202, p. 158, no. 13]. By (2) § 11.10, if $K_{2n} = p_{2n}/A_0^{(2n)}$, (2) is the dominant term in the asymptotic expansion of $Ce_{2n}(z,q)$. Thus we obtain†

$$Ce_{2n}(z,q) = (p_{2n}/A_0^{(2n)}) \sum_{r=0}^{\infty} (-1)^r A_{2r}^{(2n)} J_r(v_1) J_r(v_2). \tag{3}$$

When $\beta \to 1$, by (4) § 4.711, the first member of (16) § 13.10 vanishes, while the second becomes

$$K_{2n+1} \sum_{r=0}^{\infty} (-1)^r B_{2r+1}^{(2n+1)} [J_r(v_1) J_{r+1}(v_2) - J_{r+1}(v_1) J_r(v_2)] \quad (b_{2n+1}). \tag{4}$$

This series, odd in z with period $2\pi i$, is a solution of (1) § 13.10 with $a = b_{2n+1}$, so we infer it to be a constant multiple of $Se_{2n+1}(z,q)$. Then procedure akin to that above yields

$$Se_{2n+1}(z,q)$$
$$= (s_{2n+1}/B_1^{(2n+1)}) \sum_{r=0}^{\infty} (-1)^r B_{2r+1}^{(2n+1)} [J_r(v_1) J_{r+1}(v_2) - J_{r+1}(v_1) J_r(v_2)]. \tag{5}$$

Writing $\nu = \beta+1$ in (16) § 13.10, letting $\beta \to 0$ and 1 in turn, using (6), (8) § 4.711, and following the procedure already set out, leads to

$$Ce_{2n+1}(z,q)$$
$$= (p_{2n+1}/A_1^{(2n+1)}) \sum_{r=0}^{\infty} (-1)^r A_{2r+1}^{(2n+1)} [J_r(v_1) J_{r+1}(v_2) + J_{r+1}(v_1) J_r(v_2)] \quad (a_{2n+1})$$

and $\tag{6}$

$$Se_{2n+2}(z,q)$$
$$= -(s_{2n+2}/B_2^{(2n+2)}) \sum_{r=0}^{\infty} (-1)^r B_{2r+2}^{(2n+2)} [J_r(v_1) J_{r+2}(v_2) - J_{r+2}(v_1) J_r(v_2)]$$
$$(b_{2n+2}). \tag{7}$$

Solutions of the type herein may be derived by means of integral relations, as shown in § 10.34 et seq.

13.12. Series for $Ce_{2n+\beta}(z,q)$, $Se_{2n+\beta}(z,q)$. If in (16) § 13.10, $\nu = \beta$, $0 < \beta < 1$, comparison of the first solution therein with the series for $Ce_{2n+\beta}(z,q)$ at (13) § 13.10 shows: (a) both are even in z; (b) any A in (16) § 13.10 is the same as the corresponding coefficient in (13) § 13.10; (c) if $\beta = p/s$, a rational fraction in its lowest terms, both solutions have period $2s\pi i$. (b), (c) apply also to the odd solution in (16) § 13.10 and $Se_{2n+\beta}(z,q)$ at (12) § 4.71. Further, the solutions at (16) § 13.10 constitute a fundamental system, as also do $Ce_{2n+\beta}$, $Se_{2n+\beta}$. Hence we infer that they are constant multiples of each other, so we write

$$\begin{matrix} Ce \\ Se \end{matrix}_{2n+\beta}(z,q) = \frac{K_{2n+\beta}}{\overline{K}_{2n+\beta}} \sum_{r=-\infty}^{\infty} (-1)^r A_{2r}^{(2n+\beta)} [J_r(v_1) J_{r+\beta}(v_2) \pm J_{r+\beta}(v_1) J_r(v_2)]$$
$$(a_{2n+\beta}). \tag{1}$$

† See Appendix I for p_{2n}.

Let $z = 0$, and we get

$$K_{2n+\beta} = \text{ce}_{2n+\beta}(0, q) \Big/ 2 \sum_{r=-\infty}^{\infty} (-1)^r A_{2r}^{(2n+\beta)} J_r(k) J_{r+\beta}(k). \qquad (2)$$

Differentiating and putting $z = 0$ gives

$$\bar{K}_{2n+\beta} = \text{se}'_{2n+\beta}(0, q) \Big/ 2k \sum_{r=-\infty}^{\infty} (-1)^r A_{2r}^{(2n+\beta)} [J_r(k) J'_{r+\beta}(k) - J_{r+\beta}(k) J'_r(k)]. \qquad (3)$$

The series for $\text{Ce}_{2n+1+\beta}$, $\text{Se}_{2n+1+\beta}$ are obtained from above by writing $(1+\beta)$ for β. Analysis similar to that in § 13.60 shows that the series (1) are absolutely and uniformly convergent for z finite.

13.20. Second solutions of (1) § 13.10: functions of integral order. Y_ρ and J_ρ satisfy the same D.E. and recurrence relations of the same type. Since it is by virtue of these that the B.F. product series satisfy (1) § 13.10, it follows that a second linearly independent solution may be obtained on replacing $J_m(v_2)$ by $Y_m(v_2)$ in the first solution in § 13.11. Thus, corresponding to (3) § 13.11, we get

$$\text{Fey}_{2n}(z, q) = (p_{2n}/A_0^{(2n)}) \sum_{r=0}^{\infty} (-1)^r A_{2r}^{(2n)} J_r(v_1) Y_r(v_2). \qquad (1)$$

This function is non-periodic owing to the term $\log_e(ke^z)$ in the expansion of $Y_r(v_2)$ [203, p. 161, no. 61]; for $\log_e(ke^z) = \log_e k + z$. Using the said expansion gives

$$J_r(ke^{-z}) Y_r(ke^z) = \frac{2}{\pi}(\gamma + \log \tfrac{1}{2}k) J_r(ke^{-z}) J_r(ke^z) +$$

$$+ \frac{2}{\pi} z J_r(ke^{-z}) J_r(ke^z) + \sum \cosh \text{ terms} + \sum \sinh \text{ terms}. \qquad (2)$$

The arguments of the cosh, sinh terms are even multiples of z, and result from the relation $e^{\pm 2mz} = \cosh 2mz \pm \sinh 2mz$. Applying (2) to (1) leads to the representation

$$\text{Fey}_{2n}(z, q) = \left[\frac{2}{\pi}(\gamma + \log \tfrac{1}{2}k) \text{Ce}_{2n}(z, q) + (p_{2n}/A_0^{(2n)}) \sum \cosh \text{ terms} \right] +$$

$$+ \left[\frac{2}{\pi} z \, \text{Ce}_{2n}(z, q) + (p_{2n}/A_0^{(2n)}) \sum \sinh \text{ terms} \right] \qquad (3)$$

$$= \text{even function of } z, \text{ with period } \pi i + \text{odd non-periodic}$$
$$\text{function of } z. \qquad (4)$$

In Chapter VII it is shown that if one solution of (1) § 13.10 is even and periodic in z with period πi, the other is odd in z but non-periodic. A combination with two *arbitrary* constants constitutes a fundamental system. Accordingly on comparing (3) with the solutions in §§ 2.30,

7.61 we infer that the first $\sum$ is a multiple of $\mathrm{Ce}_{2n}(z,q)$, while the odd function is a multiple of $\mathrm{Fe}_{2n}(z,q)$. Thus we may write

$$\mathrm{Fey}_{2n}(z,q) = A\,\mathrm{Ce}_{2n}(z,q) + B\,\mathrm{Fe}_{2n}(z,q), \tag{5}$$

where A, B are *particular* constants. A similar relation pertains to functions of order $(2n+1)$: also

$$\mathrm{Gey}_m(z,q) = \bar{A}\,\mathrm{Se}_m(z,q) + \bar{B}\,\mathrm{Ge}_m(z,q). \tag{6}$$

It appears, therefore, that $\mathrm{Fey}_m(z,q)$, $\mathrm{Gey}_m(z,q)$ include the first and second solutions, but none of these functions constitutes a fundamental system in itself. The A, B, are determined in § 13.21.

Proceeding as heretofore we obtain:

$$\mathrm{Fey}_{2n+1}(z,q) = (p_{2n+1}/A_1^{(2n+1)}) \times$$
$$\times \sum_{r=0}^{\infty} (-1)^r A_{2r+1}^{(2n+1)}[J_r(v_1)Y_{r+1}(v_2) + J_{r+1}(v_1)Y_r(v_2)], \tag{7}$$

$$\mathrm{Gey}_{2n+1}(z,q) = (s_{2n+1}/B_1^{(2n+1)}) \times$$
$$\times \sum_{r=0}^{\infty} (-1)^r B_{2r+1}^{(2n+1)}[J_r(v_1)Y_{r+1}(v_2) - J_{r+1}(v_1)Y_r(v_2)]; \tag{8}$$

$$\mathrm{Gey}_{2n+2}(z,q) = -(s_{2n+2}/B_2^{(2n+2)}) \times$$
$$\times \sum_{r=0}^{\infty} (-1)^r B_{2r+2}^{(2n+2)}[J_r(v_1)Y_{r+2}(v_2) - J_{r+2}(v_1)Y_r(v_2)]. \tag{9}$$

Series for $\mathrm{Fek}_m(z,q)$, $\mathrm{Gek}_m(z,q)$ may be derived from (1), (7)–(9) by aid of (4), (7), (10), (13) § 8.14.

13.21. Relationships between Fey_m, Fe_m; Gey_m, Ge_m.

Writing $z = 0$ in (5) § 13.20, with m for $2n$, we get

$$A = \mathrm{Fey}_m(0,q)/\mathrm{Ce}_m(0,q) \tag{1}$$

since $\mathrm{Fe}_m(0,q) = 0$. Also

$$\mathrm{Fey}_m' = A\,\mathrm{Ce}_m' + B\,\mathrm{Fe}_m'; \tag{2}$$

so when $z = 0$, $\mathrm{Ce}_m' = 0$ and

$$B = \mathrm{Fey}_m'(0,q)/\mathrm{Fe}_m'(0,q). \tag{3}$$

Hence by (1), (3) above, and (5) § 13.20, we find that

$$\mathrm{Fey}_m(z,q) = \frac{\mathrm{Fey}_m(0,q)}{\mathrm{Ce}_m(0,q)}\,\mathrm{Ce}_m(z,q) + \frac{\mathrm{Fey}_m'(0,q)}{\mathrm{Fe}_m'(0,q)}\,\mathrm{Fe}_m(z,q). \tag{4}$$

Similarly we obtain

$$\mathrm{Gey}_m(z,q) = \frac{\mathrm{Gey}_m'(0,q)}{\mathrm{Se}_m'(0,q)}\,\mathrm{Se}_m(z,q) + \frac{\mathrm{Gey}_m(0,q)}{\mathrm{Ge}_m(0,q)}\,\mathrm{Ge}_m(z,q). \tag{5}$$

See § 13.31 respecting $\mathrm{Fey}_m'(0,q)$, $\mathrm{Gey}_m(0,q)$.

By (4) §8.14 we have

$$\mathrm{Fey}_{2n} = i\,\mathrm{Ce}_{2n} - 2\,\mathrm{Fek}_{2n} \tag{6}$$

$$= A\,\mathrm{Ce}_{2n} + B\,\mathrm{Fe}_{2n}. \tag{7}$$

Hence $\quad \mathrm{Fek}_{2n}(z,q) = \tfrac{1}{2}(i-A)\mathrm{Ce}_{2n}(z,q) - \tfrac{1}{2}B\,\mathrm{Fe}_{2n}(z,q). \tag{8}$

A, B being given by (1), (3). It may be remarked that by §8.14, $\mathrm{Fek}_{2n}(z,q)$ is complex for z real. Relations of the type (8) may be found for Fek_{2n+1}, Gek_m.

13.30. Integral order solutions of $y'' - (a + 2q\cosh 2z)y = 0$. Applying (1), (11), (21), (31) §8.30 to (3), (5)–(7) §13.11, each to each, we obtain the first solutions:

$$\mathrm{Ce}_{2n}(z,-q)$$
$$= (p'_{2n}/A_0^{(2n)}) \sum_{r=0}^{\infty} (-1)^r A_{2r}^{(2n)} I_r(v_1) I_r(v_2), \tag{1}$$

$$\mathrm{Ce}_{2n+1}(z,-q)$$
$$= (s'_{2n+1}/B_1^{(2n+1)}) \sum_{r=0}^{\infty} (-1)^r B_{2r+1}^{(2n+1)} [I_r(v_1)I_{r+1}(v_2) + I_{r+1}(v_1)I_r(v_2)], \tag{2}$$

$$\mathrm{Se}_{2n+1}(z,-q)$$
$$= (p'_{2n+1}/A_1^{(2n+1)}) \sum_{r=0}^{\infty} (-1)^r A_{2r+1}^{(2n+1)} [I_r(v_1)I_{r+1}(v_2) - I_{r+1}(v_1)I_r(v_2)], \tag{3}$$

$$\mathrm{Se}_{2n+2}(z,-q)$$
$$= (s'_{2n+2}/B_2^{(2n+2)}) \sum_{r=0}^{\infty} (-1)^r B_{2r+2}^{(2n+2)} [I_r(v_1)I_{r+2}(v_2) - I_{r+2}(v_1)I_r(v_2)]. \tag{4}$$

The second solutions involving the K-Bessel function may be obtained from the series in §§13.20, 13.30 by applying (4), (10); (14), (20); (24), (30); (34), (40) §8.30 and (2) §8.14. They are as follow:

$$\mathrm{Fek}_{2n}(z,-q)$$
$$= (p'_{2n}/\pi A_0^{(2n)}) \sum_{r=0}^{\infty} A_{2r}^{(2n)} I_r(v_1) K_r(v_2), \tag{5}$$

$$\mathrm{Fek}_{2n+1}(z,-q)$$
$$= (s'_{2n+1}/\pi B_1^{(2n+1)}) \sum_{r=0}^{\infty} B_{2r+1}^{(2n+1)} [I_r(v_1)K_{r+1}(v_2) - I_{r+1}(v_1)K_r(v_2)], \tag{6}$$

$$\mathrm{Gek}_{2n+1}(z,-q)$$
$$= (p'_{2n+1}/\pi A_1^{(2n+1)}) \sum_{r=0}^{\infty} A_{2r+1}^{(2n+1)} [I_r(v_1)K_{r+1}(v_2) + I_{r+1}(v_1)K_r(v_2)], \tag{7}$$

$$\mathrm{Gek}_{2n+2}(z,-q)$$
$$= (s'_{2n+2}/\pi B_2^{(2n+2)}) \sum_{r=0}^{\infty} B_{2r+2}^{(2n+2)} [I_r(v_1)K_{r+2}(v_2) - I_{r+2}(v_1)K_r(v_2)]. \tag{8}$$

Absence of $(-1)^r$ in these series should be noted.

Series for $\mathrm{Fey}_m(z, -q)$, $\mathrm{Gey}_m(z, -q)$ may be derived from (1)–(8) using (10), (20), (30), (40) § 8.30. Relationships of the type in § 13.21 may be obtained also, e.g.

$$\mathrm{Fek}_{2n}(z, -q) = \frac{\mathrm{Fek}_{2n}(0, -q)}{\mathrm{Ce}_{2n}(0, -q)} \mathrm{Ce}_{2n}(z, -q) + \frac{\mathrm{Fek}'_{2n}(0, -q)}{\mathrm{Fe}'_{2n}(0, -q)} \mathrm{Fe}_{2n}(z, -q).$$

$$\tag{9}$$

$\mathrm{Fek}'_m(0, -q)$, $\mathrm{Gek}_m(0, -q)$ are given in § 13.31: note that

$$\mathrm{Ce}_{2n}(0, -q) = \mathrm{ce}_{2n}(\tfrac{1}{2}\pi, q).$$

13.31. Evaluation of $\mathrm{Fey}'_m(0, q)$, $\mathrm{Gey}_m(0, q)$, $\mathrm{Fek}'_m(0, -q)$, $\mathrm{Gek}_m(0, -q)$. These are obtained from the series in §§ 13.20, 13.30, by aid of the following B.F. relations, with argument k:

$$J_r Y'_r - J'_r Y_r = 2/\pi k$$

$$\text{(the Wronskian relation),} \quad (1)$$

$$J_r Y'_{r+1} - J'_r Y_{r+1} + J_{r+1} Y'_r - J'_{r+1} Y_r = 2(2r+1)/\pi k^2, \tag{2}$$

$$J_r Y_{r+1} - J_{r+1} Y_r = -2/\pi k, \tag{3}$$

$$J_r Y_{r+2} - J_{r+2} Y_r = -4(r+1)/\pi k^2, \tag{4}$$

$$I_r K'_r - I'_r K_r = -1/k$$

$$\text{(Wronskian for modified B.F.),} \quad (5)$$

$$I_r K'_{r+1} + I'_{r+1} K_r - I_{r+1} K'_r - I'_r K_{r+1} = -(2r+1)/k^2, \tag{6}$$

$$I_r K_{r+1} + I_{r+1} K_r = 1/k, \tag{7}$$

$$I_r K_{r+2} - I_{r+2} K_r = (2r+2)/k^2. \tag{8}$$

It will be seen that the r.h.s. of (5)–(8) are given by $-\tfrac{1}{2}\pi$ times (1)–(4), each to each. For (1), (5) see [203, p. 156, ex. 60, 61]. The remainder may be derived therefrom by aid of recurrence relations.

The results obtained are as follow:

$$\mathrm{Fey}'_{2n}(0, q) = \frac{2p_{2n}}{\pi A_0^{(2n)}} \mathrm{ce}_{2n}(\tfrac{1}{2}\pi, q), \tag{9}$$

$$\mathrm{Fey}'_{2n+1}(0, q) = -\frac{2p_{2n+1} \mathrm{ce}'_{2n+1}(\tfrac{1}{2}\pi, q)}{\pi k A_1^{(2n+1)}}, \tag{10}$$

$$\mathrm{Gey}_{2n+1}(0, q) = -\frac{2s_{2n+1} \mathrm{se}_{2n+1}(\tfrac{1}{2}\pi, q)}{\pi k B_1^{(2n+1)}}, \tag{11}$$

$$\mathrm{Gey}_{2n+2}(0, q) = -\frac{2s_{2n+2} \mathrm{se}'_{2n+2}(\tfrac{1}{2}\pi, q)}{\pi k^2 B_2^{(2n+2)}}, \tag{12}$$

$$\mathrm{Fek}'_{2n}(0, -q) = -\frac{p'_{2n} \mathrm{ce}_{2n}(0, q)}{\pi A_0^{(2n)}}, \tag{13}$$

$$\operatorname{Fek}'_{2n+1}(0,-q) = -\frac{s'_{2n+1}\operatorname{se}'_{2n+1}(0,q)}{\pi k B_1^{(2n+1)}}, \tag{14}$$

$$\operatorname{Gek}_{2n+1}(0,-q) = \frac{p'_{2n+1}\operatorname{ce}_{2n+1}(0,q)}{\pi k A_1^{(2n+1)}}, \tag{15}$$

$$\operatorname{Gek}_{2n+2}(0,-q) = \frac{s'_{2n+2}\operatorname{se}'_{2n+2}(0,q)}{\pi k^2 B_2^{(2n+2)}}. \tag{16}$$

13.40. Combination solutions. In problems on wave motion using elliptical coordinates, it is expedient to have solutions akin to the Hankel functions $H_m^{(1),(2)}(z)$. The latter are used to represent incoming and outgoing waves in problems pertaining to circular cylinders. Accordingly for wave-motion problems involving elliptical cylinders we shall adopt the following definitions:

$$\operatorname{Me}_m^{(1),(2)}(z,q) = \operatorname{Ce}_m(z,q) \pm i \operatorname{Fey}_m(z,q) \quad (a_m), \tag{1}$$

and
$$\operatorname{Ne}_m^{(1),(2)}(z,q) = \operatorname{Se}_m(z,q) \pm i \operatorname{Gey}_m(z,q) \quad (b_m). \tag{2}$$

Then by aid of §§ 8.10–8.13, 13.11, 13.20 we get

$$\operatorname{Me}_{2n}^{(1),(2)}(z,q) = \frac{\operatorname{ce}_{2n}(\tfrac{1}{2}\pi,q)}{A_0^{(2n)}} \sum_{r=0}^{\infty} (-1)^r A_{2r}^{(2n)} H_{2r}^{(1),(2)}(2k\cosh z) \tag{3}$$

$$= \frac{\operatorname{ce}_{2n}(0,q)}{A_0^{(2n)}} \sum_{r=0}^{\infty} A_{2r}^{(2n)} H_{2r}^{(1),(2)}(2k\sinh z) \tag{4}$$

$$= (p_{2n}/A_0^{(2n)}) \sum_{r=0}^{\infty} (-1)^r A_{2r}^{(2n)} J_r(v_1) H_r^{(1),(2)}(v_2). \tag{5}$$

$$\operatorname{Me}_{2n+1}^{(1),(2)}(z,q) = -\frac{\operatorname{ce}'_{2n+1}(\tfrac{1}{2}\pi,q)}{k A_1^{(2n+1)}} \sum_{r=0}^{\infty} (-1)^r A_{2r+1}^{(2n+1)} H_{2r+1}^{(1),(2)}(2k\cosh z) \tag{6}$$

$$= \frac{\operatorname{ce}_{2n+1}(0,q)}{k A_1^{(2n+1)}} \coth z \sum_{r=0}^{\infty} (2r+1) A_{2r+1}^{(2n+1)} H_{2r+1}^{(1),(2)}(2k\sinh z) \tag{7}$$

$$= (p_{2n+1}/A_1^{(2n+1)}) \sum_{r=0}^{\infty} (-1)^r A_{2r+1}^{(2n+1)} [J_r(v_1) H_{r+1}^{(1),(2)}(v_2) + J_{r+1}(v_1) H_r^{(1),(2)}(v_2)]. \tag{8}$$

$$\operatorname{Ne}_{2n+1}^{(1),(2)}(z,q) = \frac{\operatorname{se}_{2n+1}(\tfrac{1}{2}\pi,q)}{k B_1^{(2n+1)}} \tanh z \times$$

$$\times \sum_{r=0}^{\infty} (-1)^r (2r+1) B_{2r+1}^{(2n+1)} H_{2r+1}^{(1),(2)}(2k\cosh z) \tag{9}$$

$$= \frac{\operatorname{se}'_{2n+1}(0,q)}{k B_1^{(2n+1)}} \sum_{r=0}^{\infty} B_{2r+1}^{(2n+1)} H_{2r+1}^{(1),(2)}(2k\sinh z) \tag{10}$$

$$= (s_{2n+1}/B_1^{(2n+1)}) \sum_{r=0}^{\infty} (-1)^r B_{2r+1}^{(2n+1)}[J_r(v_1)H_{r+1}^{(1),(2)}(v_2) -$$
$$- J_{r+1}(v_1)H_r^{(1),(2)}(v_2)]. \quad (11)$$

$$\mathrm{Ne}_{2n+2}^{(1),(2)}(z,q) = -\frac{\mathrm{se}_{2n+2}'(\tfrac{1}{2}\pi, q)}{k^2 B_2^{(2n+2)}} \tanh z \times$$

$$\times \sum_{r=0}^{\infty} (-1)^r (2r+2) B_{2r+2}^{(2n+2)} H_{2r+2}^{(1),(2)}(2k \cosh z) \quad (12)$$

$$= \frac{\mathrm{se}_{2n+2}'(0, q)}{k^2 B_2^{(2n+2)}} \coth z \times$$

$$\times \sum_{r=0}^{\infty} (2r+2) B_{2r+2}^{(2n+2)} H_{2r+2}^{(1),(2)}(2k \sinh z) \quad (13)$$

$$= -(s_{2n+2}/B_2^{(2n+2)}) \sum_{r=0}^{\infty} (-1)^r B_{2r+2}^{(2n+2)}[J_r(v_1)H_{r+2}^{(1),(2)}(v_2) -$$
$$- J_{r+2}(v_1)H_r^{(1),(2)}(v_2)]. \quad (14)$$

Series for $q < 0$. These may be obtained by aid of the following definitions:

$$\mathrm{Me}_{2n}^{(1),(2)}(z, -q) = (-1)^n \mathrm{Me}_{2n}^{(1),(2)}(\tfrac{1}{2}\pi i + z, q)$$
$$= \mathrm{Ce}_{2n}(z, -q) \pm i \mathrm{Fey}_{2n}(z, -q), \quad (15)$$

$$\mathrm{Ne}_{2n+2}^{(1),(2)}(z, -q) = (-1)^{n+1} \mathrm{Ne}_{2n+2}^{(1),(2)}(\tfrac{1}{2}\pi i + z, q)$$
$$= \mathrm{Se}_{2n+2}(z, -q) \pm i \mathrm{Gey}_{2n+2}(z, -q), \quad (16)$$

$$\mathrm{Me}_{2n+1}^{(1),(2)}(z, -q) = (-1)^{n+1}i \, \mathrm{Ne}_{2n+1}^{(1),(2)}(\tfrac{1}{2}\pi i + z, q)$$
$$= \mathrm{Ce}_{2n+1}(z, -q) \pm i \mathrm{Fey}_{2n+1}(z, -q), \quad (17)$$

$$\mathrm{Ne}_{2n+1}^{(1),(2)}(z, -q) = (-1)^{n+1}i \, \mathrm{Me}_{2n+1}^{(1),(2)}(\tfrac{1}{2}\pi i + z, q)$$
$$= \mathrm{Se}_{2n+1}(z, -q) \pm i \mathrm{Gey}_{2n+1}(z, -q). \quad (18)$$

13.41. Relationship between $\mathrm{Me}_m^{(1)}$, Fek_m; $\mathrm{Ne}_m^{(1)}$, Gek_m. Applying (4), (7), (10), (13) § 8.14, and (10), (20), (30), (40), § 8.30 to (1), (2) § 13.40 leads to

$$\mathrm{Me}_{2n}^{(1)}(z, \pm q) = -2i \, \mathrm{Fek}_{2n}(z, \pm q), \quad (1)$$

$$\mathrm{Me}_{2n+1}^{(1)}(z, q) = -2 \, \mathrm{Fek}_{2n+1}(z, q), \quad (2)$$

$$\mathrm{Me}_{2n+1}^{(1)}(z, -q) = 2i \, \mathrm{Fek}_{2n+1}(z, -q), \quad (3)$$

$$\mathrm{Ne}_{2n+1}^{(1)}(z, q) = -2 \, \mathrm{Gek}_{2n+1}(z, q), \quad (4)$$

$$\mathrm{Ne}_{2n+1}^{(1)}(z, -q) = 2i \, \mathrm{Gek}_{2n+1}(z, -q), \quad (5)$$

$$\mathrm{Ne}_{2n+2}^{(1)}(z, \pm q) = -2i \, \mathrm{Gek}_{2n+2}(z, \pm q). \quad (6)$$

13.50. Series for $\dfrac{\mathrm{ce}}{\mathrm{se}_m}(z,q)$, $\dfrac{\mathrm{ce}}{\mathrm{se}_{m+\beta}}(z,q)$. Writing $-iz$ for z in (3) § 13.11 gives

$$\mathrm{ce}_{2n}(z,q) = (p_{2n}/A_0^{(2n)}) \sum_{r=0}^{\infty} (-1)^r A_{2r}^{(2n)} J_r(v_1') J_r(v_2'), \tag{1}$$

where $v_1' = ke^{iz}$, $v_2' = ke^{-iz}$. The r.h.s. of (1) is even in z. If z is real, v_1' and v_2' are conjugate, so the r.h.s. is real, as we should expect. If z is complex, v_1', v_2' are not conjugate and (1) is, therefore, complex.

Writing $-iz$ for z in (6) § 13.11 yields

$$\mathrm{ce}_{2n+1}(z,q) = (p_{2n+1}/A_1^{(2n+1)}) \times$$
$$\times \sum_{r=0}^{\infty} (-1)^r A_{2r+1}^{(2n+1)} [J_r(v_1') J_{r+1}(v_2') + J_{r+1}(v_1') J_r(v_2')], \tag{2}$$

the r.h.s. being even in z. If z is real the two product pairs are conjugate, since one is derived from the other by changing the sign of i. Thus the part in [ ] takes the form

$$(x+iy)+(x-iy) = 2x, \tag{3}$$

a real function expressible in a cosine series, since $e^{\pm iz} = \cos z \pm i \sin z$. By virtue of (3), if z is real,

$$\mathrm{ce}_{2n+1}(z,q) = (2p_{2n+1}/A_1^{(2n+1)}) \sum_{r=0}^{\infty} (-1)^r A_{2r+1}^{(2n+1)} \,\mathrm{Real}[J_r(v_1') J_{r+1}(v_2')]. \tag{4}$$

Similarly we obtain

$$\mathrm{se}_{2n+1}(z,q) = (s_{2n+1}/iB_1^{(2n+1)}) \times$$
$$\times \sum_{r=0}^{\infty} (-1)^r B_{2r+1}^{(2n+1)} [J_r(v_1') J_{r+1}(v_2') - J_{r+1}(v_1') J_r(v_2')], \tag{5}$$

and, if z is real,

$$\mathrm{se}_{2n+1}(z,q) = (2s_{2n+1}/B_1^{(2n+1)}) \times$$
$$\times \sum_{r=0}^{\infty} (-1)^r B_{2r+1}^{(2n+1)} \,\mathrm{Imag}[J_r(v_1') J_{r+1}(v_2')]; \tag{6}$$

$$\mathrm{se}_{2n+2}(z,q) = -(s_{2n+2}/iB_2^{(2n+2)}) \times$$
$$\times \sum_{r=0}^{\infty} (-1)^r B_{2r+2}^{(2n+2)} [J_r(v_1') J_{r+2}(v_2') - J_{r+2}(v_1') J_r(v_2')], \tag{7}$$

and, if z is real,

$$\mathrm{se}_{2n+2}(z,q) = -(2s_{2n+2}/B_2^{(2n+2)}) \times$$
$$\times \sum_{r=0}^{\infty} (-1)^r B_{2r+2}^{(2n+2)} \,\mathrm{Imag}[J_r(v_1') J_{r+2}(v_2')]. \tag{8}$$

Series for $\mathrm{ce}_{m+\beta}(z,q)$, $\mathrm{se}_{m+\beta}(z,q)$ may be derived from § 13.12 by using the above substitutions.

13.51. Series for $ce_m(z, -q)$, $se_m(z, -q)$. Applying the relationships (2)–(5) § 2.18 to the formulae in § 13.50 yields the results given below.

$$ce_{2n}(z, -q) = (p'_{2n}/A_0^{(2n)}) \sum_{r=0}^{\infty} (-1)^r A_{2r}^{(2n)} I_r(v'_1) I_r(v'_2). \tag{1}$$

This function, as represented by the r.h.s., is even in z, real or complex with z.

$$ce_{2n+1}(z, -q) = -(s'_{2n+1}/B_1^{(2n+1)}) \times$$
$$\times \sum_{r=0}^{\infty} (-1)^r B_{2r+1}^{(2n+1)}[I_r(v'_1)I_{r+1}(v'_2) + I_{r+1}(v'_1)I_r(v'_2)], \tag{2}$$

and, if z is real,

$$ce_{2n+1}(z, -q) = -(2s'_{2n+1}/B_1^{(2n+1)}) \times$$
$$\times \sum_{r=0}^{\infty} (-1)^r B_{2r+1}^{(2n+1)} \operatorname{Real}[I_r(v'_1)I_{r+1}(v'_2)]; \tag{3}$$

$$se_{2n+1}(z, -q) = -(p'_{2n+1}/iA_1^{(2n+1)}) \times$$
$$\times \sum_{r=0}^{\infty} (-1)^r A_{2r+1}^{(2n+1)}[I_r(v'_1)I_{r+1}(v'_2) - I_{r+1}(v'_1)I_r(v'_2)], \tag{4}$$

and, if z is real,

$$se_{2n+1}(z, -q) = -(2p'_{2n+1}/A_1^{(2n+1)}) \times$$
$$\times \sum_{r=0}^{\infty} (-1)^r A_{2r+1}^{(2n+1)} \operatorname{Imag}[I_r(v'_1)I_{r+1}(v'_2)]; \tag{5}$$

$$se_{2n+2}(z, -q) = (s'_{2n+2}/iB_2^{(2n+2)}) \times$$
$$\times \sum_{r=0}^{\infty} (-1)^r B_{2r+2}^{(2n+2)}[I_r(v'_1)I_{r+2}(v'_2) - I_{r+2}(v'_1)I_r(v'_2)], \tag{6}$$

and, if z is real,

$$se_{2n+2}(z, -q) = (2s'_{2n+2}/B_2^{(2n+2)}) \times$$
$$\times \sum_{r=0}^{\infty} (-1)^r B_{2r+2}^{(2n+2)} \operatorname{Imag}[I_r(v'_1)I_{r+2}(v'_2)]. \tag{7}$$

13.52. Series for $fe_{2n}(z, q)$. Substituting $-iz$ for z in (1) § 13.20 gives

$$\operatorname{Fey}_{2n}(-iz, q) = (p_{2n}/A_0^{(2n)}) \sum_{r=0}^{\infty} (-1)^r A_{2r}^{(2n)} J_r(v'_1) Y_r(v'_2). \tag{1}$$

Consider the product $J_r(v'_1)Y_r(v'_2)$; substitute the expansion of the Y function [ref. 202, p. 161, no. 61], and we get

$$J_r(v'_1)Y_r(v'_2) = \frac{2}{\pi}[\gamma + \log_e \tfrac{1}{2}k]J_r(v'_1)J_r(v'_2) + \sum \text{cosines} -$$
$$-i\left[\frac{2}{\pi}zJ_r(v'_1)J_r(v'_2) + \sum \text{sines}\right]. \tag{2}$$

Using (2) in (1) leads to

$\mathrm{Fey}_{2n}(-iz,q)$

$$= \frac{2}{\pi}(\gamma + \log_e \tfrac{1}{2}k)\mathrm{ce}_{2n}(z,q) + (p_{2n}/A_0^{(2n)}) \sum_{r=0}^{\infty}(-1)^r A_{2r}^{(2n)} \sum \text{cosines} -$$

$$- i\left[\frac{2}{\pi}z\,\mathrm{ce}_{2n}(z,q) + (p_{2n}/A_0^{(2n)})\sum_{r=0}^{\infty}(-1)^r A_{2r}^{(2n)}\sum \text{sines}\right]. \quad (3)$$

Now, if z is real, the real and imaginary parts (even and odd functions, respectively) of (3) are linearly independent solutions of $y'' + (a_{2n} - 2q\cos z)y = 0$. Thus the second member of the r.h.s. must be a constant multiple of $\mathrm{ce}_{2n}(z,q)$, while the imaginary member must be a constant multiple of $\mathrm{fe}_{2n}(z,q)$. Hence for z real we define

$$\mathrm{fe}_{2n}(z,q) = \text{multiple of } \mathrm{Imag}\{\mathrm{Fey}_{2n}(-iz,q)\}. \quad (4)$$

Now by (1) § 7.22

$$\mathrm{fe}_{2n}(z,q) = C_{2n}(q)\left[z\,\mathrm{ce}_{2n}(z,q) + \sum_{r=0}^{\infty}f_{2r+2}^{(2n)}\sin(2r+2)z\right], \quad (5)$$

so by (1) we obtain

$$\mathrm{fe}_{2n}(z,q) = C_{2n}'(p_{2n}/A_0^{(2n)})\sum_{r=0}^{\infty}(-1)^r A_{2r}^{(2n)}\mathrm{Imag}[J_r(ke^{iz})Y_r(ke^{-iz})]. \quad (6)$$

In this and the sections which follow, the series in B.F. products are valid only if $k \neq 0$.

13.53. Determination of C_{2n}'. Differentiation term by term in (6) § 13.52 is valid since by § 13.60 the series is uniformly convergent, as also is the resulting series. Thus

$$\mathrm{fe}_{2n}'(0,q) = C_{2n}'(p_{2n}/A_0^{(2n)})\sum_{r=0}^{\infty}(-1)^r A_{2r}^{(2n)}\mathrm{Imag}[ike^{iz}J_r'(ke^{iz})Y_r(ke^{-iz}) -$$

$$- ike^{-iz}J_r(ke^{iz})Y_r'(ke^{-iz})]_{z=0}, \quad (1)$$

where $J_r'(v) = dJ_r(v)/dv$. Now $J_r'(k)Y_r(k) - J_r(k)Y_r'(k) = -2/\pi k$, by (1) § 13.31, so (1) gives

$$\mathrm{fe}_{2n}'(0,q) = -C_{2n}'(p_{2n}/A_0^{(2n)})\frac{2}{\pi}\sum_{r=0}^{\infty}(-1)^r A_{2r}^{(2n)}, \quad (2)$$

and, therefore,

$$C_{2n}' = -\tfrac{1}{2}\pi A_0^{(2n)}\,\mathrm{fe}_{2n}'(0,q)/p_{2n}\,\mathrm{ce}_{2n}(\tfrac{1}{2}\pi,q). \quad (3)$$

13.54. Relationship between $\mathrm{Fey}_{2n}(-iz,q)$, $\mathrm{ce}_{2n}(z,q)$, **and** $\mathrm{fe}_{2n}(z,q)$. (3) § 13.52 may be written

$$\mathrm{Fey}_{2n}(-iz,q) = A\,\mathrm{ce}_{2n}(z,q) + iB\,\mathrm{fe}_{2n}(z,q). \quad (1)$$

Since $\mathrm{fe}_{2n}(0, q) = 0$, we get

$$A = \mathrm{Fey}_{2n}(0, q)/\mathrm{ce}_{2n}(0, q). \tag{2}$$

Differentiating (1), and putting $z = 0$, yields

$$B = -\mathrm{Fey}'_{2n}(0, q)/\mathrm{fe}'_{2n}(0, q). \tag{3}$$

Hence by (1)–(3)

$$\mathrm{Fey}_{2n}(-iz, q) = \frac{\mathrm{Fey}_{2n}(0, q)}{\mathrm{ce}_{2n}(0, q)} \mathrm{ce}_{2n}(z, q) - i\frac{\mathrm{Fey}'_{2n}(0, q)}{\mathrm{fe}'_{2n}(0, q)} \mathrm{fe}_{2n}(z, q). \tag{4}$$

This will be clear from (4) § 13.21.

13.55. Series for $\mathrm{fe}_{2n+1}(z, q)$, $\mathrm{ge}_m(z, q)$. Analysis similar to that in § 13.52 leads to the following results for real values of z:

$$\mathrm{fe}_{2n+1}(z, q) = C'_{2n+1}(p_{2n+1}/A_1^{(2n+1)}) \times$$
$$\times \sum_{r=0}^{\infty} (-1)^r A_{2r+1}^{(2n+1)} \mathrm{Imag}[J_r(v'_1)Y_{r+1}(v'_2) + J_{r+1}(v'_1)Y_r(v'_2)], \tag{1}$$

with
$$C'_{2n+1} = \tfrac{1}{2}\pi k A_1^{(2n+1)} \mathrm{fe}'_{2n+1}(0, q)/p_{2n+1} \mathrm{ce}'_{2n+1}(\tfrac{1}{2}\pi, q). \tag{2}$$

The relationship corresponding to (4) § 13.54 is obtained by writing $2n+1$ for $2n$.

$$\mathrm{ge}_{2n+1}(z, q) = S'_{2n+1}(s_{2n+1}/B_1^{(2n+1)}) \times$$
$$\times \sum_{r=0}^{\infty} (-1)^r B_{2r+1}^{(2n+1)} \mathrm{Real}[J_r(v'_1)Y_{r+1}(v'_2) - J_{r+1}(v'_1)Y_r(v'_2)], \tag{3}$$

$$S'_{2n+1} = -\tfrac{1}{2}\pi k B_1^{(2n+1)} \mathrm{ge}_{2n+1}(0, q)/s_{2n+1} \mathrm{se}_{2n+1}(\tfrac{1}{2}\pi, q), \tag{4}$$

$$\mathrm{Gey}_{2n+1}(-iz, q) = \frac{\mathrm{Gey}'_{2n+1}(0, q)}{\mathrm{se}'_{2n+1}(0, q)} \mathrm{se}_{2n+1}(z, q) + \frac{\mathrm{Gey}_{2n+1}(0, q)}{\mathrm{ge}_{2n+1}(0, q)} \mathrm{ge}_{2n+1}(z, q), \tag{5}$$

$$\mathrm{ge}_{2n+2}(z, q) = S'_{2n+2}(s_{2n+2}/B_2^{(2n+2)}) \times$$
$$\times \sum_{r=0}^{\infty} (-1)^r B_{2r+2}^{(2n+2)} \mathrm{Real}[J_r(v'_1)Y_{r+2}(v'_2) - J_{r+2}(v'_1)Y_r(v'_2)], \tag{6}$$

$$S'_{2n+2} = -\tfrac{1}{2}\pi k^2 B_2^{(2n+2)} \mathrm{ge}_{2n+2}(0, q)/s_{2n+2} \mathrm{se}'_{2n+2}(\tfrac{1}{2}\pi, q). \tag{7}$$

The relationship corresponding to (5) is found therefrom if $2n+2$ is written for $2n+1$.

13.56. Series for $\mathrm{fe}_{2n}(z, -q)$. By (1) § 7.60

$$\mathrm{fe}_{2n}(z, -q) = (-1)^{n+1} \mathrm{fe}_{2n}(\tfrac{1}{2}\pi - z, q). \tag{1}$$

Applying the r.h.s. of (1) to (6) § 13.52 gives

$$\mathrm{fe}_{2n}(z, -q) = (-1)^{n+1} C'_{2n}(p_{2n}/A_0^{(2n)}) \times$$
$$\times \sum_{r=0}^{\infty} (-1)^r A_{2r}^{(2n)} \mathrm{Imag}[J_r(ike^{-iz})Y_r(-ike^{iz})]. \tag{2}$$

The part in [ ] has the form $x+iy$, so if z is real, (2) is unaltered if we write $-i$ for i and $(-1)^n$ for $(-1)^{n+1}$. Thus for z real

$$\mathrm{fe}_{2n}(z, -q) = (-1)^n C'_{2n}(p_{2n}/A_0^{(2n)}) \times$$

$$\times \sum_{r=0}^{\infty} (-1)^r A_{2r}^{(2n)} \, \mathrm{Imag}[J_r(-ike^{iz})Y_r(ike^{-iz})]. \quad (3)$$

Now
$$J_r(-ike^{iz}) = i^{-r} I_r(ke^{iz}) \quad (4)$$

and
$$Y_r(ike^{-iz}) = i^{-r}\left[-\frac{2}{\pi} K_r(ke^{-iz})+(-1)^r i I_r(ke^{-iz})\right]. \quad (5)$$

Using (4), (5) in (3) leads to

$$\mathrm{fe}_{2n}(z, -q) = C'_{2n}(p'_{2n}/A_0^{(2n)}) \times$$

$$\times \left\{\sum_{r=0}^{\infty} (-1)^r A_{2r}^{(2n)} I_r(ke^{iz})I_r(ke^{-iz}) - \frac{2}{\pi} \sum_{r=0}^{\infty} A_{2r}^{(2n)} \, \mathrm{Imag}[I_r(ke^{iz})K_r(ke^{-iz})]\right\}$$

$$(6)$$

$$= C'_{2n}[\mathrm{ce}_{2n}(z, -q) - 2\,\mathrm{Imag}\{\mathrm{Fek}_{2n}(-iz, -q)\}] \quad (7)$$

$$= C'_{2n}[\mathrm{ce}_{2n}(z, -q) - 2\,\mathrm{fek}_{2n}(z, -q)], \quad (8)$$

where the definition of $\mathrm{fek}_{2n}(z, -q)$ is obvious.

Replacing the K functions in (6) by their expansions [ref. 202, p. 165] leads to

$$\mathrm{fe}_{2n}(z, -q) = \mathrm{const.}[(\tfrac{1}{2}\pi - z)\mathrm{ce}_{2n}(z, -q) + \text{a sine series}], \quad (9)$$

and this has the same *form* as (2) § 7.60.

13.57. Series for $\mathrm{fe}_{2n+1}(z, -q)$**,** $\mathrm{ge}_m(z, -q)$**.** Applying (3) § 7.60 to (3) § 13.55 gives

$$\mathrm{fe}_{2n+1}(z, -q) = S'_{2n+1}(s'_{2n+1}/B_1^{(2n+1)}) \times$$

$$\times \sum_{r=0}^{\infty} (-1)^r B_{2r+1}^{(2n+1)} \, \mathrm{Real}[J_r(iv'_2)Y_{r+1}(-iv'_1) - J_{r+1}(iv'_2)Y_r(-iv'_1)]. \quad (1)$$

If z is real, (1) is unaltered if we write $-i$ for i, since the real part in [ ] is unaffected. Doing this and following on the lines of § 13.56 leads to

$$\mathrm{fe}_{2n+1}(z, -q) = S'_{2n+1}[\mathrm{ce}_{2n+1}(z, -q) - 2\,\mathrm{Imag}\{\mathrm{Fek}_{2n+1}(-iz, -q)\}] \quad (2)$$

$$= S'_{2n+1}[\mathrm{ce}_{2n+1}(z, -q) - 2\,\mathrm{fek}_{2n+1}(z, -q)] \quad (z \text{ real}). \quad (3)$$

Similarly we obtain (z real)

$$\mathrm{ge}_{2n+1}(z, -q) = C'_{2n+1}[\mathrm{se}_{2n+1}(z, -q) - 2\,\mathrm{Real}\{\mathrm{Gek}_{2n+1}(-iz, -q)\}] \quad (4)$$

$$= C'_{2n+1}[\mathrm{se}_{2n+1}(z, -q) - 2\,\mathrm{gek}_{2n+1}(z, -q)] \quad (z \text{ real}), \quad (5)$$

$$\text{ge}_{2n+2}(z, -q) = S'_{2n+2}[\text{se}_{2n+2}(z, -q) - 2\,\text{Real}\{\text{Gek}_{2n+2}(-iz, -q)\}] \quad (6)$$

$$= S'_{2n+2}[\text{se}_{2n+2}(z, -q) - 2\,\text{gek}_{2n+2}(z, -q)] \quad (z \text{ real}). \quad (7)$$

In each case by using the expansions for the K-Bessel functions, as at (9) § 13.56, the forms in § 7.60 may be obtained.

13.60. Convergence of solutions. By analysis similar to that given below, all the B.F. product series in this chapter may be proved absolutely and uniformly convergent in any finite region of the z-plane. We shall exemplify this point, using the series

$$\sum_{r=0}^{\infty} (-1)^r A_{2r}^{(2n)} J_r(v_1) Y_r(v_2). \quad (1)$$

Then by (1), (2) § 8.50 we get

$$J_r(v_1) Y_r(v_2) \sim r^{-1} e^{-2rz} \quad (r \gg |v_1| \text{ or } |v_2|). \quad (2)$$

Using (2), and (4) § 3.21, the ratio of the $(r+1)$th to the rth term is

$$\left| \frac{J_{r+1}(v_1) Y_{r+1}(v_2) A_{2r+2}^{(2n)}}{J_r(v_1) Y_r(v_2) A_{2r}^{(2n)}} \right| \simeq \frac{|k^2 e^{-2z}|}{4(r+1)^2} \to 0, \quad \text{as } r \to +\infty, \quad (3)$$

for all real or complex z provided $R(z)$ is finite. Hence under this condition series (1) is absolutely convergent By applying the 'M' test the convergence may be proved uniform. It follows that

$$\sum_{r=0}^{\infty} (-1)^r A_{2r}^{(2n)} J_r(ke^{iz}) Y_r(ke^{-iz}) \quad (4)$$

is absolutely and uniformly convergent, provided $R(iz)$ is finite, i.e. Imag(z) is finite.

By virtue of uniform convergence, it follows that the functions represented by the B.F. product series are continuous in any finite region of the z-plane.

13.61. Advantages of B.F. product series over those in Chapter VIII. These are as follows:

1. The product series converge more rapidly than those with argument $2k \cosh z$, $2k \sinh z$. The rate of convergence increases with increase in z (real).

2. The product series for Fey_m, Fek_m, Gey_m, Gek_m converge uniformly in any finite region of the z-plane, including the origin. The other series do not converge uniformly in a restricted region, including the origin.

3. By virtue of (1), (2), the product series are preferable for calculating the values of the functions. This feature is illustrated vividly in Table 22.

TABLE 22. *Computation of* $\mathrm{Fek}_0(z, -4)$; $k = 2$, $q = 4$

	$z = 0$, $2k \cosh z = 4$		$z = \log_e 2$, $2k \cosh z = 5$	
r	$\dfrac{\mathrm{ce}_0(0,4)}{A_0}(-1)^r \times$ $\times K_{2r}(2k \cosh z)$	$\dfrac{\mathrm{ce}_0(0,4)\mathrm{ce}_0(\frac{1}{2}\pi,4)}{A_0^2} \times$ $\times I_r(ke^{-z})K_r(ke^z)$	*As in* *column 2*	*As in* *column 3*
0	0·00078 0079	+0·04189 15	0·00025 801	+0·00227 970
1	130 1687	−0·03841 39	39 706	−0· 121 818
2	93 6560	+0·00607 35	22 965	+0· 8 215
3	67 359 .	−0· 47 80	12 127	−0· 230
4	50 25 ..	+0· 2 27	6 306	
5	39 90 ..	−0· 07	3 30 .	
6			1 7 ..	
Sum	+0·0046	+0·00909 51	0·00111 905	+0·00114 137

When $z = 0$ the K_{2r} series, being non-uniformly convergent, converges so slowly that six terms contribute much less than three of the $I_r K_r$ series. In columns 3, 5 the rapidity of convergence of the $I_r K_r$ series is strikingly displayed, the value of the function being obtained to at least seven decimal places using only four terms. See also [8].

MISCELLANEOUS INTEGRALS INVOLVING MATHIEU FUNCTIONS

14.10. Evaluation of $\int_0^z y \cosh 2u\, du$, **when** y **satisfies**

$$y'' - (a - 2q \cosh 2u)y = 0.$$

Integrating the D.E. with respect to u from 0 to z, we obtain

$$[y']_0^z - a \int_0^z y\, du + 2q \int_0^z y \cosh 2u\, du = 0, \tag{1}$$

so
$$\int_0^z y \cosh 2u\, du = \frac{a}{2q} \int_0^z y\, du - \frac{1}{2q}[y'(z) - y'(0)], \tag{2}$$

where y is *any* solution. In particular, if $y = \mathrm{Ce}_{2n}(u, q)$,

$$\int_0^z \mathrm{Ce}_{2n}(u, q)\, du = A_0^{(2n)}z + \sum_{r=1}^\infty \frac{1}{2r} A_{2r}^{(2n)} \sinh 2rz, \tag{3}$$

$$\frac{d}{du} \mathrm{Ce}_{2n}(u, q)\Big|_{u=0}^{u=z} = \sum_{r=1}^\infty 2r A_{2r}^{(2n)} \sinh 2rz. \tag{4}$$

Substituting (3), (4) into (2) gives

$$\int_0^z \mathrm{Ce}_{2n}(u, q)\cosh 2u\, du = \tfrac{1}{2}A_2^{(2n)}z + \tfrac{1}{4}A_0^{(2n)}\sinh 2z +$$

$$+ \frac{1}{4} \sum_{r=1}^\infty \frac{1}{r}(A_{2r+2}^{(2n)} + A_{2r-2}^{(2n)})\sinh 2rz, \tag{5}$$

by (1) § 3.10.

In a similar way for $y'' + (a - 2q \cos 2u)y = 0$, we find that

$$\int_0^z y \cos 2u\, du = \frac{a}{2q} \int_0^z y\, du + \frac{1}{2q}[y'(z) - y'(0)], \tag{6}$$

and in particular, when $y = \mathrm{ce}_{2n}(u, q)$, the r.h.s. is

$$\tfrac{1}{2}A_2^{(2n)}z + \tfrac{1}{4}A_0^{(2n)}\sin 2z + \frac{1}{4} \sum_{r=1}^\infty \frac{1}{r}(A_{2r+2}^{(2n)} + A_{2r-2}^{(2n)})\sin 2rz. \tag{7}$$

14.20. Product integrals. We commence with the equations

$$y_1'' - (a - 2q_1 \cosh 2u)y_1 = 0 \tag{1}$$

and

$$y_2'' - (a - 2q_2 \cosh 2u)y_2 = 0, \tag{2}$$

the a being the same but $q_1 \neq q_2$. Multiplying (1) by y_2, (2) by y_1, subtracting and integrating with respect to u from z_1 to z_2, we get

$$2(q_2 - q_1) \int_{z_1}^{z_2} y_1(u)y_2(u)\cosh 2u \, du = [y_1'(u)y_2(u) - y_2'(u)y_1(u)]_{z_1}^{z_2}. \tag{3}$$

When the fundamental ellipse becomes a circle, (3) degenerates to the well-known form for the Bessel functions [202, chap. vi].

If in (1), (2) $q_1 = q_2$ and y_1, y_2 are independent solutions of the same equation, with z_1 constant and $z_2 = z$ variable, we get

$$y_1'(z)y_2(z) - y_2'(z)y_1(z) = y_1'(z_1)y_2(z_1) - y_2'(z_1)y_1(z_1) = c^2, \text{ a constant.}† \tag{4}$$

For given functions y_1, y_2, c^2 is independent of z, but not of q. By (4)

$$\frac{d}{du}[\log(y_1/y_2)] = c^2/y_1 y_2, \tag{5}$$

so

$$\int^{z} du/y_1 y_2 = \frac{1}{c^2}\log(y_1/y_2). \tag{6}$$

Taking $y_1 = \mathrm{Ce}_{2n+1}(u, q)$, $y_2 = \mathrm{Fey}_{2n+1}(u, q)$, (6) asserts that

$$\int^{z} du/[\mathrm{Ce}_{2n+1}(u)\,\mathrm{Fey}_{2n+1}(u)] = \frac{1}{c^2}\log[\mathrm{Ce}_{2n+1}(z)/\mathrm{Fey}_{2n+1}(z)]. \tag{7}$$

Again, from (4), $y_1' y_2 - y_2' y_1 = c^2$, so dividing throughout by y_2^2 gives

$$(y_1'/y_2) - (y_2' y_1/y_2^2) = c^2/y_2^2, \tag{8}$$

or

$$\frac{d(y_1/y_2)}{du} = c^2/y_2^2. \tag{9}$$

Integrating (9) leads to

$$y_1/y_2 = c^2 \int^{z} du/y_2^2 + A, \tag{10}$$

or

$$y_1 = c^2 y_2 \int^{z} du/y_2^2 + Ay_2. \tag{11}$$

This gives one solution in terms of the other, but it is a troublesome form to use in practice. The lower limit is an arbitrary constant, related to A.

---

† For solutions of Bessel's equation the equivalent of (4) takes the form [203, p. 156] $y_1' y_2 - y_2' y_1 = a$ constant$/z$. The absence of z^{-1} on the r.h.s. of (4) is by virtue of Mathieu's equation having no differential of the first order.

The results herein are valid for solutions of
$$y'' + (a - 2q \cos 2u)y = 0,$$
provided that $\cosh 2u$ is replaced by $-\cos 2u$.

14.21. Theorem. If $y_1(u)$, $y_2(u)$ are solutions of
$$y'' - (a - 2q \cosh 2u)y = 0$$
for the same a, corresponding respectively to q_1, q_2, such that $y_1'(0)y_2(0) - y_2'(0)y_1(0) = 0$, and either $y_1(z, q_1) = y_2(z, q_2) = 0$ or $y_1'(z, q_1) = y_2'(z, q_2) = 0$, then

$$\int_0^z y_1(u)y_2(u)\cosh 2u \, du = 0. \tag{1}$$

This follows from (3) § 14.20. If $y_1(u) = y_2(u)$,

$$\int_0^z y_1^2(u)\cosh 2u \, du \neq 0. \tag{2}$$

We now proceed to evaluate this integral.

In (3) § 14.20 take $\Delta q = (q_2 - q_1)$ to be small,† $z_1 = 0$, $z_2 = z$, then we have

$$[y_1'(u)y_2(u) - y_2'(u)y_1(u)]_0^z - 2\Delta q \int_0^z y_1(u)y_2(u)\cosh 2u \, du = 0. \tag{3}$$

By Taylor's theorem

$$y_2 = y_1 + \Delta q \frac{\partial y_1}{\partial q} + \frac{(\Delta q)^2}{2!}\frac{\partial^2 y_1}{\partial q^2} + \dots. \tag{4}$$

Substituting into (3) and neglecting terms in $(\Delta q)^2, \dots$ leads to

$$\left[y_1'\left(y_1 + \Delta q \frac{\partial y_1}{\partial q}\right) - y_1\left(y_1' + \Delta q \frac{\partial}{\partial u}\frac{\partial y_1}{\partial q}\right) \right]_0^z -$$
$$- 2\Delta q \int_0^z y_1\left(y_1 + \Delta q \frac{\partial y_1}{\partial q}\right)\cosh 2u \, du = 0. \tag{5}$$

Dividing throughout by Δq and letting Δq tend to zero yields, with y for y_1,

$$\left[\frac{\partial y}{\partial u}\frac{\partial y}{\partial q} - y\frac{\partial}{\partial u}\frac{\partial y}{\partial q} \right]_0^z - 2\int_0^z y^2(u)\cosh 2u \, du = 0. \tag{6}$$

Hence
$$\int_0^z y^2(u)\cosh 2u \, du = \frac{1}{2}\left[\frac{\partial y}{\partial u}\frac{\partial y}{\partial q} - y\frac{\partial}{\partial u}\left(\frac{\partial y}{\partial q}\right) \right]_0^z. \tag{7}$$

$\partial y/\partial q$ is not found by differentiating the coefficients in the series for y, since both q, a vary on a characteristic curve.

† $y_2 \to y_1$ as $\Delta q \to 0$.

14.22. Example. *Evaluate* (7) § 14.21 *when* $y = \mathrm{Ce}_{2n}(u)$, *given that* $\mathrm{Ce}_{2n}(\xi_0, q) = 0$, *the upper limit being* $z = \xi_0$. Here $\partial y/\partial u|_{u=0} = 0$, since all terms in the series vanish at the origin. Then

$$\int_0^{\xi_0} y^2 \cosh 2u \, du = \frac{1}{2}\left[\frac{\partial y}{\partial u}\frac{\partial y}{\partial q}\right]_{u=\xi_0} + \frac{1}{2}\left[y\frac{\partial}{\partial u}\left(\frac{\partial y}{\partial q}\right)\right]_{u=0} \tag{1}$$

$$= \tfrac{1}{2}\,\mathrm{Ce}'_{2n}(\xi_0, q)\left(\frac{\partial y}{\partial q}\right)_{u=\xi_0} + \tfrac{1}{2}\,\mathrm{Ce}_{2n}(0, q)\left[\frac{\partial}{\partial u}\left(\frac{\partial y}{\partial q}\right)\right]_{u=0}, \tag{2}$$

where, with a constant,

$$\partial y/\partial q = \lim_{\substack{\Delta q \to 0 \\ \beta \to 0}}\{[\mathrm{Ce}_{2n+\beta}(u, q+\Delta q) - \mathrm{Ce}_{2n}(u, q)]/\Delta q\}. \tag{3}$$

The only way of evaluating (2) seems to be by a numerical process.

14.23. Evaluation of $\int_0^z (y'^2 + ay^2)\, du$, **when** y **satisfies**

$$y'' - (a - 2q\cosh 2u)y = 0.$$

The D.E. may be written

$$-y'' + ay = (2q\cosh 2u)y. \tag{1}$$

Multiplying both sides of (1) by y, and integrating with respect to u from 0 to z, yields

$$-\int_0^z y\, dy' + a\int_0^z y^2\, du = 2q\int_0^z y^2 \cosh 2u\, du. \tag{2}$$

Thus

$$\int_0^z (y'^2 + ay^2)\, du = [yy']_0^z + 2q\int_0^z y^2 \cosh 2u\, du \tag{3}$$

$$= [yy']_0^z + q\left[\frac{\partial y}{\partial u}\frac{\partial y}{\partial q} - y\frac{\partial}{\partial u}\left(\frac{\partial y}{\partial q}\right)\right]_0^z, \tag{4}$$

by (7) § 14.21.

14.24. Evaluate (4) § 14.23 if $y = \mathrm{Ce}_{2n}(u, q)$, **given that** $\mathrm{Ce}_{2n}(\xi_0, q) = 0$, $z = \xi_0$. Since $\mathrm{Ce}_{2n}(\xi_0, q) = 0$, and $\mathrm{Ce}'_{2n}(0, q) = 0$, the first member on the r.h.s. of (4) § 14.23 vanishes. Hence by (7) § 14.21, (2) § 14.22 and (4) § 14.23

$$\int_0^{\xi_0} [\mathrm{Ce}'^2_{2n}(u, q) + a\,\mathrm{Ce}^2_{2n}(u, q)]\, du = 2q \text{ times (2) § 14.22.} \tag{1}$$

14.30. Integrals involving $\sinh 2u$. Let y be a solution of the differential equation in § 14.23. Differentiating

$$\phi(u) = y'^2(u) - (a - 2q \cosh 2u) y^2(u) \tag{1}$$

with respect to u, we obtain

$$\frac{d\phi}{du} = 2y'y'' + 4q(yy' \cosh 2u + y^2 \sinh 2u) - 2ayy' \tag{2}$$

$$= 2y'[y'' - (a - 2q \cosh 2u)y] + 4qy^2 \sinh 2u = 4qy^2 \sinh 2u. \tag{3}$$

Hence

$$4q \int^z y^2 \sinh 2u \, du = y'^2(z) - (a - 2q \cosh 2z) y^2(z)$$

$$= y'^2(z) - y(z)y''(z). \tag{4}$$

Integrating by parts gives

$$\int^z y^2 \sinh 2u \, du = 2 \int^z y^2 \cosh u \, d \cosh u \tag{5}$$

$$= 2\left[y^2 \cosh^2 z - \tfrac{1}{2} \int^z y^2 \sinh 2u \, du - 2 \int^z yy' \cosh^2 u \, du \right]. \tag{6}$$

Therefore

$$\int^z y^2 \sinh 2u \, du = y^2(z)\cosh^2 z - 2 \int^z yy' \cosh^2 u \, du. \tag{7}$$

Hence by (4), (7) we find that

$$4q \int^z yy' \cosh^2 u \, du = (q + \tfrac{1}{2}a) y^2(z) - \tfrac{1}{2} y'^2(z). \tag{8}$$

Since $\cosh^2 u = \tfrac{1}{2}(\cosh 2u + 1)$, (8) may be written

$$4q \int^z yy' \cosh 2u \, du = (2q + a) y^2(z) - y'^2(z) - 4q \int^z yy' \, du \tag{9}$$

$$= ay^2(z) - y'^2(z). \tag{10}$$

14.40. Integrals for the ordinary Mathieu functions. If v is a solution of $v'' + (a - 2q \cos 2u)v = 0$, the integrals corresponding to (4), (8), (10) § 14.30 are

$$4q \int^z v^2 \sin 2u \, du = v'^2(z) + (a - 2q \cos 2z) v^2(z) \tag{1}$$

$$= v'^2(z) - v(z)v''(z), \tag{2}$$

$$4q \int^z vv' \cos^2 u \, du = (q + \tfrac{1}{2}a) v^2(z) + \tfrac{1}{2} v'^2(z), \tag{3}$$

$$4q \int^z vv' \cos 2u \, du = av^2(z) + v'^2(z). \tag{4}$$

Using (2) with $v = ce_m(u, q)$ or $se_m(u, q)$, we find that

$$\int_0^{2\pi} ce_m^2(u)\sin 2u\, du = \int_0^{2\pi} se_m^2(u)\sin 2u\, du = 0. \tag{5}$$

Using (4) leads to

$$\int_0^{2\pi} ce_m(u)ce_m'(u)\cos 2u\, du = \int_0^{2\pi} se_m(u)se_m'(u)\cos 2u\, du = 0. \tag{6}$$

From § 9.40 we have

$$\int_0^{2\pi} ce_m^2(u)\cos 2u\, du = \pi\Theta_m; \qquad \int_0^{2\pi} se_m^2(u)\cos 2u\, du = \pi\Psi_m. \tag{7}$$

14.41. Evaluation of $\int_0^{2\pi} ce_m'^2(z, q)\, dz,\ \int_0^{2\pi} se_m'^2(z, q)\, dz.$ We have

$$\int_0^{2\pi} y'^2(z)\, dz = \int_0^{2\pi} y'\, dy = [yy']_0^{2\pi} - \int_0^{2\pi} yy''\, dy. \tag{1}$$

If $y = ce_m(z, q)$ or $se_m(z, q)$, the third member of (1) vanishes at both limits. Since y is a solution of $y'' + (a - 2q\cos 2z)y = 0$, the first and last members. of (1) give

$$\int_0^{2\pi} y'^2(z)\, dz = \int_0^{2\pi} (a - 2q\cos 2z)y^2\, dy. \tag{2}$$

The evaluation of the r.h.s. is obtained from (1) § 2.21, and (7) § 14.40, so we get

$$\int_0^{2\pi} y'^2(z)\, dz = \pi\left[a - 2q\left\{\begin{matrix}\Theta_m\\\Psi_m\end{matrix}\right\}\right] = \pi\left(\begin{matrix}\vartheta_m\\\varpi_m\end{matrix}\right), \tag{3}$$

if $y = ce_m$ or se_m.

14.42. Evaluation of $\int_0^{2\pi} ce_m(z, q)se_n'(z, q)\, dz,\ \int_0^{2\pi} se_n(z, q)ce_m'(z, q)\, dz.$
First we have

$$\int_0^{2\pi} ce_m\, se_n'\, dz = [ce_m\, se_n]_0^{2\pi} - \int_0^{2\pi} se_n\, ce_m'\, dz, \tag{1}$$

by partial integration. The member in [ ] vanishes at the limits. Hence

$$\int_0^{2\pi} ce_m\, se_n'\, dz = -\int_0^{2\pi} se_n\, ce_m'\, dz. \tag{2}$$

Now

$$\int_0^{2\pi} \mathrm{ce}_{2m}\,\mathrm{se}'_{2n}\,dz = \int_0^{2\pi}\left[\sum_{r=0}^{\infty} A_{2r}^{(2m)}\cos 2rz \sum_{r=1}^{\infty} 2rB_{2r}^{(2n)}\cos 2rz\right]dz \qquad (3)$$

$$= \sum_{r=1}^{\infty} 2r \int_0^{2\pi} A_{2r}^{(2m)}B_{2r}^{(2n)}\cos^2 2rz\,dz, \qquad (4)$$

since the other integrals vanish, $\sum$ being moved outside the integral sign by virtue of uniform convergence. Therefore by (2), (4)

$$\int_0^{2\pi} \mathrm{ce}_{2m}\,\mathrm{se}'_{2n}\,dz = -\int_0^{2\pi} \mathrm{se}_{2n}\,\mathrm{ce}'_{2m}\,dz = \pi\sum_{r=1}^{\infty} 2rA_{2r}^{(2m)}B_{2r}^{(2n)}. \qquad (5)$$

In a similar way we find that

$$\int_0^{2\pi} \mathrm{ce}_{2m+1}\,\mathrm{se}'_{2n+1}\,dz = -\int_0^{2\pi} \mathrm{se}_{2n+1}\,\mathrm{ce}'_{2m+1}\,dz$$

$$= \pi\sum_{r=0}^{\infty}(2r+1)A_{2r+1}^{(2m+1)}B_{2r+1}^{(2n+1)} \qquad (6)$$

and

$$\int_0^{2\pi} \mathrm{ce}_m\,\mathrm{ce}'_n\,dz = \int_0^{2\pi} \mathrm{se}_m\,\mathrm{se}'_n\,dz = 0. \qquad (7)$$

These results are valid for $m \neq n$ or $m = n$.

14.50. An integral identity. In § 14.20 we showed that if y_1, y_2 were solutions of $y''-(a-2q\cosh 2u)y = 0$ for the same a, q, then for all u

$$y_1'y_2 - y_2'y_1 \equiv c^2, \quad \text{a constant.} \qquad (1)$$

Squaring both sides of (1) gives

$$y_1'^2y_2^2 + y_2'^2y_1^2 - 2y_1'y_2'y_1y_2 \equiv c^4. \qquad (2)$$

Now, by § 10.76,

$$y_1'y_2' = \xi_{1,2}(0) - y_1(z)y_2(z)\chi(z) + 4q\int_0^z y_1(u)y_2(u)\sinh 2u\,du, \qquad (3)$$

where $\xi_{1,2}(0) = y_1'(0)y_2'(0) + y_1(0)y_2(0)\chi(0)$. Using (3) in (2) leads† to

$$c^4 \equiv y_2^2(z)\xi_{1,1}(0) + y_1^2(z)\xi_{2,2}(0) - 2y_1(z)y_2(z)\xi_{1,2}(0) +$$

$$+ 4q\int_0^z [y_2(z)y_1(u) - y_1(z)y_2(u)]^2\sinh 2u\,du. \qquad (4)$$

† With the aid of (4) § 14.30.

Taking the initial conditions $y_1(0) = y_2'(0) = 1$, $y_1'(0) = y_2(0) = 0$, we find that $\xi_{1,1}(0) = (2q-a)$, $\xi_{2,2}(0) = 1$, $\xi_{1,2}(0) = 0$, $c^4 = 1$. Hence (4) becomes

$$y_1^2(z)+(2q-a)y_2^2(z)+4q \int_0^z [y_2(z)y_1(u)-y_1(z)y_2(u)]^2 \sinh 2u \, du \equiv 1,$$
(5)

or

$$4q \int_0^z [y_2(z)y_1(u)-y_1(z)y_2(u)]^2 \sinh 2u \, du \equiv 1-y_1^2(z)+(a-2q)y_2^2(z).$$
(6)

For the equation $y''+(a-2q\cos 2z)y = 0$, the identity corresponding to (6) is

$$4q \int_0^z [y_2(z)y_1(u)-y_1(z)y_2(u)]^2 \sin 2u \, du \equiv 1-y_1^2(z)-(a-2q)y_2^2(z).$$
(7)

If a, q are fixed, (6), (7) are valid for all real finite values of z. When $q = 0$, (7) degenerates to

$$y_1^2(z)+ay_2^2(z) = 1,$$
(8)

while the equation becomes

$$y''+ay = 0,$$
(9)

and the appropriate solutions which conform with (8) are

$$y_1(z) = \cos a^{\frac{1}{2}}z, \quad \text{and } y_2(z) = \sin a^{\frac{1}{2}}z/a^{\frac{1}{2}}$$
(10)

respectively.

PART II

APPLICATIONS OF MATHIEU FUNCTIONS

XV

APPLICATIONS OF $y'' + (a - 2q\cos 2z)y = 0$

15.10. Amplitude distortion in moving-coil loud-speaker. A conventional diagram of this apparatus is shown in Fig. 20 A. A sinusoidal current of low audio frequency in the coil, causes it to vibrate axially about a central or equilibrium position. For absence of distortion arising from amplitude of motion, the amplitude must be proportional to that of the coil current. This condition is satisfied if the total magnetic flux passing radially through the coil remains constant throughout its travel.† When the axial length of the coil is equal to that of the outer pole face (Fig. 20 B), and the amplitude is relatively great, i.e. the sound output is large, an appreciable length of the coil moves into the leakage field at each side of the outer pole. The amplitude cannot then be proportional to the current, since the field decreases rapidly with increase in axial distance from either side of the outer pole. In practice the coil usually tends to move into the weaker part of the field, but its excursion is limited by the axial restoring force exerted by the centring spider (not shown), and the outer surround which supports the diaphragm. By virtue of this superimposed unidirectional motion, speech and music are reproduced with perceptible distortion because the axial constraint is non-linear for large coil displacement.‡ If, however, the axial length of the coil is adequately greater than that of the outer pole (Fig. 20 D), the magnetic flux passing radially through the coil is almost constant throughout the travel. Then the effect described above is negligible, being counteracted easily by the axial restoring force. A well-designed loud-speaker satisfies this requirement [202], provided the coil amplitude does not exceed the linearity limits of the axial control.

---

† It has been tacitly assumed that the axial constraint is proportional to the displacement of the coil.

‡ When the coil current arises from speech or music, intermodulation occurs between the various component frequencies, owing to the constraint-displacement relationship being non-linear. The distortion is unpleasant aurally.

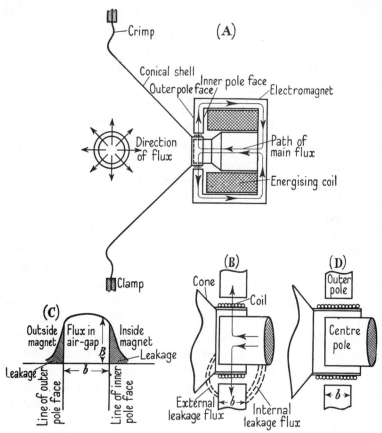

FIG. 20 A–D. Schematic diagrams for moving-coil loud-speaker.

15.11. The equation of motion. To study the phenomenon described in § 15.10, analytically, we consider a relatively narrow coil situated in a radial magnetic field which decreases linearly† from the outer side of the centre pole (Fig. 21) towards the left, i.e. away from the magnet. The axial force on the coil due to a current $I_0 \cos 2\omega t$ is

$$f = 2\pi r n c \xi I_0 \cos 2\omega t, \tag{1}$$

where

$r =$ mean coil radius,

$n =$ number of coil turns, uniformly spaced,

---

† In practice the relationship between flux and axial distance takes the form shown in Fig. 20 c.

$B = c\xi$ = magnetic flux density when coil centre is distant ξ from the origin,

c = slope of line in Fig. 21.

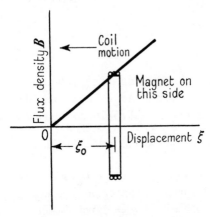

FIG. 21. Assumed relation between flux density B and distance from outer face of magnet in Fig. 20.

For simplicity we assume that:

(a) the axial mechanical restoring force on the diaphragm is negligible;

(b) the mechanical loss is negligible;

(c) the electrical impedance of the circuit external to the coil is large enough to preserve constant current whatever ξ, i.e. the back e.m.f. induced in the coil by virtue of motion in the magnetic field is small compared with the potential difference applied to the circuit.

If m_e is the effective mass of the coil and diaphragm, the equation of motion is

$$m_e \frac{d^2\xi}{dt^2} - 2\pi r n c\xi I_0 \cos 2\omega t = 0. \tag{2}$$

Writing $z = \omega t$, $q = \pi r n c I_0 / \omega^2 m_e$, (2) becomes

$$\frac{d^2\xi}{dz^2} - (2q \cos 2z)\xi = 0. \tag{3}$$

If a linear axial mechanical restoring force s per unit axial displacement is present, the term $s\xi$ must be added to the l.h.s. of (2). Then we have

$$\frac{d^2\xi}{dz^2} + (a - 2q \cos 2z)\xi = 0 \tag{4}$$

with $a = s/\omega^2 m_e$. In addition, if linear damping r_e per unit axial velocity is present, the equation of motion is

$$m_e \frac{d^2\xi}{dt^2} + r_e \frac{d\xi}{dt} + s\xi - 2\pi rnc\xi I_0 \cos 2\omega t = 0, \qquad (5)$$

or

$$\frac{d^2\xi}{dz^2} + 2\kappa \frac{d\xi}{dz} + (a - 2q \cos 2z)\xi = 0, \qquad (6)$$

where $2\kappa = r_e/\omega m_e$.

Under the simplifying assumptions given above, the motion of the coil in a linearly decreasing radial magnetic field is defined by (3). As a practical value of q we take $0 \cdot 16$, so the equation to be solved is

$$\frac{d^2\xi}{dz^2} - (0 \cdot 32 \cos 2z)\xi = 0. \qquad (7)$$

15.12. Solution of (7) § 15.11. From Fig. 8 we see that the point $a = 0$, $q = 0 \cdot 16$ lies in a stable region of the plane between a_0 and b_1. By (1) § 4.74 with $\nu = \beta$, $a = 0$, we obtain

$$\beta^2 \simeq q^2/2(1 - \beta^2),$$

from which we find that

$$\beta \simeq 0 \cdot 1138. \qquad (1)$$

For the first solution, in accordance with 1° § 4.70 we take

$$\xi_1 = \sum_{r=-\infty}^{\infty} c_{2r} \cos(2r + 0 \cdot 114)z. \qquad (2)$$

By (1) § 4.17 the recurrence formula for the c is

$$(2r + 0 \cdot 114)^2 c_{2r} + 0 \cdot 16(c_{2r+2} + c_{2r-2}) = 0. \qquad (3)$$

Neglecting c_6, with $r = 2$, we get

$$c_2 = -4 \cdot 114^2 \times 6 \cdot 25 c_4$$
$$= -1 \cdot 057 \times 10^2 c_4. \qquad (4)$$

$r = 1$
$$c_0 = 2 \cdot 114^2 \times 6 \cdot 25 \times 1 \cdot 057 \times 10^2 c_4 - c_4$$
$$= 2 \cdot 95 \times 10^3 c_4. \qquad (5)$$

Thus
$$c_2 = -3 \cdot 58 \times 10^{-2} c_0 \qquad (6)$$

and
$$c_4 = 3 \cdot 39 \times 10^{-4} c_0. \qquad (7)$$

Neglecting c_{-8}, with $r = -3$

$$c_{-4} = -5 \cdot 886^2 \times 6 \cdot 25 c_{-6}$$
$$= -2 \cdot 165 \times 10^2 c_{-6}. \qquad (8)$$

$r = -2$
$$c_{-2} = 3 \cdot 886^2 \times 6 \cdot 25 \times 2 \cdot 165 \times 10^2 c_{-6} - c_{-6}$$
$$= 2 \cdot 04 \times 10^4 c_{-6}. \qquad (9)$$

$$r = -1 \qquad c_0 = -1\!\cdot\!886^2 \times 6\!\cdot\!25 \times 2\!\cdot\!04 \times 10^4 c_{-6} - c_{-4}$$
$$= -4\!\cdot\!55 \times 10^5 c_{-6}. \tag{10}$$

Thus
$$c_{-2} = -4\!\cdot\!5 \times 10^{-2} c_0, \tag{11}$$
$$c_{-4} = 4\!\cdot\!77 \times 10^{-4} c_0, \tag{12}$$
$$c_{-6} = -2\!\cdot\!2 \times 10^{-6} c_0. \tag{13}$$

If in (3) we put $r = 0$, β for $0\!\cdot\!114$, and insert the values of c_2, c_{-2}, we obtain
$$c_0 \beta^2 = -0\!\cdot\!16(c_2 + c_{-2}) = 0\!\cdot\!16 \times 8\!\cdot\!08 \times 10^{-2} c_0,$$
so
$$\beta = 0\!\cdot\!1137, \tag{14}$$

which checks the value at (1) and also the computation in general—up to a point!

Substituting for β and the c in (2), the first solution is
$$\xi_1 = c_0[\cos 0\!\cdot\!114z - 4\!\cdot\!5 \times 10^{-2} \cos 1\!\cdot\!886z -$$
$$-3\!\cdot\!58 \times 10^{-2} \cos 2\!\cdot\!114z + ...]. \tag{15}$$

By $1°$ § 4.70 the second solution is
$$\xi_2 = c_0[\sin 0\!\cdot\!114z + 4\!\cdot\!5 \times 10^{-2} \sin 1\!\cdot\!886z -$$
$$-3\!\cdot\!58 \times 10^{-2} \sin 2\!\cdot\!114z - ...]. \tag{16}$$

By § 4.71, (15), (16) are multiples of $ce_{0\cdot114}(z, 0\!\cdot\!16)$ and $se_{0\cdot114}(z, 0\!\cdot\!16)$, respectively. Using (3) § 4.72, we have
$$K \simeq 1/c_0[1 + 0\!\cdot\!045^2 + 0\!\cdot\!036^2]^{\frac{1}{2}} \simeq 1/1\!\cdot\!002 c_0. \tag{17}$$

Hence
$$\xi_1 = 1\!\cdot\!002 c_0 \, ce_{0\cdot114}(z, 0\!\cdot\!16) \quad \text{and} \quad \xi_2 = 1\!\cdot\!002 c_0 \, se_{0\cdot114}(z, 0\!\cdot\!16), \tag{18}$$

and the complete solution with two arbitrary constants is
$$\xi = A\xi_1 + B\xi_2. \tag{19}$$

15.13. Initial conditions. We take $\xi = \xi_0$, $\dot{\xi} = 0$ at $t = 0$, i.e. when $z = 0$. Then by (15), (16), (19) § 15.12 the first condition gives
$$\xi_0 = Ac_0(1 - 0\!\cdot\!045 - 0\!\cdot\!0358),$$
so
$$A = 1\!\cdot\!088\xi_0/c_0. \tag{1}$$

The second condition gives $B = 0$. Hence the appropriate solution of the problem is
$$\xi = 1\!\cdot\!088\xi_0[\cos 0\!\cdot\!114z - 0\!\cdot\!045 \cos 1\!\cdot\!886z - 0\!\cdot\!036 \cos 2\!\cdot\!114z + ...] \tag{2}$$
$$= 1\!\cdot\!09\xi_0 \, ce_{0\cdot114}(z, 0\!\cdot\!16), \tag{3}$$

where $z = \omega t$. Since $\beta = 0\!\cdot\!114 = 57/500$, by § 4.71 the period of (2), (3) is 1000π.

15.14. Interpretation of (2) § 15.13. Cos $0{\cdot}114z$ is the dominant term, and as the coefficients of the other terms are comparatively small, these terms may be considered to represent ripples of pulsatance $> 0{\cdot}114\omega$. The motion of the coil is illustratèd by the heavy curve of Fig. 22. The coil reaches the position $\xi = 0$ after a time

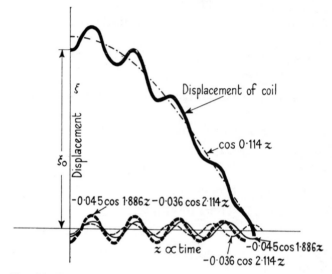

Fig. 22. Curve showing displacement of L.S. coil outside magnet.

lapse of approximately the first quarter period of $\cos 0{\cdot}114\omega t$, i.e. $\tau = \pi/0{\cdot}228\omega$. If the pulsatance of the coil current were $\omega = 35\pi$, $\tau \simeq 1/8$ second. Since we assumed absence of constraint and loss, if we make the additional assumption that the magnetic field is zero when $\xi < 0$, the coil having reached $\xi = 0$ will move onwards by virtue of its momentum. The time taken for the coil to travel the distance $\xi = \xi_0$ may be increased by reducing q [202].

15.15. Electro-mechanical rectification. The effect described above has been called by this name because a sinusoidal current in the coil causes a unidirectional motion. If, however, the magnetic field were negative behind the origin—antisymmetrical about 0—the coil would oscillate about 0, so the question of rectification would not arise.

Attention is drawn to the following features:

(a) In (2) § 15.13 there is no term of pulsatance equal to that of the current, 2ω.

(b) On the dominant component $\cos 0\cdot114\omega t$ is superimposed an infinite number of ripples of different pulsatances, which are non-integral multiples of $0\cdot114\omega$.

15.16. Parametric point in unstable region of Fig. 8. The solution in §15.12 pertains to a stable region. If (a,q) lies in an unstable region the form of solution is given at (1) or (3), 2° §4.70. This entails the rate of oscillation of the coil being the same as the frequency of the current, while ξ_{max} increases with increase in time. The reader may find it of interest to investigate the unstable case with and without damping.

15.17. Pulsatance multiplication. In Fig. 11 each iso-β curve (if continued far enough) intersects the q-axis. Between the intersections of a_0, b_1 with this axis, $0 < \beta < 1$, $a = 0$, and each β corresponds to a different pulsatance of the dominant term in (2) §15.13. Hence in this range, by varying q we may obtain any pulsatance in the range $0 < \beta\omega < \omega$. When the point is in any other stable region ($q > 0$) the dominant term will not always have the lowest pulsatance, e.g. in (2) §5.310 the dominant term has a pulsatance about four times that of the first term. Thus in a system satisfying (4) §15.11, by varying the driving force (proportional to q) and/or the constraint (proportional to a), the pulsatance of the dominant component may be any multiple or sub-multiple of 2ω, the pulsatance of the driving force.

15.20. Frequency modulation. In radio telephony, e.g. broadcasting, a wave train of constant frequency and amplitude is radiated from the aerial at the transmitting station during intervals. This is called the 'carrier' wave. The process at the transmitter whereby this wave is made to 'carry' signals, which become audible at the receiver, is known as *modulation*, i.e. the signal characters modulate the carrier wave. In the receiver there is a circuital arrangement for demodulating the radio frequency, thereby reproducing the original signals, usually rendered audible by a loud-speaker. There are three types of modulation, (a) frequency, (b) amplitude, (c) phase. We shall deal with (a), where it is implied that signals cause a variation in the frequency of the radio oscillations at the transmitter. The same principle is used in the case of the audio warble tone employed in acoustical test rooms to reduce standing wave effect. Instead of using a constant test frequency, the latter undergoes cyclic variation covering a band of 50 cycles per second or more,† at a rate which may be altered.

15.21. Classification. Frequency modulation may be classified under three heads: 1°. Direct capacitance modulation; 2°. Exact frequency modulation; 3°. Inverse capacitance modulation [2].

1°. *Direct capacitance modulation.* Consider the loss-free circuit shown schematically in Fig. 23 A. Inductance L is in series with

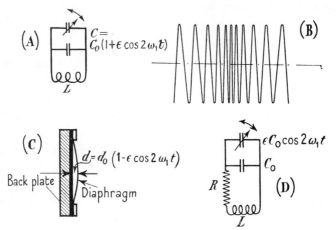

FIG. 23. (A) Schematic of loss-free electrical circuit with periodically variable capacitance.
(B) Illustrating frequency modulation *without* amplitude modulation.
(C) Illustrating capacitance type microphone.
(D) As at (A) but with resistance R in circuit.

capacitance C, which varies with time, so we write $C = C(t)$, a function of t. We assume that in practice the loss in L, C, and the connecting wires would be neutralized by the negative resistance effect of a thermionic valve. If Q denotes the quantity of electricity in the capacitance, the circuital differential equation is

$$\frac{d^2Q}{dt^2} + \frac{Q}{LC(t)} = 0. \tag{1}$$

We shall assume that $C(t) = C_0(1 + \epsilon \cos 2\omega_1 t)$, C_0 being constant and $\epsilon \ll 1$. If $\epsilon = 0$, the central or carrier pulsatance of the circuit is $\omega_0 = 1/(LC_0)^{\frac{1}{2}}$. As $C(t)$ alters from $C_0(1 - \epsilon)$ to $C_0(1 + \epsilon)$ and back again periodically, the pulsatance varies over the range $1/[LC_0(1 - \epsilon)]^{\frac{1}{2}}$ to $1/[LC_0(1 + \epsilon)]^{\frac{1}{2}}$, and the central or carrier wave is said to be frequency modulated. A frequency modulated wave is illustrated in Fig. 23 B.

† Usually a percentage of the central or test frequency.

Using the binomial expansion of $(1 + \epsilon \cos 2\omega_1 t)^{-1}$, (1) takes the form

$$\frac{d^2Q}{dt^2} + \omega_0^2(1 - \epsilon \cos 2\omega_1 t + \epsilon^2 \cos^2 2\omega_1 t - \epsilon^3 \cos^3 2\omega_1 t + ...)Q = 0.$$

$$(2)$$

If we write $z = \omega_1 t$, expand the circular functions, and put $\theta_0 = (\omega_0/\omega_1)^2[1 + \frac{1}{2}\epsilon^2 + ...]$, $2\theta_2 = -(\omega_0/\omega_1)^2[\epsilon + \frac{3}{4}\epsilon^3 + ...]$, etc., (2) becomes

$$\frac{d^2Q}{dz^2} + \left(\theta_0 + 2\sum_{r=1}^{\infty} \theta_{2r} \cos 2rz\right)Q = 0, \tag{3}$$

which is Hill's equation, whose solution is treated in § 6.11 et seq., and § 15.25.

Since the extreme values of $C(t)$ are $C_0(1 \pm \epsilon)$, we have

$$\omega_{\max}^2 = 1/LC_0(1 - \epsilon),$$

so $\omega_{\max} \simeq \omega_0(1 + \frac{1}{2}\epsilon)$: also $\omega_{\min} \simeq \omega_0(1 - \frac{1}{2}\epsilon)$. Thus the pulsatance variation on either side of ω_0 is approximately

$$\tfrac{1}{2}(\omega_{\max} - \omega_{\min}) = \Delta\omega = \tfrac{1}{2}\omega_0 \epsilon,$$

so $\epsilon = 2\Delta\omega/\omega_0$. Substituting this in (2) and omitting terms in ϵ^2, ϵ^3,..., as a first approximation we obtain

$$\frac{d^2Q}{dt^2} + (\omega_0^2 - 2\omega_0 \Delta\omega \cos 2\omega_1 t)Q = 0. \tag{4}$$

Writing $z = \omega_1 t$, $Q = y$ in (4) leads to the canonical form

$$\frac{d^2y}{dz^2} + (a - 2q \cos 2z)y = 0, \tag{5}$$

with $a = (\omega_0/\omega_1)^2$, $q = \omega_0 \Delta\omega/\omega_1^2$. The solution is in § 15.26. If C were fixed and L varied cyclically, an equation similar to (5) would be obtained.

2^0. *Exact frequency modulation.* This is a mathematical concept, and so far as the analysis is concerned, we need not consider the method by which the desired practical result is obtained. The differential equation takes the form

$$\frac{d^2Q}{dt^2} + \psi(t)Q = 0, \tag{1}$$

where $\psi(t)$ is a periodic continuous or piecewise continuous function of t. If $[\psi(t)]^{\frac{1}{2}} = \omega_0 - \Delta\omega \cos 2\omega_1 t$, the pulsatance varies from

$(\omega_0+\Delta\omega)$ to $(\omega_0-\Delta\omega)$ *exactly*, and not approximately as in 1°. Substituting this value of $\psi(t)$ in (1) leads to

$$\frac{d^2Q}{dt^2}+(\omega_0^2+\tfrac{1}{2}\Delta^2\omega-2\omega_0\Delta\omega\cos 2\omega_1 t+\tfrac{1}{2}\Delta^2\omega\cos 4\omega_1 t)Q=0, \quad (2)$$

which is an extended form of Mathieu equation, with

$$\theta_0=(\omega_0^2+\tfrac{1}{2}\Delta^2\omega)/\omega_1^2, \qquad \theta_2=-2\omega_0\Delta\omega/\omega_1^2, \qquad \theta_4=\tfrac{1}{2}\Delta^2\omega/\omega_1^2,$$

$\theta_6=\theta_8=\ldots=0,\ z=\omega_1 t$. If $\Delta\omega$ is small enough, the terms in $\Delta^2\omega$ may be neglected and (2) is then identical with (4) § 1°. Otherwise the equation must be solved without this reduction.

3°. *Inverse capacitance modulation.* An example of this class is found in a certain type of condenser microphone shown schematically in Fig. 23c. Assuming a sound wave of pulsatance $2\omega_1$ impinges on the diaphragm, the capacitance of the microphone varies *inversely* as the distance $d=d_0(1-\epsilon\cos 2\omega_1 t)$ from the back-plate. Then the capacitance at any instant is given by $C(t)=K/d_0(1-\epsilon\cos 2\omega_1 t)$, where d_0 is the separation between the diaphragm and back-plate in quiescent intervals, and K is a constant for the microphone. By (1) § 1° the differential equation for the system is, with $C_0=K/d_0$,

$$\frac{d^2Q}{dt^2}+\frac{Q}{LC_0}(1-\epsilon\cos 2\omega_1 t)=0, \tag{1}$$

or

$$\frac{d^2Q}{dt^2}+\omega_0^2(1-\epsilon\cos 2\omega_1 t)Q=0, \tag{2}$$

where $\omega_0^2=1/LC_0$. The nomenclature 'inverse capacitance modulation' is due to $(1-\epsilon\cos 2\omega_1 t)$ being in the numerator in (1), whereas in (1) § 1° it is in the denominator.

15.22. Modulation zones.

The differential equation for the three classes of modulation considered in § 15.21 may for present purposes be expressed in the form

$$\frac{d^2y}{dz^2}+a(1-2\gamma\cos 2z)y=0, \tag{1}$$

where $z=\omega_1 t$, $2\omega_1$ being the modulating or signal pulsatance; $a=(\omega_0/\omega_1)^2$, ω_0 being the central or carrier pulsatance which is modulated; $\gamma=\Delta\omega/\omega_0$, $\Delta\omega$ being the deviation on either side of ω_0. $2\omega_1$ is the rate at which the deviation occurs. Equation (1) may be used for 1°, 2°, § 15.21 provided the requisite approximation is permissible.

Referring to the stability chart Fig. 8, it is expedient for present purposes to use that half where $q \geqslant 0$, and to interchange the a, q

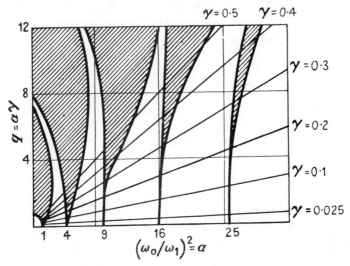

FIG. 24. Stability chart for frequency modulation [2].

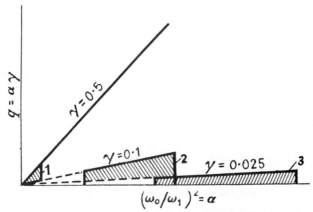

FIG. 25. Modulation zones in Fig. 24 [2].

axes. Then we have the diagram Fig. 24, and by giving γ a series of values, the lines $q = a\gamma$ may be inserted as shown.

It is convenient to divide Fig. 24 into three zones as illustrated in Fig. 25. Zone 1, covering the range $0 \cdot 1 \leqslant \gamma < 0 \cdot 5$, is of theoretical interest only. $2\Delta\omega$ approaches to ω_0, and $2\omega_1$ to ω_0. The line $\gamma = 0 \cdot 5$

may be regarded as a boundary, since in practice $\gamma < 0.5$, in fact it is usually much less than 0.5. The second zone includes the audio warble tone and covers the range $2 \times 10^2 \leqslant a \leqslant 2.4 \times 10^6$, with $0 < \gamma \leqslant 0.1$, $\Delta\omega < \omega_0$, $\omega_1 \ll \omega_0$. Zone 3 covers the range of frequency modulation in radio transmission, where $9 \times 10^5 \leqslant a \leqslant 1.2 \times 10^{13}$, $0 < \gamma \leqslant 0.025$, $\Delta\omega \ll \omega_0$, $\omega_1 \ll \omega_0$. For a given value of ω_0, since $\gamma = \Delta\omega/\omega_0$, any of the straight lines in Fig. 24 represents a condition of constant pulsatance deviation. 2γ may be regarded as the modulation coefficient; the signal strength is proportional thereto.

15.23. Stability of oscillations.

Consider the circuit of Fig. 23A in conjunction with the line $\gamma = 0.025$ in Figs. 24, 25. Imagine the circuital parameters to be continuously variable so that as $\omega_0 = 1/(LC_0)^{\frac{1}{2}}$ increases, the ratio $(\omega_0/\omega_1)^2 = a$ does likewise, but γ, the fractional deviation, remains constant at 0.025. Commencing at $a = 0$, the line $\gamma = 0.025$ intersects the (a, q) curves where they are close to each other, and as a increases, the intercepts in the stable regions steadily increase, while those in the unstable regions decrease. As a rough approximation the intersections occur when $a = m^2$, m a positive integer. With $a > 10^6$, the probability of instability in a radio circuit, whose parameters are chosen at random, is small. Moreover, if a is large enough, the operating point (a, q) will probably lie in a stable region between two characteristics for Mathieu functions of integral order.

This statement is based on the assumption that changes in $a = (\omega_0/\omega_1)^2$ are likely to be small. The curves a_{1000}, b_{1001} cross the a-axis at $a = 10^6$ and $a = (10^3+1)^2 = 10^6+2001$, respectively. Thus when q is small and positive, if we select a point midway between a_{1000}, b_{1001}, the permissible variation in pulsatance ratio $a^{\frac{1}{2}} = \omega_0/\omega_1$, to avoid encroaching upon an unstable region would be less than 1 part in 2,000. When $q > 0$ exceeds a certain value, the two characteristics begin to approach each other rapidly, and the permissible variation in (ω_0/ω_1) to avoid instability then decreases with increase in q. In precision work, where thermostatic control and temperature-compensated components are used, the pulsatance variation of an oscillator would be very small.

The greater γ, e.g. 0.5, the wider the intercept in an unstable region and the higher the probability of unstable operation. It is clear, therefore, to ensure stable operation over a wide range of a, and consequently of the signal pulsatance $2\omega_1$, that $\gamma = \Delta\omega/\omega_0$ should be small compared with $1/2$.

15.24. The line spectrum in radio frequency modulation

[21]. We have mentioned that in this case a is very large. If $\gamma \ll 1$, then $a \gg 2a\gamma = 2q > 0$, and the condition for validity of (13) § 4.80 is fulfilled. Apart from a constant multiplier, this series represents Q, the quantity of electricity in the electrical circuit Fig. 23 A. Thus writing Q for y, and $\omega_1 t$ for z in (1), (13) § 4.80, we obtain the current

$$I = \frac{dQ}{dt} = -\omega_1 \sum_{r=-r_0}^{r_0} C_r J_r(q/2a^{\frac{1}{2}})\sin[(a^{\frac{1}{2}}-2r)\omega_1 t-\alpha], \tag{1}$$

where $C_r = C(a^{\frac{1}{2}}-2r) \simeq Ca^{\frac{1}{2}}$, since in § 4.80, $a^{\frac{1}{2}} \gg r_0$. Now $q = a\gamma$, $a = (\omega_0/\omega_1)^2$, $\gamma = \Delta\omega/\omega_0$, so (1) may be written

$$I \simeq -\omega_0 C \sum_{r=-r_0}^{r_0} J_r(\Delta\omega/2\omega_1)\sin[(\omega_0-2r\omega_1)t-\alpha]. \tag{2}$$

Taking $\Delta\omega/2\omega_1 = h$, $J_{-r} = (-1)^r J_r$, (2) may be set out in the form

Discrete components		Pulsatances	
$-I/\omega_0 C =$			
$J_0(h)\sin(\omega_0 t-\alpha)+$		$\omega_0,$	the carrier
$+J_1(h)\{\sin[(\omega_0-2\omega_1)t-\alpha] - \sin[(\omega_0+2\omega_1)t-\alpha]\}+$		$\omega_0-2\omega_1,$	$\omega_0+2\omega_1$
$+J_2(h)\{\sin[(\omega_0-4\omega_1)t-\alpha] + \sin[(\omega_0+4\omega_1)t-\alpha]\}+$		$\omega_0-4\omega_1,$	$\omega_0+4\omega_1$
$+\ .\ .\ .\ .\ .\ .\ .\ .\ .\ .\ .\ .\ +$		$.\ .\ .$	
$+J_{r_0}(h)\{\sin[(\omega_0-2r_0\,\omega_1)t-\alpha]\pm\sin[(\omega_0+2r_0\,\omega_1)t-\alpha]\}$		$\omega_0-2r_0\omega_1,$	$\omega_0+2r_0\omega_1$

$$\tag{3}$$

It follows from (3) that when the carrier of pulsatance ω_0 is modulated by an oscillation of pulsatance $2\omega_1 \ll \omega_0$, there results a line spectrum or series of discrete pulsatance components. These are spaced at equal intervals $2\omega_1$ on each side of the carrier or central oscillation of pulsatance ω_0, as illustrated in Fig. 26. The amplitude of the component of pulsatance $(\omega_0\pm2r\omega_1)$ is proportional to the J-Bessel function of order r, namely, $J_r(\Delta\omega/2\omega_1)$. In Fig. 26, $\Delta\omega/2\omega_1 = 0\cdot1$. When > 1, the amplitudes of some components may exceed that of the carrier, as will be seen from tables of $J_r(u)$.

15.25. Approximate stable solution of (1) 1° § 15.21. The

equation may be written

$$Q''+a\rho^2 Q = 0, \tag{1}$$

with $a = \omega_0^2 = 1/LC_0$, $\rho = (1+\epsilon\cos 2\omega_1 t)^{-\frac{1}{2}}$. If the conditions $a \gg 1$,

$0 < \epsilon < 1$ are satisfied, then by (13) §4.82 an approximate stable solution is

$$Q_1(t) = A(1+\epsilon\cos 2\omega_1 t)^{\frac{1}{4}}\cos\left[\omega_0\int_0^t dt/(1+\epsilon\cos 2\omega_1 t)^{\frac{1}{2}}\right] \tag{2}$$

$$= A(1+\epsilon\cos 2\omega_1 t)^{\frac{1}{4}}\cos\left[\{\omega_0/(1+\epsilon)^{\frac{1}{2}}\}\int_0^t dt/(1-\lambda^2\sin^2\omega_1 t)^{\frac{1}{2}}\right], \tag{3}$$

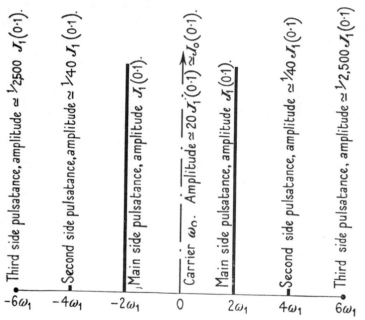

FIG. 26. Illustrating relative amplitudes of side bands in frequency modulation due to a single modulating wave.

with $\lambda^2 = 2\epsilon/(1+\epsilon)$, A being an arbitrary constant, the second one not being needed here. Thus, with $\omega_0/\omega_1 = \bar{\omega}_0$,

$$Q_1(t) = A(1+\epsilon\cos 2\omega_1 t)^{\frac{1}{4}}\cos[\{\bar{\omega}_0/(1+\epsilon)^{\frac{1}{2}}\}F(\lambda, \omega_1 t)], \tag{4}$$

where F is an incomplete elliptic integral of the first kind with modulus λ, i.e. the integral part in (3).

The type of function represented by (4) is depicted in Fig. 10 A. Both amplitude and frequency modulation are exhibited. The former is associated with the factor $(1+\epsilon\cos 2\omega_1 t)^{\frac{1}{4}}$, and the latter with $F(\lambda, \omega_1 t)$. These expressions are periodic in t, with period π/ω_1. The ratio max./min. amplitude for $\epsilon = 0.75$ is $[(1+0.75)/(1-0.75)]^{\frac{1}{4}} = 1.63/1$. This is an extreme case and corresponds to $\gamma = 0.375$ (see

Fig. 25). If ϵ were 0·02 for radio frequency modulation, the amplitude ratio would be 1·01, i.e. 1 per cent. amplitude modulation.

By (2) above and (16) § 4.82 the 'instantaneous frequency' is

$$f(t) = \frac{d}{dt}\left[\frac{\omega_0}{2\pi}\int_0^t dt/(1+\epsilon\cos 2\omega_1 t)^{\frac{1}{2}}\right] = (\omega_0/2\pi)/(1+\epsilon\cos 2\omega_1 t)^{\frac{1}{2}}. \quad (5)$$

If $\epsilon = 0.5$ the max. and min. frequencies are approximately $1.41f_0$ and $0.82f_0$, with $f_0 = \omega_0/2\pi$. Thus the variation is asymmetrical about f_0. For $\epsilon = 0.02$ the values are nearly $(1\pm0.01)f_0$, so if f_0 were 10 megacycles per second, the frequency would vary 10^5 cycles per second on each side of the carrier, at a rate ω_1/π c.p.s.

The number of oscillations in one period of the modulating frequency ω_1/π is the integral of the 'instantaneous frequency' over the period. Thus by (5)

$$N = \frac{\omega_0}{2\pi}\int_0^{\pi/\omega_1} dt/(1+\epsilon\cos 2\omega_1 t)^{\frac{1}{2}} = \frac{\omega_0}{2\pi(1+\epsilon)^{\frac{1}{2}}}\int_0^{\pi/\omega_1} dt/(1-\lambda^2\sin^2\omega_1 t)^{\frac{1}{2}}. \quad (6)$$

Writing $\omega_1 t = \tau$, (6) becomes

$$N = \frac{(\omega_0/\omega_1)}{\pi(1+\epsilon)^{\frac{1}{2}}}\int_0^{\frac{1}{2}\pi} d\tau/(1-\lambda^2\sin^2\tau)^{\frac{1}{2}} = \frac{(\omega_0/\omega_1)}{\pi(1+\epsilon)^{\frac{1}{2}}}F(\lambda,\tfrac{1}{2}\pi). \quad (7)$$

Taking $\omega_0 = 2\pi\times10^7$, $\omega_1 = 2\pi\times10^3$, by (7) the oscillations per period ω_1/π are

$$N = \frac{10^4}{\pi\times1\cdot01}\times1\cdot5874 \simeq 5000. \quad (8)$$

Current corresponding to (4). Since $I_1(t) = \dfrac{d}{dt}Q_1(t)$, differentiation of (4) leads to

$$I_1(t) = -\frac{A}{(1+\epsilon\cos 2\omega_1 t)^{\frac{1}{2}}}\left[\frac{\omega_0}{(1+\epsilon)^{\frac{1}{2}}}\sin\left\{\frac{\bar{\omega}_0}{(1+\epsilon)^{\frac{1}{2}}}F(\lambda,\omega_1 t)\right\}+\right.$$

$$\left.+\frac{\epsilon\omega_1\sin 2\omega_1 t}{2(1+\epsilon\cos 2\omega_1 t)^{\frac{1}{2}}}\cos\left\{\frac{\bar{\omega}_0}{(1+\epsilon)^{\frac{1}{2}}}F(\lambda,\omega_1 t)\right\}\right]. \quad (9)$$

The type of function represented by (9) is illustrated in Fig. 10 B. When $\omega_0 \gg \omega_1$, and ϵ is such that the second term in [ ] may be neglected in comparison with the first, $I_1(t)_{\max}$ occurs approximately at the same t as $Q_1(t)_{\min}$ (see Figs. 10 A, B).

15.26. Approximate solution of (4) 1° § 15.21. Referring to (1) § 15.25, we now take $\rho^2 = [1-(2\Delta\omega/\omega_0)\cos 2\omega_1 t]$. Writing

$$\epsilon = 2\Delta\omega/\omega_0,$$

the solution is

$$Q_1(t) = [B/(1-\epsilon\cos 2\omega_1 t)^{\frac{1}{4}}]\cos\left[\omega_0 \int_0^t (1-\epsilon\cos 2\omega_1 t)^{\frac{1}{2}}\, dt\right]. \quad (1)$$

Now

$$\int_0^t (1-\epsilon\cos 2\omega_1 t)^{\frac{1}{2}}\, dt = (1+\epsilon)^{\frac{1}{2}} \int_0^t (1-\lambda^2\cos^2\omega_1 t)^{\frac{1}{2}}\, dt = \frac{E_1(\lambda,\omega_1 t)}{\omega_1(1+\epsilon)^{-\frac{1}{2}}},$$

where E_1 is an incomplete elliptic integral defined at (14) § 4.82, with $\lambda^2 = 2\epsilon/(1+\epsilon)$. Thus

$$Q_1(t) = [B/(1-\epsilon\cos 2\omega_1 t)^{\frac{1}{4}}]\cos[\bar{\omega}_0(1+\epsilon)^{\frac{1}{2}}E_1(\lambda,\omega_1 t)], \quad (2)$$

B being an arbitrary constant, the second one not being required here.

The 'instantaneous frequency' is given by

$$f(t) = (\omega_0/2\pi)(1-\epsilon\cos 2\omega_1 t)^{\frac{1}{2}}, \quad (3)$$

and

$$N = \frac{1}{\pi}(\omega_0/\omega_1)(1+\epsilon)^{\frac{1}{2}}E(\lambda, \tfrac{1}{2}\pi). \quad (4)$$

15.30. Circuit having resistance. Hitherto we have discussed resistanceless circuits, the differential equation having the form at (1), 1° § 15.21. Suppose that a constant resistance R is included in circuit, as shown schematically in Fig. 23 D. The p.d. across R is $RI = R\, dQ/dt$, so the equation for this case is

$$\frac{d^2Q}{dt^2} + \frac{R}{L}\frac{dQ}{dt} + \frac{Q}{LC(t)} = 0. \quad (1)$$

If ϵ is small enough, we may take $1/C(t) \simeq (1-\epsilon\cos 2\omega_1 t)/C_0$, and (1) becomes

$$\frac{d^2Q}{dt^2} + \frac{R}{L}\frac{dQ}{dt} + \frac{Q}{LC_0}(1-\epsilon\cos 2\omega_1 t) = 0. \quad (2)$$

Writing $Q = y$, $1/LC_0 = \omega_0^2$, $z = \omega_1 t$, $R/\omega_1 L = 2\kappa$, $\bar{a} = (\omega_0/\omega_1)^2$, $2q = \bar{a}\epsilon$, (2) takes the form

$$y'' + 2\kappa y' + (\bar{a} - 2q\cos 2z)y = 0. \quad (3)$$

The solution of equations of this type is treated in §§ 4.83–4.86, 5.60, and stability conditions are given in § 4.83. An unstable oscillatory circuit† may be stabilized by adjusting R to some suitable value depending upon the other parameters. Moreover, as shown in § 4.84, the stable regions for (3) cover a greater area than those if $\kappa = 0$. They increase in extent with increase in R and, therefore, κ. When the point $(\bar{a}, q)$ is on a characteristic curve *for equation* (3), $\kappa = \mu$ in § 4.84, and the motion is periodic, i.e. a neutral condition. Once started, the oscillation would (in theory) continue unaltered. In practice, however, it would usually either decay to zero or increase until its growth was arrested by the natural limitations of the system.

If $(\bar{a}, q)$ lies in a $\left.\begin{array}{c}\text{stable}\\ \text{unstable}\end{array}\right\}$ region of Fig. 11,‡ $\left.\begin{array}{c}\kappa > \mu\\ \mu > \kappa\end{array}\right\}$ and the oscillation$\left.\begin{array}{c}\to 0\\ \to \pm\infty\end{array}\right\}$ as $t \to +\infty$.

15.31. Approximate stable solution of (1) § 15.30.

Substitute $Q = ve^{-\kappa t}$, with $R/L = 2\kappa$, and we get

$$\frac{d^2v}{dt^2} + (a\rho^2 - \kappa^2)v = 0, \tag{1}$$

where $a = \omega_0^2 = 1/LC_0$, $\rho^2 = 1/(1+\epsilon\cos 2\omega_1 t)$. Now write $(a\rho^2 - \kappa^2) = a\varphi^2$, with $\varphi^2 = (\rho^2 - \kappa^2/a)$, and (1) becomes

$$\frac{d^2v}{dt^2} + a\varphi^2 v = 0. \tag{2}$$

If $a \gg 1$, $0 < \epsilon < 1$, $\kappa^2/a \ll 1$, by (13) § 4.82 an approximate stable solution of (2) is

$$v_1(t) = B\varphi^{-\frac{1}{2}}\cos\left[\omega_0\int_0^t \varphi\, dt\right], \tag{3}$$

B being an arbitrary constant. But

$$\varphi = (1+\epsilon\cos 2\omega_1 t)^{-\frac{1}{2}}[1-(\kappa^2/a)(1+\epsilon\cos 2\omega_1 t)]^{\frac{1}{2}} \tag{4}$$

$$\simeq (1+\epsilon\cos 2\omega_1 t)^{-\frac{1}{2}} - (\kappa^2/2a)(1+\epsilon\cos 2\omega_1 t)^{\frac{1}{2}}, \tag{5}$$

and by (4)

$$\varphi^{\frac{1}{2}} \simeq (1+\epsilon\cos 2\omega_1 t)^{-\frac{1}{4}}[1-(\kappa^2/4a)(1+\epsilon\cos 2\omega_1 t)]; \tag{6}$$

also

$$(1+\epsilon\cos 2\omega_1 t)^{\frac{1}{2}} = (1+\epsilon)^{\frac{1}{2}}(1-\lambda^2\sin^2\omega_1 t)^{\frac{1}{2}} \tag{7}$$

† It is tacitly implied in such circuits that a thermionic valve is incorporated, so that a negative resistance effect may be obtained.

‡ Reference is made here to the stability diagram for (3). The boundary lines are $\mu = \kappa$.

with $\lambda^2 = 2\epsilon/(1+\epsilon)$. Hence from (3)–(7), on substituting $Q_1 = v_1 e^{-\kappa t}$, we obtain

$$Q_1(t) \simeq \frac{Be^{-\kappa t}(1+\epsilon\cos 2\omega_1 t)^{\frac{1}{4}}}{[1-(\kappa^2/4a)(1+\epsilon\cos 2\omega_1 t)]}\cos\left\{\bar{\omega}_0\left[\frac{F(\lambda,\omega_1 t)}{(1+\epsilon)^{\frac{1}{2}}} - \frac{\kappa^2 E(\lambda,\omega_1 t)}{2a(1+\epsilon)^{-\frac{1}{2}}}\right]\right\}.$$

(8)

The type of function represented by (8) is that of Fig. 10 A but having an exponential decay, i.e. the influence of R is to cause extinction of the oscillation, unless a negative resistance effect were introduced to counteract it.

15.32. Circuit with periodically varying resistance.
By (1) § 15.30, the equation for the free oscillations is

$$\frac{d^2Q}{dt^2} + \frac{R}{L}\frac{dQ}{dt} + \frac{Q}{LC} = 0,$$

(1)

where L, C are constant, but $R = R_0 + R_1\varphi(\omega_1 t)$, φ having period $2\pi/\omega_1$, mean value zero, $|\varphi| \leqslant 1$.

Write $Q = e^{-\kappa(t)}u(t)$, with $\kappa(t) = \frac{1}{2L}\int^t R(\tau)\,d\tau$, then (1) becomes

$$u'' + \left(\frac{1}{LC} - \frac{R^2}{4L^2} - \frac{R'}{2L}\right)u = 0.$$

(2)

Now $R^2 = R_0^2 + 2R_0 R_1\varphi + R_1^2\varphi^2$, $R' = dR/dt = \omega_1 R_1\varphi'$, and if we put $\kappa_0 = R_0/2L$, $\kappa_1 = R_1/2L$, $\omega_0^2 = (1/LC) - (R_0^2/4L^2) = a$, we obtain

$$\left(\frac{1}{LC} - \frac{R^2}{4L^2} - \frac{R'}{2L}\right) = \omega_0^2 - \kappa_1[2\kappa_0\varphi + \kappa_1\varphi^2 + \omega_1\varphi']$$

(3)

$$= a - 2q\,\psi(\omega_1 t).$$

(4)

Thus from (2), (4)

$$u'' + [a - 2q\,\psi(\omega_1 t)]u = 0,$$

(5)

which is a standard form of Hill's equation, whose solution may be obtained by the procedure in Chapter VI.

If we commence with the circuital equation

$$L\frac{dI}{dt} + RI + \frac{1}{C}\int I\,dt = 0$$

(6)

and write $I = e^{-\kappa(t)}w(t)$, we obtain

$$w'' + \left(\frac{1}{LC} - \frac{R^2}{4L^2} + \frac{R'}{2L}\right)w = 0,$$

(7)

which is identical in form with (2) except for the sign of $R'/2L$. Then (7) may be written

$$w''+[a-2q\,\psi_1(\omega_1 t)]w = 0, \tag{8}$$

where $2q\,\psi_1(\omega_1 t) = \kappa_1\{2\kappa_0\,\varphi+\kappa_1\,\varphi^2-\omega_1\,\varphi'\}$.

If a driving e.m.f. $E(t)$ is injected into the circuit, the coupling with the generator being negligible, the circuital differential equation is

$$L\frac{dI}{dt}+RI+\frac{1}{C}\int I\,dt = E(t). \tag{9}$$

Then with the above substitution we get

$$w''+[a-2q\,\psi_1(\omega_1 t)]w = (e^{\kappa(t)}/L)(dE/dt), \tag{10}$$

which may be solved by aid of Chapter VI.

These equations occur in the theory of the super-regenerative radio receiver, and reference [45] should be consulted for further details which are too extensive for inclusion here.

15.40. Dynamical system satisfying Mathieu's equation. A simple link-mass-spring mechanism is shown schematically in Fig. 5 A. The mass m slides over a frictionless horizontal plane, along the straight line CA. The links are massless and the pin-joints at A, O, B are frictionless. Also the spring is massless and unstressed when m is at D, while AB, OA are long enough for motion parallel to BD to be negligible in comparison with that along the axis of the spring.

The driving force $F_0 = lf_0\cos 2\omega t$ is applied to the cross-head B. It may be resolved into two components, one along AB, the other along DA. The latter is nearly $(f_0\cos 2\omega t)y$, and it causes m to slide along the line CDA. Three forces are to be considered in connexion with m, namely, (1) the inertia $m\,d^2y/dt^2$, (2) the constraint sy due to the spring, (3) the driving force $(f_0\cos 2\omega t)y$. Then the equation of motion is

$$m\frac{d^2y}{dt^2}+sy = (f_0\cos 2\omega t)y. \tag{1}$$

Substituting $z = \omega t$, $a = s/\omega^2 m$, $2q = f_0/\omega^2 m$, we obtain the standard form

$$\frac{d^2y}{dz^2}+(a-2q\cos 2z)y = 0. \tag{2}$$

If we write $q = a\gamma$, where $\gamma = f_0/2s$, (2) becomes

$$y''+a(1-2\gamma\cos 2z)y = 0. \tag{3}$$

15.41. Behaviour of system in § 15.40. Draw a line $a = q/\gamma$ in Fig. 27. Since $a = s/\omega^2 m$, ω will be large at points on the line near the origin, but will decrease gradually in passing along the positive direction. When ω is such that the line intersects one of the curves b_m, a_m, e.g. the points 1–8, the motion of m is periodic and neutral.

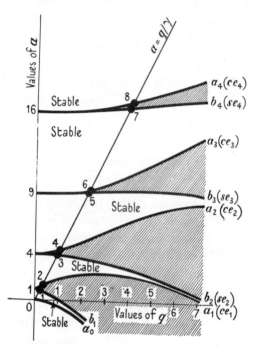

FIG. 27. Stability diagram for mechanism in Fig. 5 A.

Otherwise it is either stable or unstable according to the region in which the point (a, q) lies. The remarks in § 15.17 on variation of pulsatance apply in the present case when (a, q) lies within or on a border-line of a stable region. For a component of given pulsatance to have an amplitude greater than that of any other, (a, q) must be suitably selected. For instance, suppose the motion includes the first sub-harmonic of the driving force. Since all Mathieu functions of odd integral order, namely, $ce_{2n+1}(\omega t, q)$ and $se_{2n+1}(\omega t, q)$, have a sub-harmonic of pulsatance ω, the values of a, q at the intersections of the respective curves a_{2n+1}, b_{2n+1}, and the line $a = q/\gamma$ fulfil the required condition. For predominance of the sub-harmonic we consider the relative magnitudes of the coefficients A, B in the series for ce_{2n+1}, se_{2n+1}, $n = 0$, 1, 2,.... From [95], with q small and positive, $A_{2n+1}^{(2n+1)}$ predominates in one series and $B_{2n+1}^{(2n+1)}$ in the other. For example, if $q = 1$, $A_1^{(1)} \simeq 0.99$, the remaining A being negligible: $B_1^{(1)} \simeq 0.994$, the remaining B being negligible. In these cases the sub-harmonic predominates. If $q = 24$, $A_1 \simeq 0.398$, $A_3 \simeq -0.744$, $A_5 \simeq 0.499$, $A_7 \simeq -0.190$, so the amplitudes of the 3/2 and 5/2 harmonics exceed that of the sub-harmonic: also $B_1 \simeq 0.818$, $B_3 \simeq -0.527$, $B_5 \simeq 0.224$, so the sub-harmonic predominates, but to a much smaller extent than for $q = 1$. Tabular values show that the amplitude of the sub-harmonic in se_1 exceeds that in ce_1, ce_3, ce_5, se_3, se_5 for q in $0 < q \leqslant 40$.

15.42. Demonstration of sub-harmonic. For this purpose the device of Fig. 28 is preferable to that of Fig. 5 A. The link-mass-spring mechanism in the latter is replaced by a relatively heavy

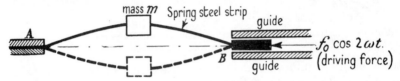

FIG. 28. Dynamical device for illustrating sub-harmonic.

mass at the centre of a light flat strip of spring steel fixed at one end A, but free to move along the direction AB at the other end. So long as the pulsatance of the driving force at B is small enough for absence of wave motion on the spring, this mechanism may be used to demonstrate the effect of varying the parameters m, s, ω, f_0 in (1) §15.40. In §15.41 we showed that the best condition for a predominant sub-harmonic was with (a,q) on b_1, q being small or moderate. Thus $a = s/\omega^2 m$ and $\gamma = f_0/2s$ must be small or moderate. To render the motion of m visible, ω should be low, so m must be relatively large and f_0 small, since we postulate s to be small. If it is not feasible to make ω low enough, the motion of m could be rendered visible stroboscopically. By using suitable values of m, s, the mechanisms of Figs. 5 A, 28 may be used to demonstrate stability and instability.

15.43. System of Fig. 5 A with linear damping. If r is a constant representing the resistance per unit velocity, (1) §15.40 takes the form

$$m\frac{d^2y}{dt^2}+r\frac{dy}{dt}+sy = (f_0\cos 2\omega t)y. \tag{1}$$

Then with $z = \omega t$ we get

$$y'' + 2\kappa y' + (\bar{a} - 2q \cos 2z)y = 0, \tag{2}$$

where $\kappa = r/2\omega m$, $\bar{a} = s/\omega^2 m$, $2q = f_0/\omega^2 m$. (2) is identical in form with (3) § 15.30, and the remarks in that section apply here also.

15.50. Vibration of stretched string. The classical case of a stretched string with immovable ends is a simple one. But when one end is held and the other is given a periodic motion along the length, the analysis is more complicated and leads to a Mathieu equation. We commence with constant tension and assume the string

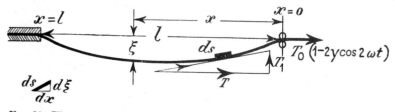

FIG. 29. Illustrating a vibrating string with periodically varying tension super-imposed upon constant tension.

to be elastic, uniform, and loss-free. Referring to Fig. 29, consider an elemental length ds. T is the horizontal component of the tension at ds, and T_1 its vertical component. By similar triangles

$$\partial \xi / \partial x = T_1/T, \quad \text{so } T_1 = T \partial \xi / \partial x. \tag{1}$$

The rate of change of T_1 with respect to x is by (1)

$$\partial T_1 / \partial x = T \partial^2 \xi / \partial x^2, \tag{2}$$

so the difference in T_1 at the ends of the element ds is

$$\partial T_1 = T \, dx \, \partial^2 \xi / \partial x^2. \tag{3}$$

When the amplitude of vibration is small, we may write dx for ds, so the vertical force to accelerate the element ds of mass $\mathbf{m} \, dx$ is

$$\partial T_1 = (\mathbf{m} \, dx) \partial^2 \xi / \partial t^2. \tag{4}$$

Equating the r.h.s. of (3), (4) leads to the equation of motion, namely,

$$\mathbf{m} \, dx \, \partial^2 \xi / \partial t^2 = T \, dx \, \partial^2 \xi / \partial x^2, \tag{5}$$

or

$$\frac{\partial^2 \xi}{\partial t^2} - \frac{T}{\mathbf{m}} \frac{\partial^2 \xi}{\partial x^2} = 0. \tag{6}$$

15.51. Solution of (6) § 15.50. During vibration there are stationary waves on the string, the boundary conditions being $\xi = 0$ at $x = 0, l$. Our solution must satisfy these. Now $e^{ib(x+\alpha t)}$, with $\alpha^2 = T/\mathbf{m}$, satisfies the equation, so its real and imaginary parts must both be solutions. Then $e^{ib(x+\alpha t)} = \cos b(x+\alpha t) + i\sin b(x+\alpha t)$, and since $\xi = 0$ at $x = 0$, the solution cannot contain $\cos bx$. Thus of the four product pairs in the expansion of the real and imaginary parts we must choose $\sin bx \sin b\alpha t$, $\sin bx \cos b\alpha t$. Hence the appropriate formal solution of (6) § 15.50 is

$$\xi = (A\sin b\alpha t + B\cos b\alpha t)\sin bx = f(t)\sin bx, \tag{1}$$

A, B being arbitrary constants. Evanescence of ξ at $x = 0, l$, entails $b = \pi n/l$, n a positive integer $\neq 0$. The pulsatances of the natural modes of vibration are given by $\omega_n = b\alpha = (\pi n/l)(T/\mathbf{m})^{\frac{1}{2}}$, $n = 1, 2, 3, \ldots$. The number of nodes *between* the ends of the string is $(n-1)$, and there are n antinodes or points of maximum displacement, corresponding to the nth mode of vibration.

15.52. Periodically varying tension. Suppose that, instead of being constant, the tension is expressed by $T = T_0(1 - 2\gamma\cos 2\omega t)$, then (6) § 15.50 becomes

$$\frac{\partial^2 \xi}{\partial t^2} - \frac{T_0}{\mathbf{m}}(1 - 2\gamma\cos 2\omega t)\frac{\partial^2 \xi}{\partial x^2} = 0 \tag{1}$$

with $\gamma < \frac{1}{2}$. By virtue of similarity we assume (1) § 15.51 as a solution and obtain the equation

$$\frac{d^2 f}{dt^2} + \frac{b^2 T_0}{\mathbf{m}}(1 - 2\gamma\cos 2\omega t)f = 0, \tag{2}$$

where $f(t)$ is different from its former value. Writing $z = \omega t$, $a = b^2 T_0/\omega^2\mathbf{m}$, $q = \gamma b^2 T_0/\omega^2\mathbf{m} = \gamma a$, (2) transforms to the standard form

$$\frac{d^2 f}{dz^2} + (a - 2q\cos 2z)f = 0. \tag{3}$$

Since $a = q/\gamma$ and $\gamma < \frac{1}{2}$, we get the case depicted in Fig. 25, where the straight line having this equation intersects all the characteristic curves. Unless the parameters a, q are specially selected, the point (a, q) will not in general lie on a characteristic for a function of integral order. Moreover, if (a, q) lies inside a stable region the motion will be represented by a Mathieu function of real fractional order, e.g. $ce_{2n+\beta}(z, q)$. In practice owing to damping, the motion once started would die away with increase in time.

15.53. Melde's experiment. This was described briefly in Chapter I. If an electrically maintained steel reed, having a frequency of the order 50 cycles per second, is used to vary the tension of the string, the rate of vibration will be sensibly constant. The tension T_0 or the length l, or both, may be adjusted so that the string vibrates without a node. Its pulsatance is then half that of the reed, i.e. a subharmonic occurs. If now the string is stopped and released, its amplitude increases with increase in time, and attains an ultimate value. By reducing the *reed* amplitude such that $q < $ some value q_0, the vibration of the string dies away. To explain these observations, terms representing both damping and non-linearity must be incorporated in the differential equation.

15.54. The modified equation. Adding viscous damping proportional to the velocity and a non-linear control term (odd in y, in virtue of symmetry of motion about the central position), we obtain

$$y'' + 2\kappa y' + (a + py^2 - 2q\cos 2z)y = 0 \quad (p > 0). \tag{1}$$

For a subharmonic to occur as in § 15.53, $a \simeq 1$ and (a, q) lies in an *unstable* region between b_1 and a_1 in Fig. 11. A first approximation solution may be obtained by taking $y = A_1\cos z + B_1\sin z$. Then, with $A = (A_1^2 + B_1^2)^{\frac{1}{2}}$, the ultimate amplitude is

$$|A| \simeq [(4/3p)\{(1-a) + (q^2 - 4\kappa^2)^{\frac{1}{2}}\}]^{\frac{1}{2}}. \tag{2}$$

The condition for maintenance of the vibration, i.e. the reality of $|A|$, is

$$q > q_0 = \{4\kappa^2 + (1-a)^2\}^{\frac{1}{2}}. \tag{3}$$

Amplitude limitation is caused by a mis-tuning effect due to the non-linear tension control py^3.†

15.55. String whose mass per unit length is periodic. If in (6) § 15.50 we write $\mathbf{m} = \mathbf{m}_0(1 - 2\gamma\cos\alpha_1 x)$ for $\mathbf{m}$, the equation becomes

$$\frac{\partial^2 \xi}{\partial t^2} - \{T/[\mathbf{m}_0(1 - 2\gamma\cos\alpha_1 x)]\}\frac{\partial^2 \xi}{\partial x^2} = 0. \tag{1}$$

Assume that $\xi = f(t)g(x)$, where f is a function of t alone, and g one of x alone. Then

$$g\frac{d^2 f}{dt^2} - \{T/[\mathbf{m}_0(1 - 2\gamma\cos\alpha_1 x)]\}f\frac{d^2 g}{dx^2} = 0. \tag{2}$$

Dividing (2) throughout by fg leads to

$$\frac{1}{f}\frac{d^2 f}{dt^2} = \{T/[\mathbf{m}_0(1 - 2\gamma\cos\alpha_1 x)]\}\frac{1}{g}\frac{d^2 g}{dx^2}. \tag{3}$$

† A detailed analysis is given in McLachlan, *Ordinary Non-linear Differential Equations in Engineering and Physical Sciences* (Oxford, 1950).

Since the l.h.s. is independent of x and the r.h.s. of t, each must be a constant, say, λ^2. Then using the l.h.s. and the separation constant λ^2, we get

$$\frac{d^2f}{dt^2}+\lambda^2 f = 0, \tag{4}$$

so

$$f = \sin\lambda t \quad \text{or} \quad \cos\lambda t. \tag{5}$$

From the r.h.s. of (3) we get

$$\frac{d^2g}{dx^2}+\frac{\lambda^2}{T}\mathbf{m}_0(1-2\gamma\cos\alpha_1 x)g = 0, \tag{6}$$

or

$$\frac{d^2g}{dz^2}+a(1-2\gamma\cos 2z)g = 0, \tag{7}$$

where $z = \tfrac{1}{2}\alpha_1 x$, $a = 4\lambda^2\mathbf{m}_0/\alpha_1^2\,T$, $q = a\gamma$, $\gamma < 0.5$.

The solution of (7) should be stable and satisfy the boundary condition $g = 0$ at $x = 0, l$. The stable solutions for $q > 0$ are given at (1)–(4) § 4.71. The boundary condition excludes (1), (3) § 4.71, so we consider (2), (4) § 4.71. Now g in (6) may or may not be periodic in x. If periodic, $\beta = p/s$, a rational fraction in its lowest terms, $0 < \beta < 1$. Write $z = s\pi x/l$, then

$$\sin(2r+p/s)(s\pi x/l) = \sin(2r+1+p/s)(s\pi x/l) = 0$$

for all r when $x = 0, l$. Hence we may take $\mathrm{se}_{m+p/s}\,(s\pi x/l, q)$ as those solutions of (6) which satisfy the boundary condition.

Before the complete solution can be written down we have to determine λ. As in §§ 15.22, 15.41 we have the relationship $a = q/\gamma$, γ being a known constant. Then the straight line so defined may be drawn as shown in Fig. 27. Its intersections with the iso-p/s curves for $\mathrm{se}_{m+p/s}\,(z,q)$—see the iso-$\beta$ curves of Fig. 11—give the values of (a, q) for which (6) satisfies the boundary condition. Then we have $\lambda_{m+p/s}^2 = a_{m+p/s}\alpha_1^2\,T/4\mathbf{m}_0$. If there is an integral number of periods of mass-distribution on the string, we may take $\alpha_1 = 2n\pi/l$, so the pulsatance of the vibration is

$$\lambda_{m+p/s} = \frac{n\pi}{l}(a_{m+p/s}\,T/\mathbf{m}_0)^{\frac{1}{2}}. \tag{8}$$

Then the complete solution of (1), with two arbitrary constants, appropriate to the boundary condition, is

$$\xi = \sum_{m=0}^{\infty}\,[A_m\cos\lambda_{m+p/s}t+B_m\sin\lambda_{m+p/s}t]\mathrm{se}_{m+p/s}\left(\frac{s\pi x}{l},a_{m+p/s}\gamma\right). \tag{9}$$

15.60. Column subjected to axial pull with periodic component [121].

Referring to Fig. 30, the pin-jointed column sustains a steady axial pull P_0, but owing to out-of-balance machinery an alternating or ripple component $-2\gamma P_0 \cos 2\omega t$ is superimposed thereon. Thus the total instantaneous axial load is $P = P_0(1 - 2\gamma \cos 2\omega t)$,

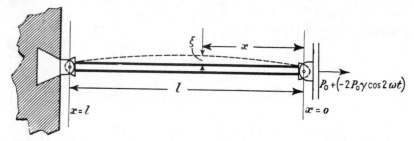

FIG. 30. Illustrating a long column with pinned ends: a periodic force is superimposed upon a constant axial pull.

where usually $\gamma < 0\cdot5$. To render the analysis tractable we make the following assumptions:

1. The column is a uniform solid or hollow homogeneous cylinder, its outer diameter being small compared with the length l.
2. The lateral displacement due to P is small compared with l.
3. The maximum stress is within the elastic limit of the material.
4. Shear stress and rotatory inertia are negligible.
5. The ripple pulsatance is well below that of the first longitudinal mode of the column, i.e. there is no longitudinal wave motion, and the column moves substantially as a whole in an *axial* direction.

Let E = Young's modulus of elasticity;

I = second moment of cross-section about a diameter;

$\mathbf{m}$ = mass of unit length of the column;

ξ = lateral displacement at any point distant x from the right end (Fig. 30).

Then it may be shown that the equation of motion is

$$EI\frac{\partial^4\xi}{\partial x^4} - P_0(1 - 2\gamma\cos 2\omega t)\frac{\partial^2\xi}{\partial x^2} + \mathbf{m}\frac{\partial^2\xi}{\partial t^2} = 0, \qquad (1)$$

or

$$\frac{\partial^2\xi}{\partial t^2} - \frac{P_0}{\mathbf{m}}(1 - 2\gamma\cos 2\omega t)\frac{\partial^2\xi}{\partial x^2} + \frac{EI}{\mathbf{m}}\frac{\partial^4\xi}{\partial x^4} = 0. \qquad (2)$$

The displacement ξ and the bending moment $EI\,\partial^2\xi/\partial x^2$ must vanish at the ends of a pinned column. Thus the boundary conditions are $\xi = 0$, $\partial^2\xi/\partial x^2 = 0$ at $x = 0$, l. From §§ 15.51, 15.52 we see that a solution of the form $\xi = f(t)\sin bx$, with $b = n\pi/l$, satisfies these conditions. Substituting this solution in (2) leads to the equation

$$\frac{d^2f}{dt^2} + \left[\frac{b^2}{\mathbf{m}}(EIb^2 + P_0) - 2\gamma\frac{P_0 b^2}{\mathbf{m}}\cos 2\omega t\right]f = 0. \tag{3}$$

Writing $z = \omega t$, $a = b^2(EIb^2 + P_0)/\omega^2\mathbf{m}$, $q = \gamma P_0 b^2/\omega^2\mathbf{m}$, (3) takes the standard form

$$\frac{d^2f}{dz^2} + (a - 2q\cos 2z)f = 0. \tag{4}$$

If now we write $\gamma_1 = \gamma P_0/(P_0 + EIb^2)$, (4) becomes

$$\frac{d^2f}{dz^2} + a(1 - 2\gamma_1\cos 2z)f = 0, \tag{5}$$

so the question of stability for a given n in $b = \pi n/l$ may be considered in the same way as in § 15.23. The stability in practice exceeds that predicted from theory owing to internal loss in the material, and an idealized equation incorporating this loss takes the form at (2) § 15.43.

The complete solution of (2), with constants A_n, may be written

$$\xi = \sum_{n=1}^{\infty} A_n f_n(t)\sin\frac{\pi nx}{l}, \tag{6}$$

$f_n(t)$ being that solution of (4) corresponding to the particular n. Proof of the convergence of a solution of type (6) will be found in reference [121].

When the inherent stiffness of the column vanishes, it may be regarded as a flexible string. To obtain this metamorphosis mathematically, we write $EI = 0$ in (3), thereby reducing it to

$$\frac{d^2f}{dt^2} + \frac{b^2 P_0}{\mathbf{m}}(1 - 2\gamma\cos 2\omega t)f = 0, \tag{7}$$

which is identical with (2) § 15.52, but with P_0 for T_0.

APPLICATION OF THE WAVE EQUATION TO VIBRATIONAL SYSTEMS

16.10. Elliptical membrane [130]. Let $\mathbf{m}$ be the constant mass per unit area, $\mathbf{T}$ the uniform tension per unit arc length,† ζ the displacement normal to the equilibrium plane of the membrane. Then *in vacuo* the equation of motion of a homogeneous loss-free membrane in the x, y plane is

$$\frac{\partial^2 \zeta}{\partial x^2} + \frac{\partial^2 \zeta}{\partial y^2} - \frac{\mathbf{m}}{\mathbf{T}} \frac{\partial^2 \zeta}{\partial t^2} = 0. \tag{1}$$

This is (6) § 15.50 with the addition of the term $-(\mathbf{T}/\mathbf{m})(\partial^2\zeta/\partial y^2)$, thereby including the coordinate y. If ζ varies sinusoidally with time t, we may take $\zeta = e^{i\omega t}f(x,y)$, so that (1) becomes

$$\frac{\partial^2 \zeta}{\partial x^2} + \frac{\partial^2 \zeta}{\partial y^2} + \frac{\mathbf{m}}{\mathbf{T}} \omega^2 \zeta = 0. \tag{2}$$

Comparison with (1) § 9.10 shows that $k_1^2 = \mathbf{m}\omega^2/\mathbf{T}$, so

$$2q = \mathbf{m}\omega^2 h^2/2\mathbf{T}.$$

Hence with this value of $2q$, (3), (4) § 9.21 are the ordinary differential equations into which (2), expressed in elliptic coordinates, may be divided. The appropriate solutions, in product form, may be selected from Tables 10–12 to satisfy the physical conditions of the problem.

16.11. Physical conditions. Referring to Fig. 31, if we start at $\eta = 0$ and move counter-clockwise round a confocal ellipse $\xi = \xi_1 < \xi_0$ the displacement ζ at any instant alters continuously. It *may* be repeated between $\eta = \pi$ and $\eta = 2\pi$, but it *is* repeated after $\eta = 2\pi$. Hence ζ is single-valued and periodic in the coordinate η. The period is either π or 2π, so that $\zeta(\xi, \eta) = \zeta(\xi, \eta+\pi)$ or $\zeta(\xi, \eta+2\pi)$ as the case may be. Thus of the product functions in $\zeta = \psi(\xi)\phi(\eta)$, we must have $\phi(\eta) = \mathrm{ce}_m(\eta)$ or $\mathrm{se}_m(\eta)$ or a constant multiple thereof.

In addition to periodicity in η, at any point $(0, \eta)$ and the corresponding point $(0, -\eta)$ on the interfocal line, we must have:

(a) continuity of displacement, i.e.

$$\zeta(0, \eta) = \zeta(0, -\eta); \tag{3}$$

† To obtain uniform radial tension per unit arc length, the membrane is stretched uniformly and clamped between circular rings. Elliptical rings are then clamped on the membrane within the circular ones. When at rest, it is assumed to be flat.

(b) continuity of gradient, i.e.

$$\frac{\partial}{\partial \xi}[\zeta(\xi, \eta)]_{\xi \to 0} = -\frac{\partial}{\partial \xi}[\zeta(\xi, -\eta)]_{\xi \to 0}. \tag{4}$$

These two conditions imply continuity of displacement and gradient in crossing the interfocal line orthogonally.

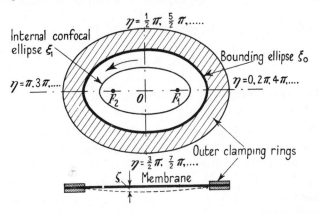

FIG. 31. Diagram for membranal problem, from which the Mathieu functions originated. F_1 and F_2 are foci.

For $\zeta = \mathrm{Ce}_m(\xi)\mathrm{ce}_m(\eta)$, $\mathrm{Ce}_m(0)$ is a non-zero constant, while $\mathrm{ce}_m(\eta) = \mathrm{ce}_m(-\eta)$. Hence (a) is satisfied. Also

$$\mathrm{ce}_m(\pm\eta)\frac{\partial}{\partial \xi}\mathrm{Ce}_m(\xi)_{\xi \to 0} = 0, \tag{5}$$

so (b) is satisfied.

For $\zeta = \mathrm{Se}_m(\xi)\mathrm{se}_m(\eta)$, $\zeta(0) = 0$, so (a) is satisfied, while

$$\mathrm{se}_m(\eta)\frac{\partial}{\partial \xi}\mathrm{Se}_m(\xi)_{\xi \to 0} = -\mathrm{se}_m(-\eta)\frac{\partial}{\partial \xi}\mathrm{Se}_m(\xi)_{\xi \to 0} \tag{6}$$

thereby satisfying (b).

For $\zeta = \mathrm{Fe}_m(\xi)\mathrm{ce}_m(\eta)$, $\mathrm{Fe}_m(0) = 0$, so (a) is satisfied, but

$$\mathrm{ce}_m(\eta)\frac{\partial}{\partial \xi}\mathrm{Fe}_m(\xi)_{\xi \to 0} = \mathrm{ce}_m(-\eta)\frac{\partial}{\partial \xi}\mathrm{Fe}_m(\xi)_{\xi \to 0} \neq 0, \tag{7}$$

except for special values of η, so in general (b) is not satisfied. Proceeding in this way, we find that the only permissible forms of solution are

$$\zeta(\xi, \eta, t) = C_m' \,\mathrm{Ce}_m(\xi, q)\mathrm{ce}_m(\eta, q)\cos(\omega_m t + \epsilon_m) \quad (a_m) \tag{8}$$

and $$\bar{\zeta}(\xi, \eta, t) = S_m' \,\mathrm{Se}_m(\xi, q)\mathrm{se}_m(\eta, q)\cos(\bar{\omega}_m t + \bar{\epsilon}_m) \quad (b_m). \tag{9}$$

C_m, S_m are arbitrary constants determinable from the conditions specified for the configuration of and velocity distribution over the membrane at $t = 0$. ω_m is the pulsatance of the mth free mode of vibration, and ϵ_m its relative phase angle. Since each integral value gives a separate solution of the differential equation, the complete solution of (1) § 16.10 when expressed in elliptic coordinates is

$$\zeta(\xi, \eta, t) = \sum_{m=0}^{\infty} C_m \, \mathrm{Ce}_m(\xi, q)\mathrm{ce}_m(\eta, q)\cos(\omega_m t + \epsilon_m) +$$

$$+ \sum_{m=1}^{\infty} S_m \, \mathrm{Se}_m(\xi, q)\mathrm{se}_m(\eta, q)\cos(\bar{\omega}_m t + \bar{\epsilon}_m). \quad (10)$$

16.12. Symmetry. In any product pair solutions, Ce or Se is constant on any confocal ellipse. Hence the symmetry is governed by ce or se. Since $\mathrm{ce}_{2n}(\eta, q) = \mathrm{ce}_{2n}(\pi \pm \eta, q) = \mathrm{ce}_{2n}(2\pi - \eta, q)$, it follows that the displacement expressed by $\mathrm{Ce}_{2n}(\xi, q)\mathrm{ce}_{2n}(\eta, q)$ is symmetrical about both the major and minor axes of the ellipse. $\mathrm{ce}_{2n+1}(\eta, q) = -\mathrm{ce}_{2n+1}(\pi \pm \eta, q) = \mathrm{ce}_{2n+1}(2\pi - \eta, q)$, so that the displacement expressed by $\mathrm{Ce}_{2n+1}(\xi, q)\mathrm{ce}_{2n+1}(\eta, q)$ is symmetrical about the major axis but anti-symmetrical about the minor axis.

$$\mathrm{se}_{2n+1}(\eta, q) = \mp \mathrm{se}_{2n+1}(\pi \pm \eta, q) = -\mathrm{se}_{2n+1}(2\pi - \eta, q),$$

so $\mathrm{Se}_{2n+1}(\xi, q)\mathrm{se}_{2n+1}(\eta, q)$ corresponds to a displacement anti-symmetrical about the major axis but symmetrical about the minor axis. Finally $\mathrm{se}_{2n+2}(\eta, q) = \pm \mathrm{se}_{2n+2}(\pi \pm \eta, q) = -\mathrm{se}_{2n+2}(2\pi - \eta, q)$, so $\mathrm{Se}_{2n+2}(\xi, q)\mathrm{se}_{2n+2}(\eta, q)$ corresponds to a displacement anti-symmetrical about both axes. These deductions will be understood more readily by reference to Figs. 1–4. As a guide to memorization, it may be remarked that the symmetry or anti-symmetry about the major and minor axes is the same as that for the degenerate forms $\cos mz$, $\sin mz$ about $z = 0$, $\frac{1}{2}\pi$, respectively (see remark at end of § 12.10).

16.13. Vibrational modes of membrane. Each individual solution in (10) § 16.11 for $m = 0, 1, 2, \ldots$ corresponds to a different mode of vibration. When q has its appropriate value, the dynamic deformation surface of the membrane and the pulsatance differ for each m. Any mode may exist separately—at least in theory—or they may all be present. The maximum displacement of the surface for a particular mode depends upon the value of C_m or S_m. These in turn are governed by the configuration of and the normal velocity distribution over the membrane at time $t = 0$. For instance, it might be pulled from the centre into a conoidal shape and released at $t = 0$.

The boundary condition for all η is that $\zeta = 0$ at the clamping rings where $\xi = \xi_0$. Since $ce_m(\eta, q)$, $se_m(\eta, q)$ are independent of ξ, we must have

$$Ce_m(\xi_0, q) = 0 \quad \text{for } m = 0, 1, 2, \dots \tag{1}$$

and

$$Se_m(\xi_0, q) = 0 \quad \text{for } m = 1, 2, \dots \tag{2}$$

Now ξ_0 is fixed, so we need those positive values of q, say $q_{m,r}$, $\bar{q}_{m,r}$ for which the respective functions in (1), (2) vanish. These may be regarded as the positive parametric zeros of the functions. They define a series of confocal nodal ellipses. There is an infinity of zeros for each m, i.e. one for each $r = 1, 2, 3, \dots$. Hence for Ce_m, if $r = p$, there are $(p-1)$ nodal ellipses *within* the clamping rings, and likewise for Se_m, but their locations differ. (1), (2) are known as the period or pulsatance equations, since their roots are used to calculate the pulsatances of the modes of the membrane.

For $q > 0$, $m \geqslant 1$, the functions $ce_m(\eta, q)$, $se_m(\eta, q)$ have zeros in η (see Chap. XII). Hence ζ in (8), (9) § 16.11 vanishes also if η satisfies the respective equations

$$ce_m(\eta, q_{m,r}) = 0 \tag{3}$$

and

$$se_m(\eta, \bar{q}_{m,r}) = 0. \tag{4}$$

The roots define a series of confocal nodal hyperbolas. Now $ce_m(\eta, q_{m,r})$, $se_m(\eta, \bar{q}_{m,r})$ each have m zeros in $0 \leqslant \eta < \pi$ (see § 12.10), so for a given m each function gives rise to m nodal hyperbolas.

16.14. Expansion of function. From physical considerations it is clear that ζ in (10) § 16.11 must be a continuous function of ξ, η, within the ellipse, which vanishes at its periphery. This suggests the *Theorem*: That any function of ξ, η, continuous and single-valued within the ellipse, which vanishes on its boundary, may be expanded at any point of the interior in the form of a double series, namely [52]

$$\zeta(\xi, \eta) = \sum_{m=0}^{\infty} \left[\sum_{r=1}^{\infty} C_{m,r} \, Ce_m(\xi, q_{m,r}) ce_m(\eta, q_{m,r}) \right] +$$
$$+ \sum_{m=1}^{\infty} \left[\sum_{r=1}^{\infty} S_{m,r} \, Se_m(\xi, \bar{q}_{m,r}) se_m(\eta, \bar{q}_{m,r}) \right]. \tag{1}$$

A formal proof of the theorem is outside our present purview.

16.15. Determination of $C_{m,r}$, $S_{m,r}$. Suppose that $\zeta(\xi, \eta)$ has the properties stated above. Multiply both sides of (1) § 16.14 by

$$(\cosh 2\xi - \cos 2\eta)\mathrm{Ce}_n(\xi, q_{n,p})\mathrm{ce}_n(\eta, q_{n,p}), \tag{1}$$

and integrate with respect to η from 0 to 2π, and with respect to ξ' from 0 to ξ_0. Then by (7) § 9.40 all terms vanish except when $n = m$, $r = p$. Hence

$$\int_0^{\xi_0}\int_0^{2\pi} \mathrm{Ce}_m(\xi, q_{m,r})\mathrm{ce}_m(\eta, q_{m,r})(\cosh 2\xi - \cos 2\eta)\zeta(\xi, \eta)\, d\xi d\eta$$

$$= C_{m,r}\int_0^{\xi_0}\int_0^{2\pi} \mathrm{Ce}_m^2(\xi, q_{m,r})\mathrm{ce}_m^2(\eta, q_{m,r})(\cosh 2\xi - \cos 2\eta)\, d\xi d\eta. \tag{2}$$

Now by (7) § 14.40

$$\int_0^{2\pi} \mathrm{ce}_m^2(\eta, q_{m,r})\cos 2\eta\, d\eta = \pi\Theta_{m,r} \tag{3}$$

so we obtain

$$C_{m,r} = \frac{\displaystyle\int_0^{\xi_0}\int_0^{2\pi} \mathrm{Ce}_m(\xi, q_{m,r})\mathrm{ce}_m(\eta, q_{m,r})\zeta(\xi, \eta)(\cosh 2\xi - \cos 2\eta)\, d\xi d\eta}{\displaystyle\pi\int_0^{\xi_0} \mathrm{Ce}_m^2(\xi, q_{m,r})[\cosh 2\xi - \Theta_{m,r}]\, d\xi}. \tag{4}$$

In like manner we can show that

$$S_{m,r} = \frac{\displaystyle\int_0^{\xi_0}\int_0^{2\pi} \mathrm{Se}_m(\xi, \bar{q}_{m,r})\mathrm{se}_m(\eta, \bar{q}_{m,r})\zeta(\xi, \eta)(\cosh 2\xi - \cos 2\eta)\, d\xi d\eta}{\displaystyle\pi\int_0^{\xi_0} \mathrm{Se}_m^2(\xi, \bar{q}_{m,r})[\cosh 2\xi - \Psi_{m,r}]\, d\xi}. \tag{5}$$

The denominators of (4), (5) may be evaluated numerically (see § 9.40).

16.16. Transition to circular membrane. Using the results in Appendix I, and omitting the time factor, (10) § 16.11 degenerates to the form [203, p. 27]

$$\zeta(r, \theta) = \sum_{m=0}^{\infty} C_m' J_m(k_1 r)\cos m\theta + \sum_{m=1}^{\infty} S_m' J_m(k_1 r)\sin m\theta, \tag{1}$$

where $C_m' = p_m' C_m$, $S_m' = s_m' S_m$. The pulsatance equations (1), (2) § 16.13 become

$$J_m(k_1 a) = 0, \tag{2}$$

whose roots define the nodal circles, while the nodal diameters are defined by the roots of

$$\cos\{m\theta - \tan^{-1}(S_m'/C_m')\} = 0. \tag{3}$$

16.17. Example. We shall consider the mode in which the displacement is proportional to $\mathrm{Ce}_1(\xi, q_{1,1})\mathrm{ce}_1(\eta, q_{1,1})$, with $a = 5$ cm., $b = 3$ cm., $e = 0\cdot8$. The first step is to calculate $q_{1,1}$, the lowest positive parametric zero, for which

$$\mathrm{Ce}_1(\xi_0, q_{1,1}) = 0. \tag{1}$$

Then $e^{-1} = \cosh \xi_0 = 1\cdot25$, and from tables $\xi_0 = 0\cdot6931$: also $e^{\xi_0} = 2$, $e^{-\xi_0} = \frac{1}{2}$, e in these latter cases being Napier's base. Writing $i\xi_0$ for z in (16) § 2.13, we obtain to order 3 in q—this being adequate for illustration—

$$\mathrm{Ce}_1(\xi_0, q) \simeq -\alpha^3(\tfrac{1}{18}\cosh 7\xi_0 - \tfrac{4}{9}\cosh 5\xi_0 + \tfrac{1}{3}\cosh 3\xi_0) +$$
$$+ \alpha^2(\tfrac{1}{3}\cosh 5\xi_0 - \cosh 3\xi_0) - \alpha\cosh 3\xi_0 + \cosh \xi_0 = 0, \tag{2}$$

where $\alpha = \frac{1}{8}q$. Using the preceding numerical values in (2) leads to the approximate equation

$$\alpha^3 + 0\cdot578\alpha^2 - 1\cdot85\alpha + 0\cdot569 = 0, \tag{3}$$

whose lowest root is found to be $\alpha \simeq 0\cdot393$. By § 16.10 the pulsatance of the mode in question is

$$\omega_1 = k_1(\mathrm{T/m})^{\frac{1}{2}}. \tag{4}$$

Now $k_1 h = 2q^{\frac{1}{2}}$, $h = ae = 4$, so with $q_{1,1} = 8\alpha = 3\cdot144$, $k_1 = 0\cdot886$, and (4) gives

$$\omega_1 = 0\cdot886(\mathrm{T/m})^{\frac{1}{2}}. \tag{5}$$

Omitting the time factor, the normal displacement of the membrane at any point (ξ, η), is expressed by

$$\zeta_1(\xi, \eta) = C_1 \, \mathrm{Ce}(\xi, q_{1,1})\mathrm{ce}(\eta, q_{1,1}), \tag{6}$$

C_1 being an arbitrary constant dependent upon the greatest amplitude. The corresponding cartesian coordinates are $x = h\cosh \xi \cos \eta$, $y = h\sinh \xi \sin \eta$, with $h = ae = 4$. Since $\mathrm{ce}_1(\eta, q_{1,1}) = 0$ when $\eta = \frac{1}{2}\pi, \frac{3}{2}\pi$, the minor axis is a nodal line. Some idea of the configuration of the membrane at any instant may be gleaned from the graph of $\mathrm{ce}_1(\eta, q)$ in Fig. 1. The displacement is symmetrical about the major, but anti-symmetrical about the minor axis.

16.18. Transition to circular membrane. If we apply the formulae in Appendix I when $e \to 0$, a remaining constant, (6) § 16.17 degenerates to

$$\zeta_1(r, \theta) = C_1' J_1(k_1 r)\cos\theta. \tag{1}$$

When $\theta = \frac{1}{2}\pi, \frac{3}{2}\pi$, $\cos\theta = 0$, so there is a nodal diameter. The first positive zero of $J_1(k_1 a)$ is $k_1 a = 3\cdot832$, and since $a = 5$ cm., $k_1 = 3\cdot832/5 = 0\cdot766$. Then

$$\omega_1 = k_1(\mathbf{T}/\mathbf{m})^{\frac{1}{2}} = 0\cdot766(\mathbf{T}/\mathbf{m})^{\frac{1}{2}}. \tag{2}$$

Comparing this with (5) § 16.17, we find that with a constant, an increase in e from 0 to $0\cdot8$ raises the pulsatance of the mode by about 16 per cent.

16.20. Free oscillations of water in elliptical lake [104]. In Fig. 32 A, ζ is the vertical displacement of the water surface from its

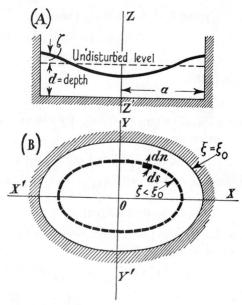

FIG. 32. (A), (B) Illustrating problem of elliptical lake.

equilibrium position, and d the uniform depth. We assume that (1) the lake is stationary in space, (2) ζ varies as $e^{i\omega t}$ with respect to time. If the displacement is small enough for its square to be neglected, it can be shown that the differential equation of motion in rectangular coordinates is

$$\frac{\partial^2\zeta}{\partial x^2} + \frac{\partial^2\zeta}{\partial y^2} + \frac{\omega^2}{c^2}\zeta = 0, \tag{1}$$

where $c^2 = gd$, c being the velocity of a free wave in a very large expanse of water of uniform depth d, and g the acceleration due to gravity. Applying the transformation in § 9.20 to (1) leads to

$$\frac{\partial^2 \zeta}{\partial \xi^2} + \frac{\partial^2 \zeta}{\partial \eta^2} + 2k^2(\cosh 2\xi - \cos 2\eta)\zeta = 0, \tag{2}$$

with $2k = \omega h/c$. Then, by an argument akin to that in §16.11, it can be shown that the required solution takes the form

$$\zeta(\xi, \eta, t) = \sum_{m=0}^{\infty} C_m \, \mathrm{Ce}_m(\xi, q)\mathrm{ce}_m(\eta, q)\cos(\omega_m t + \epsilon_m) +$$
$$+ \sum_{m=1}^{\infty} S_m \, \mathrm{Se}_m(\xi, q)\mathrm{se}_m(\eta, q)\cos(\bar{\omega}_m t + \bar{\epsilon}_m). \tag{3}$$

When the appropriate value of q is assigned, each term of the series in (3) corresponds to a normal mode of oscillation. There are two types of mode, namely, $\mathrm{Ce}_m \mathrm{ce}_m$ and $\mathrm{Se}_m \mathrm{se}_m$. An infinity of modes of either type corresponds to each m. The instantaneous displacements of the water for these modes are proportional, respectively, to

$$\mathrm{Ce}_m(\xi, q)\mathrm{ce}_m(\eta, q)\cos(\omega_m t + \epsilon_m)$$

and $\qquad \mathrm{Se}_m(\xi, q)\mathrm{se}_m(\eta, q)\cos(\bar{\omega}_m t + \bar{\epsilon}_m), \tag{4}$

q having an infinity of values for every m. Each corresponds to a distinctive dynamic deformation surface of the water. When the appropriate values C_m, S_m are used, ζ in (3) represents the configuration of the surface of the water at any instant $t \geqslant 0$. As usual C_m, S_m, are obtained by aid of the displacement and velocity distribution over the surface at $t = 0$.

16.21. Boundary condition. Consider any elemental arc length ds, and another one dn normal thereto, as depicted in Fig. 32 B. Then it may be deduced that the water-particle velocity in the direction of dn is

$$u_n = \frac{ig}{\omega} \frac{\partial \zeta}{\partial n}. \tag{1}$$

By (6) §9.12, $dn = ds_1 = l_1 d\xi$, so (1) may be written

$$u_n = \frac{ig}{\omega l_1} \frac{\partial \zeta}{\partial \xi}. \tag{2}$$

At the boundary of the lake, $\xi = \xi_0$, and the velocity of the water normal thereto is zero. Hence at $\xi = \xi_0$, $u_n = 0$, so the boundary condition is

$$\left[\frac{\partial \zeta}{\partial \xi}\right]_{\xi=\xi_0} = 0. \tag{3}$$

In the pairs of product functions $Ce_m\,ce_m$, $Se_m\,se_m$ in (3) § 16.20, ce_m, se_m are independent of ξ. Thus (3) entails

$$Ce'_m(\xi_0, q) = 0 \qquad (4)$$

and $$Se'_m(\xi_0, q) = 0, \qquad (5)$$

so we require $q_{m,p}$, $\bar{q}_{m,p}$, the positive parametric zeros of Ce'_m and Se'_m respectively. (4), (5) are designated the pulsatance or period equations.

16.22. Expansion of function. From purely physical considerations it is evident that, omitting the time factor, ζ in (3) § 16.20 must be a function continuous within the ellipse, but having zero normal gradient at its boundary. This suggests the *Theorem*: That any function of (ξ, η)-continuous and single-valued within the ellipse, having zero normal gradient at its boundary, may be expanded at any point of the interior in the form of a double series like (1) § 16.14 [52]. In the present case the values of q are designated $q_{m,p}$, $\bar{q}_{m,p}$, these being the positive parametric roots of

$$Ce'_m(\xi_0, q) = 0 \qquad (1)$$

and $$Se'_m(\xi_0, q) = 0. \qquad (2)$$

The coefficients C_m, S_m in the expansion are determined in a way similar to that in § 16.15.

16.23. Example. To illustrate the analysis in § 16.20 et seq., we shall consider the mode defined by $m = 1$, $p = 1$, the tide height being proportional to $Ce_1(\xi, q_{1,1})ce_1(\eta, q_{1,1})$. If the eccentricity of the ellipse is $e = 0.8$, then the ratio of the axes is $b/a = (1-e^2)^{\frac{1}{2}} = 0.6$. To determine the pulsatance of the water mainly parallel to the direction of the major axis, we have to find $q_{1,1}$, such that

$$Ce'_1(\xi_0, q_{1,1}) = 0. \qquad (1)$$

Differentiating (2) § 16.17 with respect to ξ and putting $\alpha = \frac{1}{8}q$, we get

$$Ce'_1(\xi_0, q) \simeq -\alpha^3(\tfrac{7}{18}\sinh 7\xi_0 - \tfrac{20}{9}\sinh 5\xi_0 + \sinh 3\xi_0) +$$
$$+\alpha^2(\tfrac{5}{3}\sinh 5\xi_0 - 3\sinh 3\xi_0) - 3\alpha\sinh 3\xi_0 + \sinh\xi_0 = 0. \quad (2)$$

Now $\cosh\xi_0 = e^{-1} = 1.25$, $\xi_0 = 0.6931$, $e^{\xi_0} = 2$, and $e^{-\xi_0} = 0.5$. Expressing the hyperbolic functions in exponentials and using these numerical values leads to the approximate equation

$$13.4\alpha^3 + 29.7\alpha^2 - 23.6\alpha + 1.5 = 0. \qquad (3)$$

The smallest positive root of (3) is $\alpha \simeq 0.07$, so $q_{1,1} \simeq 0.56$. Since $4q = \omega^2 h^2/c^2$, with $h = ae$, we have

$$\omega_1^2 = 4q_{1,1} c^2/a^2 e^2. \tag{4}$$

With the above numerical values (4) yields [104]

$$\omega_1 \simeq 1.87 c/a. \tag{5}$$

For the corresponding mode of a circular lake of radius a the

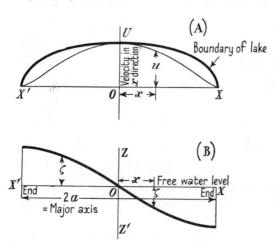

FIG. 33. Diagrams for lowest asymmetrical mode of water in elliptical lake.
(A) Velocity u in x direction.
(B) Tide height ζ.

boundary condition is given by the degenerate form of (4), (5) § 16.21 (see Appendix I), so

$$J_1'(\omega_1 a/c) = 0, \tag{6}$$

and from Bessel-function tables we find that the lowest root is

$$\omega_1 a/c \simeq 1.84 \quad \text{or} \quad \omega_1 \simeq 1.84 c/a. \tag{7}$$

Thus the pulsatance of the mode for a lake having eccentricity $e = 0.8$ is only 1.6 per cent. higher than that for $e = 0$. Moreover, in a practical sense the decrease in width of the lake from $2a$ to $1.2a = 2b$ has a negligible influence on the pulsatance of the (mainly) longitudinal oscillation. For this mode, since

$$\zeta_1 \propto \mathrm{Ce}_1(\xi, q_{1,1})\mathrm{ce}_1(\eta, q_{1,1}), \tag{8}$$

the vertical displacement of the water surface is symmetrical about the major axis, but anti-symmetrical with respect to the minor axis, as illustrated in Fig. 33 B, and demonstrated analytically in § 16.12.

The minor axis is defined by $x = 0$, so $x = h \cosh \xi \cos \eta = 0$, giving $\eta = \frac{1}{2}\pi$ or $\frac{3}{2}\pi$. Thus $\mathrm{ce_1}(\eta, q_{1,1}) = 0$, so $\zeta = 0$, and the minor axis is a nodal line.

16.24. Example. We now pass on to study the mode $m = 1$, $p = 1$ in which the tide height is proportional to $\mathrm{Se_1}(\xi, \bar{q}_{1,1})\mathrm{se_1}(\eta, \bar{q}_{1,1})$, the oscillation being mainly *across* the lake.† Since $\mathrm{se_1} = 0$ when $\eta = 0, \pi$, the major axis is a nodal line. The pulsatance equation is

$$\mathrm{Se_1'}(\xi_0, \bar{q}_{1,1}) = 0, \tag{1}$$

and we have to calculate the smallest $\bar{q} > 0$ to satisfy this. Writing iz for z in (2) § 2.14, and differentiating with respect to z, gives, with $\bar{\alpha} = \frac{1}{8}\bar{q}$,

$$\mathrm{Se_1'}(\xi_0, \bar{q}) \simeq -\bar{\alpha}^3(\tfrac{7}{18}\cosh 7\xi_0 + \tfrac{20}{9}\cosh 5\xi_0 + \cosh 3\xi_0) +$$
$$+ \bar{\alpha}^2(\tfrac{5}{3}\cosh 5\xi_0 + 3\cosh 3\xi_0) - 3\bar{\alpha}\cosh 3\xi_0 + \cosh \xi_0 = 0. \tag{2}$$

Proceeding as in § 16.23 we arrive at the approximate equation

$$129 \cdot 1\bar{\alpha}^3 - 77 \cdot 7\bar{\alpha}^2 + 24 \cdot 4\bar{\alpha} - 2 \cdot 5 = 0, \tag{3}$$

of which the smallest positive root is $\bar{\alpha} \simeq 0 \cdot 175$, giving $\bar{q}_{1,1} \simeq 1 \cdot 4$. Substituting this in the formulae $\bar{\omega}_1^2 = 4\bar{q}_{1,1}c^2/a^2e^2$ (see (4) § 16.23), we obtain [104]

$$\bar{\omega}_1 = 2 \cdot 96c/a = 1 \cdot 78c/b. \tag{4}$$

Thus $\bar{\omega}_1/\omega_1 = 2 \cdot 96/1 \cdot 87 = 1 \cdot 58$, so

$$\bar{\omega}_1 = 1 \cdot 58\omega_1. \tag{5}$$

Accordingly the pulsatance of the first mode *transverse* to the major axis is 58 per cent. greater than that of the *longitudinal* mode. This is due to the minor axis being 40 per cent. shorter than the major axis, so the time taken for the disturbance to travel across the lake is less than that to travel along it. From (4) and Table 23 we see that $\bar{\omega}_1$ is 3·3 per cent. less than that of the corresponding mode of a circular lake of radius b. It follows that if we commence with a circular lake and keep the length in the direction of the x-axis equal to $2a$, the effect of reducing the breadth is to raise the pulsatance of the longitudinal oscillation, whereas an increase in breadth causes a decrease in pulsatance. The order of the changes is small, however, even for large alterations in breadth.

For the modes of oscillation corresponding to $\mathrm{Ce_0}\,\mathrm{ce_0}$, $\mathrm{Ce_2}\,\mathrm{ce_2}$, $\mathrm{Se_2}\,\mathrm{se_2},...$ the above method of calculating the values of $q_{m,p}$, $\bar{q}_{m,p}$

† See § 16.12 regarding symmetry about the axes.

fails owing to slowness of convergence of the series in powers of q. Under appropriate conditions formulae in § 12.41 may be used.

16.30. Lake whose eccentricity $e \to 1$. The plan of the lake is now a long narrow ellipse. Since $\cosh \xi_0 = e^{-1}$, $\xi_0 > \xi \to 0$, so in (2) § 16.23, in order to obtain an approximate value of $q_{1,1}$ for the gravest longitudinal mode, we may replace $\sinh \xi_0$ by ξ_0. The tide height is given by

$$\zeta = C_1 \operatorname{Ce}_1(\xi, q_{1,1}) \operatorname{ce}_1(\eta, q_{1,1}). \tag{1}$$

Then, with an accuracy adequate for illustration, we find that the equation for $\alpha = q/8$ is

$$5{\cdot}39\alpha^3 - 0{\cdot}667\alpha^2 - 9\alpha + 1 = 0, \tag{2}$$

whose smallest positive root is $\alpha \simeq 0{\cdot}111$, i.e. $q_{1,1} = 0{\cdot}888$. Now $\omega_1^2 = 4q_{1,1}c^2/a^2e^2$, and since $e \to 1$, this value of q gives [104]

$$\omega_1 = 1{\cdot}886c/a. \tag{3}$$

16.31. Comparison of numerical results in §§ 16.23, 16.30. The three sets of results are set out in Table 23. It is obvious therefrom that the breadth of the ellipse has little influence on the frequency of the slowest longitudinal mode. When the sides of the canal are straight and parallel, however, $\omega_1 = \frac{1}{2}\pi c/a = 1{\cdot}571c/a$, which is 17 per cent. less than the pulsatance when the eccentricity of the ellipse tends to unity (see third row of Table 23).

TABLE 23

Plan of lake	Pulsatance of slowest longitudinal mode (ω_1)
Circle of radius a	$1{\cdot}84c/a$
Ellipse major axis $2a$, minor axis $1{\cdot}2a$	$1{\cdot}87c/a$
Ellipse major axis $2a$, eccentricity $e \to 1$	$1{\cdot}886c/a$

The comparatively large difference may be attributed to curvature of the sides of the ellipse, which entails a diminution in cross-sectional area towards each end of the lake. This feature introduces reflection which is progressive and continuous from the centre towards the extremities of the major axis. Consequently the relative energy of the water per unit mass near the central part of the lake exceeds that in the straight-sided canal of uniform breadth.[†] Hence the 'effective length' of the elliptical lake is less than that of a uniform canal, and the lowest pulsatance in the first case exceeds that

† Assuming the total energy to be equal in both cases.

in the second. It is of interest to remark that at any distance x from the centre, there is little difference in either the particle velocity in the x direction, or in the tide height in the two preceding cases.

16.32. Surface elevation of water (tide height) in § 16.30.

This is expressed symbolically by

$$\zeta_1 = C_1 \, \mathrm{Ce}_1(\xi, q_{1,1}) \mathrm{ce}_1(\eta, q_{1,1}), \qquad (1)$$

C_1 being an arbitrary constant, $\cos \omega_1 t$ being omitted but tacitly assumed present. Since $\xi \to 0$ and $q_{1,1}$ is fixed, Ce_1 is constant and, therefore,

$$\zeta_1 \propto \mathrm{ce}_1(\eta, q_{1,1}). \qquad (2)$$

Thus the elevation of the water surface is dependent upon the angular position η, but independent of ξ. Moreover, at any point distant x from the centre, but not too near to it, the displacement is substantially constant over the breadth of the lake.

From (2) § 2.17

$$\mathrm{ce}_1(\eta, q_{1,1}) = A_1^{(1)} \cos \eta + A_3^{(1)} \cos 3\eta + A_5^{(1)} \cos 5\eta + \dots . \qquad (3)$$

Using tabular values [52, 95], we find the A corresponding to $q_{1,1} = 0.888$ by interpolation. Substituting these in (3) yields

$$\mathrm{ce}_1(\eta, 0.888) \simeq 0.990 \cos \eta - 0.123 \cos 3\eta + 0.005 \cos 5\eta. \qquad (4)$$

In a canal of uniform breadth and length $2a$, the tide height for the slowest longitudinal mode at a distance x from the centre is proportional to $\sin \pi x/2a$. Taking $\cos \eta = x/a$, we get

$$\zeta \propto \sin \tfrac{1}{2}\pi(\cos \eta) = 2[J_1(\tfrac{1}{2}\pi)\cos \eta - J_3(\tfrac{1}{2}\pi)\cos 3\eta + J_5(\tfrac{1}{2}\pi)\cos 5\eta - \dots] \qquad (5)$$

$$\propto 0.990 \cos \eta - 0.121 \cos 3\eta + 0.0039 \cos 5\eta. \qquad (6)$$

Comparing (4), (6), the difference lies in the slightly larger coefficients of $\cos 3\eta$, $\cos 5\eta$ in the case of the elliptical lake where $e \to 1$. Consequently in passing from the right-hand ends of the lakes towards their centres, the tide heights calculated from (4), (6) are almost equal for all η in $0-\tfrac{1}{2}\pi$. A rough idea of the shape of the water surface may be gleaned from the graph of $\mathrm{ce}_1(z, 2)$ in Fig. 1. When frictional loss is taken into account there is no significant difference in the tide heights of the water at corresponding points in the two cases considered.

16.33. Pulsatances of modes corresponding to Ce_2, Ce_3,...
when $e \to 1$. In [53] it is shown that when $\xi_0 \to 0$, i.e. $e \to 1$, there is only one value of $q > 0$ for which $\mathrm{Ce}_m'(\xi, q) = 0$, $m \geqslant 1$. Thus there

is only one mode of oscillation corresponding to each m. If $q > q_{m,1}$ satisfied the pulsatance equation, we should have $\mathrm{Ce}'_m(\xi, q_{m,p}) = 0$ for $\xi < \xi_0$, thereby entailing the existence of nodal ellipses. Since there is only one parametric zero, namely, $q_{m,1}$, there are no nodal ellipses associated with the modes of oscillation of an elliptical lake whose eccentricity $e \to 1$.

To calculate the roots of $\mathrm{Ce}'_m(\xi_0, q) = 0$, we use a transcendental equation like (8) § 3.11, write $2q$ for a on the l.h.s. and in the continued fraction,† and proceed to calculate q and the A as in § 3.12 et seq. The following results were obtained [54]:

$$q_{1,1} = 0.88982\ 0 \quad \text{giving}$$

$$\mathrm{ce}_1(\eta, q_{1,1}) = 0.99241 \cos \eta - 0.12288 \cos 3\eta + 0.00471 \cos 5\eta -$$
$$- 0.00009 \cos 7\eta + \ldots; \tag{1}$$

$$q_{2,1} = 3.03907\ 36 \quad \text{giving}$$

$$\mathrm{ce}_2(\eta, q_{2,1}) = 0.39516 + 0.79032 \cos 2\eta - 0.24989 \cos 4\eta +$$
$$+ 0.02552 \cos 6\eta - 0.00134 \cos 8\eta + 0.00004 \cos 10\eta - \ldots; \tag{2}$$

$$q_{3,1} = 6.42586\ 16 \quad \text{giving}$$

$$\mathrm{ce}_3(\eta, q_{3,1}) = 0.71339 \cos \eta + 0.60237 \cos 3\eta - 0.35232 \cos 5\eta +$$
$$+ 0.06370 \cos 7\eta - 0.00604 \cos 9\eta + 0.00036 \cos 11\eta -$$
$$- 0.00001 \cos 13\eta + \ldots; \tag{3}$$

$$q_{4,1} = 11.04799\ 28 \quad \text{giving}$$

$$\mathrm{ce}_4(\eta, q_{4,1}) = 0.32544 + 0.65107 \cos 2\eta + 0.41535 \cos 4\eta -$$
$$- 0.42190 \cos 6\eta + 0.11561 \cos 8\eta - 0.01661 \cos 10\eta +$$
$$+ 0.00151 \cos 12\eta - 0.00010 \cos 14\eta + 0.00001 \cos 16\eta - \ldots; \tag{4}$$

$$q_{5,1} = 16.90474\ 0 \quad \text{giving}$$

$$\mathrm{ce}_5(\eta, q_{5,1}) = 0.61238 \cos \eta + 0.57615 \cos 3\eta + 0.23319 \cos 5\eta -$$
$$- 0.45463 \cos 7\eta + 0.17534 \cos 9\eta - 0.03485 \cos 11\eta +$$
$$+ 0.00441 \cos 13\eta - 0.00039 \cos 15\eta + 0.00003 \cos 17\eta - \ldots. \tag{5}$$

The various series (1)–(5) exemplify (a) the rapid decrease in the numerical values of the coefficients beyond a certain term, (b) the remarks at the end of § 3.33.

Using the above values of $q_{m,1}$, the pulsatances of the first five longitudinal modes of a lake whose eccentricity approaches unity were calculated, and are given in Table 24.

† This substitution is based on the result that as $e \to 1$, $a \to 2q$ [53].

TABLE 24

Mode of oscillation	Function	Value of $q_{m,1}$	Pulsatance ω_1	ω_1 for straight uniform canal
1	ce_1	0·88982 0	$1·8866c/a$	$1·5708..c/a†$
2	ce_2	3·03907 4	$3·4866c/a$	$3·1416..c/a$
3	ce_3	6·42586 2	$5·0699c/a$	$4·7124..c/a$
4	ce_4	11·04799 3	$6·6477c/a$	$6·2832..c/a$
5	ce_5	16·90474 0	$8·2231c/a$	$7·8540..c/a$

† The numbers are multiples of $\frac{1}{2}\pi$.

The tide ranges for several modes calculated by aid of (2)–(5) are portrayed in Figs. 34–7 [54, 104].

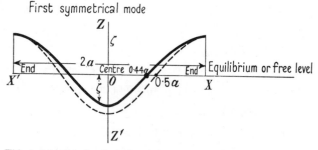

Fig. 34. Tide height ζ in lowest symmetrical mode of water in elliptical lake. The broken line is for a canal of uniform breadth.

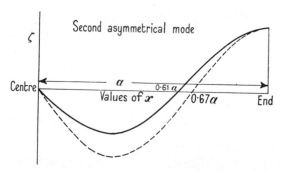

Fig. 35. Tide height ζ in second asymmetrical mode of water in elliptical lake. The broken line is for a canal of uniform breadth.

16.40. Transverse vibrational modes of gas in long hollow elliptical cylinder. If ϕ is the velocity potential at any point x, y in a cross-section, the differential equation of wave motion is

$$\frac{\partial^2\phi}{\partial x^2}+\frac{\partial^2\phi}{\partial y^2}+k_1^2\phi = 0, \tag{1}$$

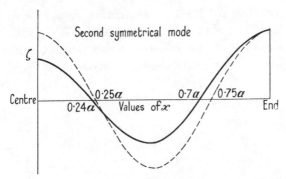

FIG. 36. Tide height ζ in second symmetrical mode of water in elliptical lake. The broken line is for a canal of uniform breadth.

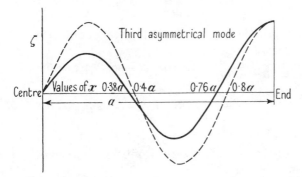

FIG. 37. Tide height ζ in third asymmetrical mode of water in elliptical lake. The broken line is for a canal of uniform breadth.

where $k_1 = \omega/c$, $\omega = 2\pi \times$ frequency, and c is the velocity of sound waves in an unconfined atmosphere of the gas, of uniform density. If the inner surface of the cylinder on which the gas particles impinge is rigid, the velocity normal thereto is zero. Hence the particle velocity $v = -(\partial\phi/\partial n) = 0$, n indicating the direction of the normal to the inner surface. Accordingly the problem is analytically similar to that of the elliptical lake studied in § 16.20 et seq., so the pulsatance equations are those at (4), (5) § 16.21. When the ellipse degenerates to a circle the vibrational modes of the gas in a hollow circular cylinder are obtained. The pulsatance equation is now (6) § 16.23. It is assumed that the cylinder is long enough for end effect to be neglected, or that practical conditions ensure absence of interference due to the ends of a short cylinder.

16.50. Vibrational modes of elliptical plate. Let ρ be the density, t the uniform thickness, σ Poisson's ratio < 1, E Young's modulus, and $c^2 = Et^2/12\rho(1-\sigma^2)$. Assume that ζ, the displacement normal to the plane of the plate, varies as $e^{i\omega t}$. Then with $k_1^4 = \omega^2/c^2$ it can be shown that the differential equation for a homogeneous loss-free plate vibrating with small amplitude *in vacuo* is

$$\frac{\partial^4 \zeta}{\partial x^4} + \frac{\partial^4 \zeta}{\partial y^4} + \frac{2\partial^4 \zeta}{\partial x^2 \partial y^2} - k_1^4 \zeta = 0, \tag{1}$$

or

$$\left(\frac{\partial^2}{\partial x^2} + \frac{\partial^2}{\partial y^2} + k_1^2\right)\left(\frac{\partial^2}{\partial x^2} + \frac{\partial^2}{\partial y^2} - k_1^2\right)\zeta = 0. \tag{2}$$

Hence

$$\frac{\partial^2 \zeta_1}{\partial x^2} + \frac{\partial^2 \zeta_1}{\partial y^2} + k_1^2 \zeta_1 = 0, \tag{3}$$

and

$$\frac{\partial^2 \zeta_2}{\partial x^2} + \frac{\partial^2 \zeta_2}{\partial y^2} - k_1^2 \zeta_2 = 0. \tag{4}$$

By § 9.20, (3), (4) expressed in elliptical coordinates are, respectively,

$$\frac{\partial^2 \zeta_1}{\partial \xi^2} + \frac{\partial^2 \zeta_1}{\partial \eta^2} + 2k^2(\cosh 2\xi - \cos 2\eta)\zeta_1 = 0, \tag{5}$$

and

$$\frac{\partial^2 \zeta_2}{\partial \xi^2} + \frac{\partial^2 \zeta_2}{\partial \eta^2} - 2k^2(\cosh 2\xi - \cos 2\eta)\zeta_2 = 0, \tag{6}$$

where $2k = k_1 h = (\omega/c)^{\frac{1}{2}}h$, giving $q = \omega h^2/4c$.

This analysis is valid for a variety of boundary conditions amongst which we may mention:

1°. Free everywhere.

2°. Clamped edge, centre free.

3°. Clamped edge, confocal elliptical hole at centre.

4°. Clamped edge, clamped at a central confocal ellipse.

5°. Clamped at a central confocal ellipse, edge free.

The solutions for all five cases must be periodic in η, with period π or 2π. For reasons akin to those given in § 16.11 a formal solution of (5) in cases 1°, 2° is (omitting the time factor)

$$\zeta_1^{(m)} = C_m \operatorname{Ce}_m(\xi, q)\operatorname{ce}_m(\eta, q) + S_m \operatorname{Se}_m(\xi, q)\operatorname{se}_m(\eta, q). \tag{7}$$

For (6) we have

$$\zeta_2^{(m)} = \bar{C}_m \operatorname{Ce}_m(\xi, -q)\operatorname{ce}_m(\eta, -q) + \bar{S}_m \operatorname{Se}_m(\xi, -q)\operatorname{se}_m(\eta, -q). \tag{8}$$

Then $\zeta^{(m)} = \zeta_1^{(m)} + \zeta_2^{(m)}$, and the complete formal solution is

$$\zeta = \sum_{m=0}^{\infty} \{C_m \operatorname{Ce}_m(\xi, q)\operatorname{ce}_m(\eta, q) + \bar{C}_m \operatorname{Ce}_m(\xi, -q)\operatorname{ce}_m(\eta, -q)\} +$$

$$+ \sum_{m=1}^{\infty} \{S_m \operatorname{Se}_m(\xi, q)\operatorname{se}_m(\eta, q) + \bar{S}_m \operatorname{Se}_m(\xi, -q)\operatorname{se}_m(\eta, -q)\}. \tag{9}$$

When the centre of the plate is removed or clamped, the solutions
Fey_m, Gey_m, Fek_m, Gek_m must be included, so we have for cases
3^0–5^0:

$$\zeta_1^{(m)} = C_m\,\mathrm{Ce}_m(\xi,q)\mathrm{ce}_m(\eta,q) + F_m\,\mathrm{Fey}_m(\xi,q)\mathrm{ce}_m(\eta,q) +$$
$$+ S_m\,\mathrm{Se}_m(\xi,q)\mathrm{se}_m(\eta,q) + G_m\,\mathrm{Gey}_m(\xi,q)\mathrm{se}_m(\eta,q) \quad (10)$$

and

$$\zeta_2^{(m)} = \bar{C}_m\,\mathrm{Ce}_m(\xi,-q)\mathrm{ce}_m(\eta,-q) + \bar{F}_m\,\mathrm{Fek}_m(\xi,-q)\mathrm{ce}_m(\eta,-q) +$$
$$+ \bar{S}_m\,\mathrm{Se}(\xi,-q)\mathrm{se}_m(\eta,-q) + \bar{G}_m\,\mathrm{Gek}_m(\xi,-q)\mathrm{se}_m(\eta,-q). \quad (11)$$

The complete solution takes a form similar to (9).

16.51. Clamped edge, centre free. Consider those modes where
the displacement is either symmetrical about both axes or about the
minor axis only. The first necessitates a solution with ce_{2n}, and
the second with ce_{2n+1} (see § 16.12), the se_m functions being inadmissible. The appropriate formal solution for the mth mode is, by
(9) § 16.50,

$$\zeta^{(m)} = C_m\,\mathrm{Ce}_m(\xi,q)\mathrm{ce}_m(\eta,q) + \bar{C}_m\,\mathrm{Ce}_m(\xi,-q)\mathrm{ce}_m(\eta,-q). \quad (1)\dagger$$

The boundary conditions are $\zeta = d\zeta/d\xi = 0$ at the clamped edge
where $\xi = \xi_0$. Using these in (1) leads to the two conditional equations

$$C_m\,\mathrm{Ce}_m(\xi_0,q)\mathrm{ce}_m(\eta,q) + \bar{C}_m\,\mathrm{Ce}_m(\xi_0,-q)\mathrm{ce}_m(\eta,-q) = 0 \quad (2)$$

and

$$C_m\,\mathrm{Ce}_m'(\xi_0,q)\mathrm{ce}_m(\eta,q) + \bar{C}_m\,\mathrm{Ce}_m'(\xi_0,-q)\mathrm{ce}_m(\eta,-q) = 0. \quad (3)$$

From (2), (3) we deduce that

$$[\mathrm{Ce}_m(\xi_0,q)\mathrm{Ce}_m'(\xi_0,-q) - \mathrm{Ce}_m'(\xi_0,q)\mathrm{Ce}_m(\xi_0,-q)]\mathrm{ce}_m(\eta,q)\mathrm{ce}_m(\eta,-q) = 0. \quad (4)$$

Hence we have the pulsatance equation

$$\mathrm{Ce}_m(\xi_0,q)\mathrm{Ce}_m'(\xi_0,-q) - \mathrm{Ce}_m'(\xi_0,q)\mathrm{Ce}_m(\xi_0,-q) = 0, \quad (5)$$

which may be written

$$\frac{d}{d\xi}[\mathrm{Ce}_m(\xi,q)/\mathrm{Ce}_m(\xi,-q)]_{\xi=\xi_0} = 0. \quad (6)$$

This equation is satisfied by $q = q_{m,s}$, $s = 1, 2,...$, and defines a
system of confocal nodal ellipses $0 < \xi \leqslant \xi_0$. From (4) we have
the equations defining a system of nodal hyperbolae, namely,

$$\mathrm{ce}_m(\eta,q) = 0 \quad \text{and} \quad \mathrm{ce}_m(\eta,-q) = 0. \quad (7)$$

† When $m = 2n+1$, and $q < 0$, in (1)–(7) write Se, se for Ce, ce: in (8), (9) write
Ce, ce for Se, se. See [225].

Nodal ellipses and nodal hyperbolae coexist, being analogous to nodal circles and radii on a freely vibrating circular plate.

For modes in which the displacement is anti-symmetrical about the major axis or about both axes, the pulsatance equation is

$$\text{Se}_m(\xi_0, q)\text{Se}'_m(\xi_0, -q) - \text{Se}'_m(\xi_0, q)\text{Se}_m(\xi_0, -q) = 0. \tag{8}$$

This defines a second system of confocal nodal ellipses. The equations for the accompanying system of nodal hyperbolae are

$$\text{se}_m(\eta, q) = 0 \quad \text{and} \quad \text{se}_m(\eta, -q) = 0. \tag{9}$$

Accordingly there is a double infinity of both classes of nodal pattern.

16.52. Determination of $q_{2n,s}$ in (6) § 16.51. If q is small, the procedure in § 16.17 may be followed. For large values of $q = k^2$ the asymptotic formula (3) § 11.42 may be used. Applying the relationship $\text{Ce}_{2n}(\xi, -q) = (-1)^n \text{Ce}_{2n}(\tfrac{1}{2}\pi i + \xi, q)$ thereto, and selecting the real part, we obtain with ξ large enough

$$\text{Ce}_{2n}(\xi, -q) \sim C_{2n}[\cosh w_1 \cos \varpi + \sinh w_1 \sin \varpi]/2^{2n} \sinh^{\frac{1}{4}} \xi, \tag{1}$$

where $w_1 = 2k \cosh \xi$, $\varpi \simeq (4n+1)\tan^{-1}(\tanh \tfrac{1}{2}\xi)$. Thus by (1) above and (3) § 11.42

$$\frac{\text{Ce}_{2n}(\xi, q)}{\text{Ce}_{2n}(\xi, -q)} \sim \frac{\tanh^{\frac{1}{4}}\xi \cos \chi}{2^{\frac{1}{4}} \cosh \chi_1}, \tag{2}$$

with $\chi = 2k \sinh \xi - (4n+1)\tan^{-1}(\tanh \tfrac{1}{2}\xi)$

and $\cosh \chi_1 = \cosh w_1 \cos \varpi + \sinh w_1 \sin \varpi.$

Differentiating (2), as indicated in (6) § 16.51, leads to the pulsatance equation

$$[\chi' \tan \chi + \chi'_1 \tanh \chi_1]_{\xi=\xi_0} = (\sinh 2\xi_0)^{-1},$$

or $$[\tan \chi + (\chi'_1/\chi')\tanh \chi_1]_{\xi=\xi_0} = (\chi' \sinh 2\xi)^{-1}_{\xi=\xi_0}. \tag{3}$$

Now k is large by hypothesis, so when ξ_0 is large enough the r.h.s. of (3) is very small, $(\chi'_1/\chi')\tanh \chi_1 \simeq 1$, and (3) approximates to

$$\tan \chi = -1 \quad \text{or} \quad \chi = s\pi - \tfrac{1}{4}\pi = (s - \tfrac{1}{4})\pi, \tag{4}$$

s being an integer. This entails

$$2k \sinh \xi_0 = (s - \tfrac{1}{4})\pi + (4n+1)\tan^{-1}(\tanh \tfrac{1}{2}\xi_0). \tag{5}$$

Then for $2k \sinh \xi_0 \to ke^{\xi_0}$ and $\tanh \tfrac{1}{2}\xi_0 \to 1$, we have

$$ke^{\xi_0} \simeq (s+n)\pi,$$

or $$k^2_{2n,s} = q_{2n,s} \simeq (s+n)^2\pi^2 e^{-2\xi_0}. \tag{6}$$

Equation (8) § 16.51 may be treated in a similar way.

16.53. Transition to circular plate. Using the degenerate forms of the modified Mathieu functions in Appendix I, both of the pulsatance equations (5), (8) § 16.51 become

$$J_m(k_1 a)I'_m(k_1 a) - J'_m(k_1 a)I_m(k_1 a) = 0 \quad (k_1^2 = \omega/c), \tag{1}$$

which is the known result for the modes of a clamped circular plate of radius a. Using the dominant terms in the asymptotic formulae for the Bessel functions, (1) gives

$$\cos(k_1 a - \tfrac{1}{4}\pi - \tfrac{1}{2}m\pi) + \sin(k_1 a - \tfrac{1}{4}\pi - \tfrac{1}{2}m\pi) = 0 \tag{2}$$

or

$$\tan(k_1 a - \tfrac{1}{4}\pi - \tfrac{1}{2}m\pi) = -1, \tag{3}$$

so, if s is an integer, $k_1 a = (s + \tfrac{1}{2}m)\pi.$ (4)

By Appendix I, as the bounding ellipse tends to a circle of radius a, $ke^{\xi_0} \to k_1 a$, so if $m = 2n$, (4) above and (6) § 16.52 agree.

Since $k_1^2 = \omega/c$, (4) gives for the higher modes of vibration of a clamped circular plate of radius a and thickness t

$$\omega = \frac{(s + \tfrac{1}{2}m)\pi t}{2a} \left[\frac{E}{3\rho(1-\sigma^2)}\right]^{\frac{1}{2}}. \tag{5}$$

Also by Appendix I, we see that (7), (8) § 16.50 degenerate to

$$\zeta_1^{(m)} = (C'_m \cos m\theta + S'_m \sin m\theta)J_m(k_1 r) \tag{6}$$

and

$$\zeta_2^{(m)} = (\bar{C}'_m \cos m\theta + \bar{S}'_m \sin m\theta)I_m(k_1 r), \tag{7}$$

the known forms for a circular plate.

16.60. Elliptical cylinder in viscous fluid [28, 116, 137, 154]. A long cylinder of elliptical cross-section† has its axis perpendicular to the plane of the paper. A viscous fluid, e.g. air, moves past the cylinder with undisturbed velocity U in a direction θ to the major axis, as illustrated in Fig. 38. In the absence of viscosity the motion of the fluid would be irrotational. Owing, however, to friction between the surface of the cylinder and the fluid, by virtue of viscosity, the flow is accompanied by vortex motion, i.e. a perturbation is superimposed upon the irrotational motion. The problem is to determine the vorticity ζ when the motion is steady. It is given by the expression

$$\zeta = \frac{\partial^2 \psi}{\partial x^2} + \frac{\partial^2 \psi}{\partial y^2}, \tag{1}$$

† The cylinder is many times longer than its major axis.

where ψ is the stream function. For *steady* motion the vorticity is known to be expressed by the differential equation

$$\frac{\partial^2 \zeta}{\partial x^2} + \frac{\partial^2 \zeta}{\partial y^2} - \frac{2}{\nu}\left(u\frac{\partial \zeta}{\partial x} + v\frac{\partial \zeta}{\partial y}\right) = 0, \tag{2}$$

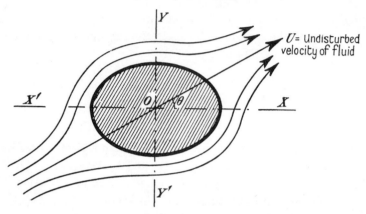

FIG. 38. Illustrating cylinder in viscous fluid.

u, v being the velocity components of the fluid parallel to the x and y axes, respectively, $\frac{1}{2}\nu = \mu/\rho$, μ the kinematic coefficient of viscosity, ρ the density of the undisturbed fluid. Then, if ϕ is the velocity potential, we have

$$u = -\frac{\partial \psi}{\partial y} = -\frac{\partial \phi}{\partial x}, \tag{3}$$

$$v = \frac{\partial \psi}{\partial x} = -\frac{\partial \phi}{\partial y}. \tag{4}$$

For the undisturbed motion,† the velocity potential and stream function expressed in rectangular coordinates are

$$\phi_0 = -U(x\cos\theta + y\sin\theta), \tag{5}$$

$$\psi_0 = -U(y\cos\theta - x\sin\theta), \tag{6}$$

these satisfying (3), (4). Substituting from the two latter into (2) yields

$$\frac{\partial^2 \zeta}{\partial x^2} + \frac{\partial^2 \zeta}{\partial y^2} + \frac{2}{\nu}\left(\frac{\partial \phi}{\partial x}\frac{\partial \zeta}{\partial x} + \frac{\partial \phi}{\partial y}\frac{\partial \zeta}{\partial y}\right) = 0. \tag{7}$$

Applying formulae in §9.20, (7) is transformed to elliptical coordinates and becomes

$$\frac{\partial^2 \zeta}{\partial \xi^2} + \frac{\partial^2 \zeta}{\partial \eta^2} + \frac{2}{\nu}\left(\frac{\partial \phi}{\partial \xi}\frac{\partial \zeta}{\partial \xi} + \frac{\partial \phi}{\partial \eta}\frac{\partial \zeta}{\partial \eta}\right) = 0. \tag{8}$$

† In the absence of friction between the fluid and the surface of the cylinder.

16.61. Solution of (8) § 16.60. Assume that the solution takes the form $\zeta = e^{-\phi/\nu}f(\xi, \eta)$. Then since $\dfrac{\partial^2\phi}{\partial\xi^2}+\dfrac{\partial^2\phi}{\partial\eta^2} = 0$, we obtain

$$e^{-\phi/\nu}\left\{\frac{\partial^2 f}{\partial\xi^2}+\frac{\partial^2 f}{\partial\eta^2}-\frac{1}{\nu^2}\left[\left(\frac{\partial\phi}{\partial\xi}\right)^2+\left(\frac{\partial\phi}{\partial\eta}\right)^2\right]f\right\} = 0. \tag{1}$$

Expressing (5), (6) § 16.60 in elliptical coordinates by aid of the substitutions $x = h\cosh\xi\cos\eta$; $y = h\sinh\xi\sin\eta$, leads to

$$\phi_0 = -Uh(\cosh\xi\cos\eta\cos\theta+\sinh\xi\sin\eta\sin\theta) \tag{2}$$

and $\qquad \psi_0 = -Uh(\sinh\xi\sin\eta\cos\theta-\cosh\xi\cos\eta\sin\theta).$ (3)

From these we find that ϕ_0 and ψ_0 satisfy

$$\left(\frac{\partial\varphi}{\partial\xi}\right)^2+\left(\frac{\partial\varphi}{\partial\eta}\right)^2 = \frac{U^2h^2}{2}(\cosh 2\xi-\cos 2\eta). \tag{4}$$

Now (2), (3) are for undisturbed motion, so that if (4) is substituted into (1), a first approximation, based on Oseen's analysis, is

$$\frac{\partial^2 f}{\partial\xi^2}+\frac{\partial^2 f}{\partial\eta^2}-\frac{U^2h^2}{2\nu^2}(\cosh 2\xi-\cos 2\eta)f = 0. \tag{5}$$

As in § 9.21 assume that $f(\xi, \eta) = f_1(\xi)f_2(\eta)$, and we get

$$f_2\frac{d^2 f_1}{d\xi^2}+f_1\frac{d^2 f_2}{d\eta^2}-\frac{U^2h^2}{2\nu^2}(\cosh 2\xi-\cos 2\eta)f_1 f_2 = 0. \tag{6}$$

Dividing throughout by $f_1 f_2$ yields

$$\frac{1}{f_1}\frac{d^2 f_1}{d\xi^2}-2k^2\cosh 2\xi = -\frac{1}{f_2}\frac{d^2 f_2}{d\eta^2}-2k^2\cos 2\eta = a, \quad\text{a constant,} \tag{7}$$

with $U^2h^2/2\nu^2 = 2k^2$, or $k^2 = U^2h^2/4\nu^2$. Then we get the two Mathieu equations

$$\frac{d^2 f_1}{d\xi^2}-(a+2k^2\cosh 2\xi)f_1 = 0, \tag{8}$$

$$\frac{d^2 f_2}{d\eta^2}+(a+2k^2\cos 2\eta)f_2 = 0. \tag{9}$$

16.62. Conditions to be satisfied. (a) As in § 16.11 the solution must be periodic in η with period π or 2π; (b) the amplitude of the motion must tend to zero as $\xi \to +\infty$; (c) the circulation of the fluid at $\xi = \infty$ must be bounded, otherwise the force on a finite length of cylinder would be infinite. (a) is satisfied if we choose $ce_n(z, -q)$, $se_n(z, -q)$ as the solutions of (9) § 16.61. Now

$$\zeta = e^{-\phi/\nu}f_1(\xi)f_2(\eta), \tag{1}$$

and to fulfil (*b*), $e^{-\phi/\nu}f_1(\xi)$ must $\to 0$ as $\xi \to +\infty$. Suppose we select the solutions $\mathrm{Fek}_n(\xi, -q)$, $\mathrm{Gek}_n(\xi, -q)$ for (8) § 16.61. Then, using their asymptotic forms from § 11.12 with ϕ_0 from (2) § 16.61, we must have

$$e^{-\phi/\nu}f_1(\xi) \propto e^{2k(\cosh\xi\cos\eta\cos\theta + \sinh\xi\sin\eta\sin\theta) - ke^\xi}\sqrt{\left(\frac{1}{2ke^\xi}\right)} \to 0. \qquad (2)$$

From § 9.12, $h\cosh\xi \sim r$, $h\sinh\xi \sim r$, as $\xi \to +\infty$; also by § 2 Appendix I, since $\tfrac{1}{2}he^\xi \sim r$, $ke^\xi \sim k_1 r$ as $\xi \to +\infty$. Writing $2k = k_1 h$ and substituting in (2) we obtain

$$e^{-\phi/\nu}f_1(\xi) \propto \frac{e^{k_1 r\{\cos(\eta-\theta)-1\}}}{\sqrt{(2k_1 r)}}. \qquad (3)$$

Now $\{\cos(\eta-\theta)-1\} < 0$ except for $(\eta-\theta) = 0$ when it vanishes. Hence (3) tends to zero as $r \to +\infty$, and, therefore, as $\xi \to +\infty$. Accordingly a solution of the form

$$\zeta = e^{-\phi/\nu}\Big\{ \sum_{n=0}^{\infty} C_n \mathrm{Fek}_n(\xi, -q)\mathrm{ce}_n(\eta, -q) +$$

$$+ \sum_{n=1}^{\infty} D_n \mathrm{Gek}_n(\xi, -q)\mathrm{se}_n(\eta, -q)\Big\} \qquad (4)$$

complies with conditions (*a*), (*b*). We shall now demonstrate that a modification of (4) is necessary, in order that condition (*c*) may be satisfied.

16.63. Circulation of fluid as $\xi \to +\infty$ [116]. We shall evaluate the difference in circulation of fluid over the ring defined by the confocal ellipses $\xi = \xi_1$ and $\xi = \xi_2$ as $\xi_2 \to +\infty$, which arises from one term in (4) § 16.62. We take the term $C_n e^{-\phi/\nu} \mathrm{Fek}_n(\xi, -q)\mathrm{ce}_n(\eta, -q)$, and the circulation is proportional to

$$\iint e^{-\phi/\nu} \mathrm{Fek}_n(\xi, -q)\mathrm{ce}_n(\eta, -q)\, ds_1\, ds_2, \qquad (1)$$

where ds_1, ds_2 are elemental arcs, as defined in § 9.12, the integration extending over the ring. From § 9.12, when ξ is large enough, $ds_1 ds_2 \sim r\,dr d\eta$, so using (3) § 16.62 and the series for $\mathrm{ce}_n(\eta, -q)$, (1) may be written

$$I_n = \mathrm{const.} \int_{r_1}^{r_2} e^{-k_1 r} r^{\frac{1}{2}} \chi_n\, dr \int_0^{2\pi} e^{k_1 r\cos(\eta-\theta)}\Big[\sum_{m=0}^{\infty} (-1)^m A_m^{(n)} \cos m\eta \Big]\, d\eta,$$

$$(2)\dagger$$

† For $\mathrm{ce}_{2n}(\eta, -q)$, $A_m^{(n)} = A_{2m}^{(2n)}$, and for $\mathrm{ce}_{2n+1}(\eta, -q)$, $A_m^{(n)} = B_{2m+1}^{(2n+1)}$.

where r_1 corresponds to ξ_1, r_2 to ξ_2, and

$$\chi_n = 1 + \frac{(4a_n-1)}{8k_1 r} + \frac{(4a_n-1)(4a_n-9)}{2!\,(8k_1 r)^2} + \frac{(4a_n-1)...(4a_n-25)}{3!\,(8k_1 r)^3} + ...,$$
(3)

which is the series part of the asymptotic expansion of $\mathrm{Fek}_n(z, -q)$ in (10) § 11.23, if the term in k^4 in (8) § 11.20 is neglected.

Now

$$e^{k_1 r \cos(\eta-\theta)} \cos m\eta = \left\{ I_0(k_1 r) + 2\sum_{p=1}^{\infty} I_p(k_1 r)\cos p(\eta-\theta) \right\}\cos m\eta$$

$$= I_0(k_1 r)\cos m\eta + \sum_{p=1}^{\infty} I_p(k_1 r)[\cos\{\eta(p+m)-p\theta\} +$$

$$+ \cos\{\eta(p-m)-p\theta\}]. \quad (4)$$

Using (4) in (2), all the integrals vanish except when $p = m$, so

$$\int_0^{2\pi} e^{k_1 r \cos(\eta-\theta)} \cos m\eta \, d\eta = 2\pi I_m(k_1 r)\cos m\theta. \quad (5)$$

But when $k_1 r$ is very large [ref. 202, p. 163]

$$I_m(k_1 r) \sim \frac{e^{k_1 r}}{\sqrt{(2\pi k_1 r)}}\left\{1 - \frac{(4m^2-1)}{8k_1 r} + \frac{(4m^2-1)(4m^2-9)}{2!\,(8k_1 r)^2} - ...\right\}. \quad (6)$$

Substituting from (5), (6) into (2) yields

$$I_n = \mathrm{const.} \int_{r_1}^{r_2} \chi_n\left[\sum_{m=0}^{\infty} (-1)^m A_m^{(n)} \cos m\theta \times \right.$$

$$\left. \times \left\{1 - \frac{(4m^2-1)}{8k_1 r} + \frac{(4m^2-1)(4m^2-9)}{2!\,(8k_1 r)^2} - ...\right\}\right] dr. \quad (7)$$

Since $\sum_{m=0}^{\infty} (-1)^{s+m} A_m^{(n)} m^{2s} \cos m\theta = (d^{2s}/d\theta^{2s})[\mathrm{ce}_n(\theta, -q)]$, the integrand of (7) may be written

$$\chi_n\left[\mathrm{ce}_n + \frac{1}{8k_1 r}(\mathrm{ce}_n + 4\mathrm{ce}_n'') + \frac{1}{2!\,(8k_1 r)^2}(16\mathrm{ce}_n^{iv} + 40\mathrm{ce}_n'' + 9\mathrm{ce}_n) + ...\right]. \quad (8)$$

Designating the coefficients of $1/r$, $1/r^2$,... in (3), (8) by α_1, α_2,..., β_1, β_2,..., respectively, (8) yields

$$(1 + \alpha_1 r^{-1} + \alpha_2 r^{-2} + ...)(\beta_0 + \beta_1 r^{-1} + \beta_2 r^{-2} + ...)$$

$$= \beta_0 + (\alpha_1\beta_0 + \beta_1)r^{-1} + (\alpha_2\beta_0 + \alpha_1\beta_1 + \beta_2)r^{-2} + ... \quad (9)$$

Inserting this in (7) and integrating with respect to r leads to

$$I_n = \text{const.}\left\{\beta_0(r_2-r_1)+(\alpha_1\beta_0+\beta_1)\log\frac{r_2}{r_1}+\right.$$

$$\left.+(\alpha_2\beta_0+\alpha_1\beta_1+\beta_2)\left(\frac{1}{r_1}-\frac{1}{r_2}\right)+...\right\} \quad (10)$$

$$= \Lambda_n\beta_0\left\{(r_2-r_1)+(\alpha_1+\beta_1/\beta_0)\log(r_2/r_1)+\right.$$

$$\left.+(\alpha_2+\alpha_1\beta_1/\beta_0+\beta_2/\beta_0)\left(\frac{1}{r_1}-\frac{1}{r_2}\right)+...\right\}. \quad (11)$$

Since $(11) \to \infty$ with r_2, it follows that the presence of a term of the form $e^{-\phi/\nu}C_n\,\mathrm{Fek}_n(\xi,-q)\mathrm{ce}_n(\eta,-q)$, as in (4) §16.62, introduces an infinite circulation as $r_2 \to \infty$, which is physically impossible. It is necessary, therefore, to modify the term in question to give a finite solution.

Only the first two terms in (11) yield infinities, so we consider these and disregard the remainder of the series, because it is convergent and finite. Then

$$\alpha_1+\beta_1/\beta_0 = \frac{1}{8k_1}\left\{(4a_n-1)+1+\frac{4\mathrm{ce}_n''}{\mathrm{ce}_n}\right\} = \frac{1}{2k_1}(a_n+\mathrm{ce}_n''/\mathrm{ce}_n). \quad (12)$$

Now $\mathrm{ce}_n''+(a_n+2k^2\cos 2\theta)\mathrm{ce}_n = 0$, so that

$$a_n+\mathrm{ce}_n''/\mathrm{ce}_n = -2k^2\cos 2\theta, \quad (13)$$

which gives

$$(\alpha_1+\beta_1/\beta_0) = -\frac{k^2}{k_1}\cos 2\theta = -\frac{Uh^2}{4\nu}\cos 2\theta. \quad (14)$$

Using (14) in (11), if θ is fixed—as it would be in practice—with $\beta_0 = \mathrm{ce}_n$ or ce_{n+1}, we get

$$I_n/\Lambda_n\,\mathrm{ce}_n$$

$$= \left\{(r_2-r_1)-\frac{Uh^2}{4\nu}\cos 2\theta\log r_2/r_1+L_n \text{ (finite as } r_2 \to \infty)\right\}, \quad (15)$$

$$I_{n+1}/\Lambda_{n+1}\,\mathrm{ce}_{n+1}$$

$$= \left\{(r_2-r_1)-\frac{Uh^2}{4\nu}\cos 2\theta\log r_2/r_1+L_{n+1} \text{ (finite as } r_2 \to \infty)\right\}. \quad (16)$$

Although both (15), $(16) \to \infty$ with r_2, their difference

$$(I_n/\Lambda_n\,\mathrm{ce}_n)-(I_{n+1}/\Lambda_{n+1}\,\mathrm{ce}_{n+1}) = L_n-L_{n+1}, \quad (17)$$

is finite. Hence the first part of the solution (4) §16.62 must be taken in the form

$$\mathrm{Fk}_{n,n+1} = e^{-\phi/\nu}[C_n \,\mathrm{Fek}_n \,\mathrm{ce}_n - C_{n+1} \,\mathrm{Fek}_{n+1} \,\mathrm{ce}_{n+1}], \qquad (18)$$

where C_n, C_{n+1} are constants whose ratio is chosen to annul the first two terms at (15), (16).

The results for the second part of the solution at (4) §16.62, namely, $e^{-\phi/\nu} D_n \,\mathrm{Gek}_n \,\mathrm{se}_n$ are identical in form with those above, except that sin is written for cos, and se for ce. Thus to preserve finite circulation we take

$$\mathrm{Gk}_{n,n+1} = e^{-\phi/\nu}[D_n \,\mathrm{Gek}_n \,\mathrm{se}_n - D_{n+1} \,\mathrm{Gek}_{n+1} \,\mathrm{se}_{n+1}]. \qquad (19)$$

Finally the complete solution which satisfies conditions (a), (b), (c) in §16.62 is given by

$$\zeta = e^{-\phi/\nu}\Big\{ \sum_{n=0}^{\infty} \mathrm{Fk}_{n,n+1} + \sum_{n=1}^{\infty} \mathrm{Gk}_{n,n+1} \Big\}. \qquad (20)$$

The arbitrary constants C, D in (18), (19) are found from the boundary conditions as usual.

ELECTRICAL AND THERMAL DIFFUSION

17.10. Eddy current loss in core of solenoid. When a sinusoidal current flows in a solenoid having a metal core of elliptical cross-section, the varying magnetic field induces eddy currents therein, the core behaving like the secondary winding of a transformer. To calculate the loss arising from these currents we assume that:

1. The current in the winding is everywhere in phase.
2. The core is a uniform metal bar of elliptical cross-section, having resistivity ρ and permeability μ, the latter being independent of H the magnetizing force.
3. The uniformly wound solenoid of n turns is long compared with its cross-sectional dimensions.
4. H is uniform at the curved surface of the bar.

Differential equation for H. It can be shown that, in rectangular coordinates, the equation for H at any point (x, y) of a cross-section of the bar is [167]

$$\frac{\partial^2 H}{\partial x^2} + \frac{\partial^2 H}{\partial y^2} - \frac{4\pi\mu}{\rho}\frac{\partial H}{\partial t} = 0. \tag{1}$$

If $H = H_1 e^{i\omega t}$, $\partial H/\partial t = i\omega H$, and (1) becomes

$$\frac{\partial^2 H}{\partial x^2} + \frac{\partial^2 H}{\partial y^2} - i\left(\frac{4\pi\mu\omega}{\rho}\right)H = 0. \tag{2}$$

Introducing elliptical coordinates as in § 9.20, this equation is transformed to

$$\frac{\partial^2 H}{\partial \xi^2} + \frac{\partial^2 H}{\partial \eta^2} + 2k^2(\cosh 2\xi - \cos 2\eta)H = 0, \tag{3}$$

where $4k^2 = k_1^2 h^2 = -ih^2(4\pi\mu\omega/\rho)$. Thus k^2 is negative imaginary and $2k = i^{\frac{3}{2}}hm$, with $m = (4\pi\mu\omega/\rho)^{\frac{1}{2}}$. Then by § 9.21 a suitable solution of (3) is $H = \chi(\xi)\phi(\eta)$, χ being a solution of

$$\frac{d^2\chi}{d\xi^2} - (a - 2k^2\cosh 2\xi)\chi = 0, \tag{4}$$

and ϕ a solution of

$$\frac{d^2\phi}{d\eta^2} + (a - 2k^2\cos 2\eta)\phi = 0. \tag{5}$$

17.11. Physical conditions. The distribution of H round any confocal ellipse in a cross-section of the core is symmetrical about the major and minor axes. Also H is single-valued and periodic in η with period π. Hence ϕ must be a multiple of $ce_{2n}(\eta, q)$. Further, to satisfy (b) § 16.11 the solution

$$\chi = Fe_{2n}(\xi, q)$$

must be excluded. Thus $Ce_{2n}(\xi, q)ce_{2n}(\eta, q)$ is the only admissible type of solution of (3) § 17.10. Accordingly at any point (ξ, η) of the cross-section we have

$$H = \sum_{n=0}^{\infty} C_{2n} Ce_{2n}(\xi, q)ce_{2n}(\eta, q), \tag{1}$$

the constants C_{2n} being determinable from the boundary conditions.

17.12. Determination of C_{2n} in (1) § 17.11. At the surface of the core, $H = H_0$, a constant given by $4\pi n I_{\text{r.m.s.}}/l$, $I_{\text{r.m.s.}}$ being the root mean square value of the current† and l the axial length of the solenoid. Thus at $\xi = \xi_0$

$$H_0 = \sum_{n=0}^{\infty} C_{2n} Ce_{2n}(\xi_0, q)ce_{2n}(\eta, q). \tag{1}$$

Multiplying both sides of (1) by $ce_{2n}(\eta, q)$ and integrating with respect to η from 0 to 2π, we get

$$H_0 \int_0^{2\pi} ce_{2n}(\eta, q) \, d\eta = C_{2n} Ce_{2n}(\xi_0, q) \int_0^{2\pi} ce_{2n}^2(\eta, q) \, d\eta$$
$$= C_{2n} Ce_{2n}(\xi_0, q)\mathfrak{L}_{2n}, \tag{2}$$

where $\mathfrak{L}_{2n} = \int_0^{2\pi} ce_{2n}^2(\eta, q) \, d\eta$, the other integrals vanishing by virtue of orthogonality.‡ The value of the first integral in (2) is $2\pi H_0 A_0^{(2n)}$, it being understood that since k^2 is negative imaginary, the A in the series for $ce_{2n}(\eta, q)$ are complex (see § 3.40 et seq.). Thus we obtain

$$C_{2n} = 2\pi H_0 A_0^{(2n)}/Ce_{2n}(\xi_0, q)\mathfrak{L}_{2n}. \tag{3}$$

Hence by (1) § 17.11, (3) the magnetizing force at any point (ξ, η) of a core-section is given by

$$H_{\xi, \eta} = 2\pi H_0 \sum_{n=0}^{\infty} A_0^{(2n)} Ce_{2n}(\xi, q)ce_{2n}(\eta, q)/\mathfrak{L}_{2n} Ce_{2n}(\xi_0, q). \tag{4}$$

Since all quantities under the $\sum$ sign are complex, so also is $H_{\xi, \eta}$, in general.

---

† The r.m.s. value is selected merely for convenience, since it is used in § 17.20.
‡ When $q = k^2$ is real the value of the integral is π. In (2), q is negative imaginary.

17.13. Transition to circular cross-section. By Appendix I
$Ce_{2n}(\xi, q) \to p'_{2n} J_{2n}(k_1 r)$, $Ce_{2n}(\xi_0, q) \to p'_{2n} J_{2n}(k_1 a)$, a being the radius
of the core. Also $ce_{2n}(\eta, q) \to \cos 2n\theta$, $n \geqslant 1$, $ce_0(\eta, q) \to A_0^{(0)} = 1$,
$A_0^{(2n)} \to 0$, $n \geqslant 1$, and $\mathfrak{L}_{2n} \to \int_0^{2\pi} \cos^2 2n\theta \, d\theta = \pi$. Hence all terms of
(4) §17.12 vanish except when $n = 0$, and for a core of circular
section we get

$$H = H_0 J_0(k_1 r)/J_0(k_1 a). \tag{1}$$

Now $k_1 = i^{\frac{3}{2}} m$, so (1) becomes

$$H = H_0 J_0(i^{\frac{3}{2}} mr)/J_0(i^{\frac{3}{2}} ma). \tag{2}$$

Expressing the J function in polar form, with

$$J_\nu(i^{\frac{3}{2}} z) = \mathrm{ber}_\nu z + i\, \mathrm{bei}_\nu z = M_\nu(z) e^{i\theta_\nu(z)},$$

leads to

$$H = H_0 \frac{M_0(mr)}{M_0(ma)} e^{i[\theta_0(mr) - \theta_0(ma)]}. \tag{3}$$

$M_0(z)$, $\theta_0(z)$ are tabulated in reference [203].

17.14. Total flux in elliptical core. This is found by integrating
μH over a cross-section. Thus the total flux is, with $k_1 = i^{\frac{3}{2}} m$,

$$\Phi = \mu \int H \, dA = -\frac{\mu}{k_1^2} \int \int \left(\frac{\partial^2 H}{\partial x^2} + \frac{\partial^2 H}{\partial y^2} \right) dx dy, \tag{1}$$

by (2) §17.10. Now if n is the outward normal and ds an elemental
surface arc, (1) may be written

$$\Phi = -\frac{\mu}{k_1^2} \oint \frac{\partial H}{\partial n} ds = -\frac{\mu}{k_1^2} \int_0^{2\pi} \frac{\partial H}{\partial \xi} d\eta, \tag{2}$$

by virtue of the relationships $ds = l_1 d\eta$, $\partial n = l_1 \partial \xi$ in §9.12. Substituting in (2) for H from (4) §17.12 leads to

$$\Phi = -\frac{2\pi\mu H_0}{k_1^2} \sum_{n=0}^{\infty} \frac{A_0^{(2n)} Ce'_{2n}(\xi, q)}{\mathfrak{L}_{2n} \, Ce_{2n}(\xi_0, q)} \int_0^{2\pi} ce_{2n}(\eta) \, d\eta, \tag{3}$$

$$= -\frac{4\pi^2\mu H_0}{k_1^2} \sum_{n=0}^{\infty} \frac{[A_0^{(2n)}]^2 \, Ce'_{2n}(\xi, q)}{\mathfrak{L}_{2n} \, Ce_{2n}(\xi_0, q)}. \tag{4}$$

This represents the total flux within an ellipse defined by $\xi < \xi_0$.
The total core flux is (4) with ξ_0 for ξ in the numerator.

17.15. Transition to circular cross-section radius a.

By aid of Appendix I, (4) § 17.14 degenerates to the form

$$\Phi = -\frac{2\pi a\mu H_0}{k_1}\frac{J_0'(k_1 a)}{J_0(k_1 a)} = \frac{2\pi a\mu H_0}{mi^{\frac{3}{2}}}\frac{J_1(i^{\frac{3}{2}}ma)}{J_0(i^{\frac{3}{2}}ma)} \tag{1}$$

$$= \pi a^2\mu H_0\left[\frac{2}{ma}\frac{M_1(ma)}{M_0(ma)}\right]e^{i[\theta_1(ma)-\theta_0(ma)-\frac{3}{4}\pi]}. \tag{2}$$

M_0, θ_0, M_1, θ_1 are tabulated in reference [203].

17.20. Effective resistance R_e and effective inductance L_e due to core.

If $I_{\text{r.m.s.}}$ is the root mean square value of the current in the solenoid, the p.d. across its ends is $E_{\text{r.m.s.}} = (R_e + i\omega L_e)I_{\text{r.m.s.}}$, so

$$I_{\text{r.m.s.}} = E_{\text{r.m.s.}}\left(\frac{R_e - i\omega L_e}{R_e^2 + \omega^2 L_e^2}\right) = \frac{E_{\text{r.m.s.}}}{Z_e^2}(R_e - i\omega L_e). \tag{1}$$

Accordingly we assume that $I_{\text{r.m.s.}}$ has two components in phase quadrature. One of these causes a flux Φ_e (equal but of opposite phase to that arising from eddy currents induced in the core) such that $n\, d\Phi_e/dt = R_e I_{\text{r.m.s.}}$. Thus the core loss is given by

$$R_e I_{\text{r.m.s.}}^2 = n\frac{d\Phi_e}{dt}I_{\text{r.m.s.}}. \tag{2}$$

Substituting $H_0 = 4\pi n I_{\text{r.m.s.}}/l$ in (4) § 17.14 the *total* r.m.s. core flux is

$$\Phi = -\frac{16\pi^3\mu n I_{\text{r.m.s.}}}{k_1^2 l}\sum_{n=0}^{\infty}\frac{[A_0^{(2n)}]^2\,\mathrm{Ce}_{2n}'(\xi_0, q)}{\mathfrak{L}_{2n}\,\mathrm{Ce}_{2n}(\xi_0, q)}. \tag{3}$$

Φ_e is the real part of (3), so if the flux varies as $e^{i\omega t}$, the core loss is, by (2), (3),

$$P = n\frac{d\Phi_e}{dt}I_{\text{r.m.s.}} = -\frac{16\pi^3\mu\omega n^2 I_{\text{r.m.s.}}^2}{l}\,\mathrm{Real}\left[i\sum_{n=0}^{\infty}\frac{[A_0^{(2n)}]^2\,\mathrm{Ce}_{2n}'(\xi_0, q)}{k_1^2\,\mathfrak{L}_{2n}\,\mathrm{Ce}_{2n}(\xi_0, q)}\right]. \tag{4}$$

Substituting $k_1 = i^{\frac{3}{2}}m$ in (4), the power dissipated in the core is represented by

$$P = \frac{16\pi^3\mu\omega n^2}{m^2 l}I_{\text{r.m.s.}}^2\,\mathrm{Real}\left[\sum_{n=0}^{\infty}\frac{[A_0^{(2n)}]^2\,\mathrm{Ce}_{2n}'(\xi_0, q)}{\mathfrak{L}_{2n}\,\mathrm{Ce}_{2n}(\xi_0, q)}\right]. \tag{5}$$

Since $P = R_e I_{\text{r.m.s.}}^2$, the effective resistance due to the metal core is given by (5), if $I_{\text{r.m.s.}}^2$ is omitted.

The so-called 'imaginary' power or energy per unit time stored in the solenoid and restored to the power source periodically is found by similar analysis, using the imaginary part of (3), to be

$$\omega L_e\, I_{\text{r.m.s.}}^2 = \frac{16\pi^3\mu\omega n^2}{m^2 l}\, I_{\text{r.m.s.}}^2\, \text{Imag}\Bigg[\sum_{n=0}^{\infty} \frac{[A_0^{(2n)}]^2 \text{Ce}_{2n}'(\xi_0, q)}{\mathfrak{L}_{2n}\, \text{Ce}_{2n}(\xi_0, q)}\Bigg]. \qquad (6)$$

Hence the effective inductance of the solenoid due to the metal core alone is given by (6), provided $\omega I_{\text{r.m.s.}}^2$ is omitted.

17.21. Transition to circular cross-section. By § 2 Appendix I we find that

$$\sum_{n=0}^{\infty} \frac{[A_0^{(2n)}]^2\, \text{Ce}_{2n}'(\xi_0, q)}{\mathfrak{L}_{2n}\, \text{Ce}_{2n}(\xi_0, q)} \rightarrow -\frac{k_1\, a J_1(k_1 a)}{2\pi J_0(k_1 a)}, \qquad (1)$$

so with $k_1^2 = -im^2$, (5) § 17.20 degenerates to

$$P = \frac{8\pi^2\mu\omega a n^2}{ml}\, I_{\text{r.m.s.}}^2\, \text{Real}\Bigg[\frac{J_1(i^{\frac{3}{2}}ma)}{J_0(i^{\frac{3}{2}}ma)}\, e^{-\frac{1}{4}\pi i}\Bigg] \qquad (2)$$

$$= \frac{8\pi^2\mu\omega a n^2}{ml}\, I_{\text{r.m.s.}}^2\, \frac{M_1(ma)}{M_0(ma)}\cos(\theta_1 - \theta_0 - \tfrac{1}{4}\pi). \qquad (3)$$

The effective resistance is given by (3), devoid of $I_{\text{r.m.s.}}^2$. In a similar way (6) § 17.20 degenerates to

$$L_e = \frac{8\pi^2\mu a n^2}{ml}\, \frac{M_1(ma)}{M_0(ma)}\sin(\theta_1 - \theta_0 - \tfrac{1}{4}\pi). \qquad (4)$$

17.30. Resistance of long straight conductors of elliptical and rectangular section to high-frequency alternating currents. At sufficiently high frequencies the current is confined mainly to a surface layer of the conductor, and the current density is negligible *within* the conductor. Thus the component of magnetic force normal to the surface tends to evanescence, and the magnetic force may be assumed wholly tangential thereto. It follows that, at the surface, the vector potential is constant and satisfies the same conditions as the scalar potential. Consequently the surface distribution of current density is identical with that of an electrostatic charge. The total current flowing axially through the conductor *corresponds* to the total surface charge [169].

17.31. Formula for charge and current density. We have now to find a formula for the charge at any point on the cylinder, bearing in mind that the surface potential ϕ is constant. Using elliptical coordinates (ξ, η)—see Fig. 39 A—the potential function constant on the surface is, apart from a constant multiplier,

$$\phi = \xi \quad \text{at} \quad \xi = \xi_0. \tag{1}$$

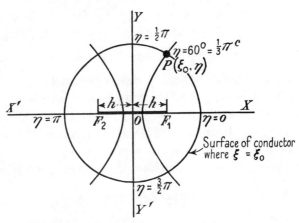

FIG. 39. (A) Illustrating conductor of elliptical cross-section foci F_1, F_2. The hyperbola determines the coordinate η at the surface where $\xi = \xi_0$.

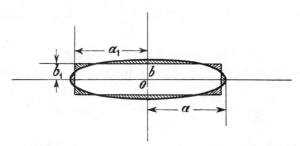

FIG. 39. (B) Ellipse having same area and axes ratio as rectangular section.

Now the charge at any point P whose coordinates are (ξ_0, η) is

$$\sigma_1 = K_1 \, d\phi/dn, \tag{2}$$

where K_1 is a constant and n denotes the direction of the normal to the surface. By §9.12, $dn = h(\cosh^2\xi_0 - \cos^2\eta)^{\frac{1}{2}} \, d\xi$, so from (1), (2)

$$\sigma_1 = K_1\left(\frac{d\phi}{d\xi}\right)\frac{d\xi}{dn} = K_1/h(\cosh^2\xi_0 - \cos^2\eta)^{\frac{1}{2}}. \tag{3}$$

(3) is proportional to the charge at any surface point (ξ_0, η). Since ξ_0 is constant, σ_1 is a maximum when $\eta = 0$, π at the ends of the major axis. It is a minimum at the ends of the minor axis, where

$\eta = \frac{1}{2}\pi, \frac{3}{2}\pi$. The values of σ_1 at these respective points are

$$\sigma_{1(\text{max})} = K_1/h(\cosh^2\xi_0 - 1)^{\frac{1}{2}} = K_1/(a^2 - h^2)^{\frac{1}{2}} \tag{4}$$

and $\qquad \sigma_{1(\text{min})} = K_1/h \cosh \xi_0 = K_1/a. \tag{5}$

Using σ for current density, the magnetic force tangential to the surface at (ξ_0, η) is, with an appropriate multiplier K [169],

$$H_t = 4\pi\sigma = 4\pi K/h(\cosh^2\xi_0 - \cos^2\eta)^{\frac{1}{2}}. \tag{6}$$

17.32. Power loss. When H_t varies sinusoidally at high-frequency, it is shown in § 18.53 that the power loss per unit *surface* area of a conductor of unit permeability is $(1/8\pi)H_t^2(\rho f)^{\frac{1}{2}}$, where $\rho = $ resistivity, $f = $ frequency, H_t is the r.m.s. value, and the radius of curvature does not vanish at any point on the surface. The length of an elemental arc on the surface of the conductor (Fig. 17) is by § 9.12

$$ds = h(\cosh^2\xi_0 - \cos^2\eta)^{\frac{1}{2}}d\eta. \tag{1}$$

Thus the power loss over the periphery, per unit axial length, is, by (1) above and (6) § 17.31,

$$P = \frac{(\rho f)^{\frac{1}{2}}}{8\pi} \int H_t^2 \, ds = 8\pi K^2(\rho f)^{\frac{1}{2}} \int\limits_0^{\frac{1}{2}\pi} d\eta/h(\cosh^2\xi_0 - \cos^2\eta)^{\frac{1}{2}}. \tag{2}$$

Now $h \cosh \xi_0 = a$, the semi-major axis, while $(\cosh \xi_0)^{-1} = e$, the eccentricity of the bounding ellipse. Accordingly (2) may be written

$$P = \frac{8\pi K^2(\rho f)^{\frac{1}{2}}}{a} \int\limits_0^{\frac{1}{2}\pi} d\eta/(1 - e^2 \cos^2\eta)^{\frac{1}{2}} \tag{3}$$

$$= \frac{8\pi K^2(\rho f)^{\frac{1}{2}}}{a} F(e, \tfrac{1}{2}\pi) \tag{4}$$

[169], where F is a complete elliptic integral of the first kind with modulus e. The total current in the conductor corresponds to the total charge on unit length, i.e.

$$\int \sigma \, ds = K \int\limits_0^{2\pi} d\eta = 2\pi K. \tag{5}$$

Hence the resistance per unit length of conductor to high-frequency alternating current is, by (4), (5),

$$R_{\text{a.c.}} = P/4\pi^2 K^2 = \frac{2(\rho f)^{\frac{1}{2}}}{\pi a} F(e, \tfrac{1}{2}\pi). \tag{6}$$

17.33. Ratio $R_{a.c.}/R_{d.c.}$. The resistance to a constant unidirectional current is

$$R_{d.c.} = \rho/\pi ab \qquad (1)$$

per unit length of conductor. Thus by (1) and (6) § 17.32 we have

$$R_{a.c.}/R_{d.c.} = 2b(f/\rho)^{\frac{1}{2}}F(e, \tfrac{1}{2}\pi). \qquad (2)$$

When the eccentricity $e \to 1$, it can be shown that [215]

$$F(e, \tfrac{1}{2}\pi) \simeq \log_e 4a/b. \qquad (3)$$

Hence for an ellipse with $a/b \gg 1$, (2) may be written

$$R_{a.c.}/R_{d.c.} \simeq 2b(f/\rho)^{\frac{1}{2}}\log_e(4a/b). \qquad (4)$$

When $e \to 0$ the ellipse degenerates to a circle, $F(e, \tfrac{1}{2}\pi) \to \tfrac{1}{2}\pi$, and (2) becomes

$$R_{a.c.}/R_{d.c.} \simeq \pi a(f/\rho)^{\frac{1}{2}}, \qquad (5)$$

a being the radius. By (6) § 17.32 the a.c. resistance per unit length is

$$R_{a.c.} \simeq (\rho f)^{\frac{1}{2}}/a. \qquad (6)$$

17.34. Resistance of rectangular strip. Referring to Fig. 39 B we suppose that $a_1/b_1 \gg 1$ and assume that the strip may be replaced by an elliptical conductor of equal cross-sectional area with $a/b = a_1/b_1$. Then it follows that

$$b = 2b_1 \pi^{-\frac{1}{2}}. \qquad (1)$$

Substituting this in (4) § 17.33 leads to the result that for a rectangular strip, at an adequately high frequency

$$R_{a.c.}/R_{d.c.} \simeq 4b_1(f/\pi\rho)^{\frac{1}{2}}\log_e(4a_1/b_1). \qquad (2)$$

Numerical example. Let

$$\left.\begin{array}{l} 2a_1 = 2\cdot 5 \text{ cm.} \\ 2b_1 = 0\cdot 2 \text{ cm.} \end{array}\right\} \quad 4a_1/b_1 = 50.$$

$$f = 40\times 10^6 \text{ cycles per second.}$$

$$\rho = 1600 \text{ absolute units, for copper.}$$

Then

$$\log_e(4a_1/b_1) = 2\cdot 3026 \log_{10} 50$$
$$\simeq 3\cdot 92. \qquad (3)$$

Hence by (2)

$$R_{a.c.}/R_{d.c.} \simeq 2\times 0\cdot 2(40\times 10^6/\pi\times 1600)^{\frac{1}{2}}\times 3\cdot 92$$
$$\simeq 140, \qquad (4)$$

so

$$R_{a.c.} \simeq 140 R_{d.c.}. \qquad (5)$$

17.40. Heat conduction in elliptical cylinder [135]. We treat the case where the cylinder is long enough in comparison with its major axis for end effect to be neglected. If θ is temperature, κ diffusivity, and t time, the two-dimensional equation for heat transmission, expressed in rectangular coordinates, is

$$\frac{\partial^2\theta}{\partial x^2}+\frac{\partial^2\theta}{\partial y^2}-\frac{1}{\kappa}\frac{\partial\theta}{\partial t} = 0. \tag{1}$$

Let $(\theta-\theta_0) = \theta_1 = f(x,y)e^{-\kappa\nu^2t}$, where $f(x,y)$ is a function independent of t, and the purpose of ν will appear later. Then

$$\frac{\partial\theta}{\partial t} = -\kappa\nu^2\theta, \tag{2}$$

and on substituting into (1) we obtain

$$\frac{\partial^2 f}{\partial x^2}+\frac{\partial^2 f}{\partial y^2}+\nu^2 f = 0. \tag{3}$$

Transforming (3) to elliptical coordinates, by § 9.20 we get

$$\frac{\partial^2 f_1}{\partial\xi^2}+\frac{\partial^2 f_1}{\partial\eta^2}+2k^2(\cosh 2\xi-\cos 2\eta)f_1 = 0, \tag{4}$$

where $k^2 = q = \frac{1}{4}\nu^2 h^2$, and f_1 is a function of ξ, η.

17.41. Particular form of solution of (4) § 17.40. If $\chi(\xi)$, $\psi(\eta)$ are functions of ξ, η alone, respectively, the appropriate solution takes the form $\chi(\xi)\psi(\eta)$. Herein we consider a case where the temperature distribution is symmetrical about both axes of the ellipse. Thus $\psi(\eta)$ must be even and periodic in η, with period π. The only solution of (4) § 17.40 having these properties involves $ce_{2n}(\eta,q)$ as a factor. For reasons similar to those given in § 17.11, the other factor is $Ce_{2n}(\xi,q)$. Hence a formal solution of (1) § 17.40, expressed in elliptical coordinates is

$$\theta_1 = (\theta-\theta_0) = f_1(\xi,\eta)e^{-\kappa\nu^2t} = \sum_{n=0}^{\infty} C_{2n}\,Ce_{2n}(\xi,q)ce_{2n}(\eta,q)e^{-\kappa\nu^2t}. \tag{1}$$

17.42. Boundary conditions. We take the simple conditions that

(a) $\theta = 0$, $t < 0$, throughout the cylinder;

(b) $\theta = \theta_0$, $t \geqslant 0$, at the surface where $\xi = \xi_0$;

(c) $\theta \to \theta_0$, $t \to +\infty$, $0 \leqslant \xi \leqslant \xi_0$.

The problem is to determine the temperature at any internal point when $t > 0$. At the surface $\xi = \xi_0$, and when $t \geqslant 0$, $(\theta - \theta_0) = \theta_1 = 0$, so by (1) §17.41 we must have

$$\text{Ce}_{2n}(\xi_0, q) = 0. \tag{1}$$

Thus q has those values $q_{2n,m}$ which make $\text{Ce}_{2n}(\xi_0, q)$ vanish, i.e. the parametric zeros of the function. Now as $t \to -0$, $\theta = 0$, $\theta_1 = -\theta_0$, and (1) §17.41 becomes

$$-\theta_0 = \sum_{n=0}^{\infty} \sum_{m=1}^{\infty} C_{2n} \, \text{Ce}_{2n}(\xi, q_{2n,m}) \text{ce}_{2n}(\eta, q_{2n,m}), \tag{2}$$

so we have to determine the C_{2n}.

17.43. Determination of C_{2n}. We employ the orthogonality theorem in §9.40. Accordingly we multiply each side of (2) §17.42 by $\text{Ce}_{2p}(\xi, q_{2p,r}) \text{ce}_{2p}(\eta, q_{2p,r})(\cosh 2\xi - \cos 2\eta)$ and integrate with respect to η from 0 to 2π, and with respect to ξ from 0 to ξ_0. Then the r.h.s. vanishes except when $p = n$, $r = m$, so

$$-\theta_0 \int_0^{\xi_0} \int_0^{2\pi} \text{Ce}_{2n}(\xi, q_{2n,m}) \text{ce}_{2n}(\eta, q_{2n,m})(\cosh 2\xi - \cos 2\eta) \, d\xi d\eta$$

$$= C_{2n} \int_0^{\xi_0} \int_0^{2\pi} \text{Ce}_{2n}^2(\xi, q_{2n,m}) \text{ce}_{2n}^2(\eta, q_{2n,m})(\cosh 2\xi - \cos 2\eta) d\xi d\eta. \tag{1}$$

Taking individual integrals, we have (see (9) § 9.40 for Θ_{2n})

$$\int_0^{2\pi} \text{ce}_{2n}(\eta, q_{2n,m}) \cos 2\eta \, d\eta = \pi A_2^{(2n)}; \qquad \int_0^{2\pi} \text{ce}_{2n}^2(\eta, q_{2n,m}) \, d\eta = \pi;$$

$$\int_0^{2\pi} \text{ce}_{2n}(\eta, q_{2n,m}) \, d\eta = 2\pi A_0^{(2n)}; \qquad \int_0^{2\pi} \text{ce}_{2n}^2(\eta, q_{2n,m}) \cos 2\eta \, d\eta = \pi \Theta_{2n}. \tag{2}$$

Hence (1) may be written

$$-\pi\theta_0 \int_0^{\xi_0} \text{Ce}_{2n}(\xi, q_{2n,m})[2A_0^{(2n)} \cosh 2\xi - A_2^{(2n)}] \, d\xi$$

$$= \pi C_{2n} \int_0^{\xi_0} \text{Ce}_{2n}^2(\xi, q_{2n,m})[\cosh 2\xi - \Theta_{2n}] \, d\xi, \tag{3}$$

so $$C_{2n} = \frac{-\theta_0 \int_0^{\xi_0} \text{Ce}_{2n}(\xi, q_{2n,m})[2A_0^{(2n)} \cosh 2\xi - A_2^{(2n)}] \, d\xi}{\int_0^{\xi_0} \text{Ce}_{2n}^2(\xi, q_{2n,m})[\cosh 2\xi - \Theta_{2n}] \, d\xi}. \tag{4}$$

The first integral in the numerator is evaluated in § 14.10; for that in the denominator see § 14.22.

Using (4) in (1) § 17.41 we obtain

$$\theta = \theta_0 \left\{ 1 - \sum_{n=0}^{\infty} \sum_{m=1}^{\infty} e^{-\kappa v_{2n,m}^2 t} \, \mathrm{Ce}_{2n}(\xi, q_{2n,m}) \mathrm{ce}_{2n}(\eta, q_{2n,m}) \times \right. $$
$$\left. \times \frac{\int_0^{\xi_0} \mathrm{Ce}_{2n}(\xi, q_{2n,m}) [2A_0^{(2n)} \cosh 2\xi - A_2^{(2n)}] \, d\xi}{\int_0^{\xi_0} \mathrm{Ce}_{2n}^2(\xi, q_{2n,m}) [\cosh 2\xi - \Theta_{2n}] \, d\xi} \right\}, \quad (5)$$

where $v_{2n,m}^2 h^2 = 4q_{2n,m}$. This gives the temperature at any point (ξ, η) of the cross-section when $t \geqslant 0$. Since the factor in (5) involving the integrals is independent of ξ, η, (5) is a solution of (1) § 17.40 expressed in elliptical coordinates. Also (1) $\theta = \theta_0$ for $t \geqslant 0$ at the surface where $\xi = \xi_0$, since $\mathrm{Ce}_{2n}(\xi_0, q_{2n,m}) = 0$; (2) $\theta \to \theta_0$ everywhere when $t \to +\infty$, since $e^{-\kappa v_{2n,m}^2 t} \to 0$. Hence the boundary conditions (b), (c) § 17.42 are satisfied.

17.44. Transition to circular cylinder. We commence with (1) § 17.41 and by aid of Appendix I find that it degenerates to

$$\theta_1 = \sum_{n=0}^{\infty} C_{2n} p'_{2n} e^{-\kappa k_1^2 t} J_{2n}(k_1 r) \cos 2n\phi, \quad (1)$$

with $k_1 = v_{2n,m}$. Since θ_1 is now independent of ϕ, by virtue of condition (b) § 17.42, all terms in (1) must vanish except $n = 0$.† Thus

$$\theta_1 = C_0 p'_0 J_0(k_1 r) e^{-\kappa k_1^2 t}. \quad (2)$$

At the surface $r = a$, $\theta = \theta_0$, so $k_1 a = \alpha_{0,m}$, $m = 1, 2, 3, ...$, these being the roots of $J_0(k_1 a) = 0$. Also as $e \to 0$, $\xi \to +\infty$, $\sinh \xi \to \cosh \xi$, $r \to h \cosh \xi$ ($h \to 0$), $dr \to h \sinh \xi \, d\xi$ (see § 9.12),

$$\cosh 2\xi \, d\xi \to 2 \cosh \xi \sinh \xi \, d\xi \simeq 2r \, dr / h^2.$$

Using these and $\mathrm{Ce}_0(\xi, q_{0,m}) \to p'_0 J_0(\alpha_{0,m} r/a)$, $\mathrm{ce}_0(\eta, q_{0,m}) \to 2^{-\frac{1}{2}}$, $A_0^{(0)} \to 2^{-\frac{1}{2}}$, $A_2^{(0)} \to 0$, $\Theta_{2n} \to 0$, $v_{0,m}^2 \to \alpha_{0,m}^2/a^2$ (since by Appendix I, $q \to 0$ as $e \to 0$), (5) § 17.43 degenerates to

$$\theta = \theta_0 \left\{ 1 - \sum_{m=1}^{\infty} e^{-\kappa \alpha_m^2 t / a^2} J_0(\alpha_m r/a) \frac{\int_0^a r J_0(\alpha_m r/a) \, dr}{\int_0^a r J_0^2(\alpha_m r/a) \, dr} \right\}, \quad (3)$$

where α_m has been written for $\alpha_{0,m}$.

Now
$$\int_0^a r J_0(\alpha_m r/a) \, dr = \frac{a^2}{\alpha_m} J_1(\alpha_m), \quad (4)$$

---

† A mathematical proof is given in [135].

and

$$\int_0^a rJ_0^2(\alpha_m r/a)\,dr = \tfrac{1}{2}a^2[J_1^2(\alpha_m)+J_0^2(\alpha_m)] = \tfrac{1}{2}a^2J_1^2(\alpha_m), \tag{5}$$

since $J_0(\alpha_m) = 0$. Substituting from (4), (5) into (3) leads to the well-known result for a circular cylinder, namely,

$$\theta = \theta_0\Big[1-2\sum_{m=1}^{\infty}\frac{J_0(\alpha_m r/a)}{\alpha_m J_1(\alpha_m)}e^{-\kappa\alpha_m^2 t/a^2}\Big]. \tag{6}$$

17.50. An electromagnetic problem analogous to heat conduction [135]. The problems in § 17.10 and § 17.40 are analogous, provided the conditions are analogous. For the electromagnetic problem they are as follow:

(a) $H = 0$, $t < 0$, throughout the metal core;

(b) $H = H_0 = 4\pi nI_0/l$, $t \geqslant 0$, at the surface where $\xi = \xi_0$;

(c) $H \to H_0$, $t \to +\infty$, $0 \leqslant \xi \leqslant \xi_0$.

Interpreted physically these conditions imply that at $t = 0$ a battery is connected to the solenoid through a high resistance R, such that the time taken for the current to attain a substantially steady value I_0 is small enough to be ignored. Thus for analytical purposes the current-time relationship is represented by Heaviside's unit function. The problem is to find H at any point of the cross-section of the metal core, and thence to calculate the inductance (variable) of the solenoid due to the core alone, when $t > 0$.

The differential equation for H is (1) § 17.10. If in (1) § 17.40 we write H for θ and $4\pi\mu/\rho$ for $1/\kappa$, the two equations are alike. Hence *mutatis mutandis*, (1) § 17.41 is a formal solution of (1) § 17.10, so we have

$$H-H_0 = \sum_{n=0}^{\infty} C_{2n}\,\mathrm{Ce}_{2n}(\xi,q)\mathrm{ce}_{2n}(\eta,q)e^{-\rho\nu^2 t/4\pi\mu}. \tag{1}$$

The solution which satisfies the above boundary conditions is (5) § 17.43, with H written for θ. Thus we get

$$H = \frac{4\pi nI_0}{l}\Big[1-\sum_{n=0}^{\infty}\sum_{m=1}^{\infty}e^{-\rho\nu_{2n,m}^2 t/4\pi\mu}\,\mathrm{Ce}_{2n}(\xi,q_{2n,m})\mathrm{ce}_{2n}(\eta,q_{2n,m})\times$$
$$\times\frac{\displaystyle\int_0^{\xi_0}\mathrm{Ce}_{2n}(\xi)[A_0^{(2n)}\cosh 2\xi-A_0^{(2n)}]\,d\xi}{\displaystyle\int_0^{\xi_0}\mathrm{Ce}_{2n}^2(\xi)[\cosh 2\xi-\Theta_{2n}]\,d\xi}\Big]. \tag{2}$$

When the ellipse tends to a circle, this expression degenerates to a known form for a metal core of circular cross-section [204; (4) p. 242].

17.51. Inductance due to core flux alone. This is defined to be the flux interlinkage due to magnetization of the core, when unit current (unidirectional) flows in the n turn winding. If Φ is the total *core*† flux, then

$$L = \Phi n/I_0 = \frac{\mu n}{I_0} \int\int H \, ds_1 ds_2, \tag{1}$$

where $ds_1 ds_2$ is an elemental area of cross-section. Now by §9.12

$$ds_1 = \frac{h}{2^{\frac{1}{2}}} (\cosh 2\xi - \cos 2\eta)^{\frac{1}{2}} \, d\xi \tag{2}$$

and

$$ds_2 = \frac{h}{2^{\frac{1}{2}}} (\cosh 2\xi - \cos 2\eta)^{\frac{1}{2}} \, d\eta, \tag{3}$$

so

$$L = \frac{h^2 \mu n}{2I_0} \int_0^{\xi_0} \int_0^{2\pi} H (\cosh 2\xi - \cos 2\eta) \, d\xi d\eta. \tag{4}$$

Substituting for H from (2) §17.50 into (4) and using the analysis in §17.43 leads to

$$L = \frac{4\pi^2 n^2 ab\mu}{l} \left[1 - \frac{h^2}{2ab} \sum_{n=0}^{\infty} \sum_{m=1}^{\infty} e^{-\rho \nu_{2n,m}^2 l/4\pi\mu} \times \right.$$
$$\left. \times \frac{\left\{ \int_0^{\xi_0} \mathrm{Ce}_{2n}(\xi, q_{2n,m})[2A_0^{(2n)} \cosh 2\xi - A_2^{(2n)}] \, d\xi \right\}^2}{\int_0^{\xi_0} \mathrm{Ce}_{2n}^2(\xi, q_{2n,m})[\cosh 2\xi - \Theta_{2n}] \, d\xi} \right]. \tag{5}$$

For evaluation of some of the integrals, see §§14.10, 14.22.

When the ellipse tends to a circle, (5) degenerates to a known form [204; (13) p. 281].

---

† The flux in the air space between the core and the winding is not included in (1).

ELECTROMAGNETIC WAVE GUIDES

18.10. Introduction. From 1888, when electromagnetic waves were first demonstrated, till about 1936, attention was concentrated chiefly on their propagation in the atmosphere surrounding the earth. It is possible, however, to confine electromagnetic waves to the air space *within* a metal tube. Propagation of this nature was treated experimentally and theoretically more than half a century ago. The subject has been retrieved from the academical archives, owing to developments in ultra high-frequency technique. There are now ultra high-frequency electronic devices for generating frequencies exceeding 3×10^9 cycles per second, i.e. wave-lengths less than 10 cm. Analysis has revealed that if the electromagnetic power is transmitted to an aerial by a *transmission line*, e.g. a parallel wire or a coaxial cylinder system, the loss† exceeds appreciably that incurred when the power is transmitted as *electromagnetic waves through the air in a uniform highly conducting tube*. Since the power is confined within the tube, it is guided, so the tube is called a wave guide. The subject has now attained considerable importance, and deserves detailed treatment here. Moreover, we shall not confine our analysis to the case where Mathieu functions are involved, but lead up to it from two simpler cases, thereby introducing a difficult subject gradually. References to numerous papers dealing with wave guides will be found in [200].

18.11. Rectangular wave guide. Analytically this is the simplest case. The convention adopted for cartesian coordinates is illustrated in Fig. 40, the z-axis being parallel to the axis of the guide and constituting the inner left lower corner. At the near end, containing the origin O, we suppose that there is a device for exciting electromagnetic waves, which are propagated parallel to the z-axis, in the direction of the arrow. We assume that the guide is so long that the influence of reflection from the far end at an intermediate point may be disregarded. Alternatively we may consider the guide to be relatively short, but terminated at its far end by an appropriate

† Expressed as a percentage of the input power at the transmitting end of the line.

impedance, such that reflection is negligible, as is the case in practice. Moreover, the transmission is unidirectional.

Power is transmitted down the guide in one or more of the 'modes' to which the system responds.† To investigate these we have to solve Maxwell's equations for the electromagnetic field, subject to the particular condition which obtains at the inner surface of the guide. Unless we postulate absence of loss due to eddy currents in

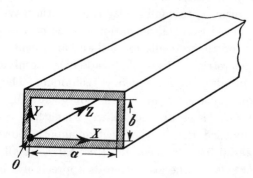

FIG. 40. Coordinate system in rectangular wave guide.

the wall of the guide, it is difficult to formulate a precise boundary condition.‡ Assuming zero resistivity for the metal of the guide, the condition is that the tangential component of the electric field in the air must vanish at the inner surface.

18.20. Maxwell's equations. For an isotropic non-conducting dielectric of permeability μ and dielectric constant ϵ, the 'curl' equations in vector form (heavy type) are

$$\epsilon \frac{\partial \mathbf{E}}{\partial t} = \text{curl}\,\mathbf{H}, \tag{1}$$

$$\mu \frac{\partial \mathbf{H}}{\partial t} = -\text{curl}\,\mathbf{E}, \tag{2}$$

where $\mathbf{E}$ designates an electric, and $\mathbf{H}$ a magnetic force space vector.

The vectors $\mathbf{E}$ and $\mathbf{H}$ can each be resolved into components parallel to the axes X, Y, Z of Fig. 40. Let the scalar components be denoted

---

† For power to be propagated down the guide, it may be shown using § 18.24 that the width must be $> \frac{1}{2}\lambda$, where λ is the wavelength in an *unbounded* dielectric.

‡ Loss in the dielectric (air) is also assumed to be zero, i.e. it is a perfect insulator.

by E_x, E_y, E_z, and H_x, H_y, H_z, respectively. Then in terms of cartesian coordinates, (1) yields the equations:

$$\epsilon \frac{\partial E_x}{\partial t} = -\frac{\partial H_y}{\partial z} + \frac{\partial H_z}{\partial y}, \tag{3}$$

$$\epsilon \frac{\partial E_y}{\partial t} = -\frac{\partial H_z}{\partial x} + \frac{\partial H_x}{\partial z}, \tag{4}$$

$$\epsilon \frac{\partial E_z}{\partial t} = -\frac{\partial H_x}{\partial y} + \frac{\partial H_y}{\partial x}. \tag{5}$$

To aid memorization it should be observed that in (1), (2) **E** and **H** are interchanged, ϵ is on the l.h.s. with **E**, and μ on the l.h.s. with **H**, but with a negative curl. Equations (3)–(5) come from (1), and their subscripts are in cyclic order. The subscripts and coordinates (in denominators) in the last two members of each equation are interchanged. Thus by memorizing (1)–(3) all formulae of the set (3)–(8) may be written down.

For the components of magnetic force we have from (2)—using (3) as a pattern—

$$\mu \frac{\partial H_x}{\partial t} = \frac{\partial E_y}{\partial z} - \frac{\partial E_z}{\partial y}, \tag{6}$$

$$\mu \frac{\partial H_y}{\partial t} = \frac{\partial E_z}{\partial x} - \frac{\partial E_x}{\partial z}, \tag{7}$$

$$\mu \frac{\partial H_z}{\partial t} = \frac{\partial E_x}{\partial y} - \frac{\partial E_y}{\partial x}. \tag{8}$$

18.21. Cosinusoidal variation of E and H. It is expedient to make this choice so that various transmission modes may be segregated. At any section distant z from O in Fig. 40 the electric and magnetic force vectors are in phase and vary in accordance with the real part of $e^{i\omega t}$. If the phase at any z is referred to O, account must be taken of the velocity of *phase* propagation down the guide. The instantaneous distribution of **E** and **H** along the guide depends upon the real part of $e^{i\omega t}e^{-i\beta z}$, i.e. $\cos(\omega t - \beta z)$, where β is a coefficient such that βz defines the phase at z with respect to its value at O. For transmission of power down the guide, it can be shown that β must be real [see 210].

18.22. Simplification of equations in § 18.20. This is effected by writing $i\omega$ for $\partial/\partial t$, and $-i\beta$ for $\partial/\partial z$, in accordance with § 18.21. Then (3)–(8) § 18.20 become

$$i\omega\epsilon E_x = i\beta H_y + \frac{\partial H_z}{\partial y}, \tag{1}$$

$$i\omega\epsilon E_y = -\frac{\partial H_z}{\partial x} - i\beta H_x, \tag{2}$$

$$i\omega\epsilon E_z = -\frac{\partial H_x}{\partial y} + \frac{\partial H_y}{\partial x}, \tag{3}$$

$$i\omega\mu H_x = -i\beta E_y - \frac{\partial E_z}{\partial y}, \tag{4}$$

$$i\omega\mu H_y = \frac{\partial E_z}{\partial x} + i\beta E_x, \tag{5}$$

$$i\omega\mu H_z = \frac{\partial E_x}{\partial y} - \frac{\partial E_y}{\partial x}. \tag{6}$$

Substituting for iE_y from (2) into (4), and for iE_x from (1) into (5), gives

$$k_1^2 H_x = -i\beta\frac{\partial H_z}{\partial x} + i\omega\epsilon\frac{\partial E_z}{\partial y} \tag{7}$$

and

$$k_1^2 H_y = -i\beta\frac{\partial H_z}{\partial y} - i\omega\epsilon\frac{\partial E_z}{\partial x}, \tag{8}$$

where $k_1^2 = \mu\epsilon\omega^2 - \beta^2 = (\omega/c)^2 - \beta^2$ and $c = 1/(\mu\epsilon)^{\frac{1}{2}}$, the velocity of light. Substituting for iH_y from (5) into (1), and for iH_x from (4) into (2), gives

$$k_1^2 E_x = -i\beta\frac{\partial E_z}{\partial x} - i\omega\mu\frac{\partial H_z}{\partial y} \tag{9}$$

and

$$k_1^2 E_y = -i\beta\frac{\partial E_z}{\partial y} + i\omega\mu\frac{\partial H_z}{\partial x}. \tag{10}$$

Using (7), (8) in (3) for H_x, H_y leads to the two-dimensional wave equation

$$\frac{\partial^2 E_z}{\partial x^2} + \frac{\partial^2 E_z}{\partial y^2} + k_1^2 E_z = 0. \tag{11}$$

Similarly from (9), (10), and (6), we obtain

$$\frac{\partial^2 H_z}{\partial x^2} + \frac{\partial^2 H_z}{\partial y^2} + k_1^2 H_z = 0. \tag{12}$$

18.23. Solution of (11) § 18.22. Write $E_z = \psi(x)\xi(y)$, where ψ is a function of x alone, and ξ is a function of y alone. Then

$$\xi\frac{d^2\psi}{dx^2} + \psi\frac{d^2\xi}{dy^2} = -k_1^2\psi\xi, \qquad (1)$$

where $k_1^2 = (\omega/c)^2 - \beta^2$. Dividing throughout by $\psi\xi$, (1) becomes

$$\frac{1}{\psi}\frac{d^2\psi}{dx^2} + k_1^2 = -\frac{1}{\xi}\frac{d^2\xi}{dy^2}. \qquad (2)$$

Introducing a separation constant l^2, as in § 9.21, we obtain two ordinary differential equations, namely,

$$\frac{d^2\psi}{dx^2} + (k_1^2 - l^2)\psi = 0 \qquad (3)$$

and

$$\frac{d^2\xi}{dy^2} + l^2\xi = 0. \qquad (4)$$

The formal solutions of (3), (4) are: (a) $\cos[x(k_1^2 - l^2)^{\frac{1}{2}}]$, $\sin[x(k_1^2 - l^2)^{\frac{1}{2}}]$; (b) $\cos ly$, $\sin ly$, respectively. From these we have to construct a solution which satisfies the boundary condition $E_z = 0$, at the inner plane faces of the guide, i.e. at $x = 0, a$; $y = 0, b$. Since $\cos(0) = 1$, the cosine solutions are inadmissible, so we take

$$E_z = \psi\xi = A\sin[x(k_1^2 - l^2)^{\frac{1}{2}}]\sin ly, \qquad (5)$$

A being an arbitrary constant. Now E_z vanishes when $x = 0$ or $y = 0$. For it to vanish at $x = a$, $y = b$, we must have, respectively, $a(k_1^2 - l^2)^{\frac{1}{2}} = m\pi$, $bl = n\pi$, m and n being any positive integers. Then ·eliminating l by squaring and adding, we get

$$k_1^2 = \pi^2\left[\left(\frac{m}{a}\right)^2 + \left(\frac{n}{b}\right)^2\right]. \qquad (6)$$

Selecting the real part of the phase factor $e^{i(\omega t - \beta z)}$, an appropriate solution of (11) § 18.22 is

$$E_z = A\sin\frac{\pi m x}{a}\sin\frac{\pi n y}{b}\cos(\omega t - \beta z). \qquad (7)$$

This defines a wave system in the rectangular guide. By assigning integral values to m, n the modes of transmission may be specified. There is, however, a limitation associated with β, which we shall now investigate.

18.24. Cut-off or critical pulsatance. Since $\beta^2 = (\omega/c)^2 - k_1^2$, from (6) § 18.23 we get

$$\beta^2 = (\omega/c)^2 - \pi^2[(m/a)^2 + (n/b)^2]. \qquad (1)$$

For power to be transmitted down the guide, β must be real [210], so it follows that

$$\omega > \pi c[(m/a)^2+(n/b)^2]^{\frac{1}{2}}. \tag{2}$$

Hence, if m, n be assigned, there is a pulsatance

$$\omega_c = \pi c[(m/a)^2+(n/b)^2]^{\frac{1}{2}}, \tag{3}$$

below which transmission of power ceases. This is termed the cut-off or critical pulsatance, and it corresponds to $\beta = 0$. Its value depends for a given guide upon m, n. If ω is fixed but exceeds ω_c, there is only a finite number of m, n combinations (modes of transmission) for which the inequality can be satisfied.

18.25. E or transverse magnetic wave. (11), (12) § 18.22 are two linearly independent equations, so the solution of (11) holds if that of (12) is $H_z \equiv 0$, which implies $\partial H_z/\partial x \equiv 0 \equiv \partial H_z/\partial y$. Then from (9), (10) § 18.22

$$E_x = -\frac{i\beta}{k_1^2}\frac{\partial E_z}{\partial x}; \quad \text{and} \quad E_y = -\frac{i\beta}{k_1^2}\frac{\partial E_z}{\partial y}. \tag{1}$$

Applying these to (7) § 18.23 yields, using $e^{i(\omega t-\beta z)}$ for $\cos(\omega t-\beta z)$, $-i = e^{-\frac{1}{2}\pi i}$, and taking the real part,

$$E_x = A\frac{\beta}{k_1^2}\frac{\pi m}{a}\cos\frac{\pi m x}{a}\sin\frac{\pi n y}{b}\sin(\omega t-\beta z);$$

$$E_y = A\frac{\beta}{k_1^2}\frac{\pi n}{b}\sin\frac{\pi m x}{a}\cos\frac{\pi n y}{b}\sin(\omega t-\beta z). \tag{2}$$

Also from (1), (2) § 18.22

$$H_x = -(\omega\epsilon/\beta)E_y; \qquad H_y = (\omega\epsilon/\beta)E_x. \tag{3}$$

Collecting the six results, we have

$$E_x = A(\beta/k_1^2)(\pi m/a)\cos(\pi m x/a)\sin(\pi n y/b)\sin(\omega t-\beta z), \tag{4}$$

$$E_y = A(\beta/k_1^2)(\pi n/b)\sin(\pi m x/a)\cos(\pi n y/b)\sin(\omega t-\beta z), \tag{5}$$

$$E_z = A\sin(\pi m x/a)\sin(\pi n y/b)\cos(\omega t-\beta z); \tag{6}$$

$$H_x = -A(\omega\epsilon/k_1^2)(\pi n/b)\sin(\pi m x/a)\cos(\pi n y/b)\sin(\omega t-\beta z), \tag{7}$$

$$H_y = A(\omega\epsilon/k_1^2)(\pi m/a)\cos(\pi m x/a)\sin(\pi n y/b)\sin(\omega t-\beta z), \tag{8}$$

$$H_z \equiv 0. \tag{9}$$

In the type of wave to which these results refer, the electric force at any non-boundary point has components in the x, y, z directions. The magnetic force, however, has components in the x, y directions only, so it is wholly transverse to the direction of propagation. For this reason the wave is called an E or *transverse magnetic type*. It may conveniently be denoted by the symbol $E_{m,n}$, m, n indicating the particular mode of transmission. When $m = 0$ for any n, or vice versa, (4)–(8) vanish. Hence transverse magnetic waves of the types $E_{0,n}$, $E_{m,0}$ do not exist. The lowest mode possible is with $m = n = 1$, i.e. $E_{1,1}$, which has the lowest cut-off frequency.

18.26. H or transverse electric wave. The linear independence of (11), (12) § 18.22 permits us to take $E_z \equiv 0$, which implies $\partial E_z/\partial x \equiv 0 \equiv \partial E_z/\partial y$. Then from (9), (10) § 18.22

$$\frac{\partial H_z}{\partial y} = \frac{ik_1^2}{\omega\mu} E_x; \qquad \frac{\partial H_z}{\partial x} = -\frac{ik_1^2}{\omega\mu} E_y. \tag{1}$$

Since $E_x = 0$ at $y = 0, b$, whilst $E_y = 0$ at $x = 0, a$, it follows from (1) that the appropriate conditions to be satisfied by H_z are

$$\partial H_z/\partial y = 0 \quad \text{at } y = 0, b; \qquad \partial H_z/\partial x = 0 \quad \text{at } x = 0, a. \tag{2}$$

Referring back to § 18.23 we now use the cosine solutions of (12) § 18.22 and obtain, with an arbitrary constant B,

$$H_z = B \cos\frac{\pi mx}{a} \cos\frac{\pi ny}{b} \cos(\omega t - \beta z), \tag{3}$$

which satisfies the conditions (2).

Then from (7), (8) § 18.22

$$H_x = -\frac{i\beta}{k_1^2}\frac{\partial H_z}{\partial x}; \qquad H_y = -\frac{i\beta}{k_1^2}\frac{\partial H_z}{\partial y}, \tag{4}$$

while from (4), (5) § 18.22

$$E_x = \frac{\omega\mu}{\beta} H_y; \qquad E_y = -\frac{\mu\omega}{\beta} H_x. \tag{5}$$

Applying (4), (5) to (3), we obtain

$$E_x = -B\frac{\omega\mu}{k_1^2}\frac{\pi n}{b}\cos\frac{\pi mx}{a}\sin\frac{\pi ny}{b}\sin(\omega t - \beta z), \tag{6}$$

$$E_y = B\frac{\mu\omega}{k_1^2}\frac{\pi m}{a}\sin\frac{\pi mx}{a}\cos\frac{\pi ny}{b}\sin(\omega t - \beta z), \tag{7}$$

$$E_z \equiv 0; \tag{8}$$

$$H_x = -B\frac{\beta}{k_1^2}\frac{\pi m}{a}\sin\frac{\pi mx}{a}\cos\frac{\pi ny}{b}\sin(\omega t - \beta z), \tag{9}$$

$$H_y = -B\frac{\beta}{k_1^2}\frac{\pi n}{b}\cos\frac{\pi mx}{a}\sin\frac{\pi ny}{b}\sin(\omega t - \beta z), \tag{10}$$

$$H_z = B\cos\frac{\pi mx}{a}\cos\frac{\pi ny}{b}\cos(\omega t - \beta z). \tag{11}$$

In the type of wave to which these results pertain, the magnetic force at any non-boundary point has components in the x, y, z

directions. The electric force, however, has components in the x, y directions only, so it is wholly transverse to the direction of propagation. For this reason the wave is called an H or *transverse electric*

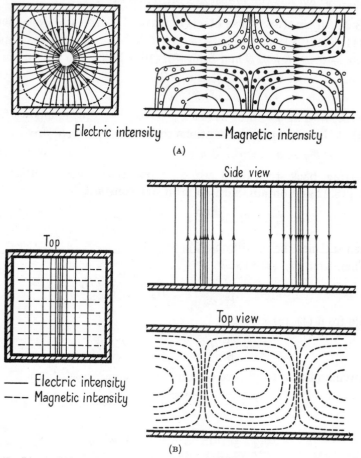

Fig. 41. Lines of electric (——) and magnetic force (– – – –) in rectangular wave guide: (A) $E_{1,1}$ wave; (B) $H_{1,0}$ wave.

type. It may conveniently be denoted by the symbol $H_{m,n}$, m, n indicating the particular mode of transmission. When $m = n = 0$, all components in (6)–(11) vanish except H_z. Since the electric and magnetic components cannot exist independently, there is no wave of type $H_{0,0}$. But if $m = 0$, $n = 1$, or $m = 1$, $n = 0$, the waves exist. If $b > a$, the $H_{0,1}$ wave has the lowest cut-off frequency, but if $b < a$, $H_{1,0}$ possesses this attribute, as will be evident from (3) § 18.24.

The lines of electric and magnetic force in a rectangular wave guide are illustrated in Fig. 41.

18.30. Orthogonal curvilinear coordinates. In solving Maxwell's equations for the electromagnetic field, the equations for the components of electric and magnetic force must be expressed in terms of the appropriate coordinates. For a rectangular wave guide, the equations may be written down immediately in cartesian coordinates. When the guide has a curved cross-section it is expedient

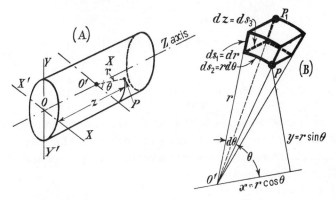

FIG. 42. Orthogonal curvilinear coordinates.

to employ orthogonal curvilinear coordinates. These are determined by the common point of three surfaces which intersect mutually at right angles. This may be illustrated by aid of Fig. 42 which refers to the cylindrical polar coordinates r, θ, z. The point P is the common intersection of (1) the curved surface of the cylinder of radius r, (2) a plane through P perpendicular to the axis Oz, (3) a plane containing Oz and passing through P. These three surfaces intersect orthogonally. Then from Fig. 42 A, B we see that $x = r\cos\theta$, $y = r\sin\theta$, $z = z$ itself. The lengths of the edges of the elemental solid in Fig. 42 B are, respectively, dr, $r\,d\theta$, and dz. The first and third are straight, but the second is *curved*.

Now consider the coordinates from a general viewpoint (each of the three *curves* at the intersection having finite curvature), and let them be $\varphi_1, \varphi_2, \varphi_3$, respectively. The lengths of the edges of the solid are $ds_1 = l_1\,d\varphi_1$, $ds_2 = l_2\,d\varphi_2$, $ds_3 = l_3\,d\varphi_3$, where l_1, l_2, l_3 are multiplying factors depending upon the particular system of coordinates. In general they will vary with the position of P in space. For cylindrical polars $\varphi_1 = r$, $\varphi_2 = \theta$, $\varphi_3 = z$, $ds_1 = dr$, $ds_2 = r\,d\theta$, $ds_3 = dz$; so $l_1 = 1$, $l_2 = r$, and $l_3 = 1$. For elliptical coordinates, Fig. 16, $\varphi_1 = \xi$, $\varphi_2 = \eta$, $\varphi_3 = z$; so by (4) § 9.12, $l_1 = l_2 = h[(\cosh 2\xi - \cos 2\eta)/2]^{\frac{1}{2}}$, and since $z = z$, $l_3 = 1$.

18.31. Vector differential formulae.

We now introduce general formulae by means of which the scalar components A_1, A_2, A_3 of a vector quantity $\mathbf{A}$ may be expressed in terms of orthogonal curvilinear coordinates:

$$(\text{curl }\mathbf{A})_1 = \frac{1}{l_2 l_3}\left[-\frac{\partial(l_2 A_2)}{\partial \varphi_3} + \frac{\partial(l_3 A_3)}{\partial \varphi_2}\right], \tag{1}$$

$$(\text{curl }\mathbf{A})_2 = \frac{1}{l_3 l_1}\left[-\frac{\partial(l_3 A_3)}{\partial \varphi_1} + \frac{\partial(l_1 A_1)}{\partial \varphi_3}\right], \tag{2}$$

and

$$(\text{curl }\mathbf{A})_3 = \frac{1}{l_1 l_2}\left[-\frac{\partial(l_1 A_1)}{\partial \varphi_2} + \frac{\partial(l_2 A_2)}{\partial \varphi_1}\right]. \tag{3}$$

As an aid to memorization, note that, (a) the A occur in cyclic order, (b) the subscript on the l.h.s. does not occur on the r.h.s., (c) the subscripts on the r.h.s. are interchanged in denominator and numerator of the two differentials.

In the wave guides treated herein $l_3 = 1$, $\partial/\partial \varphi_3 = \partial/\partial z$ may be replaced (as in § 18.22) by $-i\beta$, whilst $A_3 = A_z$. Thus (1)–(3) become

$$(\text{curl }\mathbf{A})_1 = i\beta A_2 + \frac{1}{l_2}\frac{\partial A_z}{\partial \varphi_2}, \tag{4}$$

$$(\text{curl }\mathbf{A})_2 = -\frac{1}{l_1}\frac{\partial A_z}{\partial \varphi_1} - i\beta A_1, \tag{5}$$

and

$$(\text{curl }\mathbf{A})_z = \frac{1}{l_1 l_2}\left\{-\frac{\partial(l_1 A_1)}{\partial \varphi_2} + \frac{\partial(l_2 A_2)}{\partial \varphi_1}\right\}. \tag{6}$$

These three formulae enable us to write down the components of the electric and magnetic fields for *any* type of uniform cylindrical wave guide.

18.32. Form of general differential equation.

From (1), (2) § 18.20 and (4), (5), (6) § 18.31 we obtain

$$i\omega\epsilon E_1 = i\beta H_2 + \frac{1}{l_2}\frac{\partial H_z}{\partial \varphi_2}, \tag{1}$$

$$i\omega\epsilon E_2 = -\frac{1}{l_1}\frac{\partial H_z}{\partial \varphi_1} - i\beta H_1, \tag{2}$$

$$i\omega\epsilon E_z = \frac{1}{l_1 l_2}\left\{-\frac{\partial(l_1 H_1)}{\partial\varphi_2}+\frac{\partial(l_2 H_2)}{\partial\varphi_1}\right\};\tag{3}$$

$$i\mu\omega H_1 = -i\beta E_2 - \frac{1}{l_2}\frac{\partial E_z}{\partial\varphi_2},\tag{4}$$

$$i\mu\omega H_2 = \frac{1}{l_1}\frac{\partial E_z}{\partial\varphi_1}+i\beta E_1,\tag{5}$$

$$i\mu\omega H_z = \frac{1}{l_1 l_2}\left\{\frac{\partial(l_1 E_1)}{\partial\varphi_2}-\frac{\partial(l_2 E_2)}{\partial\varphi_1}\right\}.\tag{6}$$

Substituting from (4) into (2) for iE_2 gives

$$k_1^2 H_1 = i\left\{\frac{\omega\epsilon}{l_2}\frac{\partial E_z}{\partial\varphi_2}-\frac{\beta}{l_1}\frac{\partial H_z}{\partial\varphi_1}\right\},\tag{7}$$

with $k_1^2 = (\omega/c)^2-\beta^2$.

Substituting from (5) into (1) for iE_1 gives

$$k_1^2 H_2 = -i\left\{\frac{\omega\epsilon}{l_1}\frac{\partial E_z}{\partial\varphi_1}+\frac{\beta}{l_2}\frac{\partial H_z}{\partial\varphi_2}\right\}.\tag{8}$$

Using the values of H_1, H_2 from (7), (8) in (3) leads to the general differential equation

$$\frac{1}{l_1^2}\frac{\partial^2 E_z}{\partial\varphi_1^2}+\frac{1}{l_2^2}\frac{\partial^2 E_z}{\partial\varphi_2^2}+\frac{1}{l_1 l_2}\left\{\frac{\partial(l_2/l_1)}{\partial\varphi_1}\frac{\partial E_z}{\partial\varphi_1}+\frac{\partial(l_1/l_2)}{\partial\varphi_2}\frac{\partial E_z}{\partial\varphi_2}\right\}+k_1^2 E_z = 0.\tag{9}$$

In like manner an identical equation can be deduced for H_z.

18.33. General formulae for E waves. In accordance with § 18.25 we put $H_z \equiv 0$. Then from (1), (2) § 18.32 we get

$$E_1 = \frac{\beta}{\omega\epsilon}H_2\tag{1}$$

and

$$E_2 = -\frac{\beta}{\omega\epsilon}H_1.\tag{2}$$

By (7), (8) § 18.32

$$H_1 = \frac{i\omega\epsilon}{k_1^2 l_2}\frac{\partial E_z}{\partial\varphi_2}\tag{3}$$

and

$$H_2 = -\frac{i\omega\epsilon}{k_1^2 l_1}\frac{\partial E_z}{\partial\varphi_1}.\tag{4}$$

From (1), (4) and (2), (3) we have

$$E_1 = -\frac{i\beta}{k_1^2 l_1}\frac{\partial E_z}{\partial\varphi_1}\tag{5}$$

and

$$E_2 = -\frac{i\beta}{k_1^2 l_2}\frac{\partial E_z}{\partial\varphi_2}.\tag{6}$$

Hence if E_z is determined from (9) § 18.32, the remaining components follow immediately from (3)–(6).

18.34. General formulae for H waves. In accordance with § 18.26 we put $E_z \equiv 0$. Then from (5), (4) § 18.32

$$E_1 = \frac{\mu\omega H_2}{\beta} \tag{1}$$

and

$$E_2 = -\frac{\mu\omega H_1}{\beta}. \tag{2}$$

By (7), (8) § 18.32

$$H_1 = -\frac{i\beta}{k_1^2 l_1} \frac{\partial H_z}{\partial \varphi_1} \tag{3}$$

and

$$H_2 = -\frac{i\beta}{k_1^2 l_2} \frac{\partial H_z}{\partial \varphi_2}. \tag{4}$$

From (1), (4) and (2), (3)

$$E_1 = -\frac{i\mu\omega}{k_1^2 l_2} \frac{\partial H_z}{\partial \varphi_2} \tag{5}$$

and

$$E_2 = \frac{i\mu\omega}{k_1^2 l_1} \frac{\partial H_z}{\partial \varphi_1}. \tag{6}$$

Hence, if H_z is determined from (9) § 18.32, the remaining components follow immediately from (3)–(6).

Having derived general formulae from E and H waves, we are now in a position to obtain the scalar components of the electric and magnetic forces in any uniform cylindrical wave guide whose cross-section is expressible in terms of two orthogonal curvilinear coordinates.

18.40. Application of formulae in preceding sections to circular wave guide. Referring to § 18.30 we have $\varphi_1 = r$, $\varphi_2 = \theta$, $l_1 = 1$, $l_2 = r$, so $\partial(l_1/l_2)/\partial\varphi_2 = \partial(1/r)/\partial\theta = 0$, and (9) § 18.32 becomes

$$\frac{\partial^2 E_z}{\partial r^2} + \frac{1}{r} \frac{\partial E_z}{\partial r} + \frac{1}{r^2} \frac{\partial^2 E_z}{\partial \theta^2} + k_1^2 E_z = 0. \tag{1}$$

Assume that $E_z = \zeta(r)\chi(\theta)$, where ζ is a function of r alone, and χ one of θ alone. Proceeding as in § 9.21 we get

$$\frac{r^2}{\zeta} \frac{d^2\zeta}{dr^2} + \frac{r}{\zeta} \frac{d\zeta}{dr} + r^2 k_1^2 = -\frac{1}{\chi} \frac{d^2\chi}{d\theta^2} = m^2, \quad \text{say,} \tag{2}$$

m^2 being the separation constant. Then the equation for ζ is

$$\frac{d^2\zeta}{dr^2} + \frac{1}{r} \frac{d\zeta}{dr} + \left(k_1^2 - \frac{m^2}{r^2}\right)\zeta = 0, \tag{3}$$

which is the standard differential equation for the Bessel functions of the two kinds of order m, namely, $J_m(k_1 r)$, $Y_m(k_1 r)$. Now E_z must be finite on the axis of the guide, but $Y_m(0) = -\infty$, so the Y solution is inadmissible, and we retain only $J_m(k_1 r)$.

The equation for χ is

$$\frac{d^2\chi}{d\theta^2} + m^2\chi = 0, \tag{4}$$

whose formal solutions $\cos m\theta$, $\sin m\theta$ are appropriate here. Accordingly as a composite solution of (1), with two arbitrary constants, we take

$$\zeta_m \chi_m = J_m(k_1 r)[\bar{A}_m \cos m\theta + \bar{B}_m \sin m\theta] = A_m J_m(k_1 r)\cos(m\theta - \alpha_m), \tag{5}$$

where $A_m = (\bar{A}_m^2 + \bar{B}_m^2)^{\frac{1}{2}}$, $\alpha_m = \tan^{-1}(\bar{B}_m/\bar{A}_m)$. By suitable choice of datum line for θ we can, without loss of generality, write $m\theta$ for $(m\theta - \alpha_m)$. Then a formal solution of (1) is

$$E_{z_m} = A_m J_m(k_1 r)\cos m\theta \cos(\omega t - \beta z). \tag{6}$$

Now E_{z_m} is single-valued and periodic in the coordinate θ, so we must have $\cos m\theta = \cos m(\theta + 2\pi)$. Hence m must be an integer, and since $J_m = (-1)^m J_{-m}$, we need consider positive integers only. Then (6) is a solution of (1) for $m \geqslant 0$, so a complete formal solution for the problem under consideration is

$$E_z = \sum_{m=0}^{\infty} A_m J_m(k_1 r)\cos(m\theta - \alpha_m), \tag{7}$$

the time factor being omitted.

The boundary condition is $E_z = 0$ when $r = a$ at the inner surface of the guide. Hence $J_m(k_1 a) = 0$, so that $k_1 a$ must be a positive real zero of the B.F. of order m. For each m the B.F. has an infinite number of zeros, i.e. writing $k_{m,r}$ for k_1, $J_m(k_{m,r} a) = 0$ for $r = 1$, 2, 3,.... Also there are an infinite number of B.F. corresponding to $m = 0$, 1, 2,.... Hence a double infinity of zeros is obtained. For power to be transmitted down the guide, by [210] β must be real. But $\beta^2 = (\omega/c)^2 - k_{m,r}^2$, so for the reality of β we must have $\omega/c > k_{m,r}$. Hence for each m, power is transmitted only in those modes, finite in number, for which ω satisfies this inequality.

If $m = 0$, the first zero [203, p. 9] occurs when $k_{0,1} a = 2\cdot405$, so $k_{0,1} = 2\cdot405 a^{-1}$. Then for an $E_{0,1}$ wave

$$E_{z_{0,1}} = A_0 J_0(k_{0,1} r)\cos(\omega t - \beta z). \tag{8}$$

Now $\beta^2 = (\omega/c)^2 - k_{0,1}^2$, so the cut-off or lowest possible frequency for an $E_{0,1}$ wave in an air dielectric is ($\beta = 0$),

$$\omega_c/2\pi = k_{0,1}c/2\pi = 2 \cdot 405 \times 3 \times 10^{10}/2\pi a = 1 \cdot 15 \times 10^{10}/a$$

cycles per second if a is in centimetres. This is equivalent to a wave-length of $2 \cdot 62a$ cm. in free space.

E waves in circular guide. Applying the formulae in § 18.33 to (6), and including the time factor, leads to the following results:

$$E_r = A_m \frac{\beta}{k_1} J'_m(k_1 r)\cos m\theta \sin(\omega t - \beta z), \tag{9}$$

$$E_\theta = -\frac{A_m \beta m}{k_1^2 r} J_m(k_1 r)\sin m\theta \sin(\omega t - \beta z), \tag{10}$$

$$E_z = A_m J_m(k_1 r)\cos m\theta \cos(\omega t - \beta z); \tag{11}$$

$$H_r = A_m \frac{\omega \epsilon m}{k_1^2 r} J_m(k_1 r)\sin m\theta \sin(\omega t - \beta z), \tag{12}$$

$$H_\theta = A_m \frac{\omega \epsilon}{k_1} J'_m(k_1 r)\cos m\theta \sin(\omega t - \beta z), \tag{13}$$

$$H_z \equiv 0, \quad \text{by hypothesis.} \tag{14}$$

From a purely mathematical viewpoint the complete solution in each of the preceding cases involves a double summation like (1) § 16.14, in m and in r (not to be confused with r the radius). In practice, as we have seen, for any m, power is transmitted down the guide in a finite number of modes, i.e. the range of r is finite. In (9)–(13), $k_1 = k_{m,r}$ is such that $J_m(k_{m,r}a) = 0$.

18.41. H waves in circular guide. Using (1) § 18.40 for H_z, the formal solution is identical in type with (7) § 18.40, so

$$H_{z_m} = B_m J_m(k_1 r)\cos m\theta \cos(\omega t - \beta z), \tag{1}$$

where $m = 0, 1, 2,....$. From (6) § 18.34

$$E_\theta = \frac{i\mu\omega}{k_1^2} \frac{\partial H_z}{\partial r}, \tag{2}$$

and this must vanish when $r = a$, since E_θ is then tangential to the inner surface of the guide. Hence $\partial H_z/\partial r = 0$, and from (1) with $k'_{m,r}$ for k_1 we get

$$J'_m(k'_{m,r}a) = 0. \tag{3}$$

If $m = 0$, the first zero occurs when $k'_{0,1}a \simeq 3 \cdot 832$, so $k'_{0,1} \simeq 3 \cdot 832a^{-1}$. Substituting this in (1) gives for an $H_{0,1}$ wave

$$H_{z_{0,1}} = B_0 J_0(k'_{0,1} r)\cos(\omega t - \beta z). \tag{4}$$

The cut-off frequency ($\beta = 0$) for this mode is (air-dielectric)

$$\omega_c/2\pi = k'_{0,1}c/2\pi = 3\cdot832\times3\times10^{10}/2\pi a = 1\cdot83\times10^{10}/a$$

cycles per second if a is in centimetres. This is equivalent to a wavelength of $1\cdot64a$ cm. in free space.

Applying the formulae in § 18.34 to (1) yields the results:

$$E_r = -B_m\frac{\mu\omega m}{k_1^2 r}J_m(k_1 r)\sin m\theta\sin(\omega t-\beta z), \tag{5}$$

$$E_\theta = -B_m\frac{\mu\omega}{k_1}J'_m(k_1 r)\cos m\theta\sin(\omega t-\beta z), \tag{6}$$

$$E_z \equiv 0, \quad \text{by hypothesis;} \tag{7}$$

$$H_r = B_m\frac{\beta}{k_1}J'_m(k_1 r)\cos m\theta\sin(\omega t-\beta z), \tag{8}$$

$$H_\theta = -B_m\frac{\beta m}{k_1^2 r}J_m(k_1 r)\sin m\theta\sin(\omega t-\beta z), \tag{9}$$

$$H_z = B_m J_m(k_1 r)\cos m\theta\cos(\omega t-\beta z). \tag{10}$$

The remarks in the last paragraph of § 18.40 are applicable here, except that now $k_1 = k'_{m,r}$, such that $J'_m(k_{m,r}a) = 0$. The lines of electric and magnetic force in a circular wave guide are depicted in Fig. 43.

18.50. Elliptical wave guide [22]. The system of coordinates used is illustrated in Fig. 16. From § 18.30 we get $\varphi_1 = \xi$, $\varphi_2 = \eta$, $\varphi_3 = z$, $l_1 = l_2 = h[\frac{1}{2}(\cosh 2\xi-\cos 2\eta)]^{\frac{1}{2}}$. Using these in (9) § 18.32 leads to the equation

$$\frac{\partial^2 E_z}{\partial\xi^2}+\frac{\partial^2 E_z}{\partial\eta^2}+\frac{1}{2}k_1^2 h^2(\cosh 2\xi-\cos 2\eta)E_z = 0, \tag{1}$$

which has the same form as (2) § 16.20. For reasons similar to those given in § 16.11, the appropriate formal solution of (1) is

$$E_z = \sum_{m=0}^\infty C_m\,\mathrm{Ce}_m(\xi,q)\mathrm{ce}_m(\eta,q)+\sum_{m=1}^\infty S_m\,\mathrm{Se}_m(\xi,q)\mathrm{se}_m(\eta,q), \tag{2}$$

the time factor being omitted, but see (3), (4) below. For any m there are two types of solution, namely,

$$E_{z_{mc}} = C_m\,\mathrm{Ce}_m(\xi,q)\mathrm{ce}_m(\eta,q)\cos(\omega t-\beta z) \tag{3}$$

and $\qquad E_{z_{ms}} = S_m\,\mathrm{Se}_m(\xi,q)\mathrm{se}_m(\eta,q)\cos(\omega t-\beta z) \tag{4}$

where $k_1^2 h^2 = 4q$ and C_m, S_m are arbitrary constants determinable in the usual way. For E waves the boundary condition is that $E_z = 0$ at the inner surface of the guide where $\xi = \xi_0$. Hence we must have

$$\text{Ce}_m(\xi_0, q) = 0 \tag{5}$$

and
$$\text{Se}_m(\xi_0, q) = 0. \tag{6}$$

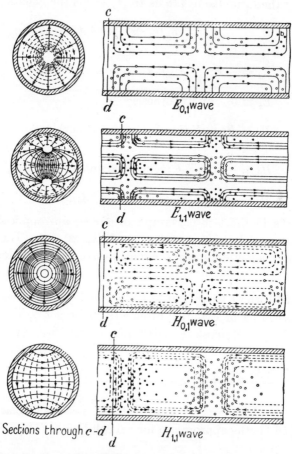

FIG. 43. Approximate configuration of lines of electric (——) and magnetic force (– – – –) in circular wave guide: small solid circles represent lines of force directed towards observer. Propagation is towards the r.h.s. of page.

Let $q_{m,r}$, $\bar{q}_{m,r}$ be the respective rth roots of these equations for a given m. Then the appropriate solutions of (1) corresponding thereto are

$$E_{z_{mc}} = C_{m,r}\,\text{Ce}_m(\xi, q_{m,r})\text{ce}_m(\eta, q_{m,r})\cos(\omega t - \beta z) \tag{7}$$

and
$$E_{z_{ms}} = S_{m,r}\,\text{Se}_m(\xi, \bar{q}_{m,r})\text{se}_m(\eta, \bar{q}_{m,r})\cos(\omega t - \beta z), \tag{8}$$

where $m \geqslant 0$ in (7), $m \geqslant 1$ in (8), and $r \geqslant 1$. For each m, in (7)

$$\text{Ce}_m(\xi, q_{m,r}) = 0,$$

with $r = 1, 2, \dots$. Also for each r, m has an infinity of values. Hence there is a double infinity of zeros. Power is transmitted down the guide only if β is real, so $\omega/c > k_{m,r}$, where $k_{m,r}^2 h^2 = 4q_{m,r}$, or $k_{m,r} = 2q_{m,r}^{\frac{1}{2}}/ae$. Thus for each m, power is transmitted in those modes, finite in number, for which the above inequality is satisfied. Similar remarks apply in connexion with $\text{Se}_m(\xi, \bar{q}_{m,r})$ in (8).

For a $\text{Ce}_m \text{ce}_m$ mode of transmission the lowest pulsatance occurs when $m = 0$, $r = 1$. Thus $k_{0,1}^2 h^2 = 4q_{0,1}$, so $k_{0,1} = 2q_{0,1}^{\frac{1}{2}}/h = 2q_{0,1}^{\frac{1}{2}}/ae$ (e being the eccentricity of the ellipse), and

$$\omega_c = k_{0,1} c = 2cq_{0,1}^{\frac{1}{2}}/ae. \tag{9}$$

Applying the formulae in §18.33 to (7), (8), *the results for E waves* are:

$$E_\xi = \frac{\beta}{k_1^2 l_1} \begin{Bmatrix} C_{m,r}\, \text{Ce}'_m(\xi, q_{m,r})\text{ce}_m(\eta, q_{m,r}) \\ S_{m,r}\, \text{Se}'_m(\xi, \bar{q}_{m,r})\text{se}_m(\eta, \bar{q}_{m,r}) \end{Bmatrix} \sin(\omega t - \beta z), \tag{10}$$

$$E_\eta = \frac{\beta}{k_1^2 l_1} \begin{Bmatrix} C_{m,r}\, \text{Ce}_m(\xi, q_{m,r})\text{ce}'_m(\eta, q_{m,r}) \\ S_{m,r}\, \text{Se}_m(\xi, \bar{q}_{m,r})\text{se}'_m(\eta, \bar{q}_{m,r}) \end{Bmatrix} \sin(\omega t - \beta z), \tag{11}$$

$$E_z = \begin{Bmatrix} C_{m,r}\, \text{Ce}_m(\xi, q_{m,r})\text{ce}_m(\eta, q_{m,r}) \\ S_{m,r}\, \text{Se}_m(\xi, \bar{q}_{m,r})\text{se}_m(\eta, \bar{q}_{m,r}) \end{Bmatrix} \cos(\omega t - \beta z); \tag{12}$$

$$H_\xi = -\frac{\omega \epsilon}{\beta} E_\eta, \tag{13}$$

$$H_\eta = \frac{\omega \epsilon}{\beta} E_\xi, \tag{14}$$

$$H_z \equiv 0, \quad \text{by hypothesis.} \tag{15}$$

The respective arbitrary constants in (10)–(14) are the same. Convenient symbols for E-wave modes are $E_{cm,r}$, $E_{sm,r}$, m, r having the values stated below (8), so that $\omega/c > k_{m,r}$ or $\bar{k}_{m,r}$.

18.51. H waves in elliptical guide. Here $E_z \equiv 0$ by hypothesis, and H_z satisfies an equation like (1) §18.50. Thus the formal solution for the mth mode is

$$H_z = \begin{Bmatrix} \bar{C}_m \text{Ce}_m(\xi, q)\text{ce}_m(\eta, q) \\ \bar{S}_m \text{Se}_m(\xi, q)\text{se}_m(\eta, q) \end{Bmatrix} \cos(\omega t - \beta z). \tag{1}$$

The tangential component of E must vanish at the inner surface of the guide, so $E_\eta = 0$ when $\xi = \xi_0$. Then by (6) §18.34, since $\varphi_1 = \xi$, it follows that

$$\left[\frac{\partial H_z}{\partial \xi}\right]_{\xi=\xi_0} = 0, \quad \text{so} \quad \text{Ce}'_m(\xi_0, q) = 0, \tag{2}$$

$$\text{and} \quad \text{Se}'_m(\xi_0, q) = 0. \tag{3}$$

Let $q_{m,p}$, $\bar{q}_{m,p}$ be the respective pth roots of these equations for a given m. Then the appropriate solutions of the differential equation corresponding to the pth modes are

$$H_z = \begin{Bmatrix} \bar{C}_{m,p}\,\mathrm{Ce}_m(\xi, q_{m,p})\mathrm{ce}_m(\eta, q_{m,p}) \\ \bar{S}_{m,p}\,\mathrm{Se}_m(\xi, \bar{q}_{m,p})\mathrm{se}_m(\eta, \bar{q}_{m,p}) \end{Bmatrix} \cos(\omega t - \beta z), \qquad (4)$$

with $m \geqslant 0$ for $\mathrm{Ce}_m\,\mathrm{ce}_m$, $m \geqslant 1$ for $\mathrm{Se}_m\,\mathrm{se}_m$, and $p \geqslant 1$, such that

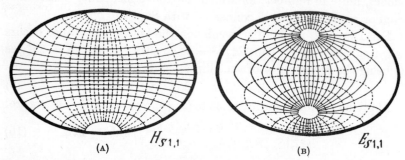

$$H_{\mathcal{S}1,1} \qquad\qquad E_{\mathcal{S}1,1}$$

(A)   (B)

FIG. 44. Lines of electric (——) and magnetic force (– – – –) in elliptical wave guide: eccentricity of ellipse is 0·75. (A) $H_{s1,1}$ wave; (B) $E_{s1,1}$ wave.

$\omega/c > k_{m,p}$ or $\bar{k}_{m,p}$. The lowest pulsatance is obtained by the procedure given in § 16.23. Applying the formulae in § 18.34 to (4), the *results for H waves* are:

$$E_\xi = \frac{\mu\omega}{k_1^2\,l_1} \begin{Bmatrix} \bar{C}_{m,p}\,\mathrm{Ce}_m(\xi, q_{m,p})\mathrm{ce}_m'(\eta, q_{m,p}) \\ \bar{S}_{m,p}\,\mathrm{Se}_m(\xi, \bar{q}_{m,p})\mathrm{se}_m'(\eta, \bar{q}_{m,p}) \end{Bmatrix} \sin(\omega t - \beta z), \qquad (5)$$

$$E_\eta = -\frac{\mu\omega}{k_1^2\,l_1} \begin{Bmatrix} \bar{C}_{m,p}\,\mathrm{Ce}_m'(\xi, q_{m,p})\mathrm{ce}_m(\eta, q_{m,p}) \\ \bar{S}_{m,p}\,\mathrm{Se}_m'(\xi, \bar{q}_{m,p})\mathrm{se}_m(\eta, \bar{q}_{m,p}) \end{Bmatrix} \sin(\omega t - \beta z), \qquad (6)$$

$$E_z \equiv 0; \qquad (7)$$

$$H_\xi = -\frac{\beta}{\mu\omega}\,E_\eta, \qquad (8)$$

$$H_\eta = \frac{\beta}{\mu\omega}\,E_\xi, \qquad (9)$$

H_z as at (4) above. $\qquad (10)$

The constants $\bar{C}_{m,p}$, $\bar{S}_{m,p}$ are the same throughout. Convenient symbols for H waves are $H_{cm,p}$, $H_{sm,p}$, m, p having the values given below (4).

The lines of electric and magnetic force in an elliptical wave guide are portrayed in Fig. 44.

18.52. Power transmitted down elliptical wave guide. The power passing through each unit area of cross-section in the direction of the z-axis, i.e. the time rate of energy flow per unit area, may be calculated by aid of the Poynting vector $\mathbf{p}$. If $\mathbf{E}$, $\mathbf{H}$ are the electric and magnetic force vectors at any point (ξ, η) in the cross-section, then

$$\mathbf{p} = \mathbf{E}\mathbf{H}/4\pi, \qquad (1)$$

where the vector product is to be taken. Expressed in terms of scalar quantities

$$p_z = \frac{1}{4\pi}[E_\xi H_\eta - E_\eta H_\xi]. \qquad (2)$$

Substituting from (10), (11), (13), (14) § 18.50 for the various quantities, (2) becomes

$$p_z = \frac{1}{4\pi}\frac{\beta\omega\epsilon}{k_1^4 l_1^2}|C_m|^2[\mathrm{Ce}_m'^2(\xi, q_{m,r})\mathrm{ce}_m^2(\eta, q_{m,r}) + $$
$$+ \mathrm{Ce}_m^2(\xi, q_{m,r})\mathrm{ce}_m'^2(\eta, q_{m,r})]\sin^2(\omega t - \beta z) \qquad (3)$$

for an $E_{cm,r}$ type of wave, C_m being a constant. The mean power transmitted through unit area, taken over a cycle of $\sin \omega t$ at any z, is one-half the maximum value of (3). Hence the total mean power for the m mode in question is found by omitting $\sin^2(\omega t - \beta z)$ and halving the integral of (3) over the cross-section. Thus, omitting $q_{m,r}$ for brevity,

$$P_z = \frac{|C_m|^2\beta\omega\epsilon}{8\pi k_1^4}\int\int[\mathrm{Ce}_m'^2(\xi)\mathrm{ce}_m^2(\eta) + \mathrm{Ce}_m^2(\xi)\mathrm{ce}_m'^2(\eta)]\frac{ds_1 ds_2}{l_1^2}, \qquad (4)$$

ds_1, ds_2, and l_1 being defined in § 9.12. But $ds_1 ds_2/l_1^2 = d\xi d\eta$, so (4) may be written

$$P_z = \frac{|C_m|^2\beta\omega\epsilon}{8\pi k_1^4}\int\limits_0^{\xi_0}\int\limits_0^{2\pi}[\mathrm{Ce}_m'^2(\xi)\mathrm{ce}_m^2(\eta) + \mathrm{Ce}_m^2(\xi)\mathrm{ce}_m'^2(\eta)]\,d\xi d\eta. \qquad (5)$$

By (1) § 2.21, $\int\limits_0^{2\pi}\mathrm{ce}_m^2(\eta)\,d\eta = \pi$, and by (3) § 14.41, $\int\limits_0^{2\pi}\mathrm{ce}_m'^2(\eta)\,d\eta = \vartheta_m\pi$.

Thus $$P_z = \frac{|C_m|^2\beta\omega\epsilon}{8k_1^4}\int\limits_0^{\xi_0}[\mathrm{Ce}_m'^2(\xi, q_{m,r}) + \vartheta_m\,\mathrm{Ce}_m^2(\xi, q_{m,r})]\,d\xi. \qquad (6)$$

For an $E_{sm,r}$ type of wave, P_z is given by (6) on replacing Ce_m by Se_m, $q_{m,r}$ by $\bar{q}_{m,r}$, and ϑ_m by ϖ_m. Formulae for H waves are obtained from (6) if ϵ is replaced by μ, and $q_{m,r}$, $\bar{q}_{m,r}$ by $q_{m,p}$, $\bar{q}_{m,p}$, respectively.

18.53. Attenuation of waves due to imperfect conductor [200]. Hitherto the metal of the guide has been assumed a perfect conductor, so that waves travel from end to end without loss. In practice, however, loss must be taken into account. We confine our attention to metallic loss and assume absence of loss in the air dielectric. If the resistivity of the metal is included in Maxwell's

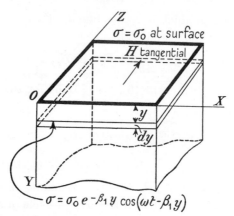

Fig. 45. Illustrating penetration of current into very large flat slab, induced by sinusoidally varying magnetic field tangential to free surface.

equations the loss may be determined, but not without undue complication. It is adequate for practical purposes to assume that the magnetic field at the inner surface of the guide is the same as it would be if the metal had zero resistivity. Then introducing $\rho_1 > 0$ into the analysis, we calculate the eddy-current loss as in the case of a metal slab.

Consider a very large metal slab of resistivity ρ_1 whose upper face lies in the XZ plane, Fig. 45. Let a sinusoidal electromagnetic field exist above the slab, the maximum value of the magnetic component tangential thereto being H_t. This induces a *surface* current of density σ in a *non-resistive slab*, such that

$$H_t = 4\pi\sigma, \quad \text{or} \quad \sigma = H_t/4\pi. \tag{1}$$

Since $\rho_1 > 0$ in practice, there is a *volume* distribution of current whose density at a depth y below the surface is σ_1. This depends upon ρ_1, the magnetic permeability μ_1, and f the frequency of the electromagnetic field. The propagation of power *into* the slab perpendicular to its surface is similar to that along a uniform transmission line. If $\sigma_0 \cos \omega t$ is the surface-current density, it may be shown that at any depth y below the surface

$$\sigma_1 = \sigma_0 e^{-\beta_1 y} \cos(\omega t - \beta_1 y), \tag{2}$$

where $\beta_1 = 2\pi(\mu_1 f/\rho_1)^{\frac{1}{2}}$. We have now to determine σ_0, so that the volume distribution of current in the slab is equal to σ, i.e.

$$\text{maximum value of } \int_0^\infty \sigma_1 \, dy = H_t/4\pi. \tag{3}$$

Substituting from (2) for σ_1 into the integral in (3) and evaluating yields† $\sigma_0 \cos(\omega t - \frac{1}{4}\pi)/2^{\frac{1}{2}}\beta_1$. The angle $\frac{1}{4}\pi$ is due to the current not being in phase throughout the depth of the slab. The loss is unaffected by omitting $\frac{1}{4}\pi$, so equating the maximum values in (3) leads to $\sigma_0 = \beta_1 H_t/2^{\frac{1}{2}}\pi$. Thus the equivalent root mean square value of σ_1 in (2) is

$$\sigma_{\text{r.m.s.}} = \beta_1 H_t e^{-\beta_1 y}/4\pi. \tag{4}$$

Then the power loss per unit surface area of the slab is given by

$$\rho_1 \int_0^\infty \sigma_{\text{r.m.s.}}^2 \, dy = \frac{\rho_1 \beta_1^2 H_t^2}{16\pi^2} \int_0^\infty e^{-2\beta_1 y} \, dy, \tag{5}$$

so

$$P_{\text{cm.}^2} = \beta_1 \rho_1 H_t^2/32\pi^2 = (\mu_1 \rho_1 f)^{\frac{1}{2}} H_t^2/16\pi. \tag{6}$$

Since the depth of penetration into the metal of a guide at ultra high frequency is very small, the preceding analysis is applicable to curved surfaces, provided the curvature is not excessive. This condition obtains in practical wave guides where the ratio (depth of penetration/radius of curvature) is of the order 2×10^{-5} or less, except in the region of a corner. The proportionate surface area affected is then quite small.

18.54. Application of analysis in § 18.53 to wave guide. If ds is an elemental arc-length of a cross-section at the inner surface of the guide, the area of a surface element of unit axial length is $dA = ds \times 1$. The magnetic field component tangential to the element is H_t. Then by (6) § 18.53 the power loss in the element is $dP = (\mu_1 \rho_1 f)^{\frac{1}{2}} H_t^2 \, ds/16\pi$, so the total loss in unit length of the guide is

$$P = \frac{1}{16\pi}(\mu_1 \rho_1 f)^{\frac{1}{2}} \int H_t^2 \, ds, \tag{1}$$

the integration being taken round the inner surface.

† $\displaystyle\int_0^\infty e^{-\beta_1 y} \cos(\beta_1 y - \alpha_1) \, dy = \frac{1}{2\beta_1}(\cos\alpha_1 + \sin\alpha_1) = \frac{1}{2^{\frac{1}{2}}\beta_1}\cos(\alpha_1 - \frac{1}{4}\pi).$

As the waves travel down the guide, the power absorbed by the metal per unit length is given by (1). Consequently it represents $-dP_z/dz$,† the distance rate of power loss sustained by the waves. If we define this loss to be

$$P = -dP_z/dz = 2\alpha P_z, \tag{2}$$

then α is known as the attenuation constant. The multiplier 2 arises as follows: If H_m is the maximum magnetic field at the transmitter where $z = 0$, its value at a point $z > 0$ is $H_m e^{-\alpha z}$. The power, however, is proportional to $(H_m e^{-\alpha z})^2 = H_m^2 e^{-2\alpha z}$, i.e. $P_z = P_m e^{-2\alpha z}$, so

$$-dP_z/dz = 2\alpha P_m e^{-2\alpha z} = 2\alpha P_z, \tag{3}$$

giving

$$\alpha = P/2P_z. \tag{4}$$

For purposes of calculation the value of z is immaterial, since α is constant.

18.55. Attenuation in elliptical wave guide. For an $E_{cm,r}$ type of wave the tangential component of magnetic force at the inner surface of the guide, where $\xi = \xi_0$, is

$$H_\eta = \frac{C_m \, \omega\epsilon}{k_1^2 \, l_1} \, \mathrm{Ce}_m'(\xi_0, q_{m,r}) \mathrm{ce}_m(\eta, q_{m,r}), \tag{1}$$

C_m being a constant.

Also by § 9.12, $ds = l_1 d\eta$, so by aid of (1) § 18.54 we get the loss per unit length as

$$P = |C_m|^2 \frac{(\mu_1 \rho_1 f)^{\frac{1}{2}} \omega^2 \epsilon^2}{16\pi k_1^4} \left[\mathrm{Ce}_m'^2(\xi_0, q_{m,r})\right] \int_0^{2\pi} \mathrm{ce}_m^2(\eta, q_{m,r}) \, d\eta/l_1. \tag{2}$$

Now

$$l_1 = h(\cosh^2\xi - \cos^2\eta)^{\frac{1}{2}} = h \cosh \xi_0 [1 - (\cos \eta/\cosh \xi_0)^2]^{\frac{1}{2}}$$
$$= a(1 - e^2 \cos^2\eta)^{\frac{1}{2}},$$

e being the eccentricity of the bounding ellipse. Substituting this value of l_1 into (2) leads to

$$P = |C_m|^2 \frac{(\mu_1 \rho_1 f)^{\frac{1}{2}} \omega^2 \epsilon^2}{16\pi a k_1^4} \left[\mathrm{Ce}_m'^2(\xi_0, q_{m,r})\right] \int_0^{2\pi} \mathrm{ce}_m^2(\eta, q_{m,r}) \, d\eta/(1 - e^2 \cos^2\eta)^{\frac{1}{2}}.$$

$$\tag{3}$$

---

† The negative sign indicates decrease in P_z with increase in z. P_z is the total power passing a section distant z from the transmitter.

Since $e < 1$, the denominator of the integrand may be expanded binomially, and we get for the integral

$$I = \int_0^{2\pi} \mathrm{ce}_m^2(\eta, q_{m,r}) \times$$

$$\times \left[1 + \tfrac{1}{2}e^2\cos^2\eta + \frac{1.3}{2^2.2!}e^4\cos^4\eta + \frac{1.3.5}{2^3.3!}e^6\cos^6\eta + \ldots \right] d\eta. \quad (4)$$

On substituting the series for $\mathrm{ce}_{2n}(\eta, q_{2n,r})$ in (4) and using (9) § 9.40, we obtain

$$I = \pi\left[1 + \frac{1}{2^2}e^2\{1 + \Theta_{2n}\} + \ldots \right]. \quad (5)$$

Inserting (5) into (3), with $m = 2n$ the expression for the power loss per unit length of guide is

$$P = |C_{2n}|^2 \frac{(\mu_1\rho_1 f)^{\frac{1}{2}}\omega^2\epsilon^2}{16ak_1^4}[\mathrm{Ce}_{2n}'^2(\xi_0, q_{2n,r})]\left[1 + \frac{1}{2^2}e^2\{1 + \Theta_{2n}\} + \ldots \right]. \quad (6)$$

From (6) § 18.52 and (6) above, the attenuation constant is

$$\alpha = \frac{1}{4a}\left(\frac{\mu_1\rho_1 f\epsilon}{\mu}\right)^{\frac{1}{2}}\frac{\mathrm{Ce}_{2n}'^2(\xi_0, q_{2n,r})}{[1 - (f_c/f)^2]^{\frac{1}{2}}}\frac{\left[1 + \frac{1}{2^2}e^2\{1 + \Theta_{2n}\} + \ldots \right]}{\displaystyle\int_0^{\xi_0}[\mathrm{Ce}_{2n}'^2(\xi, q_{2n,r}) + \vartheta_{2n}\,\mathrm{Ce}_{2n}^2(\xi, q_{2n,r})]\,d\xi}.$$

$$\quad (7)$$

In (7) f_c is the cut-off frequency.

For H_{cm} waves the attenuation constant may be shown to be

$$\alpha = \frac{(\mu_1\rho_1 f)^{\frac{1}{2}}}{4\pi a\beta\mu\omega}\,\mathrm{Ce}_m^2(\xi_0, q_{m,p}) \times$$

$$\times \frac{\left[\beta^2\displaystyle\int_0^{2\pi}\frac{\mathrm{ce}_m'^2(\eta, q_{m,p})\,d\eta}{(1 - e^2\cos^2\eta)^{\frac{1}{2}}} + k_1^4 a^2\displaystyle\int_0^{2\pi}\mathrm{ce}_m^2(\eta, q_{m,p})(1 - e^2\cos^2\eta)^{\frac{1}{2}}\,d\eta \right]}{\displaystyle\int_0^{\xi_0}[\mathrm{Ce}_m'^2(\xi, q_{m,p}) + \vartheta_m\,\mathrm{Ce}_m^2(\xi, q_{m,p})]\,d\xi}, \quad (8)$$

which may be evaluated by procedure akin to that above (7), a numerical process being used for the denominator.

18.56. Transition to circular cross-section. The results in Appendix I may be used to reproduce the formulae for a circular section given in §§ 18.40, 18.41 from those in §§ 18.50, 18.51.

18.57. Influence of deviation of cross-section from circularity [22, 200]. Using the formulae in (12) § 18.50, when the ellipse tends towards a circle, by Appendix I—omitting the time factor—we have

$$E_{z_{cm}} = C_m \operatorname{Ce}_m(\xi, q_{m,r}) \operatorname{ce}_m(\eta, q_{m,r}) \to C_m p'_m J_m(k_1 r) \cos m\theta, \qquad (1)$$

for an E_{cm} type wave, and

$$E_{z_{sm}} = S_m \operatorname{Se}_m(\xi, \bar{q}_{m,r}) \operatorname{se}_m(\eta, \bar{q}_{m,r}) \to S_m s'_m J_m(k_1 r) \sin m\theta, \qquad (2)$$

for an E_{sm} type wave. Consider both solutions in (5) § 18.40 for

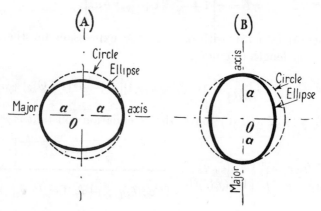

Fig. 46. (A, B) Illustrating deformation of circular wave guide to elliptical form.

waves in a circular guide for the modes $m = 1$, $r = 1, 2,...$, and suppose that the deformation occurs in the position shown in Fig. 46 A. If the orientation of the wave—looking down the guide—is such that $S_1 = 0$, then

$$E_z = C_1 p'_1 J_1(k_1 r) \cos \theta \leftarrow C_1 \operatorname{Ce}_1(\xi, q_{1,r}) \operatorname{ce}_1(\eta, q_{1,r}) \qquad (3)$$

and at the deformation the wave will tend to an E_{c_1} type. In the same way, if the deformation occurs as shown in Fig. 46 B, i.e. $\frac{1}{2}\pi$ away from the position indicated in Fig. 46 A, and the orientation of the wave is such that $C_1 = 0$,

$$E_z = S_1 s'_1 J_1(k_1 r) \sin \theta \leftarrow S_1 \operatorname{Se}_1(\xi, \bar{q}_{1,r}) \operatorname{se}_1(\eta, \bar{q}_{1,r}), \qquad (4)$$

so the wave will tend to an E_{s_1} type. Generally the deformation will occur in a position such that neither C_1 nor S_1 is zero, so that both E_{c_1}, E_{s_1} waves may be created. Now these corresponding types have different phase velocities.† Consequently in travelling down the guide the two waves will fall out of step progressively. It follows, therefore, that unless $C_1 = S_1 = 0$, i.e. the deformation occurs along an axis of symmetry of the wave pattern (see Fig. 44), non-circularity introduces a degree of instability. Since there is no E_{sm} wave of order $m = 0$, slight deformation will not cause splitting of an E_{c_0} wave. For $m = 1, 2,...$ splitting of the wave into two components with unequal phase velocities will occur. Similar conclusions apply for H waves. It may be remarked that with an E_1 or an H_1 wave, after splitting occurs, one component has a higher attenuation than the other, and after travelling an adequate distance down the guide, the component with the greater attenuation will be of negligible comparative amplitude.

† From § 18.24, $\beta^2 = (\omega/c)^2 - (\omega_c/c)^2$, so $\beta = (\omega/c)[1 - (\omega_c/\omega)^2]^{\frac{1}{2}}$, where $\omega_c/2\pi$ is the cut-off frequency for the transmission mode concerned. The phase velocity is $v_p = \omega/\beta = c[1 - (\omega_c/\omega)^2]^{-\frac{1}{2}}$. As $\omega \to \omega_c + 0$, $v_p \to +\infty$, which is a well-known phenomenon in geometrical optics.

DIFFRACTION OF SOUND AND ELECTROMAGNETIC WAVES

19.10. Scattering of sound by elliptical cylinder.

Referring to Fig. 47, a plane sound wave in air travels towards the origin from the lower side and impinges at an angle θ on a right elliptical cylinder with axis $Z'OZ$, normal to the plane of the paper. The cylinder is long compared with its major axis, being immobile and non-absorbent. Its presence causes the sound to be scattered.

Analytically we may for convenience consider the wave to have two components. There is (1) a plane wave identical with that in absence of the cylinder, (2) a scattered wave, diverging away from O, for which we have to derive a symbolical representation.

19.11. Equation of sound propagation.

The two-dimensional equation is

$$\frac{\partial^2 \phi}{\partial x^2} + \frac{\partial^2 \phi}{\partial y^2} + k_1^2 \phi = 0, \tag{1}$$

where ϕ is the velocity potential, $k_1 = \omega/c$, and c is the velocity of sound in the medium [see reference 202, chap. ii]. Since we are dealing with an elliptical cylinder, we transform (1) to elliptical coordinates. Thus by §9.20 we obtain

$$\frac{\partial^2 \phi}{\partial \xi^2} + \frac{\partial^2 \phi}{\partial \eta^2} + 2k^2(\cosh 2\xi - \cos 2\eta)\phi = 0, \tag{2}$$

with $2k = k_1 h$.

19.12. Velocity potential of plane wave.

For a plane sound wave travelling as shown in Fig. 47 the root mean square value† of the velocity potential at any point on the wave front at a perpendicular distance σ from the origin O, in absence of the cylinder, is represented by

$$\phi_1 = \phi_0 \, e^{i(k_1 \sigma - \omega t)}. \tag{1}$$

From Fig. 47

$$\sigma = x \cos \theta + y \sin \theta, \tag{2}$$

† Sinusoidal variation implied.

and by (7) § 10.53, (1) expressed in elliptical coordinates is

$$\phi_1 = 2\phi_0 e^{-i\omega t} \times$$

$$\times \sum_{n=0}^{\infty} \left[\frac{1}{p_{2n}} \mathrm{Ce}_{2n}(\xi)\mathrm{ce}_{2n}(\eta)\mathrm{ce}_{2n}(\theta) + \frac{1}{s_{2n+2}} \mathrm{Se}_{2n+2}(\xi)\mathrm{se}_{2n+2}(\eta)\mathrm{se}_{2n+2}(\theta) + \right.$$

$$\left. +i\left\{ \frac{1}{p_{2n+1}} \mathrm{Ce}_{2n+1}(\xi)\mathrm{ce}_{2n+1}(\eta)\mathrm{ce}_{2n+1}(\theta) + \frac{1}{s_{2n+1}} \mathrm{Se}_{2n+1}(\xi)\mathrm{se}_{2n+1}(\eta)\mathrm{se}_{2n+1}(\theta) \right\} \right].$$

$$(3)$$

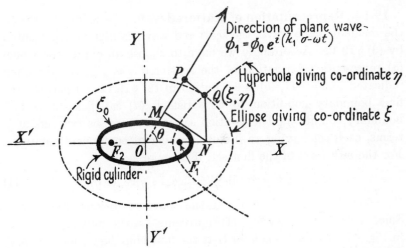

FIG. 47. Illustrating plane sound wave impinging on a very long rigid elliptical cylinder. Q has coordinates ξ, η, defined by orthogonal intersection of confocal ellipse and hyperbola.

$$ON = x, \quad NQ = y, \quad OM = x \cos \theta, \quad MP = y \sin \theta,$$
$$\sigma = OP = x \cos \theta + y \sin \theta = h(\cosh \xi \cos \eta \cos \theta + \sinh \xi \sin \eta \sin \theta).$$
F_1, F_2 are foci and $F_1 F_2 = 2h$. MN and PQ are perpendicular to OP.

This is a solution of (2) § 19.11 and represents the velocity potential of the plane wave in absence of the cylinder.

19.13. Boundary conditions. Since the surface of the cylinder is immobile, the velocity of the air particles normal thereto must be zero. Thus the first boundary condition is that the sum of the normal velocities of the incident and scattered waves shall vanish at $\xi = \xi_0$. If u_{n_1} is the normal velocity of the incident wave and u_{n_2} that of the scattered wave, whose velocity potential is ϕ_2, we must have

$$u_{n_1} + u_{n_2} = -\left(\frac{\partial \phi_1}{\partial n} + \frac{\partial \phi_2}{\partial n} \right)_{\xi=\xi_0} = 0, \tag{1}$$

n indicating the direction of the normal. From § 9.12 $\partial n = l_1 \partial \xi$, so the first boundary condition may be written

$$\left(\frac{\partial \phi_1}{\partial \xi} + \frac{\partial \phi_2}{\partial \xi}\right)_{\xi=\xi_0} = 0. \tag{2}$$

The second boundary condition is

$$\phi_2 \to 0 \quad \text{as} \quad \xi \to +\infty, \tag{3}$$

since the influence of the cylinder is nil at infinity.

19.14. Representation of scattered wave. Being different from the incident plane wave, the scattered wave cannot be represented by (3) § 19.12. Accordingly we have to choose an expression which (a) represents propagation of the scattered wave in the direction indicated in Fig. 47, (b) is a solution of (2) § 19.11, (c) permits the first boundary condition to be satisfied, (d) satisfies the second boundary condition. The solution selected comprises two sets of $\sum$ terms, each set having an infinite number of component solutions. For the mth term of the first set, if we take

$$\psi_{c_m} = C_m e^{-i\omega t} \text{Me}_m^{(1)}(\xi, q)\text{ce}_m(\eta, q)\text{ce}_m(\theta, q), \tag{1}$$

C_m being a complex constant, all the above conditions are satisfied. Since $\text{Me}_m^{(1)} = \text{Ce}_m + i\,\text{Fey}_m$, (1) represents a wave moving as shown in Fig. 47. We shall see later that the first boundary condition may be satisfied if C_m is correctly chosen. From the asymptotic formulae for $\text{Me}_m^{(1)}(\xi)$ in § 11.11 it is seen that $\psi_{c_m} \to 0$ as $\xi \to +\infty$.

In the second set of $\sum$ terms in the proposed solution we incorporate the function $\text{Ne}_m^{(1)} = \text{Se}_m + i\,\text{Gey}_m$. The required form of solution which represents wave propagation away from the origin as in Fig. 47, is

$$\psi_{s_m} = S_m e^{-i\omega t} \text{Ne}_m^{(1)}(\xi, q)\text{se}_m(\eta, q)\text{se}_m(\theta, q), \tag{2}$$

which has the properties (a)–(d) given above. Thus for the scattered wave we take the solution

$$\phi_2 = e^{-i\omega t} \times$$

$$\times \sum_{n=0}^{\infty} [C_{2n} \text{Me}_{2n}^{(1)}(\xi)\text{ce}_{2n}(\eta)\text{ce}_{2n}(\theta) + C_{2n+1} \text{Me}_{2n+1}^{(1)}(\xi)\text{ce}_{2n+1}(\eta)\text{ce}_{2n+1}(\theta) +$$

$$+ S_{2n+1} \text{Ne}_{2n+1}^{(1)}(\xi)\text{se}_{2n+1}(\eta)\text{se}_{2n+1}(\theta) +$$

$$+ S_{2n+2} \text{Ne}_{2n+2}^{(1)}(\xi)\text{se}_{2n+2}(\eta)\text{se}_{2n+2}(\theta)]. \tag{3}$$

Using condition (2) § 19.13 and equating the sum of the derivatives of functions of the same kind and order to zero, gives for $\xi = \xi_0$:

$$C_{2n} = -\frac{2\phi_0}{p_{2n}} \frac{\mathrm{Ce}'_{2n}(\xi_0)}{\mathrm{Me}^{(1)'}_{2n}(\xi_0)} = -\frac{2\phi_0 \cos \alpha_{2n} e^{-i\alpha_{2n}}}{p_{2n}}, \qquad (4)$$

where $\cos \alpha_{2n} = \mathrm{Ce}'_{2n}(\xi_0)/[\mathrm{Ce}'^2_{2n}(\xi_0) + \mathrm{Fey}'^2_{2n}(\xi_0)]^{\frac{1}{2}}$;

$$C_{2n+1} = -\frac{2i\phi_0}{p_{2n+1}} \frac{\mathrm{Ce}'_{2n+1}(\xi_0)}{\mathrm{Me}^{(1)'}_{2n+1}(\xi_0)} = -\frac{2\phi_0 \cos \alpha_{2n+1} e^{-i(\alpha_{2n+1}-\frac{1}{2}\pi)}}{p_{2n+1}}, \qquad (5)$$

where $\cos \alpha_{2n+1} = \mathrm{Ce}'_{2n+1}(\xi_0)/[\mathrm{Ce}'^2_{2n+1}(\xi_0) + \mathrm{Fey}'^2_{2n+1}(\xi_0)]^{\frac{1}{2}}$;

$$S_{2n+1} = -\frac{2i\phi_0}{s_{2n+1}} \frac{\mathrm{Se}'_{2n+1}(\xi_0)}{\mathrm{Ne}^{(1)'}_{2n+1}(\xi_0)} = -\frac{2\phi_0 \cos \beta_{2n+1} e^{-i(\beta_{2n+1}-\frac{1}{2}\pi)}}{s_{2n+1}}, \qquad (6)$$

where $\cos \beta_{2n+1} = \mathrm{Se}'_{2n+1}(\xi_0)/[\mathrm{Se}'^2_{2n+1}(\xi_0) + \mathrm{Gey}'^2_{2n+1}(\xi_0)]^{\frac{1}{2}}$;

$$S_{2n+2} = -\frac{2\phi_0}{s_{2n+2}} \frac{\mathrm{Se}'_{2n+2}(\xi_0)}{\mathrm{Ne}^{(1)'}_{2n+2}(\xi_0)} = -\frac{2\phi_0 \cos \beta_{2n+2} e^{-i\beta_{2n+2}}}{s_{2n+2}}, \qquad (7)$$

where $\cos \beta_{2n+2} = \mathrm{Se}'_{2n+2}(\xi_0)/[\mathrm{Se}'^2_{2n+2}(\xi_0) + \mathrm{Gey}'^2_{2n+2}(\xi_0)]^{\frac{1}{2}}$, and p_m, s_m are defined in Appendix I.

The velocity potential at any point on or outside the cylinder is

$$\phi = \phi_1 + \phi_2$$
$$= \phi_0 e^{i(k_1\sigma - \omega t)} + \phi_2 \quad \text{[as at (3) above].} \qquad (8)$$

This may be regarded as a general solution of the problem. If $\theta = 0$, and the incident wave travels parallel to the X-axis, the terms in (3) involving S_{2n+1}, S_{2n+2} vanish, leaving

$$\phi_2 = e^{-i\omega t} \sum_{m=0}^{\infty} C_m \mathrm{Me}^{(1)}_m(\xi) \mathrm{ce}_m(\eta) \mathrm{ce}_m(0). \qquad (9)$$

When $\theta = \frac{1}{2}\pi$, the incident wave travels parallel to the Y-axis, and we get

$$\phi_2 = e^{-i\omega t} \sum_{n=0}^{\infty} [C_{2n} \mathrm{Me}^{(1)}_{2n}(\xi) \mathrm{ce}_{2n}(\eta) \mathrm{ce}_{2n}(\tfrac{1}{2}\pi) +$$
$$+ S_{2n+1} \mathrm{Ne}^{(1)}_{2n+1}(\xi) \mathrm{se}_{2n+1}(\eta) \mathrm{se}_{2n+1}(\tfrac{1}{2}\pi)]. \qquad (10)$$

19.20. Long rigid ribbon. This case is obtained when $\xi_0 \to 0$, the width of the ellipse of evanescent minor axis then tending to $2h$, the interfocal distance. When $\xi_0 = 0$, $\mathrm{Ce}'_m(\xi_0) = 0$, and in (3) § 19.14 $C_{2n} = C_{2n+1} = 0$, while

$$S_{2n+1} = -2i\phi_0 k B_1^{(2n+1)}/\mathrm{se}_{2n+1}(\tfrac{1}{2}\pi) \mathrm{Ne}^{(1)'}_{2n+1}(0) \qquad (1)$$

and

$$S_{2n+2} = -2\phi_0 k^2 B_2^{(2n+2)}/\mathrm{se}'_{2n+2}(\tfrac{1}{2}\pi) \mathrm{Ne}^{(1)'}_{2n+2}(0). \qquad (2)$$

Inserting these in (3) § 19.14 we obtain the velocity potential of the scattered wave at any point, whose coordinates are ξ, η, on or outside the ribbon. Thus

$$\phi_2 = -2e^{-i\omega t}\phi_0 k \sum_{n=0}^{\infty} \left[i B_1^{(2n+1)} \frac{\mathrm{Ne}_{2n+1}^{(1)}(\xi)\mathrm{se}_{2n+1}(\eta)\mathrm{se}_{2n+1}(\theta)}{\mathrm{se}_{2n+1}(\tfrac{1}{2}\pi, q)\mathrm{Ne}_{2n+1}^{(1)'}(0)} + \right.$$

$$\left. + k B_2^{(2n+2)} \frac{\mathrm{Ne}_{2n+2}^{(1)}(\xi)\mathrm{se}_{2n+2}(\eta)\mathrm{se}_{2n+2}(\theta)}{\mathrm{se}_{2n+2}'(\tfrac{1}{2}\pi, q)\mathrm{Ne}_{2n+2}^{(1)'}(0)} \right]. \quad (3)$$

At the surface of the ribbon $\xi = 0$, so by (3) § 19.12 the velocity potential due to the plane wave is

$$\phi_1 = 2e^{-i\omega t}\phi_0 \sum_{n=0}^{\infty} \left[\frac{A_0^{(2n)}\,\mathrm{ce}_{2n}(\eta)\mathrm{ce}_{2n}(\theta)}{\mathrm{ce}_{2n}(\tfrac{1}{2}\pi, q)} - \frac{ikA_1^{(2n+1)}\,\mathrm{ce}_{2n+1}(\eta)\mathrm{ce}_{2n+1}(\theta)}{\mathrm{ce}_{2n+1}'(\tfrac{1}{2}\pi, q)} \right].$$

$$(4)$$

Since $\mathrm{Se}_m(0) = 0$, by (3) above the velocity potential due to the scattered wave is

$$\phi_2 = 2e^{-i\omega t}\phi_0 k \sum_{n=0}^{\infty} \left[\frac{B_1^{(2n+1)}\,\mathrm{Gey}_{2n+1}(0)\mathrm{se}_{2n+1}(\eta)\mathrm{se}_{2n+1}(\theta)}{\mathrm{Ne}_{2n+1}^{(1)'}(0)\mathrm{se}_{2n+1}(\tfrac{1}{2}\pi, q)} - \right.$$

$$\left. - \frac{ikB_2^{(2n+2)}\,\mathrm{Gey}_{2n+2}(0)\mathrm{se}_{2n+2}(\eta)\mathrm{se}_{2n+2}(\theta)}{\mathrm{Ne}_{2n+2}^{(1)'}(0)\mathrm{se}_{2n+2}'(\tfrac{1}{2}\pi, q)} \right]. \quad (5)$$

The resultant velocity potential at the ribbon surface due to both the incident and scattered waves is the sum of (4) and (5). If p_0 is the root mean square pressure of the incident wave, then, since $p = \rho_0 \partial\phi/\partial t = -i\rho_0\omega\phi$,[†] the pressure is obtained from (4), (5) by writing p_0 for ϕ_0, p_1, p_2 for ϕ_1, ϕ_2, respectively.

Polar diagrams for plane sound waves scattered by a ribbon of width $2h$ for various wave-lengths (as a function of $2h$) and angles of incidence are shown in Fig. 48.

The solution for the diffraction of sound waves at a slit of width $2h$ in an infinite rigid plane may be obtained by analysis akin to that above, but the boundary condition corresponding to (2) § 19.13 is now that the velocity of the sound waves normal to the plane is zero.

---

† ρ_0 is the density of the undisturbed medium, while p is not to be confused with the multipliers in (4), (5), § 19.14.

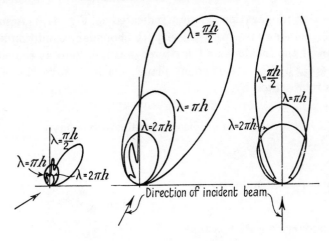

FIG. 48. Polar diagrams for sound scattered by a long ribbon [144].

19.21. Formulae for large distance from ribbon. The confocal ellipses are now sensibly concentric circles, and we may use the asymptotic formulae for the Ne functions, with $k_1 r = v$ (see § 9.12 and Appendix I). Thus from (3), (4) § 11.11, if $|v| \gg n$,

$$\mathrm{Ne}^{(1)}_{2n+1}(\xi) \sim -\frac{\mathrm{se}'_{2n+1}(0)\mathrm{se}_{2n+1}(\tfrac{1}{2}\pi)}{kB_1^{(2n+1)}}\left(\frac{2}{\pi v}\right)^{\frac{1}{2}} e^{i(v+\frac{1}{4}\pi)} \tag{1}$$

and

$$\mathrm{Ne}^{(1)}_{2n+2}(\xi) \sim -i\frac{\mathrm{se}'_{2n+2}(0)\mathrm{se}'_{2n+2}(\tfrac{1}{2}\pi)}{k^2B_2^{(2n+2)}}\left(\frac{2}{\pi v}\right)^{\frac{1}{2}} e^{i(v+\frac{1}{4}\pi)}. \tag{2}$$

Substituting (1), (2) into (3) § 19.20 leads to the formula

$$\phi_2 \sim 2\phi_0\left(\frac{2}{\pi k_1 r}\right)^{\frac{1}{2}} e^{i(k_1 r-\omega t+\frac{1}{4}\pi)} \sum_{m=1}^{\infty} \mathrm{se}_m(\eta, q)\mathrm{se}_m(\theta, q)\frac{\mathrm{se}'_m(0, q)}{\mathrm{Ne}_m^{(1)'}(0, q)}. \tag{3}$$

This represents the velocity potential of the scattered wave at a great distance r from the ribbon. The pressure is $\rho_0 \partial\phi_2/\partial t$, so

$$p_2 = -i\rho_0\omega\phi_2 \sim 2\rho\omega\phi_0\left(\frac{2}{\pi k_1 r}\right)^{\frac{1}{2}} e^{i(k_1 r-\omega t+\frac{1}{4}\pi)} \times$$

$$\times \sum_{m=1}^{\infty} \mathrm{se}_m(\eta, q)\mathrm{se}_m(\theta, q)\frac{\mathrm{se}'_m(0, q)}{\mathrm{Ne}_m^{(1)'}(0, q)}. \tag{4}$$

19.30. Scattering of electromagnetic waves by long elliptical metal cylinder. Consider the incident wave to be plane polarized, the electric force vector being parallel to the axis $Z'OZ$, and let the direction of propagation be that indicated in Fig. 47.† Assuming that the cylinder has zero resistivity, the boundary condition is that the sum of the incident and scattered waves is zero at the surface where $\xi = \xi_0$. For the incident plane polarized wave the electric force is represented by

$$E_1 = E_0 e^{i(k_1 \sigma - \omega t)}, \tag{1}$$

so by § 19.12, in terms of elliptical coordinates we have

$$E_1 = 2e^{-i\omega t} E_0 \sum_{n=0}^{\infty} \text{ [as at (3) § 19.12].} \tag{2}$$

For the scattered wave we take

$$E_2 = \text{the r.h.s. of (3) § 19.14.} \tag{3}$$

The boundary condition is that

$$E_1 + E_2 = 0 \quad \text{when} \quad \xi = \xi_0, \tag{4}$$

so from (2), (3) we obtain

$$C_{2n} = -\frac{2E_0}{p_{2n}} \frac{C_{2n}(\xi_0)}{\text{Me}_{2n}^{(1)}(\xi_0)}, \qquad C_{2n+1} = -\frac{2iE_0}{p_{2n+1}} \frac{\text{Ce}_{2n+1}(\xi_0)}{\text{Me}_{2n+1}^{(1)}(\xi_0)}; \tag{5}$$

$$S_{2n+1} = -\frac{2iE_0}{s_{2n+1}} \frac{\text{Se}_{2n+1}(\xi_0)}{\text{Ne}_{2n+1}^{(1)}(\xi_0)}, \qquad S_{2n+2} = -\frac{2E_0}{s_{2n+2}} \frac{S_{2n+2}(\xi_0)}{\text{Ne}_{2n+2}^{(1)}(\xi_0)}. \tag{6}$$

Writing

$$\text{Ce}_m(\xi_0)/\text{Me}_m^{(1)}(\xi_0) = \cos \alpha_m e^{-i\alpha_m},$$

$$\cos \alpha_m = \text{Ce}_m(\xi_0)/[\text{Ce}_m^2(\xi_0) + \text{Fey}_m^2(\xi_0)]^{\frac{1}{2}}; \tag{7}$$

$$\text{Se}_m(\xi_0)/\text{Ne}_m^{(1)}(\xi_0) = \cos \beta_m e^{-i\beta_m},$$

$$\cos \beta_m = \text{Se}_m(\xi_0)/[\text{Se}_m^2(\xi_0) + \text{Gey}_m^2(\xi_0)]^{\frac{1}{2}}, \tag{8}$$

(3) may be expressed in the form

$$E_2 = -2e^{-i\omega t} E_0 \sum_{n=0}^{\infty} \left[\frac{A_0^{(2n)} e^{-i\alpha_{2n}} \cos \alpha_{2n} \, \text{Me}_{2n}^{(1)}(\xi) \text{ce}_{2n}(\eta) \text{ce}_{2n}(\theta)}{\text{ce}_{2n}(0) \text{ce}_{2n}(\frac{1}{2}\pi)} + \right.$$

$$+ \frac{k^2 B_2^{(2n+2)} e^{-i\beta_{2n+2}} \cos \beta_{2n+2} \, \text{Ne}_{2n+2}^{(1)}(\xi) \text{se}_{2n+2}(\eta) \text{se}_{2n+2}(\theta)}{\text{se}_{2n+2}'(0) \text{se}_{2n+2}'(\frac{1}{2}\pi)} +$$

$$+ i \left\{ \frac{-kA_1^{(2n+1)} e^{-i\alpha_{2n+1}} \cos \alpha_{2n+1} \, \text{Me}_{2n+1}^{(1)}(\xi) \text{ce}_{2n+1}(\eta) \text{ce}_{2n+1}(\theta)}{\text{ce}_{2n+1}(0) \text{ce}_{2n+1}'(\frac{1}{2}\pi)} + \right.$$

$$\left. \left. + \frac{kB_1^{(2n+1)} e^{-i\beta_{2n+1}} \cos \beta_{2n+1} \, \text{Ne}_{2n+1}^{(1)}(\xi) \text{se}_{2n+1}(\eta) \text{se}_{2n+1}(\theta)}{\text{se}_{2n+1}'(0) \text{se}_{2n+1}(\frac{1}{2}\pi)} \right\} \right]. \tag{9}$$

† The equation of propagation is (11) § 18.22 in rectangular coordinates, and (1) § 18.50 in elliptical coordinates.

When $\theta = \frac{1}{2}\pi$, $ce_{2n+1}(\theta) = se_{2n+2}(\theta) = 0$, and (3), (5), (6) yield

$$E_2 = -e^{-i\omega t} 2E_0 \sum_{n=0}^{\infty} \left[\frac{Ce_{2n}(\xi_0)}{p_{2n} Me_{2n}^{(1)}(\xi_0)} Me_{2n}^{(1)}(\xi)ce_{2n}(\eta)ce_{2n}(\tfrac{1}{2}\pi) + \right.$$

$$\left. + \frac{i\,Se_{2n+1}(\xi_0)}{s_{2n+1} Ne_{2n+1}^{(1)}(\xi_0)} Ne_{2n+1}^{(1)}(\xi)se_{2n+1}(\eta)se_{2n+1}(\tfrac{1}{2}\pi) \right]. \quad (10)$$

If ξ is large enough, $v = k \cosh \xi \simeq k_1 r$, and the asymptotic forms of the Me, Ne functions may be used. Then with the dominant term only (see § 11.11)

$$\frac{2Me_{2n}^{(1)}(\xi)}{p_{2n}} \sim \frac{2i\,Ne_{2n+1}^{(1)}(\xi)}{s_{2n+1}} \sim -2\left(\frac{2}{\pi k_1 r}\right)^{\frac{1}{2}} e^{i(v+\frac{1}{4}\pi)}. \quad (11)$$

Substituting from (11) into (10) leads to

$$E_2 \sim e^{-i\omega t} 2\left(\frac{2}{\pi k_1 r}\right)^{\frac{1}{2}} e^{i(k_1 r + \frac{3}{4}\pi)} E_0 \times$$

$$\times \sum_{n=0}^{\infty} \left[\frac{Ce_{2n}(\xi_0)ce_{2n}(\eta)ce_{2n}(\tfrac{1}{2}\pi)}{Me_{2n}^{(1)}(\xi_0)} + \frac{Se_{2n+1}(\xi_0)se_{2n+1}(\eta)se_{2n+1}(\tfrac{1}{2}\pi)}{Ne_{2n+1}^{(1)}(\xi_0)} \right]. \quad (12)$$

This represents the electric force due to the scattered wave at a large distance r from the axis of the cylinder. The resultant electric force at the point is $E = E_1 + E_2$.

19.31. Long rigid ribbon.

Here $\xi_0 = 0$, so in (6) § 19.30 $S_m = 0$, while from (5) § 19.30

$$C_{2n} = -\frac{2E_0\,Ce_{2n}(0)}{p_{2n} Me_{2n}^{(1)}(0)} = -\frac{2E_0 A_0^{(2n)}}{Me_{2n}^{(1)}(0)ce_{2n}(\tfrac{1}{2}\pi)}$$

and $\quad C_{2n+1} = -\dfrac{2iE_0\,Ce_{2n+1}(0)}{p_{2n+1} Me_{2n+1}^{(1)}(0)} = \dfrac{2ikA_1^{(2n+1)}E_0}{Me_{2n+1}^{(1)}(0)ce'_{2n+1}(\tfrac{1}{2}\pi)}. \quad (1)$

Substituting from (1) into (3) § 19.30 yields

$$E_2 = -2e^{-i\omega t}E_0 \sum_{n=0}^{\infty} \left[\frac{A_0^{(2n)} Me_{2n}^{(1)}(\xi)ce_{2n}(\eta)ce_{2n}(\theta)}{Me_{2n}^{(1)}(0)ce_{2n}(\tfrac{1}{2}\pi)} - \right.$$

$$\left. - \frac{ikA_1^{(2n+1)} Me_{2n+1}^{(1)}(\xi)ce_{2n+1}(\eta)ce_{2n+1}(\theta)}{Me_{2n+1}^{(1)}(0)ce'_{2n+1}(\tfrac{1}{2}\pi)} \right]. \quad (2)$$

This represents the scattered wave at any point (ξ, η) on or outside the ribbon.

Polar diagrams for electromagnetic waves scattered by a ribbon of zero resistivity and width $2h$ for various wave-lengths (as a function of $2h$) and angles of incidence are shown in Fig. 49.

The solution for the diffraction of electromagnetic waves at a slit of width $2h$ in an infinite perfectly conducting flat sheet may be obtained by analysis akin to that which precedes. The boundary

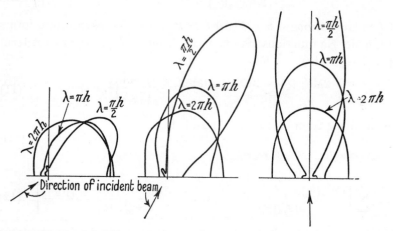

FIG. 49. Polar diagrams for electromagnetic waves scattered by a long ribbon [144].

condition is that the electric force vanishes at the surface of the sheet. In the incident wave the electric force vector is parallel to the axis of the slit.

19.32. Formula for large distance from ribbon.

We use the asymptotic approximations

$$\mathrm{Me}_{2n}^{(1)}(\xi) \sim -\frac{i\,\mathrm{ce}_{2n}(0)\mathrm{ce}_{2n}(\tfrac{1}{2}\pi)}{A_0^{(2n)}}\left(\frac{2}{\pi k_1 r}\right)^{\frac{1}{2}}e^{i(k_1 r+\frac{1}{4}\pi)} \tag{1}$$

and

$$\mathrm{Me}_{2n+1}^{(1)}(\xi) \sim \frac{\mathrm{ce}_{2n+1}(0)\mathrm{ce}_{2n+1}'(\tfrac{1}{2}\pi)}{kA_1^{(2n+1)}}\left(\frac{2}{\pi k_1 r}\right)^{\frac{1}{2}}e^{i(k_1 r+\frac{1}{4}\pi)}. \tag{2}$$

Inserting these in (2) § 19.31 leads to

$$E_2 \sim 2\left(\frac{2}{\pi k_1 r}\right)^{\frac{1}{2}}e^{i(k_1 r-\omega t+\frac{3}{4}\pi)}E_0\sum_{m=0}^{\infty}\mathrm{ce}_m(\eta)\mathrm{ce}_m(\theta)\frac{\mathrm{ce}_m(0)}{\mathrm{Me}_m^{(1)}(0)}. \tag{3}$$

This represents the scattered wave at a great distance r from the ribbon. As in (12) § 19.30 and (2) § 19.31, $e^{-i\omega t}$ may be a separate factor.

APPENDIX I

Degenerate forms of Mathieu and modified Mathieu functions

1. Mathieu functions. When the fundamental ellipse tends to a circle, by § 9.11, $h \to 0$ and, since $q^{\frac{1}{2}} = k = \frac{1}{2}k_1 h$, $q \to 0$. By § 3.32 all $A_p^{(m)}$ in the series for $ce_m(\eta, q)$ tend to zero, except that $A_m^{(m)} \to 1$. Hence as the eccentricity $e \to 0$, $q \to 0$ and

$$ce_m(\eta, q) \to \cos m\eta = \cos m\phi \quad (m \geqslant 1), \tag{1}$$

the confocal hyperbolae in Fig. 16 becoming radii of the circle, with $\eta = \phi$. For $n = 0$, $ce_0(\eta, 0) \to 2^{-\frac{1}{2}} = A_0^{(0)}$. In the same way it can be shown that as $e \to 0$,

$$se_m(\eta, q) \to \sin m\eta = \sin m\phi \quad (m \geqslant 1). \tag{2}$$

Fractional orders. As $e \to 0$, $q \to 0$, $A_p^{(m+\beta)} \to 0$ except for $p = m$, when $A_m^{(m+\beta)} \to 1$. Thus

$$ce_{m+\beta}(z, q) \to \cos(m+\beta)\phi \tag{3}$$

and
$$se_{m+\beta}(z, q) \to \sin(m+\beta)\phi. \tag{4}$$

2. Modified Mathieu functions. The equation for these functions, $q > 0$, is

$$y'' - (a - 2k^2 \cosh 2\xi)y = 0 \quad (q = k^2). \tag{1}$$

By §§ 9.11, 9.12 when a confocal ellipse of semi-major axis r tends to a circle with this radius, $\xi \to +\infty$, $h \to 0$ such that $h \cosh \xi \to r$, i.e. $\frac{1}{2}he^\xi \to r$. Then $2k^2 \cosh 2\xi \to k^2 e^{2\xi}$, while if this remains finite, $k \to 0$ and, therefore, $a \to m^2$ for a function of integral order m. Consequently (1) degenerates to

$$y'' + (k^2 e^{2\xi} - m^2)y = 0. \tag{2}$$

Putting $r = \frac{1}{2}he^\xi$, $2k = k_1 h$, (2) transforms to the standard Bessel equation

$$\frac{d^2y}{dr^2} + \frac{1}{r}\frac{dy}{dr} + \left(k_1^2 - \frac{m^2}{r^2}\right)y = 0. \tag{3}$$

With $k_1 r = ke^\xi$, the formal solutions of (3) are $J_m(k_1 r)$ and $Y_m(k_1 r)$. Then as $\xi \to +\infty$, $k \to 0$, $\cosh \xi \to \sinh \xi$, $k_1 r$ is finite and the solutions of (1) are constant multiples of the corresponding solutions of (3), each to each. Now as ξ and $r \to +\infty$, the dominant·terms in the asymptotic expansions of $Ce_m(\xi, q)$, $Se_m(\xi, q)$, and $J_m(k_1 r)$ are identical save for constant multipliers p'_m, s'_m. A similar remark applies in the case of $\mathrm{Fey}_m(\xi,q)$, $\mathrm{Gey}_m(\xi,q)$, and $Y_m(k_1 r)$. Thus we have the following degenerate cases as $\xi \to +\infty$:

$$\mathrm{Ce}_m(\xi,q) \to p'_m J_m(k_1 r) \qquad\qquad (m \geqslant 0), \quad (4)$$

$$\mathrm{Se}_m(\xi,q) \to s'_m J_m(k_1 r) \qquad\qquad (m \geqslant 1); \quad (5)$$

$$\frac{d}{d\xi}\mathrm{Ce}_m(\xi,q) \to p'_m r \frac{d}{dr} J_m(k_1 r) = p'_m k_1 r J'_m(k_1 r) \quad (m \geqslant 0), \quad (6)$$

$$\frac{d}{d\xi}\mathrm{Se}_m(\xi,q) \to s'_m r \frac{d}{dr} J_m(k_1 r) = s'_m k_1 r J'_m(k_1 r) \quad (m \geqslant 1); \quad (7)$$

$$\mathrm{Fey}_m(\xi,q) \to p'_m Y_m(k_1 r) \qquad\qquad (m \geqslant 0), \quad (8)$$

$$\mathrm{Gey}_m(\xi,q) \to s'_m Y_m(k_1 r) \qquad\qquad (m \geqslant 1); \quad (9)$$

$$\frac{d}{d\xi}\mathrm{Fey}_m(\xi,q) \to p'_m k_1 r Y'_m(k_1 r) \qquad\qquad (m \geqslant 0), \quad (10)$$

$$\frac{d}{d\xi}\mathrm{Gey}_m(\xi,q) \to s'_m k_1 r Y'_m(k_1 r) \qquad\qquad (m \geqslant 1). \quad (11)$$

Applying the foregoing to (1), (2) § 13.40 leads to

$$\mathrm{Me}_{2n}^{(1)}(z,q) = -2i\,\mathrm{Fek}_{2n}(z,q) \to p'_{2n} H_{2n}^{(1)}(k_1 r), \qquad (12)$$

$$\mathrm{Me}_{2n+1}^{(1)}(z,q) = -2\,\mathrm{Fek}_{2n+1}(z,q) \to p'_{2n+1} H_{2n+1}^{(1)}(k_1 r); \qquad (13)$$

$$\mathrm{Ne}_{2n+1}^{(1)}(z,q) = -2\,\mathrm{Gek}_{2n+1}(z,q) \to s'_{2n+1} H_{2n+1}^{(1)}(k_1 r), \qquad (14)$$

$$\mathrm{Ne}_{2n+2}^{(1)}(z,q) = -2i\,\mathrm{Gek}_{2n+2}(z,q) \to s'_{2n+2} H_{2n+2}^{(1)}(k_1 r). \qquad (15)$$

The degenerate forms of $\mathrm{Fe}_m(z,q)$, $\mathrm{Ge}_m(z,q)$ may be derived by applying (4), (5), (8), (9) to (4), (5) § 13.21, while those of the functions of order $(m+\beta)$ are identical in form with (4), (5), but m is replaced by $(m+\beta)$.

3. Determination of p'_m, s'_m. These are obtained by comparing the dominant terms in the asymptotic expansions of the corresponding functions. Thus by (1) § 11.10 and (15) § 8.10, when $\xi \to +\infty$

$$\mathrm{Ce}_{2n}(\xi,q) \sim \frac{\mathrm{ce}_{2n}(0,q)\mathrm{ce}_{2n}(\tfrac{1}{2}\pi,q)}{A_0^{(2n)}}\left(\frac{2}{\pi k e^\xi}\right)^{\frac{1}{2}}\sin(k e^\xi + \tfrac{1}{4}\pi), \qquad (1)$$

while $$J_{2n}(k_1 r) \sim (-1)^n\left(\frac{2}{\pi k_1 r}\right)^{\frac{1}{2}}\sin(k_1 r + \tfrac{1}{4}\pi). \qquad (2)$$

Remembering that as $\xi \to +\infty$, $k e^\xi \to k_1 r$, it follows from (1), (2) and (4) § 2, that

$$p'_{2n} = (-1)^n\,\mathrm{ce}_{2n}(0,q)\mathrm{ce}_{2n}(\tfrac{1}{2}\pi,q)/A_0^{(2n)} = (-1)^n p_{2n}. \qquad (3)$$

Similarly we find that

$$p'_{2n+1} = (-1)^{n+1} \operatorname{ce}_{2n+1}(0,q)\operatorname{ce}'_{2n+1}(\tfrac{1}{2}\pi,q)/kA_1^{(2n+1)} = (-1)^n p_{2n+1}, \quad (4)$$

$$s'_{2n+1} = (-1)^n \operatorname{se}_{2n+1}(0,q)\operatorname{se}_{2n+1}(\tfrac{1}{2}\pi,q)/kB_1^{(2n+1)} = (-1)^n s_{2n+1}, \quad (5)$$

and

$$s'_{2n+2} = (-1)^{n+1} \operatorname{se}'_{2n+2}(0,q)\operatorname{se}'_{2n+2}(\tfrac{1}{2}\pi,q)/k^2 B_2^{(2n+2)} = (-1)^{n+1} s_{2n+2}. \quad (6)$$

4. Results for $q < 0$. We write $-k_1^2$ for k_1^2 in (3) § 2 thereby obtaining the equation for the modified Bessel functions $I_m(k_1 r)$, $K_m(k_1 r)$. The degenerate cases are:

$$\operatorname{Ce}_{2n}(\xi, -q) \to p'_{2n} I_{2n}(k_1 r), \quad (1)$$

$$\operatorname{Ce}_{2n+1}(\xi, -q) \to s'_{2n+1} I_{2n+1}(k_1 r); \quad (2)$$

$$\operatorname{Se}_{2n+1}(\xi, -q) \to p'_{2n+1} I_{2n+1}(k_1 r), \quad (3)$$

$$\operatorname{Se}_{2n+2}(\xi, -q) \to s'_{2n+2} I_{2n+2}(k_1 r); \quad (4)$$

$$\frac{d}{d\xi}\operatorname{Ce}_{2n}(\xi, -q) \to p'_{2n} k_1 r I'_{2n}(k_1 r), \quad (5)$$

$$\frac{d}{d\xi}\operatorname{Ce}_{2n+1}(\xi, -q) \to s'_{2n+1} k_1 r I'_{2n+1}(k_1 r); \quad (6)$$

$$\frac{d}{d\xi}\operatorname{Se}_{2n+1}(\xi, -q) \to p'_{2n+1} k_1 r I'_{2n+1}(k_1 r), \quad (7)$$

$$\frac{d}{d\xi}\operatorname{Se}_{2n+2}(\xi, -q) \to s'_{2n+2} k_1 r I'_{2n+2}(k_1 r); \quad (8)$$

$$\pi \operatorname{Fek}_{2n}(\xi, -q) \to p'_{2n} K_{2n}(k_1 r), \quad (9)$$

$$\pi \operatorname{Fek}_{2n+1}(\xi, -q) \to s'_{2n+1} K_{2n+1}(k_1 r); \quad (10)$$

$$\pi \operatorname{Gek}_{2n+1}(\xi, -q) \to p'_{2n+1} K_{2n+1}(k_1 r), \quad (11)$$

$$\pi \operatorname{Gek}_{2n+2}(\xi, -q) \to s'_{2n+2} K_{2n+2}(k_1 r). \quad (12)$$

The results for $\operatorname{Me}_m^{(1)}(\xi, -q)$, $\operatorname{Ne}_m^{(1)}(\xi, -q)$ may be derived from (9)–(12) and § 13.41.

5. Degeneration of $\operatorname{ce}_m(z, -q)$, $\operatorname{se}_m(z, -q)$ to parabolic cylinder functions. When z is small, $\cos 2z \simeq 1 - 2z^2$ and Mathieu's equation, for q negative, may be written

$$y'' + (a + 2q - 4qz^2)y = 0. \quad (1)$$

Let $z = \tfrac{1}{2}xq^{-\frac{1}{4}}$, and suppose that as $q \to +\infty$, $z \to 0$ but qz^2 remains finite [91]. Then by (2) § 12.30,

$$(a_{2n} + 2q) \sim (8n + 2)q^{\frac{1}{2}}, \quad (2)$$

and with these changes (1) is transformed to

$$\frac{d^2y}{dx^2} + [(2n+\tfrac{1}{2}) - \tfrac{1}{4}x^2]y = 0, \tag{3}$$

which is the differential equation for the parabolic cylinder function $D_{2n}(x)$. Hence under the above conditions

$$\mathrm{ce}_{2n}(z, -q) \to \text{a constant} \times D_{2n}(x) = K D_{2n}(2zq^{\frac{1}{2}}). \tag{4}$$

Similarly it may be shown that

$$\mathrm{se}_{2n+1}(z, -q) \to \text{a constant} \times D_{2n+1}(x). \tag{5}$$

APPENDIX II

TABLE 25. *Characteristic numbers for*
$$ce_m(z,q),\ m = 0\text{–}5;\ se_m(z,q),\ m = 1\text{–}6$$

q	$-a_0$	$-b_1$	$-a_1$	$-b_2$	$+a_2$	$+b_3$
0	0·00000 00	−1·00000 00	−1·00000 00	−4·00000 00	4·00000 00	9·00000 00
1	0·45513 86	0·11024 88	−1·85910 81	−3·91702 48	4·37130 10	9·04773 93
2	1·51395 69	1·39067 65	−2·37919 99	−3·67223 27	5·17266 51	9·14062 77
3	2·83439 19	2·78537 97	−2·51903 91	−3·27692 20	6·04519 69	9·22313 28
4	4·28051 88	4·25918 29	−2·31800 82	−2·74688 10	6·82907 48	9·26144 61
5	5·80004 60	5·79008 06	−1·85818 75	−2·09946 04	7·44910 97	9·23632 77
6	7·36883 08	7·36391 10	−1·21427 82	−1·35138 12	7·87006 45	9·13790 58
7	8·97374 25	8·97120 24	−0·43834 91	−0·51754 54	8·08662 31	8·96238 55
8	10·60672 92	10·60536 81	0·43594 36	0·38936 18	8·11523 88	8·70991 44
9	12·26241 42	12·26166 17	1·38670 16	1·35881 01	7·98284 32	8·38311 92
10	13·93698 00	13·93655 25	2·39914 24	2·38215 82	7·71736 98	7·98606 91
12	17·33206 60	17·33191 84	4·57013 29	4·56353 99	6·87873 69	7·00056 68
14	20·77605 53	20·77600 04	6·89340 05	6·89070 07	5·73631 23	5·79262 95
16	24·25867 95	24·25865 78	9·33526 71	9·33410 97	4·37123 26	4·39789 62
18	27·77284 22	27·77283 32	11·87324 25	11·87272 65	2·83305 67	2·84599 17
20	31·31339 01	31·31338 62	14·49130 14	14·49106 33	1·15428 29	1·16070 57
24	38·45897 32	38·45897 24	19·92259 56	19·92254 03	−2·53976 57	−2·53807 79
28	45·67336 96	45·67336 94	25·56174 71	25·56173 29	−6·58806 30	−6·58758 50
32	52·94222 30	52·94222 29	31·36515 44	31·36515 05	−10·91435 34	−10·91420 90
36	60·25556 79	60·25556 79	37·30263 91	37·30263 80	−15·46677 03	−15·46672 43
40	67·60615 22	67·60615 22	43·35227 53	43·35227 49	−20·20794 08	−20·20792 54

q	a_3	b_4	a_4	b_5	a_5	b_6
0	9·00000 00	16·00000 00	16·00000 00	25·00000 00	25·00000 00	36·00000 00
1	9·07836 88	16·03297 01	16·03383 23	25·02084 08	25·02085 43	36·01428 99
2	9·37032 25	16·12768 80	16·14120 38	25·08334 90	25·08377 78	36·05720 70
3	9·91550 63	16·27270 12	16·33872 07	25·18707 98	25·19028 55	36·12887 12
4	10·67102 71	16·45203 53	16·64981 89	25·33054 49	25·34375 76	36·22941 14
5	11·54883 20	16·64821 99	17·09658 17	25·51081 60	25·54997 17	36·35886 68
6	12·46560 07	16·84460 16	17·68878 30	25·72341 07	25·81727 20	36·51706 67
7	13·35842 13	17·02666 08	18·41660 87	25·96244 72	26·15612 02	36·70350 27
8	14·18188 04	17·18252 78	19·25270 51	26·22099 95	26·57775 33	36·91721 31
9	14·90367 97	17·30301 10	20·16092 64	26·49154 72	27·09186 61	37·15669 50
10	15·50278 44	17·38138 07	21·10463 37	26·76642 64	27·70376 87	37·41985 88
12	16·30153 49	17·39524 97	22·97212 75	27·30001 24	29·20805 50	38·00600 87
14	16·59854 05	17·20711 53	24·65059 51	27·76976 67	31·00005 08	38·64847 19
16	16·48688 43	16·81868 37	26·00867 83	28·13635 59	32·93089 51	39·31501 08
18	16·06197 54	16·24208 04	26·98776 64	28·37385 82	34·85305 87	39·97235 11
20	15·39581 09	15·49397 76	27·59457 82	28·46822 13	36·64498 97	40·58966 41
24	13·52284 27	13·55279 65	27·88544 08	28·21535 94	39·51255 19	41·60570 99
28	11·11107 98	11·12062 27	27·28330 82	27·40574 88	41·23495 03	42·22484 15
32	8·29149 62	8·29467 21	26·06244 82	26·10835 26	41·95351 12	42·39394 28
36	5·14563 63	5·14673 75	24·37850 94	24·39606 65	41·92666 46	42·11835 61
40	1·72964 91	1·73004 56	22·32527 63	22·33214 85	41·34975 44	41·43300 52

APPENDIX III

Classification of Mathieu functions for a, q real $\gtrless 0$

In Tables 26–8, $m = 2n$ or $2n+1$, $n = 0, 1, 2, \ldots$; $0 < \beta < 1$; μ real and positive.

TABLE 26. *Solutions of $y'' + (a - 2q \cos 2z)y = 0$:*
ordinary functions

Order	First kind	Second kind	Alternative second kind
Integral	$\mathrm{ce}_m(z, \pm q)$	$\mathrm{fe}_m(z, \pm q)$	$\mathrm{fek}_m(z, -q)$, z real
Integral	$\mathrm{se}_m(z, \pm q)$	$\mathrm{ge}_m(z, \pm q)$	$\mathrm{gek}_m(z, -q)$, z real
Fractional	$\mathrm{ce}_{m+\beta}(z, \pm q)$	$\mathrm{se}_{m+\beta}(z, \pm q)$	

TABLE 27. *Solutions of $y'' - (a - 2q \cosh 2z)y = 0$:*
modified functions

Order	First kind	Second kind	Alternative second kind	Third kind
Integral	$\mathrm{Ce}_m(z, \pm q)$	$\mathrm{Fey}_m(z, \pm q)$; $\mathrm{Fek}_m(z, \pm q)$	$\mathrm{Fe}_m(z, \pm q)$	$\mathrm{Me}_m^{(1),(2)}(z, \pm q)$
Integral	$\mathrm{Se}_m(z, \pm q)$	$\mathrm{Gey}_m(z, \pm q)$; $\mathrm{Gek}_m(z, \pm q)$	$\mathrm{Ge}_m(z, \pm q)$	$\mathrm{Ne}_m^{(1),(2)}(z, \pm q)$
Fractional	$\mathrm{Ce}_{m+\beta}(z, \pm q)$	$\mathrm{Se}_{m+\beta}(z, \pm q)$		

TABLE 28. *Solutions of $y'' + (a - 2q \cos 2z)y = 0$:*
functions of order $(m+\mu)$

First kind	Second kind
$\mathrm{ceu}_{m+\mu}(z, \pm q)$	$\mathrm{ceu}_{m+\mu}(-z, \pm q)$

The cer, cei functions have been omitted since q is negative imaginary. Fey, Gey, Fek, Gek take priority over Fe_m, Ge_m as modified functions of the second kind because:

1. They are better suited for applications when z is large;
2. Their representations in B.F. product series converge rapidly, thereby facilitating computation;
3. They degenerate to the Y- and K-Bessel functions under the conditions in Appendix I.

Excepting Fe_m, Ge_m, alternative representations of each function are given herein. For instance, four different series and five integral relations are given for $\mathrm{Ce}_m(z, q)$. $\mathrm{Fey}_m(z, q)$ is a Y-type modified Mathieu function of the second kind of order m, q positive, whereas $\mathrm{Fek}_m(z, -q)$ is a K-type modified Mathieu function of the second kind of order m, q negative.

REFERENCES

Abbreviations used in Section A

1. *A. der P.*   *Annalen der Physik.*
2. *A. für E.*   *Archiv für Elektrotechnik.*
3. *D.*   *Inaugural Dissertation.*
4. *M.A.*   *Mathematische Annalen.*
5. *M.N.R.A.S.*   *Monthly Notices of Royal Astronomical Society.*
6. *M.T.A.C.*   *Mathematical Tables and other Aids to Computation.*
7. *M.Z.*   *Mathematische Zeitschrift.*
8. *P.C.P.S.*   *Proceedings Cambridge Philosophical Society.*
9. *P.E.M.S.*   *Proceedings Edinburgh Mathematical Society.*
10. *P.I.C.M.*   *Proceedings International Congress of Mathematicians.*
11. *P.I.R.E.*   *Proceedings Institute Radio Engineers (America).*
12. *P.L.M.S.*   *Proceedings London Mathematical Society.*
13. *P.M.*   *Philosophical Magazine.*
14. *P.R.S.ˉ*   *Proceedings Royal Society, London.*
15. *P.R.S.E.*   *Proceedings Royal Society, Edinburgh.*
16. *Q.J.M.*   *Quarterly Journal of Mathematics (Oxford).*
17. *T.C.P.S.*   *Transactions Cambridge Philosophical Society.*
18. *T.M.J.*   *Tôhoku Mathematical Journal.*
19. *Z.A.M.M.*   *Zeitschrift für angewandte Mathematik und Mechanik.*
20. *Z. für H.*   *Zeitschrift für Hochfrequenztechnik.*
21. *Z.P.*   *Zeitschrift für Physik.*

A. SCIENTIFIC PAPERS

1. Ataka, H. Super-regeneration in ultra-short wave receiver. *P.I.R.E.* **23**, 841, 1935.
2. Barrow, W. L. Frequency modulation. *P.I.R.E.* **20**, 1626, 1932.
3. —— *P.I.R.E.* **22**, 201, 1934.
4. —— Smith, D. B., and Baumann, F. W. Oscillatory circuits having periodically varying parameters. *Jour. Frank. Inst.* **221**, 403 and 509, 1936.
5. Bateman, H. Solution of linear D.E. by definite integrals. *T.C.P.S.* **21**, 171, 1909.
6. Bickley, W. G. A class of hyperbolic Mathieu functions. *P.M.* **30**, 312, 1940.
7. —— Tabulation of Mathieu functions. *M.T.A.C.* **1**, 409, 1945.
8. —— and McLachlan, N. W. Mathieu functions of integral order and their tabulation. *M.T.A.C.* **2**, 1, 1946.
9. Bôcher, M. *P.I.C.M.*, Cambridge, **1**, 163, 1912.
10. Bock, Ph. *D.*, Prague, 1932.
11. Brainerd, J. G. Note on modulation. *P.I.R.E.* **28**, 136, 1940.
12. —— and Weygandt, C. N. Solutions of Mathieu's equation. *P.M.* **30**, 458, 1940.

374 REFERENCES

13. Brainerd, J. G. Stability of oscillations in systems obeying Mathieu's equation. *Jour. Frank. Inst.* **233**, 135, 1942.
14. Bremekamp, H. Over de periodieke oplossinger der vergelÿking van Mathieu. *Nieuw. Arch. voor Wiskunde*, **15**, 138, 1925.
15. —— Over de voortplanting van een golfbeweging in een medium van periodieke structuur. *Physica*, **6**, 136, 1926.
16. —— On the solution of Mathieu's equation. *Nieuw. Arch. voor Wiskunde*, **15**, 252, 1927.
17. Bruns, H. *Astron. Nachr.*, No. 2533, 193, 1883; No. 2553, 129, 1884.
18. Burgess, A. G. Determinants for periodic solution of Mathieu's equation. *P.E.M.S.* **33**, 25, 1915.
19. Butts, W. H. Elliptic cylinder function of class *K*. *D.*, Zürich, 1908.
20. Callandreau, O. *Astron. Nachr.*, No. 2547, 1884.
21. Carson, J. R. Notes on theory of modulation. *P.I.R.E.* **10**, 62, 1922.
22. Chu, L. J. Electromagnetic waves in elliptic metal pipes. *Jour. App. Phys.* **9**, 583, 1938.
23. —— and Stratton, J. A. Elliptic and spheroidal wave functions. *Jour. Math. and Phys. Mass. Inst. Techn.* **20**, 259, 1941.
24. Couwenhoven, A. Über die Schütterlerscheinungen elektrischer Lokomotiven mit Kurbelantrieb. Forschungsarbeiten, *V.D.I.*, Heft 218, 1919. (This is a special report listed on p. xxviii, vol. 63.)
25. Curtis, M. F. Existence of the elliptic cylinder functions. *Ann. of Math.* **20**, 213, 1917.
26. Dannacher, S. Zur Theorie der Funktionen des elliptischen Zylinders. *D.*, Zürich, 1906.
27. David, S. P. *L'Onde Électrique*, **7**, 217, 1928.
28. Davies, T. V. Flow of viscous fluid past a flat plate. *P.M.* **31**, 283, 1941.
29. Dhar, S. C. Convergence of second solutions of Mathieu's equation. *Bull. Calcutta Math. Soc.* **10**, 1921.
30. —— Solutions of Mathieu's equation, of second kind. *T.M.J.* **19**, 175, 1921.
31. —— Integral equations for elliptic cylinder functions. *Jour. Dept. Sc. Calcutta Univ.* **3**, 251, 1922.
32. —— Elliptic cylinder functions of second kind. *Amer. Jour. Math.* **45**, 217, 1923.
33. —— Integral equations and expansions of elliptic cylinder functions in Bessel functions. *T.M.J.* **24**, 40, 1924.
34. —— *Jour. Indian Math. Soc.* **16**, 227, 1926.
35. —— Elliptic cylinder functions of second kind. *Bull. Calcutta Math. Soc.* **18**, 11, 1927.
36. Dougall, J. Solution of Mathieu's equation. *P.E.M.S.* **34**, 4, 1916.
37. —— Solution of Mathieu's equation and asymptotic expansions. *P.E.M.S.* **41**, 26, 1923.
38. —— Solutions of Mathieu's equation, representation by contour integrals, and asymptotic expansions. *P.E.M.S.* **44**, 57, 1926.
39. Drefus, L. Eigenschwingungen von Systemen mit periodisch veränderlicher Elastizität. *A. für E.* **11**, 207, 1920.
40. Duffing, G. Erzwungene Schwingungen bei veränderlicher Eigenfrequenz und ihre technische Bedeutung. Sammlung Vieweg. Heft 41/42.

41. Einaudi, R. Sulle configurazioni di equilibrio instabile di una piastra sollecitata da sforzi tangentiali pulsante. *Atti Accad. Gioenia Catania*, mem. **20**, 1, 1936; mem. **5**, 1, 1937.

42. Emersleben, O. Freie Schwingungen in Kondensatorkreisen. *Phys. Zeits.* **22**, 393, 1921.

43. Erdélyi, A. Über die kleinen Schwingungen eines Pendels mit oszillierendem Aufhängepunkt. *Z.A.M.M.* **14**, 435, 1934.

44. —— Über die freien Schwingungen in Kondensatorkreisen mit periodisch veränderlicher Kapazität. *A. der P.* **19**, 585, 1934.

45. —— Zur Theorie des Pendelrückkopplers. *A. der P.* **23**, 21, 1935.

46. —— Über die rechnerische Ermittlung von Schwingungsvorgängen in Kreisen mit periodisch schwankenden Parametern. *A. für E.* **29**, 473, 1935.

47. —— Über die Integration der Mathieuschen Differentialgleichung durch Laplacesche Integrale. *M.Z.* **41**, 653, 1936.

48. —— Bemerken zur Integration der Mathieuschen Differentialgleichung durch Laplacesche Integrale. *Compositio Math.* **5**, 435, 1938.

49. Floquet, G. Sur les équations différentielles linéaires. *Ann. de l'École Normale Supérieure*, **12**, 47, 1883.

50. Förster, R. Über Schüttel- und Zitterschwingungen. *A. für E.* **27**, 307, 1933.

51. Froidevaux, J., and Liénard, A. *Rev. Gén. Électrique*, **25**, 515, 1929.

52. Goldstein, S. Mathieu functions. *T.C.P.S.* **23**, 303, 1927.

53. —— Approximate solutions of linear D.E. of second order, with application to Mathieu's equation. *P.L.M.S.* **28**, 81, 1927.

54. —— Free oscillations of water in elliptical canal. *P.L.M.S.* **28**, 91, 1927.

55. —— Second solution of Mathieu's equation. *P.C.P.S.* **24**, 224, 1928.

56. —— Asymptotic expansion for the Mathieu characteristic numbers. *P.R.S.E.* **49**, 210, 1929.

57. —— and Mulholland, H. P. Characteristic numbers of Mathieu's equation with imaginary parameter. *P.M.* **8**, 834, 1929.

58. Gorelik, G., and Hintz, G. *Z. für H.* **38**, 222, 1931.

59. —— Resonanzerscheinungen in linearen Systemen mit periodisch veränderlichen Parametern. *Zeits. techn. Phys.*, Leningrad, **4**, 1783, 1934; **5**, 195, 1935; **5**, 489, 1935.

60. Hallén, F. Über die elektrischen Schwingungen in drahtförmigen Leitern. *Uppsala Univ. Årsskr. Math. Naturw.*, 1930.

61. Hamel, G. Über lineare homogene Differentialgleichungen zweiter Ordnung mit periodischen Koeffizienten. *M.A.* **73**, 371, 1913.

62. Harrison, W. J. Motion of spheres, circular and elliptic cylinders through viscous liquid. *T.C.P.S.* **23**, 71, 1924.

63. Hartenstein, H. D., Leipzig, 1887.

64. Hässler, G. *Z. für H.* **44**, 80, 1934.

65. Haupt, O. Über lineare homogene Differentialgleichungen zweiter Ordnung mit periodischen Koeffizienten. *M.A.* **79**, 278, 1919.

66. Hidaka, K. Tables for computing se_1, ce_1, ..., se_7, ce_7 and derivatives. *Mem. Imp. Marine Obser., Kobe, Japan*, **6**, 137, 1936.

67. Hilb, E. Über Kleinsche Theoreme in der Theorie der linearen Differentialgleichungen. *M.A.* **66**, 215, 1908; **68**, 24, 1909.

68. —— Über Reihenentwicklungen nach den Eigenfunktionen linearer Differentialgleichungen. *M.A.* **71**, 76, 1909.

69. Hilbert, D. *Göttinger Nachrichten*, p. 213, 1904.

70. Hill, G. W. Mean motion of the lunar perigee. *Acta. Math.* **8**, 1, 1886.

71. Hille, E. Zeros of the Mathieu functions. *P.L.M.S.* **23**, 185, 1923.

72. Hirsch, P. Das Pendel mit oszillierendem Aufhängepunkt. *Z.A.M.M.* **10**, 41, 1930.

73. Horn, J. *M.A.* **52**, 340, 1899.

74. —— Integration linearer Differentialgleichungen durch Laplacesche Integrale und Fakultätenreihen. *Jahresber. d. Deutschen Math. Ver.* **24**, 309, 1915.

75. —— Singuläre Systeme linearer Volterrascher Integralgleichungen. *M.Z.* **3**, 265, 1919.

76. —— Laplacesche Integrale und Gammaquotientenreihen in der Theorie der Differentialgleichungen und Volterrascher Integralgleichungen. *M.Z.* **8**, 110, 1920.

77. —— Laplacesche Integrale, Binomialkoeffizientenreihen und Gammaquotientenreihen in der Theorie der linearen Differentialgleichungen. *M.Z.* **21**, 85, 1924.

78. Hough, S. S. Dynamical theory of the tides. *Phil. Trans. Roy. Soc.* (A), **189**, 201, 1897.

79. Humbert, P. Mathieu functions of higher order. *P.E.M.S.* **40**, 27, 1922.

80. Ince, E. L. Elliptic cylinder functions of the second kind. *P.E.M.S.* **33**, 2, 1915.

81. —— General solution of Hill's equation. *M.N.R.A.S.* **75**, 436, 1915.

82. —— (Notes on 81.) *M.N.R.A.S.* **76**, 431, 1916.

83. —— (Further notes on 81.) *M.N.R.A.S.* **78**, 141, 1917.

84. —— Impossibility of co-existence of two Mathieu functions. *P.C.P.S.* **21**, 117, 1922.

85. —— Associated Mathieu functions. *P.E.M.S.* **41**, 94, 1923.

86. —— Linear D.E. with periodic coefficients. *P.L.M.S.* **23**, 56, 1923.

87. —— Real zeros of solutions of linear D.E. with periodic coefficients. *P.L.M.S.* **25**, 53, 1924.

88. —— Characteristic numbers of Mathieu equation (1). *P.R.S.E.* **46**, 20, 1925.

89. —— Periodic solutions of linear D.E. with periodic coefficients. *P.C.P.S.* **23**, 44, 1926.

90. —— Second solution of Mathieu's equation. *P.C.P.S.* **23**, 47, 1926.

91. —— Mathieu's equation with large parameters. *Jour. L.M.S.* **2**, 46, 1926.

92. —— Characteristic numbers of Mathieu's equation (2). *P.R.S.E.* **46**, 316, 1926.

93. —— Characteristic numbers of Mathieu's equation (3). *P.R.S.E.* **47**, 294, 1927.

94. —— Mathieu functions of stable type. *P.M.* **6**, 547, 1928.

95. —— Tables of the elliptic cylinder functions. *P.R.S.E.* **52**, 355, 1932.

96. Ince, E. L. Zeros and turning points of elliptic cylinder functions. *P.R.S.E.* **52**, 424, 1932.

97. —— Relations between the elliptic cylinder functions. *P.R.S.E.* **59**, 176, 1939.

98. Ittman, G. P. De rotatie van onsymetrische moleculen. *Physica*, **9**, 305, 1929.

99. —— and Kramers, H. A. Zur Quantelung des asymmetrischen Kreisels. *Z.P.* **58**, 217, 1929; **60**, 663, 1930.

100. —— Zur Theorie der Störungen in Bandenspektren. *Z.P.* **71**, 616, 1931.

101. Jeffreys, H. Approximate solutions of linear D.E. of second order. *P.L.M.S.* **23**, 428, 1924.

102. —— Certain solutions of Mathieu's equation. *P.L.M.S.* **23**, 437, 1924.

103. —— The modified Mathieu equation. *P.L.M.S.* **23**, 449, 1924.

104. —— Free oscillations of water in elliptical lake. *P.L.M.S.* **23**, 455, 1924.

105. Klein, F. Bemerkungen zur Theorie der linearen Differentialgleichungen zweiter Ordnung. *M.A.* **64**, 175, 1907.

106. Klotter, K., and Kotowski, G. *Z.A.M.M.* **19**, 289, 1939.

107. Klotter, K. *Forsch.-Ing. Wes.* **12**, 209, 1941.

108. —— and Kotowski, G. Über die Stabilität der Lösungen Hillscher Differentialgleichungen mit drei unabhängigen Parametern. *Z.A.M.M.* **23**, 149, 1943.

109. Kluge, F. *Ing.-Arch.* **2**, 119, 1931.

110. Kohn, K. *Z. für H.* **37**, 51 and 98, 1931.

111. Kotowski, G. Lösungen der inhomogenen Mathieuschen Differential-gleichung mit periodischer Störfunktion beliebiger Frequenz (mit besonderer Berücksichtigung der Resonanzlösungen). *Z.A.M.M.* **23**, 213, 1943.

112. Kronig, R. de L., and Penney, W. G. Quantum mechanics in crystal lattices. *P.R.S.* (A), **130**, 499, 1931.

113. Kryloff, N., and Bogoliuboff, N. Influence of resonance in transverse vibrations of rods caused by periodic normal forces at one end. *Ukrainian Sc. Res. Inst. of Armament*, Recueil, Kiev, 1935.

114. Lerch, M. *Comptes Rendus*, pp.1,325, 1906.

115. Levy, H. Analysis of empiric function into quasi-periodic constituents. *P.L.M.S.* **25**, 487, 1926.

116. Lewis, T. Solutions of Oseen's extended equation for circular and elliptic cylinders and the flat plate. *Q.J.M.* **9**, 21, 1938.

117. Liénard, A. M. Oscillations auto-entretenue. *Proc. Third Int. Cong. Applied Mech.* **3**, 173, 1931.

118. Lindemann, C. L. F. Über die Differentialgleichung der Functionen des elliptischen Zylinders. *M.A.* **22**, 117, 1883.

119. Lindstedt, A. *Astronomische Nachr.* **103, 104, 105.**

120. Lotz, I. Correction of downwash in wind tunnels of circular and ellip-tical sections. *Luftfahrtforschung*, **12**, No. 8, 1935.

121. Lubkin, S., and Stoker, J. J. Stability of columns and strings under periodically varying forces. *Quart. Appl. Math.* **1**, 215, 1943.

122. Maclaurin, R. C. Solutions of $(\nabla^2 + k^2)\psi = 0$ in elliptical coordinates, and their physical applications. *T.C.P.S.* **17**, 41, 1898.

123. Maginniss, F. J. Sinusoidal variation of parameter in single series circuit. *P.I.R.E.* **29**, 25, 1941.

124. Malmborg, M. Om integrationen af en klass af lineäre differentialekvationer med dubbel periodiska koefficienter, analog med de S. K. Hermite'ska differentialekvationerna. *Uppsala Univ. Årsskr. Math. Naturw.* 1897.

125. Mandelstam, L., and Papalexi, N. Über Resonanzerscheinungen bei Frequenzteilung. *Z.P.* **73**, 223, 1931.

126. Marković, Z. Sur la non-existence simultanée de deux fonctions de Mathieu. *P.C.P.S.* **23**, 203, 1926.

127. —— Sur les fonctions de Mathieu de période π. *Acad. des Sc. des Slaves du sud de Zagreb (Croatie)*, **21**, 34, 1925.

128. Marshall, W. Asymptotic representation of elliptic cylinder.functions. *D.*, Zürich, 1909.

129. —— Arbitrary constants in 128. *P.E.M.S.* **40**, 2, 1921.

130. **Mathieu, É. Mémoire sur le mouvement vibratoire d'une membrane de forme elliptique.** *Jour. de Math. Pures et Appliquées (Jour. de Liouville)* **13**, 137, 1868.

131. McDonald, J. H. *Trans. Amer. Math. Soc.* **29**, 647, 1927.

132. McLachlan, N. W. *P.M.* **26**, 695, 1938.

133. —— Hill's differential equation. *Math. Gaz.* **29**, 68, 1945.

134. —— Computation of solution of Mathieu's equation. *P.M.* **36**, 403, 1945.

135. —— Heat conduction in elliptical cylinder, and an analogous electromagnetic problem. *P.M.* **36**, 600, 1945; **37**, 216, 1946.

136. Meissner, E. Über Schüttelschwingungen in Systemen mit periodisch veränderlicher Elastizität. *Schweizer Bauzeitung*, **72**, 95, 1918.

137. Meksyn, D. Solution of Oseen's equation for an inclined elliptical cylinder in a viscous fluid. *P.R.S.* (A), **162**, 232, 1937.

138. Mettler, E. *Mitt. Forsch.-Anst. Gulehoffnungshütte-Konzern*, **8**, 1, 1940.

139. —— *Forschungshefte aus dem Gebiet des Stahlbaues*, Heft, **4**, 1, 1941.

140. Milne, A. Roots of the confluent hypergeometric functions. *P.E.M.S.* **33**, 48, 1915.

141. Möglich, H. Beugungserscheinungen an Körpern von ellipsoidischer Gestalt. *A. der P.* **83**, 609, 1927.

142. Morse, P. M. Quantum mechanics of electrons in crystals. *Phys. Rev.* **35**, 1310, 1930.

143. —— Addition formulae for spheroidal functions. *Proc. Nat. Acad. Sc. Wash.* **21**, 56, 1935.

144. —— and Rubenstein, P. J. Diffraction of waves by ribbons and slits. *Phys. Rev.* **54**, 895, 1938.

145. Müller, K. E. Über die Schüttelschwingungen des Kuppelstangenantriebes. *D.*, Zürich, 1919.

146. Nisino, K. *Jour. Aero. Res. Inst., Tokyo Imp. Univ.*, No. 176, May 1939.

147. Noether, F. Anwendung der Hillschen Differentialgleichung auf die Wellenfortpflanzung in elektrischen oder akustischen Kettenleitern. *Internat. Cong. Appl. Mech. Stockholm*, **3**, 143, 1931.

148. Pellam, J. R. Sound diffraction by a strip of absorbing material. *Jour. Acous. Soc. Amer.* **11**, 396, 1940.

REFERENCES 379

149. Poincaré, J. H. *Acta Mathematica*, **8**, 295, 1886.
150. Poole, E. G. C. Certain classes of Mathieu function. *P.L.M.S.* **20**, 374, 1921.
151. —— Notes on spheroidal wave functions. *Q.J.M.* **49**, 309, 1923.
152. Pol, B. van der, and Strutt, M. J. O. Stability of solutions of Mathieu's equation. *P.M.* **5**, 18, 1928.
153. Raman, C. V. Experimental investigations on the maintenance of vibrations. *Proc. Indian Assoc. for Cultivation of Sc.*, Bull. **6**, 1, 1912.
154. Ray, M. Vibration of elliptical cylinder in viscous fluid. *Z.A.M.M.* **16**, 99, 1936.
155. Rayleigh, Lord. Maintenance of vibrations by forces of double frequency, and propagation of waves through a medium with a periodic structure. *P.M.* **24**, 145, 1887.
156. Roosenstein, H. O. *Z. für H.* **42**, 85, 1933.
157. Rosenhead, L. Aerofoil in a wind tunnel of elliptical section. *P.R.S.* (A), **140**, 579, 1933.
158. Sarchinger, E. Beitrag zur Theorie der Funktionen des elliptischen Zylinders. *D.*, Leipzig, 1894.
159. Sanuki and Tani. Wall interference of wind tunnel of elliptical cross-section. *Proc. Phys. Math. Soc. Japan*, **14**, 592, 1932.
160. Schubert, J. Über die Integration der Differentialgleichung $(\nabla^2 + k^2)u = 0$, für Flächenstücke, die von konfokalen Ellipsen und Hyperbeln begrenzt werden. *D.*, Königsberg, 1886.
161. Schwerin, F. Über Schüttelschwingungen gekoppelter Systeme. *Z.T.P.* **10**, 37, 1929.
162. Sieger, B. Die Beugung einer ebenen elektrischen Wellen an einem Schirm von elliptischen Querschnitt. *A. der P.* **27**, 626, 1908.
163. Stephenson, A. A class of forced oscillations. *Q.J.M.* **37**, 353, 1906.
164. —— New type of dynamical stability. *Proc. Manchester Phil. Soc.* **52**, No. 8, 1908.
165. Stieltjes, T. J. *Astronomische Nachr.*, No. 109, 1884.
166. Stratton, J. A. Spheroidal functions. *Proc. Nat. Acad. Sc. Wash.* **21**, 51 and 316, 1935.
167. Strutt, M. J. O. Wirbelströme im elliptischen Zylinder. *A. der P.* **84**, 485, 1927.
168. —— Eigenschwingungen einer Saite mit sinusförmiger Massenverteilung. *A. der P.* **85**, 129, 1928.
169. —— Magnetische Feldverdrängung und Eigenzeitkonstanten. *A. der P.* **85**, 866, 1928.
170. —— Zur Wellenmechanik des Atomgitters. *A. der P.* **86**, 819, 1928.
171. —— Der charakteristische Exponent der Hillschen Differentialgleichung. *M.A.* **101**, 559, 1929.
172. —— Hydrodynamische Behandlung hochfrequenter elektromagnetischer Aufgaben. *A. für E.* **21**, 526, 1929.
173. —— Beugung einer ebenen Wellen an einem Spalt von endlicher Breite. *Z.P.* **69**, 597, 1931.
174. Strutt, M. J. O. Erweiterung der Siebkettentheorie. *A. für E.* **26**, 273, 1932.

175. Sturm, J. C. F. *Jour. de Math.* **1**, 106, 1836.
176. Tisserand, F. *Bull. Astronomique*, **9**, 102, 1892.
177. Utida, I., and Sezawa, K. Dynamical stability of a column under periodic longitudinal forces. *Aero. Res. Inst. Tokyo Imp. Univ.* **15**, 193, 1940.
178. Varma, R. S. On Mathieu functions. *Jour. Ind. Math. Soc.* **19**, 49, 1931.
179. —— Integral involving elliptic cylinder function. *P.M.* **12**, 280, 1931.
180. Watson, G. N. Convergence of series for Mathieu functions. *P.E.M.S.* **33**, 25, 1915.
181. Weber, H. *M.A.* **1**, 1, 1869.
182. Weinstein, D. H. Characteristic values of Mathieu's equation. *P.M.* **20**, 288, 1935.
183. Whittaker, E. T. *M.A.* **57**, 333, 1903.
184. —— Elliptic cylinder functions in harmonic analysis. *P.I.C.M.*, Cambridge, **1**, 366, 1912.
185. —— Differential equations whose solutions satisfy integral equations. *P.E.M.S.* **33**, 22, 1915.
186. —— General solution of Mathieu's equation. *P.E.M.S.* **32**, 75, 1914.
187. —— Recurrence formulae for Mathieu functions. *Jour. L.M.S.* **4**, 88, 1929.
188. Wiegand, A. Unveröffentlichter, Bericht der D.V.L., Inst. X.
189. Wiesman. *D.*, Zürich, 1909.
190. Wiman. Über die reelen Lösungen der linearen Differentialgleichungen zweiter Ordnung. *Arkiv. f. Math. Astr. o. Fys.* **12**, No. 14, 1917.
191. Young, A. W. Quasi-periodic solutions of Mathieu's equation. *P.E.M.S.* **32**, 81, 1914.

B. BOOKS

192. Courant, R., and Hilbert, D. *Methoden der Math. Phys.* Vol. I.
193. Dhar, S. C. *Mathieu Functions.* Jour. Dept. Sc., Nagpur (Calcutta Univ. Press, 1928).
194. Fletcher, A. F., Miller, J. C. P., Rosenhead, L., and Comrie, L. J. *Index of Mathematical Tables.* 2 vols. (2nd ed. 1962).
195. Föppl, A. *Vorlesungen über technische Mechanik.* Vol. 6, 4 Aufl. (1921).
196. Frenkel, J. *Lehrbuch der Elektrodynamik.* Vol. 2 (1928).
197. Heine, E. *Handbuch der Kugelfunktionen.* 2 vols. (1878/81).
198. Humbert, P. *Fonctions de Mathieu et de Lamé* (Paris, 1926).
199. Ince, E. L. *Ordinary Differential Equations* (1927; Dover reprint, 1949).
200. Lamont, H. R. L. *Wave Guides* (1942).
201. Mathieu, É. *Cours de mathématique physique* (Paris, 1873).
202. McLachlan, N. W. *Loud Speakers* (1934; Dover reprint, 1960).
203. —— *Bessel Functions for Engineers* (2nd ed. 1955).
204. —— *Complex Variable Theory and Transform Calculus* (2nd ed. 1963).
205. Pockels, H. *Über die partielle Differentialgleichung* $\Delta u + k'u = 0$ *und deren Auftreten in der Math. Phys.* (1891).
206. Poincaré, J. H. *Méthodes nouvelles de la Mécanique céleste.* Chap. 17. (Dover reprint, 1957)
207. Rayleigh, Lord. *Complete Scientific Papers.* Vol. 2, 88, 1883; vol. 3, 1, 1887. (Dover reprint, 1964)
208. —— *Theory of Sound.* Vol. 1, 82, 1926. (Dover reprint, 1945)

209. Riemann-Weber. *Differentialgleichungen der Physik* (1925).

210. Sarbacher, R. I., and Edson, W. A. *Hyper and Ultra-High Frequency Engineering* (1944).

211. Stratton, J. A., Morse, P. M., Chu, L. J., and Hutner, R. A. *Elliptic Cylinder and Spheroidal Wave Functions* (1942).

212. Strutt, M. J. O. *Lamésche, Mathieusche, und verwandte Funktionen in Physik und Technik* (1932).

213. Tisserand, F. *Traité de Mécanique céleste.* Tome 3, p. 1 (1894).

214. Watson, G. N. *Theory of Bessel Functions* (1944).

215. Whittaker, E. T., and Watson, G. N. *Modern Analysis* (1927).

C. ADDITIONAL REFERENCES

216. Baranov, V. *Contribution à l'étude des fonctions de Mathieu normées.* *Thèse.* Montpellier, 1941.

217. Blanch, G. Computation of Mathieu Functions. *Jour. Math. and Phys.*, *Mass. Inst. Techn.* **25**, 1, 1946.

218. Borg, G. Stability of a certain class of linear differential equations. *Arkiv. f. Math. Astr. o. Fys.* **31**, No. 1, Dec. 1944.

219. Brillouin, M. Théorie d'un alternateur auto-excitateur. *Éclairage électrique*, p. 49, April 1897.

220. Campbell, R. *Théorie Générale de l'Équation de Mathieu* (1955). See references therein.

221. Ferrar, W. L. *A Text Book of Convergence* (1938).

222. Flammer, C. *Spheroidal Wave Functions* (1951).

223. Marković, Z. Sur les fonctions de l'équation différentielle linéaire du second ordre à coefficient périodique. *P.L.M.S.* **31**, 417, 1930.

224. McLachlan, N. W. Mathieu Functions and their Classification. *Jour. Math. and Phys.*, *Mass. Inst. Techn.* **25**, 209, 1946.

225. —— Vibrational Problems in Elliptical Coordinates. *Quart. App. Math.* **5**, 289, 1947.

226. —— Mathieu Functions of Fractional Order. *Jour. Math. and Phys.* **26**, 29, 1947.

227. —— Computation of Solutions of $(1 + 2\epsilon \cos 2z)d^2y/dz^2 + \theta y = 0$—frequency modulation functions. *Jour. App. Phys.* **18**, 723, 1947.

228. —— Application of Mathieu's Differential Equation to the Stability of a Nonlinear Oscillator. *Math. Gazette* **35**, 105, 1951. See *Jour. Math. and Phys.* **26**, 78, 1947 for a correction.

229. Meixner, J., and Schäfke, H. *Mathieusche Funktionen und Sphäroid Funktionen* (1954).

230. Minorsky, N. On parametric excitation. *Jour. Frank. Inst.* **240**, 25, 1945.

231. Moullin, E. B. Propagation of electric waves in a rectangular wave guide. *Jour. Inst. Elec. Eng.*, Radio section, March 1945.

232. Poincaré, J. H. Sur quelques théorèmes généraux de l'électrotechnique. *Éclairage électrique*, p. 293, March 1907.

233. Poole, E. G. C. *Introduction to the Theory of Linear Differential Equations* (1936; Dover reprint, 1960).

234. Table of Characteristic Values of Mathieu's Differential Equation, AMP Report 165. IR., *Mathematical Tables Project, National Bureau of Standards, America*, September 1945.

ADDITIONAL RESULTS

THE following were obtained after the manuscript went to press. The analysis underlying the derivation of the formulae is usually omitted for brevity.

1. Evaluation of $\mathrm{Fey}'_m(0,q)/\mathrm{Fe}'_m(0,q)$ and $\mathrm{Gey}_m(0,q)/\mathrm{Ge}_m(0,q)$ in § 13.21. By comparison it follows from (1) § 7.61, (3)–(5) § 13.20, and (3), (4) § 13.21, that for q real > 0

$$B = \mathrm{Fey}'_{2n}(0,q)/\mathrm{Fe}'_{2n}(0,q) = 2/\pi C_{2n}(q). \tag{1}$$

Similarly
$$\mathrm{Fey}'_{2n+1}(0,q)/\mathrm{Fe}'_{2n+1}(0,q) = 2/\pi C_{2n+1}(q), \tag{2}$$

and
$$\mathrm{Gey}_m(0,q)/\mathrm{Ge}_m(0,q) = -2/\pi S_m(q). \tag{3}$$

2. Relations between C'_m, $C_m(q)$; S'_m, $S_m(q)$ in §§ 13.52–13.55. By aid of (3)–(6) § 13.52, we deduce that

$$C'_{2n} = -\tfrac{1}{2}\pi C_{2n}(q). \tag{1}$$

We also find that
$$C'_{2n+1} = -\tfrac{1}{2}\pi C_{2n+1}(q), \tag{2}$$

and
$$S'_m = -\tfrac{1}{2}\pi S_m(q). \tag{3}$$

From (1) § 7.22, (3) § 13.53, and (1) above, we get

$$p_{2n}\,\mathrm{ce}_{2n}(\tfrac{1}{2}\pi,q)/A_0^{(2n)} = \mathrm{ce}_{2n}(0,q) + \sum_{r=0}^{\infty}(2r+2)f_{2r+2}^{(2n)} = \mathrm{fe}'_{2n}(0,q)/C_{2n}(q).$$

Also
$$\tag{4}$$

$$-p_{2n+1}\,\mathrm{ce}'_{2n+1}(\tfrac{1}{2}\pi,q)/kA_1^{(2n+1)} = \mathrm{ce}_{2n+1}(0,q) + \sum_{r=0}^{\infty}(2r+1)f_{2r+1}^{(2n+1)}$$

$$= \mathrm{fe}'_{2n+1}(0,q)/C_{2n+1}(q), \tag{5}$$

$$s_{2n+1}\,\mathrm{se}_{2n+1}(\tfrac{1}{2}\pi,q)/kB_1^{(2n+1)} = \sum_{r=0}^{\infty}g_{2r+1}^{(2n+1)} = \mathrm{ge}_{2n+1}(0,q)/S_{2n+1}(q), \tag{6}$$

$$s_{2n+2}\,\mathrm{se}'_{2n+2}(\tfrac{1}{2}\pi,q)/k^2B_2^{(2n+2)} = \sum_{r=0}^{\infty}g_{2r}^{(2n+2)} = \mathrm{ge}_{2n+2}(0,q)/S_{2n+2}(q). \tag{7}$$

3. Limiting forms of Fey_m, Gey_m, Fek_m, Gek_m, $C_m(q)$, $S_m(q)$ as $q \to +0$.

$$\left.\begin{array}{c}\mathrm{Fey}\\2\mathrm{Fek}\end{array}\right\}_0 \begin{array}{c}(z,q)\\(z,-q)\end{array} \to \pm\frac{2^{\frac{1}{2}}}{\pi}(z+\tfrac{1}{2}\log_e q), \tag{1, 2}$$

$$\left.\begin{array}{c}\mathrm{Fey}\\\mathrm{Gey}\end{array}\right\}_m (z,q) \to -2^{2m-1}(m-1)!\,m!\,\pi^{-1}q^{-m}e^{-mz} \quad (m \geqslant 1), \tag{3, 4}$$

$$\left.\begin{array}{c}\mathrm{Fek}\\\mathrm{Gek}\end{array}\right\}_m (z,-q) \to -\tfrac{1}{2}\left.\begin{array}{c}\mathrm{Fey}\\\mathrm{Gey}\end{array}\right\}_m (z,q) \quad (m \geqslant 1). \tag{5, 6}$$

provided q and $ke^{\pm z}$ are small enough. The forms (1)–(6) show that the functions of zero order have a branch point, while those of higher integral order have a pole of equal order at $q = 0$. These formulae were derived from the B.F. product series, with the aid of (8), (9) § 3.33. Approximate representations of the J-, Y-, I-, K-Bessel functions were used, and only the dominant term in the expansion retained. More accurate formulae may be derived by retaining appropriate additional terms before and after the dominant terms. Thus

$$\left.\begin{matrix}\text{Fey}\\ 2\text{Fek}\end{matrix}\right\}_0\begin{matrix}(z,\,q)\\ (z,\,-q)\end{matrix} \simeq \pm\frac{2^{\frac{1}{2}}}{\pi}\Big\{[(\gamma-\log_e 2)+\tfrac{1}{2}\log_e q+z]\times$$
$$\times\,[1\mp\tfrac{1}{2}q\cosh 2z]-\tfrac{1}{2}q\sinh 2z\Big\},\quad (7,\,8)$$

where $(\gamma-\log_e 2) = -0.1159.... -\tfrac{1}{2}q\sinh 2z$ applies to 2 Fek$_0$ only. Also if $n \geqslant 2$

$$\left.\begin{matrix}\text{Fey}\\ 2\text{Fek}\end{matrix}\right\}_{2n}\begin{matrix}(z,\,q)\\ (z,\,-q)\end{matrix} \simeq \mp\frac{2^{4n-1}(2n-1)!\,(2n)!\,e^{-2nz}}{\pi q^{2n}}\times$$
$$\times\left\{1\pm\tfrac{1}{4}q\Big[\frac{e^{2z}}{(2n-1)}-\frac{e^{-2z}}{(2n+1)}\Big]\right\}.\quad (9,\,10)$$

When the order of the function $m \geqslant 1$, the multipliers $p_{2n}/A_0^{(2n)}$, $p_{2n+1}/A_1^{(2n+1)}$, etc. (see Appendix I), external to the B.F. product series for these functions (see Chap. XIII), have singularities at $q = 0$. For example

$$\text{Fey}_{2n+1}(z,\,q)$$
$$= [p_{2n+1}/A_1^{(2n+1)}]\sum_{r=0}^{\infty}(-1)^r A_{2r+1}^{(2n+1)}[J_r(v_1)Y_{r+1}(v_2)+J_{r+1}(v_1)Y_r(v_2)],\quad (11)$$

where $v_1 = ke^{-z}$, and $v_2 = ke^z$. As $q \to 0$, the multiplier

$$p_{2n+1}/A_1^{(2n+1)} \to (-1)^n 2^{4n}(2n)!\,(2n+1)!\,q^{-2n-\frac{1}{2}},\quad (12)$$

while

$$\sum_{r=0}^{\infty}(-1)^r A_{2r+1}^{(2n+1)}[J_r(v_1)Y_{r+1}(v_2)+J_{r+1}(v_1)Y_r(v_2)] \to (-1)^{n+1}2\pi^{-1}q^{-\frac{1}{2}}e^{-(2n+1)z}.$$
$$(13)$$

Hence, considered as independent functions of q, both (12), (13) have branch points at $q = 0$. This is true for $\text{Gey}_{2n+1}(z,\,q)$ also. The $\sum$ part in $\text{Fey}_{2n}(z,\,q)$ has no singularity in q, but that of $\text{Gey}_{2n+2}(z,\,q)$ has a pole of unit order.

As $q \to 0$, $\quad \text{Fe}_m(z,\,q) \to \sinh mz$, so $\text{Fe}'_m(0,\,q) \to m$. $\quad$ (14)

Thus from (3), (14),

$$\text{Fey}'_m(0,\,q)/\text{Fe}'_m(0,\,q) \to 2^{2m-1}(m-1)!\,m!\,\pi^{-1}q^{-m},\quad (15)$$

so from (1), (2) § 1, and (15), it follows that as $q \to 0$

$$C_m(q) \to q^m/2^{2m-2}(m-1)!\,m! \tag{16}$$

Similarly, we find that $\quad S_m(q) \to C_m(q).$ $\tag{17}$

4. Fey_m, Gey_m, Fek_m, Gek_m with argument $(z+ip\pi)$.

$$\left.\begin{matrix}\mathrm{Fey}\\ \mathrm{Gey}\end{matrix}\right\}_m (z+ip\pi, \pm q) = \left.\begin{matrix}\mathrm{Fey}\\ \mathrm{Gey}\end{matrix}\right\}_m (z, \pm q) + 2ip\left.\begin{matrix}\mathrm{Ce}\\ \mathrm{Se}\end{matrix}\right\}_m (z, \pm q), \tag{1, 2}$$

p being any integer if m is even. When m is odd, p is even.

$$\left.\begin{matrix}\mathrm{Fek}\\ \mathrm{Gek}\end{matrix}\right\}_m (z+ip\pi, \pm q) = \left.\begin{matrix}\mathrm{Fek}\\ \mathrm{Gek}\end{matrix}\right\}_m (z, \pm q) - ip\left.\begin{matrix}\mathrm{Ce}\\ \mathrm{Se}\end{matrix}\right\}_m (z, \pm q), \tag{3, 4}$$

p being any integer if m is even. When m is odd, p being even, write $+p$ for $-ip$ on the r.h.s. of (3), (4). These formulae illustrate the non-periodic nature of the functions. By applying (1)–(6) § 13.41 to (3), (4) above, relations for $\mathrm{Me}_m^{(1),(2)}(z, \pm q)$, and $\mathrm{Ne}_m^{(1),(2)}(z, \pm q)$ may be derived.

5. Integrals of the form at (9)–(12) § 9.40.

$$\Theta_{2n}^{(p)} = \frac{1}{\pi} \int_0^{2\pi} \mathrm{ce}_{2n}^2(u, q)\cos 2pu\,du$$

$$= \sum_{r=0}^{\frac{1}{2}(p-1)} A_{2r}^{(2n)}A_{2p-2r}^{(2n)} + \sum_{r=0}^{\infty} A_{2r}^{(2n)}A_{2p+2r}^{(2n)} \tag{1}$$

$$= \tfrac{1}{2}[A_p^{(2n)}]^2 + \sum_{r=0}^{\frac{1}{2}(p-2)} A_{2r}^{(2n)}A_{2p-2r}^{(2n)} + \sum_{r=0}^{\infty} A_{2r}^{(2n)}A_{2p+2r}^{(2n)}, \tag{2}$$

$$\Theta_{2n+1}^{(p)} = \frac{1}{\pi} \int_0^{2\pi} \mathrm{ce}_{2n+1}^2(u, q)\cos 2pu\,du$$

$$= \tfrac{1}{2}[A_p^{(2n+1)}]^2 + \sum_{r=0}^{\frac{1}{2}(p-3)} A_{2r+1}^{(2n+1)}A_{2p-2r-1}^{(2n+1)} + \sum_{r=0}^{\infty} A_{2r+1}^{(2n+1)}A_{2p+2r+1}^{(2n+1)} \tag{3}$$

$$= \sum_{r=0}^{\frac{1}{2}(p-2)} A_{2r+1}^{(2n+1)}A_{2p-2r-1}^{(2n+1)} + \sum_{r=0}^{\infty} A_{2r+1}^{(2n+1)}A_{2p+2r+1}^{(2n+1)}, \tag{4}$$

$$\Psi_{2n+1}^{(p)} = \frac{1}{\pi} \int_0^{2\pi} \mathrm{se}_{2n+1}^2(u, q)\cos 2pu\,du$$

$$= -\tfrac{1}{2}[B_p^{(2n+1)}]^2 - \sum_{r=0}^{\frac{1}{2}(p-3)} B_{2r+1}^{(2n+1)}B_{2p-2r-1}^{(2n+1)} + \sum_{r=0}^{\infty} B_{2r+1}^{(2n+1)}B_{2p+2r+1}^{(2n+1)} \tag{5}$$

$$= -\sum_{r=0}^{\frac{1}{2}(p-2)} B_{2r+1}^{(2n+1)}B_{2p-2r-1}^{(2n+1)} + \sum_{r=0}^{\infty} B_{2r+1}^{(2n+1)}B_{2p+2r+1}^{(2n+1)}, \tag{6}$$

$$\Psi_{2n+2}^{(p)} = \frac{1}{\pi} \int_0^{2\pi} \mathrm{se}_{2n+2}^2(u,q)\cos 2pu \, du$$

$$= -\sum_{r=0}^{\frac{1}{2}(p-3)} B_{2r+2}^{(2n+2)} B_{2p-2r-2}^{(2n+2)} + \sum_{r=0}^{\infty} B_{2r+2}^{(2n+2)} B_{2p+2r+2}^{(2n+2)} \tag{7}$$

$$= -\tfrac{1}{2}[B_p^{(2n+2)}]^2 - \sum_{r=0}^{\frac{1}{2}(p-4)} B_{2r+2}^{(2n+2)} B_{2p-2r-2}^{(2n+2)} + \sum_{r=0}^{\infty} B_{2r+2}^{(2n+2)} B_{2p+2r+2}^{(2n+2)}. \tag{8}$$

In (1), (3), (5), (7), p is an odd positive integer, while in (2), (4), (6), (8) it is even $\geqslant 2$. The results (1), (2) will enable additional terms in (5)–(7) § 18.55 to be obtained.

6. Improved asymptotic formulae, q large and positive.
These were derived from (5) § 11.43 by writing iz for z.

$$\begin{matrix}\mathrm{Ce}\\\mathrm{Fey}\end{matrix}\Big\}_m (z,q) \sim 2C_m\gamma_m\Big[(1+x_m)\begin{matrix}\cos\\\sin\end{matrix}\chi_m \pm z_m\begin{matrix}\sin\\\cos\end{matrix}\chi_m\Big], \tag{1, 2}$$

$$\begin{matrix}\mathrm{Se}\\\mathrm{Gey}\end{matrix}\Big\}_{m+1} (z,q) \sim \pm 2S_{m+1}\gamma_m\Big[(1+x_m)\begin{matrix}\sin\\\cos\end{matrix}\chi_m \mp z_m\begin{matrix}\cos\\\sin\end{matrix}\chi_m\Big], \tag{3, 4}$$

where $\chi_m = 2k\sinh z - (2m+1)\tan^{-1}(\tanh\tfrac{1}{2}z)$, $\gamma_m = 2^{-m-\frac{1}{2}}(\cosh z)^{-\frac{1}{2}}$, $x_m = (2m+1)/8k\cosh^2 z$, $z_m = (m^2+m+1)\tanh z/8k\cosh z$. The formulae in § 11.42 may be derived by omitting the terms in x_m, z_m in (1)–(4). Applying (4), (7), (10), (13) § 8.14 to (1)–(4) we obtain

$$\begin{matrix}\mathrm{Fek}_{2n}\\\mathrm{Gek}_{2n+1}\end{matrix} (z,q) \sim \begin{matrix}C_{2n}\\S_{2n+1}\end{matrix}\gamma_{2n}[(1+x_{2n})e^{i(\chi_{2n}+\frac{1}{2}\pi)}+z_{2n}e^{i\chi_{2n}}], \tag{5, 6}$$

$$\begin{matrix}\mathrm{Fek}_{2n+1}\\\mathrm{Gek}_{2n+2}\end{matrix} (z,q) \sim \begin{matrix}-C_{2n+1}\\S_{2n+2}\end{matrix}\gamma_{2n+1}[(1+x_{2n+1})e^{i\chi_{2n+1}}+z_{2n+1}e^{i(\chi_{2n+1}-\frac{1}{2}\pi)}]. \tag{7, 8}$$

The real and imaginary parts in (5)–(8) are required if z is real, since $\mathrm{Fek}_m(z,q)$, $\mathrm{Gek}_m(z,q)$ are complex. Formulae for $\mathrm{Me}^{(1),(2)}(z,q)$, $\mathrm{Ne}^{(1),(2)}(z,q)$ may be derived by applying (1), (2), (4), (6) § 13.41 to (5)–(8). See comment in § 7 on accuracy. The phase angle range for *all* asymptotic formulae in the book is $-\tfrac{1}{2}\pi < \text{phase } z < \tfrac{1}{2}\pi$, q real.

7. Improved asymptotic formulae, q large and negative.
These were derived from § 6 by applying the appropriate relations in § 8.30.

$$\begin{matrix}\mathrm{Ce}\\\mathrm{Fey}\end{matrix}\Big\}_{2n} (z,-q) \sim C_{2n}\delta_{2n}\Big[(1-X_{2n})\begin{Bmatrix}e^{\psi_{2n}}-ie^{-\psi_{2n}}\\ie^{\psi_{2n}}-e^{-\psi_{2n}}\end{Bmatrix} + Z_{2n}\begin{Bmatrix}e^{\psi_{2n}}+ie^{-\psi_{2n}}\\ie^{\psi_{2n}}+e^{-\psi_{2n}}\end{Bmatrix}\Big], \tag{1, 2}$$

$$\left.\begin{matrix}\text{Ce}\\\text{Fey}\end{matrix}\right\}_{2n+1}(z,-q) \sim S_{2n+1}\,\delta_{2n}\left[(1-X_{2n})\begin{Bmatrix}e^{\psi_{2n}}+ie^{-\psi_{2n}}\\ie^{\psi_{2n}}+e^{-\psi_{2n}}\end{Bmatrix}+Z_{2n}\begin{Bmatrix}e^{\psi_{2n}}-ie^{-\psi_{2n}}\\ie^{\psi_{2n}}-e^{-\psi_{2n}}\end{Bmatrix}\right].$$

$$(3, 4)$$

Formulae for $Se_{2n+1}(z,-q)$, $Gey_{2n+1}(z,-q)$ are given by (3), (4), respectively, if $(2n+1)$ is written on the r.h.s. for $2n$ and C_{2n+1} for S_{2n+1}. Those for the same functions of order $(2n+2)$ are derived from (1), (2) by the first change, and writing S_{2n+2} for C_{2n}.

Also $\quad \text{Fek}_{\substack{2n\\2n+1}}(z,-q) \sim \dfrac{C_{2n}}{S_{2n+1}}\,\delta_{2n}\,e^{-\psi_{2n}}(1-X_{2n}-Z_{2n}),$ $\qquad$ (5, 6)

and $\quad \text{Gek}_{\substack{2n+1\\2n+2}}(z,-q) \sim \dfrac{C_{2n+1}}{S_{2n+2}}\,\delta_{2n+1}\,e^{-\psi_{2n+1}}(1-X_{2n+1}-Z_{2n+1}).$ $\quad$ (7, 8)

In (1)–(8),

$$\psi_m = 2k\cosh z - (2m+1)y, \qquad \tanh 2y = (\cosh z)^{-1},$$

$$X_m = (2m+1)/8k\sinh^2 z, \qquad Z_m = (m^2+m+1)\coth z/8k\sinh z,$$

$$\delta_m = 2^{-m-\frac{1}{2}}(\sinh z)^{-\frac{1}{2}}.$$

If z is real, Ce, Se are real, so the imaginary part is omitted; Fey, Gey are complex, so both real and imaginary parts are used; Fek, Gek are real. Formulae for $Me_m^{(1),(2)}(z,-q)$, $Ne_m^{(1),(2)}(z,-q)$ may be derived by applying (1), (3), (5), (6) § 13.41 to (5)–(8). See § 11.44 for remarks on accuracy. For a given order m, and an assigned $\begin{pmatrix}z\\q\end{pmatrix}$, the accuracy increases with increase in $\begin{pmatrix}q\\z\end{pmatrix}$, due to reduction in the omitted terms akin to X_m, Z_m.

8. Approximate solution of $y''-(a-2q\cosh 2z)y = 0$, q **large and positive,** $\frac{1}{2}|1+a/2q| < 1$. Writing the equation in the form $y''+2q(\cosh 2z-a/2q)y = 0$, the procedure in §§ 4.82, 6.20 carried as far as w_2, leads to the second approximation

$$\begin{matrix}y_1\\y_2\end{matrix}(z) \simeq \frac{\text{a constant}}{(\cosh 2z - a/2q)^{\frac{1}{4}}}\begin{matrix}\cos\\\sin\end{matrix}\Omega,$$

$$(1, 2)$$

where

$$\Omega = 2k\sinh z - k\left[h^2\text{gd}(z) + \sum_{r=2}^{\infty}\frac{1.3...(2r-3)}{2^{r-1}r!}h^{2r}D_{2r-2}\right] +$$

$$+ \frac{1}{16k}\left[\text{gd}(z) + \tfrac{1}{2}(13h^2-6)D_2 + \tfrac{1}{8}h^2(115h^2-76)D_4 + \right.$$

$$\left. + \tfrac{5}{16}h^4(77h^2-58)D_6 + ...\right], \quad (3)$$

$h^2 = \frac{1}{2}(1+a/2q)$, $\mathrm{gd}(z) = 2\tan^{-1}e^z - \frac{1}{2}\pi$, the gudermannian of z, and

$$D_{2r} = \frac{1.3...(2r-1)}{2.4...2r}\left[\mathrm{gd}(z) + \frac{\tanh z}{\cosh z} + ... + \frac{2.4...(2r-2)}{3.5...(2r-1)}\frac{\tanh z}{\cosh^{2r-1}z}\right].$$

(1), (2) may be used as asymptotic formulae for functions of any order $(m+\beta)$, provided the constant multiplier can be found. Consider $\mathrm{Ce}_m(z,q)$, and $\mathrm{Se}_{m+1}(z,q)$. When $q \to +\infty$, by (7) § 12.30, $a \sim -2q+(4m+2)k$, so $(\cosh 2z - a/2q)^{\frac{1}{4}} \sim 2^{\frac{1}{4}}\cosh^{\frac{1}{2}}z$, and

$$\Omega \sim 2k\sinh z - (2m+1)\tfrac{1}{4}\pi.$$

Thus (1), (2) give

$$\begin{matrix}y_1\\y_2\end{matrix}(z) \sim 2^{-\frac{1}{4}}(\cosh z)^{-\frac{1}{2}}\frac{K_1\cos}{K_2\sin}[2k\sinh z - (2m+1)\tfrac{1}{4}\pi]. \qquad (4, 5)$$

These are the forms at (3), (4) § 11.42, if $\tanh\frac{1}{2}z \simeq 1$. Hence by comparison, $K_1 = C_m/2^{m-\frac{3}{4}}$, $K_2 = S_{m+1}/2^{m-\frac{3}{4}}$. With the aid of (1)–(4) § 6, we infer that

$$\left.\begin{matrix}\mathrm{Ce}\\\mathrm{Fey}\end{matrix}\right\}_m(z,q) \sim \frac{C_m}{2^{m-\frac{3}{4}}(\cosh 2z - a/2q)^{\frac{1}{4}}}\frac{\cos}{\sin}\Omega \quad (a = a_m), \qquad (6, 7)$$

and $\left.\begin{matrix}\mathrm{Se}\\\mathrm{Gey}\end{matrix}\right\}_{m+1}(z,q) \sim \dfrac{\pm S_{m+1}}{2^{m-\frac{3}{4}}(\cosh 2z - a/2q)^{\frac{1}{4}}}\dfrac{\sin}{\cos}\Omega \quad (a = b_{m+1}). \qquad (8, 9)$

9. Parametric zeros of $\mathrm{Fey}_m(z,q)$, $\mathrm{Gey}_{m+1}(z,q)$. Applying the procedure in § 12.41 to the dominant terms in (2), (4) § 6, it is found that the formulae for Fey_m, Gey_{m+1} are those for Se_{m+1}, Ce_m, each to each.

10. Pulsatance equations for elliptical ring membrane. Referring to § 16.11 et seq., the membrane is clamped at two confocal ellipses where $\xi = \xi_0$ at the outer, and $\xi = \xi_1$ at the inner. The two forms of component solution are

$$\zeta_m = [C_m\,\mathrm{Ce}_m(\xi,q)+F_m\,\mathrm{Fey}_m(\xi,q)]\mathrm{ce}_m(\eta,q)\cos(\omega_m t+\epsilon_m) \quad (a_m), \quad (1)$$

and

$$\bar{\zeta}_m = [S_m\,\mathrm{Se}_m(\xi,q)+G_m\,\mathrm{Gey}_m(\xi,q)]\mathrm{se}_m(\eta,q)\cos(\bar{\omega}_m t+\bar{\epsilon}_m) \quad (b_m). \quad (2)$$

Inserting the boundary conditions in (1), (2) leads to the pulsatance equations

$$\mathrm{Ce}_m(\xi_0,q)\mathrm{Fey}_m(\xi_1,q) - \mathrm{Ce}_m(\xi_1,q)\mathrm{Fey}_m(\xi_0,q) = 0 \quad (m \geqslant 0), \quad (3)$$

and

$$\mathrm{Se}_m(\xi_0,q)\mathrm{Gey}_m(\xi_1,q) - \mathrm{Se}_m(\xi_1,q)\mathrm{Gey}_m(\xi_0,q) = 0 \quad (m \geqslant 1). \quad (4)$$

If q is a parametric zero of (3), (4), the corresponding nodal hyperbolae are determined, respectively, by

$$\text{ce}_m(\eta, q) = 0, \quad \text{and} \quad \text{se}_m(\eta, q) = 0. \qquad (m \geqslant 1) \qquad (5)$$

For an elliptical ring lake (see § 16.20 et seq.), the pulsatance equations are obtained from (3), (4) by using the first derivatives of Ce_m, Fey_m, etc., with respect to ξ. Nodal hyperbolae are determined by (5), using the parametric zeros of the new pulsatance equations. Putting the leading terms of (1), (2) § 6 in (3), the parametric zeros are

$$q_{m,p} = k_{m,p}^2 \simeq [p\pi + \theta_m^{(0)} - \theta_m^{(1)}]^2 / 4(\sinh \xi_0 - \sinh \xi_1)^2, \qquad (6)$$

with $\theta_m^{(r)} = (2m+1)\tan^{-1}(\tanh \tfrac{1}{2}\xi_r)$, p integral $\geqslant 1$. A similar formula may be derived for (4).

11. Formulae for $\text{ce}_{2n}(\tfrac{1}{2}\pi, q)/A_0^{(2n)}$, $\text{ce}_{2n}(0, q)/A_0^{(2n)}$. From (17) § 8.10 and (3) § 13.11

$$\text{ce}_{2n}(\tfrac{1}{2}\pi, q)/A_0^{(2n)} = \sum_{r=0}^{\infty} A_{2r}^{(2n)} J_{2r}(2k \sinh z) \Big/ \sum_{r=0}^{\infty} (-1)^r A_{2r}^{(2n)} J_r(ke^{-z}) J_r(ke^z),$$

and from (15) § 8.10, (3) § 13.11   (1)

$$\text{ce}_{2n}(0, q)/A_0^{(2n)}$$

$$= \sum_{r=0}^{\infty} (-1)^r A_{2r}^{(2n)} J_{2r}(2k \cosh z) \Big/ \sum_{r=0}^{\infty} (-1)^r A_{2r}^{(2n)} J_r(ke^{-z}) J_r(ke^z). \qquad (2)$$

If k is finite and > 0, these formulae are valid for all values of z except those when the numerator and denominator vanish (zeros of $\text{Ce}_{2n}(z, q)$). Similar formulae may be derived for other multipliers in Chap. VIII. They may be used to calculate λ_{2n}, etc., on p. 185.

12. Bessel function series for $\text{Ce}_{m+\beta}(z, \pm q)$, $\text{Se}_{m+\beta}(z, \pm q)$. Using analysis of the type in §§ 8.10, 8.13, we get

$$\text{Ce}_{2n+\beta}(z, q) = C_{2n+\beta} \sum_{r=-\infty}^{\infty} (-1)^r A_{2r}^{(2n+\beta)} J_{2r+\beta}(2k \cosh z), \qquad (1)$$

and

$$\text{Se}_{2n+\beta}(z, q) = S_{2n+\beta} \tanh z \sum_{r=-\infty}^{\infty} (-1)^r (2r+\beta) A_{2r}^{(2n+\beta)} J_{2r+\beta}(2k \cosh z),$$

with   (2)

$$C_{2n+\beta} = \text{Ce}_{2n+\beta}(z_0, q) \Big/ \sum_{r=-\infty}^{\infty} (-1)^r A_{2r}^{(2n+\beta)} J_{2r+\beta}(2k \cosh z_0); \qquad (3)$$

$$S_{2n+\beta} = \text{Se}_{2n+\beta}(z_0, q) \Big/ \tanh z_0 \sum_{r=-\infty}^{\infty} (-1)^r (2r+\beta) A_{2r}^{(2n+\beta)} J_{2r+\beta}(2k \cosh z_0).$$

$$(4)$$

In these formulae $|\cosh z| > 1$, z_0 is neither imaginary nor zero, and k is finite > 0.

The r.h.s. of (1) has the following properties: (a) It is even in z; (b) it has a branch point in the u-plane $(u = 2k\cosh z)$ at the origin, and in the z-plane at $z = (2r+1)\frac{1}{2}\pi i$, $r = -\infty$ to $+\infty$, i.e. on the imaginary axis; (c) it is multivalued, and if $\beta = p/s$, a rational fraction in its lowest terms, it may be shown to have period $2s\pi i$ in z; (d) it is absolutely and uniformly convergent if $|\cosh z| > 1$, but non-uniformly convergent as $|\cosh z| \to 1$. On the imaginary axis it diverges, i.e. when $|\cosh z| \leqslant 1$. Hence there are no representations of the type (1), (2) for $\mathrm{ce}_{m+\beta}(z,q)$, $\mathrm{se}_{m+\beta}(z,q)$.

$$\mathrm{Ce}_{2n+\beta}(z,q) = \sum_{r=-\infty}^{\infty} A_{2r}^{(2n+\beta)}\cosh(2r+\beta)z$$

is analytic except at infinity where it has an essential singularity. This series and that at (1) § 13.12 in B.F. products are analytical continuations of (1) when $|\cosh z| \leqslant 1$. Series (2) has properties (b)–(d), but is odd in z.

For $q < 0$,

$$\mathrm{Ce}_{2n+\beta}(z,-q) = \bar{C}_{2n+\beta} \sum_{r=-\infty}^{\infty} (-1)^r A_{2r}^{(2n+\beta)} I_{2r+\beta}(2k\cosh z), \tag{5}$$

and

$$\mathrm{Se}_{2n+\beta}(z,-q) = \bar{S}_{2n+\beta}\tanh z \sum_{r=-\infty}^{\infty} (-1)^r(2r+\beta) A_{2r}^{(2n+\beta)} I_{2r+\beta}(2k\cosh z), \tag{6}$$

with

$$\bar{C}_{2n+\beta} = \mathrm{Ce}_{2n+\beta}(z_0,-q) \Big/ \sum_{r=-\infty}^{\infty} (-1)^r A_{2r}^{(2n+\beta)} I_{2r+\beta}(2k\cosh z_0); \tag{7}$$

$$\bar{S}_{2n+\beta} = \mathrm{Se}_{2n+\beta}(z_0,-q) \Big/ \tanh z_0 \sum_{r=-\infty}^{\infty} (-1)^r(2r+\beta) \times$$
$$\times A_{2r}^{(2n+\beta)} I_{2r+\beta}(2k\cosh z_0), \tag{8}$$

z_0 as above. (5), (6) have the same properties as (1), (2) respectively. Here and in §§ 13–16, the representations for functions of order $(2n+1+\beta)$ are obtained by writing $(1+\beta)$ for β, and using $A_{2r+1}^{(2n+1+\beta)}$ for $A_{2r}^{(2n+\beta)}$. (5), (6) were derived from (1), (2) by putting ik for k (by virtue of the altered sign of $q = k^2$ in the D.E.) and writing $(-1)^r A_{2r}^{(2n+\beta)}$ for $A_{2r}^{(2n+\beta)}$ in accordance with § 21.

13. Bessel function product series for $\mathrm{ce}_{m+\beta}(z,\pm q)$, $\mathrm{se}_{m+\beta}(z,\pm q)$, $\mathrm{Ce}_{m+\beta}(z,-q)$, $\mathrm{Se}_{m+\beta}(z,-q)$.

$$\left.\begin{matrix}\mathrm{ce}\\\mathrm{se}\end{matrix}\right\}_{2n+\beta}(z,q) = \left.\begin{matrix}K_{2n+\beta}\\iK_{2n+\beta}\end{matrix}\right\}\sum_{r=-\infty}^{\infty} (-1)^r A_{2r}^{(2n+\beta)}[J_r(v_1')J_{r+\beta}(v_2') \pm J_{r+\beta}(v_1')J_r(v_2')],$$
$$\tag{1, 2}$$

with $v_1' = ke^{iz}$, $v_2' = ke^{-iz}$, the K being defined at (2), (3) § 13.12.

$$\left.\begin{matrix} \mathrm{ce} \\ \mathrm{se} \end{matrix}\right\}_{2n+\beta}(z, -q)$$

$$= (-1)^n \left.\begin{matrix} L_{2n+\beta} \\ \bar{L}_{2n+\beta} \end{matrix}\right\} \sum_{r=-\infty}^{\infty} (-1)^r A_{2r}^{(2n+\beta)}[I_r(v_1')I_{r+\beta}(v_2') \pm I_{r+\beta}(v_1')I_r(v_2')], \quad (3, 4)$$

with

$$L_{2n+\beta} = \mathrm{ce}_{2n+\beta}(0, -q) \Big/ 2 \sum_{r=-\infty}^{\infty} (-1)^r A_{2r}^{(2n+\beta)} I_r(k) I_{r+\beta}(k); \qquad (5)$$

$$\bar{L}_{2n+\beta} = \mathrm{se}'_{2n+\beta}(0, -q) \Big/ 2k \sum_{r=-\infty}^{\infty} (-1)^r A_{2r}^{(2n+\beta)}[I_r(k)I'_{r+\beta}(k) - I_{r+\beta}(k)I'_r(k)].$$

$$\left.\begin{matrix} \mathrm{Ce} \\ \mathrm{Se} \end{matrix}\right\}_{2n+\beta}(z, -q) \qquad\qquad\qquad\qquad\qquad\qquad (6)$$

$$= (-1)^n \left.\begin{matrix} L_{2n+\beta} \\ \bar{L}_{2n+\beta} \end{matrix}\right\} \sum_{r=-\infty}^{\infty} (-1)^r A_{2r}^{(2n+\beta)}[I_r(v_1)I_{r+\beta}(v_2) \pm I_{r+\beta}(v_1)I_r(v_2)], \quad (7, 8)$$

with $v_1 = ke^{-z}$, $v_2 = ke^z$. If k is finite and positive, (1)–(4), (7), (8) are absolutely and uniformly convergent in any finite region of the z-plane. (7), (8) are analytical continuations of (5), (6) § 12 when $|\cosh z| \leqslant 1$.

14. Integral equations for $\mathrm{Ce}_{m+\beta}(z, q)$, $\mathrm{Se}_{m+\beta}(z, q)$. These were derived by analysis akin to that in § 10.40,

$$\mathrm{Ce}_{2n+\beta}(z, q) = \frac{2}{\pi} C_{2n+\beta} \int_0^\infty \sin(2k \cosh z \cosh u - \tfrac{1}{2}\beta\pi)\mathrm{Ce}_{2n+\beta}(u, q) \, du,$$
and
$$\qquad\qquad\qquad\qquad\qquad\qquad\qquad\qquad\qquad\qquad\qquad (1)$$

$$\mathrm{Se}_{2n+\beta}(z, q)$$
$$= -\frac{4}{\pi} S_{2n+\beta} k \sinh z \int_0^\infty \cos(2k \cosh z \cosh u - \tfrac{1}{2}\beta\pi)\sinh u \, \mathrm{Se}_{2n+\beta}(u, q) \, du,$$

$$\qquad\qquad\qquad\qquad\qquad\qquad\qquad\qquad\qquad\qquad\qquad (2)$$

k, z real > 0, while $C_{2n+\beta}$, $S_{2n+\beta}$ are given at (3), (4) § 12.

15. Asymptotic series for $\mathrm{Ce}_{m+\beta}(z, \pm q)$, $\mathrm{Se}_{m+\beta}(z, \pm q)$, z **large,** $0 < \beta < 1$.

$$\left.\begin{matrix} \mathrm{Ce} \\ \mathrm{Se} \end{matrix}\right\}_{2n+\beta}(z, q) \sim p_{2n+\beta}(2/\pi v)^{\frac{1}{2}}[P_{2n+\beta}^{(a)} \sin x - Q_{2n+\beta}^{(a)} \cos x], \quad (1, 2)$$

where $p_{2n+\beta} = (-1)^n p'_{2n+\beta} = C_{2n+\beta}\, \mathrm{ce}_{2n+\beta}(0, q)$, and P, Q are given at (13), (14) § 11.20, $a = a_{2n+\beta}$ being used to calculate the c in (7)–(9) § 11.20, $x = v + \tfrac{1}{4}\pi - \tfrac{1}{2}\beta\pi$, $v = ke^z$; also

$$\left.\begin{matrix} \mathrm{Ce} \\ \mathrm{Se} \end{matrix}\right\}_{2n+\beta}(z, -q) \sim p'_{2n+\beta}(2\pi v)^{-\frac{1}{2}}\Big[e^v \sum_{r=0}^{\infty} c_r v^{-r} - ie^{-i(v+\beta\pi)} \sum_{r=0}^{\infty} (-1)^r c_r v^{-r}\Big].$$

$$\qquad\qquad\qquad\qquad\qquad\qquad\qquad\qquad\qquad\qquad\qquad (3, 4)$$

The functions are real if z is real, so the second member in [ ] is omitted then. If $R(z) > 0$ is large, $\cosh(2r+\beta)z \sim \sinh(2r+\beta)z$, and since the coefficients $A_{2r}^{(2n+\beta)}$ are common to the series representations of both functions (see (12) § 4.71), under the above condition they have the same asymptotic expansion.

16. Asymptotic formulae for $Ce_{2n+\beta}(z,q)$, $Se_{2n+\beta}(z,q)$, q **large and positive,** $0 < \beta < 1$.

$$\left.\begin{array}{c}Ce\\Se\end{array}\right\}_{2n+\beta} (z,q) \sim p_{2n+\beta}(\pi k \cosh z)^{-\frac{1}{2}}\left[(1+x_{2n})\begin{array}{c}\cos \varphi_{2n}\\\sin \varphi_{2n-1}\end{array} \pm z_{2n}\begin{array}{c}\sin \varphi_{2n}\\\cos \varphi_{2n-1}\end{array}\right],$$

$$(1, 2)$$

where $\varphi_m = 2k\sinh z - \frac{1}{2}\beta\pi - (2m+1)\tan^{-1}(\tanh \frac{1}{2}z)$, x_{2n}, z_{2n} are defined in § 6 and $p_{2n+\beta}$ in § 15. See last two sentences of § 7 regarding accuracy.

17. Degenerate forms. Procedure akin to that in § 2 Appendix I, yields

$$\left.\begin{array}{c}Ce\\Se\end{array}\right\}_{m+\beta} (z,q) \to p'_{m+\beta} J_{m+\beta}(k_1 r); \tag{1, 2}$$

$$\left.\begin{array}{c}Ce\\Se\end{array}\right\}_{m} (z, -iq) \to \begin{array}{c}p'_m\\s'_m\end{array} J_m(i^{\frac{3}{2}}k_1 r); \tag{3, 4}$$

$$\left.\begin{array}{c}Cer\\Cei\end{array}\right\}_{m} (z) \to p'_m \begin{array}{c}ber\\bei\end{array}\right\}_{m} (k_1 r); \tag{5, 6}$$

$$\left.\begin{array}{c}Ser\\Sei\end{array}\right\}_{m} (z) \to s'_m \begin{array}{c}ber\\bei\end{array}\right\}_{m} (k_1 r). \tag{7, 8}$$

COMMENTS ON CERTAIN PARTS OF THE TEXT

18. $ce_m(z,q)$, $se_m(z,q)$ **as functions of** q **real** > 0. This is displayed in Figs. 167–77, pp. 288–93 in the revised American edition (1943) of *Funktionentafeln* by E. Jahnke and F. Emde. Except Figs. 167, 169, the normalization in the graphs and those of Figs. 1–4 herein is that of § 2.21. In Figs. 167, 169 the values of $ce_0(z,q)$ have been multiplied by $2^{\frac{1}{2}}$. The reader should plot similar graphs using the tabular data in references 52, 95.

19. Computation of a, β, μ, **coefficients, etc.** The procedure in Chaps. III–VII, XIII, etc., lacks the detail usually needed by the professional computer, because the text is for the general reader. The former is able to supply the missing material required in tabulation. The general reader will find that in computing β or μ (especially the latter), the recurrence formula method in § 5.32 is easier to manipulate than the continued fractions in § 5.11. For convenience in § 5.20 et seq., we have taken $c_0 = 1$, or $c_1 = 1$, as the case may be. When the order of the function is $(m+\beta)$, c_0/c_m, c_1/c_m, etc., may be small if m is large enough with q moderate. It might then be expedient to put $c_m = 1$. A similar remark applies with regard to computation of $A_p^{(m+\beta)}$ in § 4.71, since it is proportional to c_p. For instance, if $m = 12$, the computation could be started at, say, c_{20} on one side of c_{12} and at c_4 on the other. To reduce errors it is expedient to work *towards* c_{12} from each side. The whole range c_{20} to c_4 or vice versa should not be covered in one direction only. An overlap to c_{m+4} on one side of c_m, and to c_{m-4} on the other, provides a check.

20. Stability of solutions. In (b) § 4.14, a solution which tends to zero as $z \to +\infty$ is defined to be stable, although (a, q) lies in an *unstable* region of the plane. But the same solution tends to $\pm\infty$ as $z \to -\infty$, so when *the whole range of z* is considered, it is unstable. In applications where z is a multiple of the time t, which is always real and positive, it is preferable that the definition (b) § 4.14 is adopted.

21. Changing the sign of q. It is not always expedient to do this by writing $(\frac{1}{2}\pi - z)$ for z in solutions of (1) § 2.10, e.g. (5), (6) § 4.71. Now the recurrence relations for $-q$ are obtained from those for $+q$ by writing $(-1)^r A_{2r}^{(2n+\beta)}$, or $(-1)^r A_{2r+1}^{(2n+1+\beta)}$, for $A_{2r}^{(2n+\beta)}$, $A_{2r+1}^{(2n+1+\beta)}$, as the case may be. Thus, apart from the multiplier $(-1)^n$, (7), (8) § 4.71 follow immediately from (1), (2) § 4.71 if this change is made. The same artifice may be used in §§ 5.20, 5.21, 5.310 to obtain solutions for a changed sign of q. When the argument in the series is $2k \cosh z$, it is also necessary to write ik for k, since $(ik)^2 = -q$. If the external multiplier is a function of q, it should be re-determined (see § 12, where (5), (6) were derived from (1), (2) in this way).

22. Solution of (8) § 4.80. This linear difference equation is satisfied by the J- and the Y-Bessel functions. Referring to § 3.21, if we put $v_r = c_{r+1}/c_r$, we obtain

$$v_{r+1} + v_r^{-1} = 4(a^{\frac{1}{2}}/q)(r+1). \tag{1}$$

Then if a, q are finite, it follows from (1) that $v_r \to 0$ or to $\pm\infty$ as $r \to \pm\infty$. Hence one solution tends to zero, the other to infinity as $r \to \pm\infty$. Now $J_r \to 0$, while by aid of (2) 1° § 8.50 it may be shown that $Y_r \to \mp\infty$. But for convergence of (5) § 4.80, $c_r \to 0$, so the Y-Bessel function is an inadmissible solution.

23. Second solutions. Herein we have taken the first solutions of the various differential equations to be either odd or even, according to the value of a. If the first solution is *even*, there is one (and only one) linearly independent *odd* solution, and vice versa. But by virtue of the theory of linear D.E., we may construct from these two solutions as many other second solutions as we please, which are neither odd nor even. Thus if $Ce_m(z, q)$ is the first and even solution, *the* second and *odd* linearly independent solution is $Fe_m(z, q)$ in § 7.61. If γ and δ are *any* non-zero constants,

$$y_2(z) = \gamma \, Ce_m(z, q) + \delta \, Fe_m(z, q) \qquad (1)$$

represents an infinite family of linearly independent second solutions, which are neither odd nor even. Now it may happen that the most suitable second solution is obtained when γ and δ have special values. It is demonstrated in §§ 8.11, 8.12, 13.20 that $Fey_m(z, q)$ is a linearly independent solution of the same D.E. as $Ce_m(z, q)$, and by §§ 13.20, 13.21 it has the form at (1). In this instance the values of γ, δ derived in § 13.21, are fixed automatically, i.e. they are not arbitrary. $Fey_m(z, q)$ is more suitable as a standard second solution than $Fe_m(z, q)$—see analysis in Chaps. VIII, X, XI, XIII, and Appendix III.

Referring to § 9.30, $Fey_m(z, q)$, $Fek_m(z, -q)$ are preferable to $Fe_m(z, \pm q)$ in applications. They both tend to zero as $z \to +\infty$.

Fundamental system. *Any* two linearly independent solutions of a Mathieu equation constitute a fundamental system, since the Wronskian relation is non-zero (see (1) § 2.191). In the text it is stated sometimes that if $y_1(z)$, $y_2(z)$ are solutions satisfying this condition, while A, B are *arbitrary* constants,

$$y(z) = Ay_1(z) + By_2(z) \qquad (2)$$

constitutes a fundamental system. This may be regarded as an extension of the usual definition.

24. Formula (1) § 5.15 for β. If in Fig. 11, $a^{\frac{1}{2}}$ is plotted instead of a, the iso-β curves $\beta = 0\cdot1$, $0\cdot2$, $0\cdot3$,... will intersect the $a^{\frac{1}{2}}$ axis at equal intervals. Provided $|q|$ is not too large, these curves are almost parallel to the q-axis. The $|q|$ range of parallelism increases with increase in $a^{\frac{1}{2}}$, as will be evident from the last sentence of § 2.151. Then interpolation for β is almost linear in $a^{\frac{1}{2}}$, and the accuracy of (1) § 5.15 and (4) § 4.74 will be of the same order. This is the basis of (1) § 5.15, which is easily established by aid of paragraph one in § 5.13. In Fig. 11 for values of $q > 0$ beyond the maxima of the iso-β curves, where they begin to approach each other, the accuracy of (1) § 5.15 is likely to be low.

25. Remark on (4) § 7.40 in relation to § 7.50 et seq. By § 3.21, if q is finite, as $r \to +\infty$, $|A_{2r+3}/A_{2r+1}| \sim q/(2r+3)^2$. Thus the r.h.s. of (4) § 7.40 is very small when r is large enough, and we get (approximately) (1) § 7.50 but with f for c. One solution tends to zero, the other to infinity as $r \to +\infty$. Consequently, if we *assume* that $f_{2r-1} > f_{2r+1} > f_{2r+3}$, etc., in (4) § 7.40, and calculate the $f_p^{(m)}$ on this basis, we obtain a particular solution which tends to zero as $r \to +\infty$. The series involving the $f_p^{(m)}$ may now be shown to have the convergence properties deduced in §§ 3.21, 3.22. The coefficients $g_p^{(m)}$ may be treated similarly.

26. Convergence. Throughout the book, except perhaps at (2) 3° § 8.50, q is assumed to be finite. In fact $q > 0$ may usually be interpreted to mean that q is greater than zero, but *finite*. When $q \to +\infty$ an explicit statement is made to this effect.

27. Relationships between Fey_m, Ce_m, Fek_m, etc. in §§ 8.14, 8.30. These were deduced using series for Fey_m, Fek_m, convergent only if $|\cosh z| > 1$. But by virtue of the B.F. product representations, these functions are continuous when $|\cosh z| \leqslant 1$, so by analytical continuation the said relations are valid in any finite region of the z-plane. They may, of course, be derived directly from the B.F. product series. In view of the frequent occurrence of the foregoing restriction on z, it is apposite to remark that the 'forbidden neighbourhood' is the imaginary axis!

28. Remark on § 10.40. The functions represented by the r.h.s. of (4), (6), (7), (9) appear to be even in z, while those in (11), (13), (14), (16) appear to be odd. They are, however, neither odd nor even, and this point is covered by the restrictions on z at the end of the section.

INDEX

BOOKS EXPLAINING SCIENCE AND MATHEMATICS

General

WHAT IS SCIENCE?, Norman Campbell. This excellent introduction explains scientific method, role of mathematics, types of scientific laws. Contents: 2 aspects of science, science & nature, laws of science, discovery of laws, explanation of laws, measurement & numerical laws, applications of science. 192pp. 5⅜ x 8. S43 Paperbound **$1.25**

THE COMMON SENSE OF THE EXACT SCIENCES, W. K. Clifford. Introduction by James Newman, edited by Karl Pearson. For 70 years this has been a guide to classical scientific and mathematical thought. Explains with unusual clarity basic concepts, such as extension of meaning of symbols, characteristics of surface boundaries, properties of plane figures, vectors, Cartesian method of determining position, etc. Long preface by Bertrand Russell. Bibliography of Clifford. Corrected, 130 diagrams redrawn. 249pp. 5⅜ x 8.
T61 Paperbound **$1.60**

SCIENCE THEORY AND MAN, Erwin Schrödinger. This is a complete and unabridged reissue of SCIENCE AND THE HUMAN TEMPERAMENT plus an additional essay: "What is an Elementary Particle?" Nobel laureate Schrödinger discusses such topics as nature of scientific method, the nature of science, chance and determinism, science and society, conceptual models for physical entities, elementary particles and wave mechanics. Presentation is popular and may be followed by most people with little or no scientific training. "Fine practical preparation for a time when laws of nature, human institutions . . . are undergoing a critical examination without parallel," Waldemar Kaempffert, N. Y. TIMES. 192pp. 5⅜ x 8.
T428 Paperbound **$1.35**

FADS AND FALLACIES IN THE NAME OF SCIENCE, Martin Gardner. Examines various cults, quack systems, frauds, delusions which at various times have masqueraded as science. Accounts of hollow-earth fanatics like Symmes; Velikovsky and wandering planets; Hoerbiger; Bellamy and the theory of multiple moons; Charles Fort; dowsing, pseudoscientific methods for finding water, ores, oil. Sections on naturopathy, iridiagnosis, zone therapy, food fads, etc. Analytical accounts of Wilhelm Reich and orgone sex energy; L. Ron Hubbard and Dianetics; A. Korzybski and General Semantics; many others. Brought up to date to include Bridey Murphy, others. Not just a collection of anecdotes, but a fair, reasoned appraisal of eccentric theory. Formerly titled IN THE NAME OF SCIENCE. Preface. Index. x + 384pp. 5⅜ x 8. T394 Paperbound **$1.50**

A DOVER SCIENCE SAMPLER, edited by George Barkin. 64-page book, sturdily bound, containing excerpts from over 20 Dover books, explaining science. Edwin Hubble, George Sarton, Ernst Mach, A. d'Abro, Galileo, Newton, others, discussing island universes, scientific truth, biological phenomena, stability in bridges, etc. Copies limited; no more than 1 to a customer,
FREE

POPULAR SCIENTIFIC LECTURES, Hermann von Helmholtz. Helmholtz was a superb expositor as well as a scientist of genius in many areas. The seven essays in this volume are models of clarity, and even today they rank among the best general descriptions of their subjects ever written. "The Physiological Causes of Harmony in Music" was the first significant physiological explanation of musical consonance and dissonance. Two essays, "On the Interaction of Natural Forces" and "On the Conservation of Force," were of great importance in the history of science, for they firmly established the principle of the conservation of energy. Other lectures include "On the Relation of Optics to Painting," "On Recent Progress in the Theory of Vision," "On Goethe's Scientific Researches," and "On the Origin and Significance of Geometrical Axioms." Selected and edited with an introduction by Professor Morris Kline. xii + 286pp. 5⅜ x 8½. T799 Paperbound **$1.45**

BOOKS EXPLAINING SCIENCE AND MATHEMATICS

Physics

CONCERNING THE NATURE OF THINGS, Sir William Bragg. Christmas lectures delivered at the Royal Society by Nobel laureate. Why a spinning ball travels in a curved track; how uranium is transmuted to lead, etc. Partial contents: atoms, gases, liquids, crystals, metals, etc. No scientific background needed; wonderful for intelligent child. 32pp. of photos, 57 figures. xii + 232pp. 5⅜ x 8. T31 Paperbound **$1.35**

THE RESTLESS UNIVERSE, Max Born. New enlarged version of this remarkably readable account by a Nobel laureate. Moving from sub-atomic particles to universe, the author explains in very simple terms the latest theories of wave mechanics. Partial contents: air and its relatives, electrons & ions, waves & particles, electronic structure of the atom, nuclear physics. Nearly 1000 illustrations, including 7 animated sequences. 325pp. 6 x 9.
T412 Paperbound **$2.00**

CATALOGUE OF DOVER BOOKS

**FROM EUCLID TO EDDINGTON: A STUDY OF THE CONCEPTIONS OF THE EXTERNAL WORLD,
Sir Edmund Whittaker.** A foremost British scientist traces the development of theories of
natural philosophy from the western rediscovery of Euclid to Eddington, Einstein, Dirac, etc.
The inadequacy of classical physics is contrasted with present day attempts to understand
the physical world through relativity, non-Euclidean geometry, space curvature, wave mechanics, etc. 5 major divisions of examination: Space; Time and Movement; the Concepts
of Classical Physics; the Concepts of Quantum Mechanics; the Eddington Universe. 212pp.
5⅜ x 8.   T491 Paperbound **$1.35**

PHYSICS, THE PIONEER SCIENCE, L. W. Taylor. First thorough text to place all important
physical phenomena in cultural-historical framework; remains best work of its kind. Exposition of physical laws, theories developed chronologically, with great historical, illustrative
experiments diagrammed, described, worked out mathematically. Excellent physics text
for self-study as well as class work. Vol. 1: Heat, Sound: motion, acceleration, gravitation,
conservation of energy, heat engines, rotation, heat, mechanical energy, etc. 211 illus.
407pp. 5⅜ x 8. Vol. 2: Light, Electricity: images, lenses, prisms, magnetism, Ohm's law,
dynamos, telegraph, quantum theory, decline of mechanical view of nature, etc. Bibliography.
13 table appendix. Index. 551 illus. 2 color plates. 508pp. 5⅜ x 8.
Vol. 1 S565 Paperbound **$2.00**
Vol. 2 S566 Paperbound **$2.00**
The set **$4.00**

A SURVEY OF PHYSICAL THEORY, Max Planck. One of the greatest scientists of all time,
creator of the quantum revolution in physics, writes in non-technical terms of his own
discoveries and those of other outstanding creators of modern physics. Planck wrote this
book when science had just crossed the threshold of the new physics, and he communicates
the excitement felt then as he discusses electromagnetic theories, statistical methods, evolution of the concept of light, a step-by-step description of how he developed his own momen-
tous theory, and many more of the basic ideas behind modern physics. Formerly "A Survey
of Physics." Bibliography. Index. 128pp. 5⅜ x 8.   S650 Paperbound **$1.15**

THE ATOMIC NUCLEUS, M. Korsunsky. The only non-technical comprehensive account of the
atomic nucleus in English. For college physics students, etc. Chapters cover: Radioactivity,
the Nuclear Model of the Atom, the Mass of Atomic Nuclei, the Disintegration of Atomic
Nuclei, the Discovery of the Positron, the Artificial Transformation of Atomic Nuclei, Artificial Radioactivity, Mesons, the Neutrino, the Structure of Atomic Nuclei and Forces Acting
Between Nuclear Particles, Nuclear Fission, Chain Reaction, Peaceful Uses, Thermonuclear
Reactions. Slightly abridged edition. Translated by G. Yankovsky. 65 figures. Appendix includes
45 photographic illustrations. 413 pp. 5⅜ x 8.   S1052 Paperbound **$2.00**

PRINCIPLES OF MECHANICS SIMPLY EXPLAINED, Morton Mott-Smith. Excellent, highly readable
introduction to the theories and discoveries of classical physics. Ideal for the layman who
desires a foundation which will enable him to understand and appreciate contemporary developments in the physical sciences. Discusses: Density, The Law of Gravitation, Mass and
Weight, Action and Reaction, Kinetic and Potential Energy, The Law of Inertia, Effects of
Acceleration, The Independence of Motions, Galileo and the New Science of Dynamics,
Newton and the New Cosmos, The Conservation of Momentum, and other topics. Revised
edition of "This Mechanical World." Illustrated by E. Kosa, Jr. Bibliography and Chronology.
Index. xiv + 171pp. 5⅜ x 8½.   T1067 Paperbound **$1.00**

THE CONCEPT OF ENERGY SIMPLY EXPLAINED, Morton Mott-Smith. Elementary, non-technical
exposition which traces the story of man's conquest of energy, with particular emphasis on
the developments during the nineteenth century and the first three decades of our own
century. Discusses man's earlier efforts to harness energy, more recent experiments and
discoveries relating to the steam engine, the engine indicator, the motive power of heat, the
principle of excluded perpetual motion, the bases of the conservation of energy, the concept
of entropy, the internal combustion engine, mechanical refrigeration, and many other related
topics. Also much biographical material. Index. Bibliography. 33 illustrations. ix + 215pp.
5⅜ x 8½.   T1071 Paperbound **$1.25**

HEAT AND ITS WORKINGS, Morton Mott-Smith. One of the best elementary introductions to the
theory and attributes of heat, covering such matters as the laws governing the effect of heat
on solids, liquids and gases, the methods by which heat is measured, the conversion of a
substance from one form to another through heating and cooling, evaporation, the effects of
pressure on boiling and freezing points, and the three ways in which heat is transmitted
(conduction, convection, radiation). Also brief notes on major experiments and discoveries.
Concise, but complete, it presents all the essential facts about the subject in readable style.
Will give the layman and beginning student a first-rate background in this major topic in
physics. Index. Bibliography. 50 illustrations. x + 165pp. 5⅜ x 8½. T978 Paperbound **$1.00**

THE STORY OF ATOMIC THEORY AND ATOMIC ENERGY, J. G. Feinberg. Wider range of facts
on physical theory, cultural implications, than any other similar source. Completely non-
technical. Begins with first atomic theory, 600 B.C., goes through A-bomb, developments to
1959. Avogadro, Rutherford, Bohr, Einstein, radioactive decay, binding energy, radiation
danger, future benefits of nuclear power, dozens of other topics, told in lively, related,
informal manner. Particular stress on European atomic research. "Deserves special mention
. . . authoritative," Saturday Review. Formerly "The Atom Story." New chapter to 1959.
Index. 34 illustrations. 251pp. 5⅜ x 8.   T625 Paperbound **$1.45**

THE STRANGE STORY OF THE QUANTUM, AN ACCOUNT FOR THE GENERAL READER OF THE GROWTH OF IDEAS UNDERLYING OUR PRESENT ATOMIC KNOWLEDGE, B. Hoffmann. Presents lucidly and expertly, with barest amount of mathematics, the problems and theories which led to modern quantum physics. Dr. Hoffmann begins with the closing years of the 19th century, when certain trifling discrepancies were noticed, and with illuminating analogies and examples takes you through the brilliant concepts of Planck, Einstein, Pauli, de Broglie, Bohr, Schroedinger, Heisenberg, Dirac, Sommerfeld, Feynman, etc. This edition includes a new, long postscript carrying the story through 1958. "Of the books attempting an account of the history and contents of our modern atomic physics which have come to my attention, this is the best," H. Margenau, Yale University, in "American Journal of Physics."; 32 tables and line illustrations. Index. 275pp. 5⅜ x 8. T518 Paperbound **$1.50**

THE EVOLUTION OF SCIENTIFIC THOUGHT FROM NEWTON TO EINSTEIN, A. d'Abro. Einstein's special and general theories of relativity, with their historical implications, are analyzed in non-technical terms. Excellent accounts of the contributions of Newton, Riemann, Weyl, Planck, Eddington, Maxwell, Lorentz and others are treated in terms of space and time, equations of electromagnetics, finiteness of the universe, methodology of science. 21 diagrams. 482pp. 5⅜ x 8. T2 Paperound **$2.00**

THE RISE OF THE NEW PHYSICS, A. d'Abro. A half-million word exposition, formerly titled THE DECLINE OF MECHANISM, for readers not versed in higher mathematics. The only thorough explanation, in everyday language, of the central core of modern mathematical physical theory, treating both classical and modern theoretical physics, and presenting in terms almost anyone can understand the equivalent of 5 years of study of mathematical physics. Scientifically impeccable coverage of mathematical-physical thought from the Newtonian system up through the electronic theories of Dirac and Heisenberg and Fermi's statistics. Combines both history and exposition; provides a broad yet unified and detailed view, with constant comparison of classical and modern views on phenomena and theories. "A must for anyone doing serious study in the physical sciences," JOURNAL OF THE FRANKLIN INSTITUTE. "Extraordinary faculty . . . to explain ideas and theories of theoretical physics in the language of daily life," ISIS. First part of set covers philosophy of science, drawing upon the practice of Newton, Maxwell, Poincaré, Einstein, others, discussing modes of thought, experiment, interpretations of causality, etc. In the second part, 100 pages explain grammar and vocabulary of mathematics, with discussions of functions, groups, series, Fourier series, etc. The remainder is devoted to concrete, detailed coverage of both classical and quantum physics, explaining such topics as analytic mechanics, Hamilton's principle, wave theory of light, electromagnetic waves, groups of transformations, thermodynamics, phase rule, Brownian movement, kinetics, special relativity, Planck's original quantum theory, Bohr's atom, Zeeman effect, Broglie's wave mechanics, Heisenberg's uncertainty, Eigen-values, matrices, scores of other important topics. Discoveries and theories are covered for such men as Alembert, Born, Cantor, Debye, Euler, Foucault, Galois, Gauss, Hadamard, Kelvin, Kepler, Laplace, Maxwell, Pauli, Rayleigh, Volterra, Weyl, Young, more than 180 others. Indexed. 97 illustrations. ix + 982pp. 5⅜ x 8. T3 Volume 1, Paperbound **$2.00**
T4 Volume 2, Paperbound **$2.00**

SPINNING TOPS AND GYROSCOPIC MOTION, John Perry. Well-known classic of science still unsurpassed for lucid, accurate, delightful exposition. How quasi-rigidity is induced in flexible and fluid bodies by rapid motions; why gyrostat falls, top rises; nature and effect on climatic conditions of earth's precessional movement; effect of internal fluidity on rotating bodies, etc. Appendixes describe practical uses to which gyroscopes have been put in ships, compasses, monorail transportation. 62 figures. 128pp. 5⅜ x 8. T416 Paperbound **$1.00**

THE UNIVERSE OF LIGHT, Sir William Bragg. No scientific training needed to read Nobel Prize winner's expansion of his Royal Institute Christmas Lectures. Insight into nature of light, methods and philosophy of science. Explains lenses, reflection, color, resonance, polarization, x-rays, the spectrum, Newton's work with prisms, Huygens' with polarization, Crookes' with cathode ray, etc. Leads into clear statement of 2 major historical theories of light, corpuscle and wave. Dozens of experiments you can do. 199 illus., including 2 full-page color plates. 293pp. 5⅜ x 8. S538 Paperbound **$1.85**

THE STORY OF X-RAYS FROM RÖNTGEN TO ISOTOPES, A. R. Bleich. Non-technical history of x-rays, their scientific explanation, their applications in medicine, industry, research, and art, and their effect on the individual and his descendants. Includes amusing early reactions to Röntgen's discovery, cancer therapy, detections of art and stamp forgeries, potential risks to patient and operator, etc. Illustrations show x-rays of flower structure, the gall bladder, gears with hidden defects, etc. Original Dover publication. Glossary. Bibliography. Index. 55 photos and figures. xiv + 186pp. 5⅜ x 8. T662 Paperbound **$1.35**

ELECTRONS, ATOMS, METALS AND ALLOYS, Wm. Hume-Rothery. An introductory-level explanation of the application of the electronic theory to the structure and properties of metals and alloys, taking into account the new theoretical work done by mathematical physicists. Material presented in dialogue-form between an "Old Metallurgist" and a "Young Scientist." Their discussion falls into 4 main parts: the nature of an atom, the nature of a metal, the nature of an alloy, and the structure of the nucleus. They cover such topics as the hydrogen atom, electron waves, wave mechanics, Brillouin zones, co-valent bonds, radio-activity and natural disintegration, fundamental particles, structure and fission of the nucleus, etc. Revised, enlarged edition. 177 illustrations. Subject and name indexes. 407pp. 5⅜ x 8½. S1046 Paperbound **$2.25**

OUT OF THE SKY, H. H. Nininger. A non-technical but comprehensive introduction to "meteoritics", the young science concerned with all aspects of the arrival of matter from outer space. Written by one of the world's experts on meteorites, this work shows how, despite difficulties of observation and sparseness of data, a considerable body of knowledge has arisen. It defines meteors and meteorites; studies fireball clusters and processions, meteorite composition, size, distribution, showers, explosions, origins, craters, and much more. A true connecting link between astronomy and geology. More than 175 photos, 22 other illustrations. References. Bibliography of author's publications on meteorites. Index. viii + 336pp. 5⅜ x 8. T519 Paperbound **$1.85**

SATELLITES AND SCIENTIFIC RESEARCH, D. King-Hele. Non-technical account of the manmade satellites and the discoveries they have yielded up to the autumn of 1961. Brings together information hitherto published only in hard-to-get scientific journals. Includes the life history of a typical satellite, methods of tracking, new information on the shape of the earth, zones of radiation, etc. Over 60 diagrams and 6 photographs. Mathematical appendix. Bibliography of over 100 items. Index. xii + 180pp. 5⅜ x 8½. T703 Paperbound **$2.00**

BOOKS EXPLAINING SCIENCE AND MATHEMATICS

Mathematics

CHANCE, LUCK AND STATISTICS: THE SCIENCE OF CHANCE, Horace C. Levinson. Theory of probability and science of statistics in simple, non-technical language. Part I deals with theory of probability, covering odd superstitions in regard to "luck," the meaning of betting odds, the law of mathematical expectation, gambling, and applications in poker, roulette, lotteries, dice, bridge, and other games of chance. Part II discusses the misuse of statistics, the concept of statistical probabilities, normal and skew frequency distributions, and statistics applied to various fields—birth rates, stock speculation, insurance rates, advertising, etc. "Presented in an easy humorous style which I consider the best kind of expository writing," Prof. A. C. Cohen, Industry Quality Control. Enlarged revised edition. Formerly titled "The Science of Chance." Preface and two new appendices by the author. Index. xiv + 365pp. 5⅜ x 8. T1007 Paperbound **$1.85**

PROBABILITIES AND LIFE, Emile Borel. Translated by M. Baudin. Non-technical, highly readable introduction to the results of probability as applied to everyday situations. Partial contents: Fallacies About Probabilities Concerning Life After Death; Negligible Probabilities and the Probabilities of Everyday Life; Events of Small Probability; Application of Probabilities to Certain Problems of Heredity; Probabilities of Deaths, Diseases, and Accidents; On Poisson's Formula. Index. 3 Appendices of statistical studies and tables. vi + 87pp. 5⅜ x 8½. T121 Paperbound **$1.00**

GREAT IDEAS OF MODERN MATHEMATICS: THEIR NATURE AND USE, Jagjit Singh. Reader with only high school math will understand main mathematical ideas of modern physics, astronomy, genetics, psychology, evolution, etc., better than many who use them as tools, but comprehend little of their basic structure. Author uses his wide knowledge of non-mathematical fields in brilliant exposition of differential equations, matrices, group theory, logic, statistics, problems of mathematical foundations, imaginary numbers, vectors, etc. Original publication. 2 appendices. 2 indexes. 65 illustr. 322pp. 5⅜ x 8. S587 Paperbound **$1.75**

MATHEMATICS IN ACTION, O. G. Sutton. Everyone with a command of high school algebra will find this book one of the finest possible introductions to the application of mathematics to physical theory. Ballistics, numerical analysis, waves and wavelike phenomena, Fourier series, group concepts, fluid flow and aerodynamics, statistical measures, and meteorology are discussed with unusual clarity. Some calculus and differential equations theory is developed by the author for the reader's help in the more difficult sections. 88 figures. Index. viii + 236pp. 5⅜ x 8. T440 Clothbound **$3.50**

THE FOURTH DIMENSION SIMPLY EXPLAINED, edited by H. P. Manning. 22 essays, originally Scientific American contest entries, that use a minimum of mathematics to explain aspects of 4-dimensional geometry: analogues to 3-dimensional space, 4-dimensional absurdities and curiosities (such as removing the contents of an egg without puncturing its shell), possible measurements and forms, etc. Introduction by the editor. Only book of its sort on a truly elementary level, excellent introduction to advanced works. 82 figures. 251pp. 5⅜ x 8. T711 Paperbound **$1.35**

MATHEMATICS—INTERMEDIATE TO ADVANCED

General

INTRODUCTION TO APPLIED MATHEMATICS, Francis D. Murnaghan. A practical and thoroughly sound introduction to a number of advanced branches of higher mathematics. Among the selected topics covered in detail are: vector and matrix analysis, partial and differential equations, integral equations, calculus of variations, Laplace transform theory, the vector triple product, linear vector functions, quadratic and bilinear forms, Fourier series, spherical harmonics, Bessel functions, the Heaviside expansion formula, and many others. Extremely useful book for graduate students in physics, engineering, chemistry, and mathematics. Index. 111 study exercises with answers. 41 illustrations. ix + 389pp. 5⅜ x 8½.
S1042 Paperbound **$2.00**

OPERATIONAL METHODS IN APPLIED MATHEMATICS, H. S. Carslaw and J. C. Jaeger. Explanation of the application of the Laplace Transformation to differential equations, a simple and effective substitute for more difficult and obscure operational methods. Of great practical value to engineers and to all workers in applied mathematics. Chapters on: Ordinary Linear Differential Equations with Constant Coefficients;; Electric Circuit Theory; Dynamical Applications; The Inversion Theorem for the Laplace Transformation; Conduction of Heat; Vibrations of Continuous Mechanical Systems; Hydrodynamics; Impulsive Functions; Chains of Differential Equations; and other related matters. 3 appendices. 153 problems, many with answers. 22 figures. xvi + 359pp. 5⅜ x 8½.
S1011 Paperbound **$2.25**

APPLIED MATHEMATICS FOR RADIO AND COMMUNICATIONS ENGINEERS, C. E. Smith. No extraneous material here!—only the theories, equations, and operations essential and immediately useful for radio work. Can be used as refresher, as handbook of applications and tables, or as full home-study course. Ranges from simplest arithmetic through calculus, series, and wave forms, hyperbolic trigonometry, simultaneous equations in mesh circuits, etc. Supplies applications right along with each math topic discussed. 22 useful tables of functions, formulas, logs, etc. Index. 166 exercises, 140 examples, all with answers. 95 diagrams. Bibliography. x + 336pp. 5⅜ x 8.
S141 Paperbound **$1.75**

Algebra, group theory, determinants, sets, matrix theory

ALGEBRAS AND THEIR ARITHMETICS, L. E. Dickson. Provides the foundation and background necessary to any advanced undergraduate or graduate student studying abstract algebra. Begins with elementary introduction to linear transformations, matrices, field of complex numbers; proceeds to order, basal units, modulus, quaternions, etc.; develops calculus of linears sets, describes various examples of algebras including invariant, difference, nilpotent, semi-simple. "Makes the reader marvel at his genius for clear and profound analysis," Amer. Mathematical Monthly. Index. xii + 241pp. 5⅜ x 8.
S616 Paperbound **$1.50**

THE THEORY OF EQUATIONS WITH AN INTRODUCTION TO THE THEORY OF BINARY ALGEBRAIC FORMS, W. S. Burnside and A. W. Panton. Extremely thorough and concrete discussion of the theory of equations, with extensive detailed treatment of many topics curtailed in later texts. Covers theory of algebraic equations, properties of polynomials, symmetric functions, derived functions, Horner's process, complex numbers and the complex variable, determinants and methods of elimination, invariant theory (nearly 100 pages), transformations, introduction to Galois theory, Abelian equations, and much more. Invaluable supplementary work for modern students and teachers. 759 examples and exercises. Index in each volume. Two volume set. Total of xxiv + 604pp. 5⅜ x 8.
S714 Vol I Paperbound **$1.85**
S715 Vol II Paperbound **$1.85**
The set **$3.70**

COMPUTATIONAL METHODS OF LINEAR ALGEBRA, V. N. Faddeeva, translated by **C. D. Benster.** First English translation of a unique and valuable work, the only work in English presenting a systematic exposition of the most important methods of linear algebra—classical and contemporary. Shows in detail how to derive numerical solutions of problems in mathematical physics which are frequently connected with those of linear algebra. Theory as well as individual practice. Part I surveys the mathematical background that is indispensable to what follows. Parts II and III, the conclusion, set forth the most important methods of solution, for both exact and iterative groups. One of the most outstanding and valuable features of this work is the 23 tables, double and triple checked for accuracy. These tables will not be found elsewhere. Author's preface. Translator's note. New bibliography and index. x + 252pp. 5⅜ x 8.
S424 Paperbound **$1.95**

ALGEBRAIC EQUATIONS, E. Dehn. Careful and complete presentation of Galois' theory of algebraic equations; theories of Lagrange and Galois developed in logical rather than historical form, with a more thorough exposition than in most modern books. Many concrete applications and fully-worked-out examples. Discusses basic theory (very clear exposition of the symmetric group); isomorphic, transitive, and Abelian groups; applications of Lagrange's and Galois' theories; and much more. Newly revised by the author. Index. List of Theorems. xi + 208pp. 5⅜ x 8.
S697 Paperbound **$1.45**

Differential equations, ordinary and partial; integral equations

INTRODUCTION TO THE DIFFERENTIAL EQUATIONS OF PHYSICS, L. Hopf. Especially valuable to the engineer with no math beyond elementary calculus. Emphasizing intuitive rather than formal aspects of concepts, the author covers an extensive territory. Partial contents: Law of causality, energy theorem, damped oscillations, coupling by friction, cylindrical and spherical coordinates, heat source, etc. Index. 48 figures. 160pp. 5⅜ x 8.
S120 Paperbound $1.25

INTRODUCTION TO THE THEORY OF LINEAR DIFFERENTIAL EQUATIONS, E. G. Poole. Authoritative discussions of important topics, with methods of solution more detailed than usual, for students with background of elementary course in differential equations. Studies existence theorems, linearly independent solutions; equations with constant coefficients; with uniform analytic coefficients; regular singularities; the hypergeometric equation; conformal representation; etc. Exercises. Index. 210pp. 5⅜ x 8.
S629 Paperbound $1.65

DIFFERENTIAL EQUATIONS FOR ENGINEERS, P. Franklin. Outgrowth of a course given 10 years at M. I. T. Makes most useful branch of pure math accessible for practical work. Theoretical basis of D.E.'s; solution of ordinary D.E.'s and partial derivatives arising from heat flow, steady-state temperature of a plate, wave equations; analytic functions; convergence of Fourier Series. 400 problems on electricity, vibratory systems, other topics. Formerly "Differential Equations for Electrical Engineers." Index 41 illus. 307pp. 5⅜ x 8.
S601 Paperbound $1.65

DIFFERENTIAL EQUATIONS, F. R. Moulton. A detailed, rigorous exposition of all the non-elementary processes of solving ordinary differential equations. Several chapters devoted to the treatment of practical problems, especially those of a physical nature, which are far more advanced than problems usually given as illustrations. Includes analytic differential equations; variations of a parameter; integrals of differential equations; analytic implicit functions; problems of elliptic motion; sine-amplitude functions; deviation of formal bodies; Cauchy-Lipschitz process; linear differential equations with periodic coefficients; differential equations in infinitely many variations; much more. Historical notes. 10 figures. 222 problems. Index. xv + 395pp. 5⅜ x 8.
S451 Paperbound $2.00

DIFFERENTIAL AND INTEGRAL EQUATIONS OF MECHANICS AND PHYSICS (DIE DIFFERENTIAL-UND INTEGRALGLEICHUNGEN DER MECHANIK UND PHYSIK), edited by P. Frank and R. von Mises. Most comprehensive and authoritative work on the mathematics of mathematical physics available today in the United States: the standard, definitive reference for teachers, physicists, engineers, and mathematicians—now published (in the original German) at a relatively inexpensive price for the first time! Every chapter in this 2,000-page set is by an expert in his field: Carathéodory, Courant, Frank, Mises, and a dozen others. Vol I, on mathematics, gives concise but complete coverages of advanced calculus, differential equations, integral equations, and potential, and partial differential equations. Index. xxiii + 916pp. Vol. II (physics): classical mechanics, optics, continuous mechanics, heat conduction and diffusion, the stationary and quasi-stationary electromagnetic field, electromagnetic oscillations, and wave mechanics. Index. xxiv + 1106pp. Two volume set. Each volume available separately. 5⅝ x 8⅜.
S787 Vol I Clothbound $7.50
S788 Vol II Clothbound $7.50
The set $15.00

LECTURES ON CAUCHY'S PROBLEM, J. Hadamard. Based on lectures given at Columbia, Rome, this discusses work of Riemann, Kirchhoff, Volterra, and the author's own research on the hyperbolic case in linear partial differential equations. It extends spherical and cylindrical waves to apply to all (normal) hyperbolic equations. Partial contents: Cauchy's problem, fundamental formula, equations with odd number, with even number of independent variables; method of descent. 32 figures. Index. iii + 316pp. 5⅜ x 8. **S105 Paperbound $1.75**

THEORY OF DIFFERENTIAL EQUATIONS, A. R. Forsyth. Out of print for over a decade, the complete 6 volumes (now bound as 3) of this monumental work represent the most comprehensive treatment of differential equations ever written. Historical presentation includes in 2500 pages every substantial development. Vol. 1, 2: EXACT EQUATIONS, PFAFF'S PROBLEM; ORDINARY EQUATIONS, NOT LINEAR: methods of Grassmann, Clebsch, Lie, Darboux; Cauchy's theorem; branch points; etc. Vol. 3, 4: ORDINARY EQUATIONS, NOT LINEAR; ORDINARY LINEAR EQUATIONS: Zeta Fuchsian functions, general theorems on algebraic integrals, Brun's theorem, equations with uniform periodic coefficients, etc. Vol. 4, 5: PARTIAL DIFFERENTIAL EQUATIONS: 2 existence-theorems, equations of theoretical dynamics, Laplace transformations, general transformation of equations of the 2nd order, much more. Indexes. Total of 2766pp. 5⅜ x 8.
S576-7-8 Clothbound: the set $15.00

PARTIAL DIFFERENTIAL EQUATIONS OF MATHEMATICAL PHYSICS, A. G. Webster. A keystone work in the library of every mature physicist, engineer, researcher. Valuable sections on elasticity, compression theory, potential theory, theory of sound, heat conduction, wave propagation, vibration theory. Contents include: deduction of differential equations, vibrations, normal functions, Fourier's series, Cauchy's method, boundary problems, method of Riemann-Volterra. Spherical, cylindrical, ellipsoidal harmonics, applications, etc. 97 figures. vii + 440pp. 5⅜ x 8.
S263 Paperbound $2.00

ELEMENTARY CONCEPTS OF TOPOLOGY, P. Alexandroff. First English translation of the famous brief introduction to topology for the beginner or for the mathematician not undertaking extensive study. This unusually useful intuitive approach deals primarily with the concepts of complex, cycle, and homology, and is wholly consistent with current investigations. Ranges from basic concepts of set-theoretic topology to the concept of Betti groups. "Glowing example of harmony between intuition and thought," David Hilbert. Translated by A. E. Farley. Introduction by D. Hilbert. Index. 25 figures. 73pp. 5⅜ x 8. **S747 Paperbound $1.00**

Number theory

INTRODUCTION TO THE THEORY OF NUMBERS, L. E. Dickson. Thorough, comprehensive approach with adequate coverage of classical literature, an introductory volume beginners can follow. Chapters on divisibility, congruences, quadratic residues & reciprocity, Diophantine equations, etc. Full treatment of binary quadratic forms without usual restriction to integral coefficients. Covers infinitude of primes, least residues, Fermat's theorem, Euler's phi function, Legendre's symbol, Gauss's lemma, automorphs, reduced forms, recent theorems of Thue & Siegel, many more. Much material not readily available elsewhere. 239 problems. Index. I figure. viii + 183pp. 5⅜ x 8. **S342 Paperbound $1.65**

ELEMENTS OF NUMBER THEORY, I. M. Vinogradov. Detailed 1st course for persons without advanced mathematics; 95% of this book can be understood by readers who have gone no farther than high school algebra. Partial contents: divisibility theory, important number theoretical functions, congruences, primitive roots and indices, etc. Solutions to both problems and exercises. Tables of primes, indices, etc. Covers almost every essential formula in elementary number theory! Translated from Russian. 233 problems, 104 exercises. viii + 227pp. 5⅜ x 8. **S259 Paperbound $1.60**

THEORY OF NUMBERS and DIOPHANTINE ANALYSIS, R. D. Carmichael. These two complete works in one volume form one of the most lucid introductions to number theory, requiring only a firm foundation in high school mathematics. "Theory of Numbers," partial contents: Eratosthenes' sieve, Euclid's fundamental theorem, G.C.F. and L.C.M. of two or more integers, linear congruences, etc "Diophantine Analysis": rational triangles, Pythagorean triangles, equations of third, fourth, higher degrees, method of functional equations, much more. "Theory of Numbers": 76 problems. Index. 94pp. "Diophantine Analysis": 222 problems. Index. 118pp. 5⅜ x 8. **S529 Paperbound $1.35**

Numerical analysis, tables

MATHEMATICAL TABLES AND FORMULAS, Compiled by Robert D. Carmichael and Edwin R. Smith. Valuable collection for students, etc. Contains all tables necessary in college algebra and trigonometry, such as five-place common logarithms, logarithmic sines and tangents of small angles, logarithmic trigonometric functions, natural trigonometric functions, four-place antilogarithms, tables for changing from sexagesimal to circular and from circular to sexagesimal measure of angles, etc. Also many tables and formulas not ordinarily accessible, including powers, roots, and reciprocals, exponential and hyperbolic functions, ten-place logarithms of prime numbers, and formulas and theorems from analytical and elementary geometry and from calculus. Explanatory introduction. viii + 269pp. 5⅜ x 8½. **S111 Paperbound $1.00**

MATHEMATICAL TABLES, H. B. Dwight. Unique for its coverage in one volume of almost every function of importance in applied mathematics, engineering, and the physical sciences. Three extremely fine tables of the three trig functions and their inverse functions to thousandths of radians; natural and common logarithms; squares, cubes; hyperbolic functions and the inverse hyperbolic functions; $(a^2 + b^2)$ exp. ½a; complete elliptic integrals of the 1st and 2nd kind; sine and cosine integrals; exponential integrals Ei(x) and Ei(−x); binomial coefficients; factorials to 250; surface zonal harmonics and first derivatives; Bernoulli and Euler numbers and their logs to base of 10; Gamma function; normal probability integral; over 60 pages of Bessel functions; the Riemann Zeta function. Each table with formulae generally used, sources of more extensive tables, interpolation data, etc. Over half have columns of differences, to facilitate interpolation. Introduction. Index. viii + 231pp. 5⅜ x 8. **S445 Paperbound $1.75**

TABLES OF FUNCTIONS WITH FORMULAE AND CURVES, E. Jahnke & F. Emde. The world's most comprehensive 1-volume English-text collection of tables, formulae, curves of transcendent functions. 4th corrected edition, new 76-page section giving tables, formulae for elementary functions—not in other English editions. Partial contents: sine, cosine, logarithmic integral; factorial function; error integral; theta functions; elliptic integrals, functions; Legendre, Bessel, Riemann, Mathieu, hypergeometric functions, etc. Supplementary books. Bibliography. Indexed. "Out of the way functions for which we know no other source," SCIENTIFIC COMPUTING SERVICE, Ltd. 212 figures. 400pp. 5⅜ x 8. **S133 Paperbound $2.00**

CHEMISTRY AND PHYSICAL CHEMISTRY

ORGANIC CHEMISTRY, F. C. Whitmore. The entire subject of organic chemistry for the practicing chemist and the advanced student. Storehouse of facts, theories, processes found elsewhere only in specialized journals. Covers aliphatic compounds (500 pages on the properties and synthetic preparation of hydrocarbons, halides, proteins, ketones, etc.), alicyclic compounds, aromatic compounds, heterocyclic compounds, organophosphorus and organometallic compounds. Methods of synthetic preparation analyzed critically throughout. Includes much of biochemical interest. "The scope of this volume is astonishing," INDUSTRIAL AND ENGINEERING CHEMISTRY. 12,000-reference index. 2387-item bibliography. Total of x + 1005pp. 5⅜ x 8.
Two volume set.　　　　　　　　　　　　　　　　　　　　　S700 Vol I Paperbound **$2.00**
　　　　　　　　　　　　　　　　　　　　　　　　　　　　S701 Vol II Paperbound **$2.00**
　　　　　　　　　　　　　　　　　　　　　　　　　　　　　　　　　　The set **$4.00**

THE MODERN THEORY OF MOLECULAR STRUCTURE, Bernard Pullman. A reasonably popular account of recent developments in atomic and molecular theory. Contents: The Wave Function and Wave Equations (history and bases of present theories of molecular structure); The Electronic Structure of Atoms (Description and classification of atomic wave functions, etc.); Diatomic Molecules; Non-Conjugated Polyatomic Molecules; Conjugated Polyatomic Molecules; The Structure of Complexes. Minimum of mathematical background needed. New translation by David Antin of "La Structure Moleculaire." Index. Bibliography. vii + 87pp. 5⅜ x 8½.　　　　　　　　　　　　　　　　　　　　　　　　　　S987 Paperbound **$1.00**

CATALYSIS AND CATALYSTS, Marcel Prettre, Director, Research Institute on Catalysis. This brief book, translated into English for the first time, is the finest summary of the principal modern concepts, methods, and results of catalysis. Ideal introduction for beginning chemistry and physics students. Chapters: Basic Definitions of Catalysis (true catalysis and generalization of the concept of catalysis); The Scientific Bases of Catalysis (Catalysis and chemical thermodynamics, catalysis and chemical kinetics); Homogeneous Catalysis (acid-base catalysis, etc.); Chain Reactions; Contact Masses; Heterogeneous Catalysis (Mechanisms of contact catalyses, etc.); and Industrial Applications (acids and fertilizers, petroleum and petroleum chemistry, rubber, plastics, synthetic resins, and fibers). Translated by David Antin. Index. vi + 88pp. 5⅜ x 8½.　　　　　　　S998 Paperbound **$1.00**

POLAR MOLECULES, Pieter Debye. This work by Nobel laureate Debye offers a complete guide to fundamental electrostatic field relations, polarizability, molecular structure. Partial contents: electric intensity, displacement and force, polarization by orientation, molar polarization and molar refraction, halogen-hydrides, polar liquids, ionic saturation, dielectric constant, etc. Special chapter considers quantum theory. Indexed. 172pp. 5⅜ x 8.
　　　　　　　　　　　　　　　　　　　　　　　　　　　　S64 Paperbound **$1.50**

THE ELECTRONIC THEORY OF ACIDS AND BASES, W. F. Luder and Saverio Zuffanti. The first full systematic presentation of the electronic theory of acids and bases—treating the theory and its ramifications in an uncomplicated manner. Chapters: Historical Background; Atomic Orbitals and Valence; The Electronic Theory of Acids and Bases; Electrophilic and Electrodotic Reagents; Acidic and Basic Radicals; Neutralization; Titrations with Indicators; Displacement; Catalysis; Acid Catalysis; Base Catalysis; Alkoxides and Catalysts; Conclusion. Required reading for all chemists. Second revised (1961) eidtion, with additional examples and references. 3 figures. 9 tables. Index. Bibliography xii + 165pp. 5⅜ x 8.
　　　　　　　　　　　　　　　　　　　　　　　　　　　　S201 Paperbound **$1.50**

KINETIC THEORY OF LIQUIDS, J. Frenkel. Regarding the kinetic theory of liquids as a generalization and extension of the theory of solid bodies, this volume covers all types of arrangements of solids, thermal displacements of atoms, interstitial atoms and ions, orientational and rotational motion of molecules, and transition between states of matter. Mathematical theory is developed close to the physical subject matter. 216 bibliographical footnotes. 55 figures. xi + 485pp. 5⅜ x 8.　　　　　　　　S95 Paperbound **$2.55**

THE PRINCIPLES OF ELECTROCHEMISTRY, D. A. MacInnes. Basic equations for almost every subfield of electrochemistry from first principles, referring at all times to the soundest and most recent theories and results; unusually useful as text or as reference. Covers coulometers and Faraday's Law, electrolytic conductance, the Debye-Hueckel method for the theoretical calculation of activity coefficients, concentration cells, standard electrode potentials, thermodynamic ionization constants, pH, potentiometric titrations, irreversible phenomena, Planck's equation, and much more. "Excellent treatise," AMERICAN CHEMICAL SOCIETY JOURNAL. "Highly recommended," CHEMICAL AND METALLURGICAL ENGINEERING. 2 Indices. Appendix. 585-item bibliography. 137 figures. 94 tables. ii + 478pp. 5⅜ x 8⅜.
　　　　　　　　　　　　　　　　　　　　　　　　　　　　S52 Paperbound **$2.45**

THE PHASE RULE AND ITS APPLICATION, Alexander Findlay. Covering chemical phenomena of 1, 2, 3, 4, and multiple component systems, this "standard work on the subject" (NATURE, London), has been completely revised and brought up to date by A. N. Campbell and N. O. Smith. Brand new material has been added on such matters as binary, tertiary liquid equilibria, solid solutions in ternary systems, quinary systems of salts and water. Completely revised to triangular coordinates in ternary systems, clarified graphic representation, solid models, etc. 9th revised edition. Author, subject indexes. 236 figures. 505 footnotes, mostly bibliographic. xii + 494pp. 5⅜ x 8.　　　　　　　S91 Paperbound **$2.45**

PHYSICS

General physics

FOUNDATIONS OF PHYSICS, R. B. Lindsay & H. Margenau. Excellent bridge between semi-popular works & technical treatises. A discussion of methods of physical description, construction of theory; valuable for physicist with elementary calculus who is interested in ideas that give meaning to data, tools of modern physics. Contents include symbolism, mathematical equations; space & time foundations of mechanics; probability; physics & continua; electron theory; special & general relativity; quantum mechanics; causality. "Thorough and yet not overdetailed. Unreservedly recommended," NATURE (London). Unabridged, corrected edition. List of recommended readings. 35 illustrations. xi + 537pp. 5⅜ x 8.
S377 Paperbound **$2.75**

FUNDAMENTAL FORMULAS OF PHYSICS, ed. by D. H. Menzel. Highly useful, fully inexpensive reference and study text, ranging from simple to highly sophisticated operations. Mathematics integrated into text—each chapter stands as short textbook of field represented. Vol. 1: Statistics, Physical Constants, Special Theory of Relativity, Hydrodynamics, Aerodynamics, Boundary Value Problems in Math. Physics; Viscosity, Electromagnetic Theory, etc. Vol. 2: Sound, Acoustics, Geometrical Optics, Electron Optics, High-Energy Phenomena, Magnetism, Biophysics, much more. Index. Total of 800pp. 5⅜ x 8. Vol. 1 S595 Paperbound **$2.00**
Vol. 2 S596 Paperbound **$2.00**

MATHEMATICAL PHYSICS, D. H. Menzel. Thorough one-volume treatment of the mathematical techniques vital for classic mechanics, electromagnetic theory, quantum theory, and relativity. Written by the Harvard Professor of Astrophysics for junior, senior, and graduate courses, it gives clear explanations of all those aspects of function theory, vectors, matrices, dyadics, tensors, partial differential equations, etc., necessary for the understanding of the various physical theories. Electron theory, relativity, and other topics seldom presented appear here in considerable detail. Scores of definitions, conversion factors, dimensional constants, etc. "More detailed than normal for an advanced text . . . excellent set of sections on Dyadics, Matrices, and Tensors," JOURNAL OF THE FRANKLIN INSTITUTE. Index. 193 problems, with answers. x + 412pp. 5⅜ x 8. S56 Paperbound **$2.00**

THE SCIENTIFIC PAPERS OF J. WILLARD GIBBS. All the published papers of America's outstanding theoretical scientist (except for "Statistical Mechanics" and "Vector Analysis"). Vol I (thermodynamics) contains one of the most brilliant of all 19th-century scientific papers—the 300-page "On the Equilibrium of Heterogeneous Substances," which founded the science of physical chemistry, and clearly stated a number of highly important natural laws for the first time; 8 other papers complete the first volume. Vol II includes 2 papers on dynamics, 8 on vector analysis and multiple algebra, 5 on the electromagnetic theory of light, and 6 miscellaneous papers. Biographical sketch by H. A. Bumstead. Total of xxxvi + 718pp. 5⅝ x 8⅜.
S721 Vol I Paperbound **$2.00**
S722 Vol II Paperbound **$2.00**
The set **$4.00**

BASIC THEORIES OF PHYSICS, Peter Gabriel Bergmann. Two-volume set which presents a critical examination of important topics in the major subdivisions of classical and modern physics. The first volume is concerned with classical mechanics and electrodynamics: mechanics of mass points, analytical mechanics, matter in bulk, electrostatics and magnetostatics, electromagnetic interaction, the field waves, special relativity, and waves. The second volume (Heat and Quanta) contains discussions of the kinetic hypothesis, physics and statistics, stationary ensembles, laws of thermodynamics, early quantum theories, atomic spectra, probability waves, quantization in wave mechanics, approximation methods, and abstract quantum theory. A valuable supplement to any thorough course or text.
Heat and Quanta: Index. 8 figures. x + 300pp. 5⅜ x 8½. S968 Paperbound **$1.75**
Mechanics and Electrodynamics: Index. 14 figures. vii + 280pp. 5⅜ x 8½.
S969 Paperbound **$1.75**

THEORETICAL PHYSICS, A. S. Kompaneyets. One of the very few thorough studies of the subject in this price range. Provides advanced students with a comprehensive theoretical background. Especially strong on recent experimentation and developments in quantum theory. Contents: Mechanics (Generalized Coordinates, Lagrange's Equation, Collision of Particles, etc.), Electrodynamics (Vector Analysis, Maxwell's equations, Transmission of Signals, Theory of Relativity, etc.), Quantum Mechanics (the Inadequacy of Classical Mechanics, the Wave Equation, Motion in a Central Field, Quantum Theory of Radiation, Quantum Theories of Dispersion and Scattering, etc.), and Statistical Physics (Equilibrium Distribution of Molecules in an Ideal Gas, Boltzmann statistics, Bose and Fermi Distribution, Thermodynamic Quantities, etc.). Revised to 1961. Translated by George Yankovsky, authorized by Kompaneyets. 137 exercises. 56 figures. 529pp. 5⅜ x 8½. S972 Paperbound **$2.50**

ANALYTICAL AND CANONICAL FORMALISM IN PHYSICS, André Mercier. A survey, in one volume, of the variational principles (the key principles—in mathematical form—from which the basic laws of any one branch of physics can be derived) of the several branches of physical theory, together with an examination of the relationships among them. Contents: the Lagrangian Formalism, Lagrangian Densities, Canonical Formalism, Canonical Form of Electrodynamics, Hamiltonian Densities, Transformations, and Canonical Form with Vanishing Jacobian Determinant. Numerous examples and exercises. For advanced students, teachers, etc. 6 figures. Index. viii + 222pp. 5⅜ x 8½. S1077 Paperbound **$1.75**

MATHEMATICAL PUZZLES AND RECREATIONS

AMUSEMENTS IN MATHEMATICS, Henry Ernest Dudeney. The foremost British originator of mathematical puzzles is always intriguing, witty, and paradoxical in this classic, one of the largest collections of mathematical amusements. More than 430 puzzles, problems, and paradoxes. Mazes and games, problems on number manipulation, unicursal and other route problems, puzzles on measuring, weighing, packing, age, kinship, chessboards, joining, crossing river, plane figure dissection, and many others. Solutions. More than 450 illustrations. vii + 258pp. 5⅜ x 8.   T473 Paperbound **$1.25**

SYMBOLIC LOGIC and THE GAME OF LOGIC, Lewis Carroll. "Symbolic Logic" is not concerned with modern symbolic logic, but is instead a collection of over 380 problems posed with charm and imagination, using the syllogism, and a fascinating diagrammatic method of drawing conclusions. In "The Game of Logic," Carroll's whimsical imagination devises a logical game played with 2 diagrams and counters (included) to manipulate hundreds of tricky syllogisms. The final section, "Hit or Miss" is a lagniappe of 101 additional puzzles in the delightful Carroll manner. Until this reprint edition, both of these books were rarities costing up to $15 each. Symbolic Logic: Index, xxxi + 199pp. The Game of Logic: 96pp. Two vols. bound as one. 5⅜ x 8.   T492 Paperbound **$1.50**

MAZES AND LABYRINTHS: A BOOK OF PUZZLES, W. Shepherd. Mazes, formerly associated with mystery and ritual, are still among the most intriguing of intellectual puzzles. This is a novel and different collection of 50 amusements that embody the principle of the maze: mazes in the classical tradition; 3-dimensional, ribbon, and Möbius-strip mazes; hidden messages; spatial arrangements; etc.—almost all built on amusing story situations. 84 illustrations. Essay on maze psychology. Solutions. xv + 122pp. 5⅜ x 8.   T731 Paperbound **$1.00**

MATHEMATICAL RECREATIONS, M. Kraitchik. Some 250 puzzles, problems, demonstrations of recreational mathematics for beginners & advanced mathematicians. Unusual historical problems from Greek, Medieval, Arabic, Hindu sources: modern problems based on "mathematics without numbers," geometry, topology, arithmetic, etc. Pastimes derived from figurative numbers, Mersenne numbers, Fermat numbers; fairy chess, latruncles, reversi, many topics. Full solutions. Excellent for insights into special fields of math. 181 illustrations. 330pp. 5⅜ x 8.   T163 Paperbound **$1.75**

MATHEMATICAL PUZZLES OF SAM LOYD, Vol. I, selected and edited by M. Gardner. Puzzles by the greatest puzzle creator and innovator. Selected from his famous "Cyclopedia of Puzzles," they retain the unique style and historical flavor of the originals. There are posers based on arithmetic, algebra, probability, game theory, route tracing, topology, counter, sliding block, operations research, geometrical dissection. Includes his famous "14-15" puzzle which was a national craze, and his "Horse of a Different Color" which sold millions of copies. 117 of his most ingenious puzzles in all, 120 line drawings and diagrams. Solutions. Selected references. xx + 167pp. 5⅜ x 8.   T498 Paperbound **$1.00**

MY BEST PUZZLES IN MATHEMATICS, Hubert Phillips ("Caliban"). Caliban is generally considered the best of the modern problemists. Here are 100 of his best and wittiest puzzles, selected by the author himself from such publications as the London Daily Telegraph, and each puzzle is guaranteed to put even the sharpest puzzle detective through his paces. Perfect for the development of clear thinking and a logical mind. Complete solutions are provided for every puzzle. x + 107pp. 5⅜ x 8½.   T91 Paperbound **$1.00**

MY BEST PUZZLES IN LOGIC AND REASONING, H. Phillips ("Caliban"). 100 choice, hitherto unavailable puzzles by England's best-known problemist. No special knowledge needed to solve these logical or inferential problems, just an unclouded mind, nerves of steel, and fast reflexes. Data presented are both necessary and just sufficient to allow one unambiguous answer. More than 30 different types of puzzles, all ingenious and varied, many one of a kind, that will challenge the expert, please the beginner. Original publication. 100 puzzles, full solutions. x + 107pp. 5⅜ x 8½.   T119 Paperbound **$1.00**

MATHEMATICAL PUZZLES FOR BEGINNERS AND ENTHUSIASTS, G. Mott-Smith. 188 mathematical puzzles to test mental agility. Inference, interpretation, algebra, dissection of plane figures, geometry, properties of numbers, decimation, permutations, probability, all enter these delightful problems. Puzzles like the Odic Force, How to Draw an Ellipse, Spider's Cousin, more than 180 others. Detailed solutions. Appendix with square roots, triangular numbers, primes, etc. 135 illustrations. 2nd revised edition. 248pp. 5⅜ x 8.   T198 Paperbound **$1.00**

MATHEMATICS, MAGIC AND MYSTERY, Martin Gardner. Card tricks, feats of mental mathematics, stage mind-reading, other "magic" explained as applications of probability, sets, theory of numbers, topology, various branches of mathematics. Creative examination of laws and their applications with scores of new tricks and insights. 115 sections discuss tricks with cards, dice, coins; geometrical vanishing tricks, dozens of others. No sleight of hand needed; mathematics guarantees success. 115 illustrations. xii + 174pp. 5⅜ x 8.
                                                        T335 Paperbound **$1.00**

RECREATIONS IN THE THEORY OF NUMBERS: THE QUEEN OF MATHEMATICS ENTERTAINS, Albert H. Beiler. The theory of numbers is often referred to as the "Queen of Mathematics." In this book Mr. Beiler has compiled the first English volume to deal exclusively with the recreational aspects of number theory, an inherently recreational branch of mathematics. The author's clear style makes for enjoyable reading as he deals with such topics as: perfect numbers, amicable numbers, Fermat's theorem, Wilson's theorem, interesting properties of digits, methods of factoring, primitive roots, Euler's function, polygonal and figurate numbers, Mersenne numbers, congruence, repeating decimals, etc. Countless puzzle problems, with full answers and explanations. For mathematicians and mathematically-inclined laymen, etc. New publication. 28 figures. 9 illustrations. 103 tables. Bibliography at chapter ends. vi + 247pp. 5⅜ x 8½.
T1096 Paperbound **$1.85**

PAPER FOLDING FOR BEGINNERS, W. D. Murray and F. J. Rigney. A delightful introduction to the varied and entertaining Japanese art of origami (paper folding), with a full crystal-clear text that anticipates every difficulty; over 275 clearly labeled diagrams of all important stages in creation. You get results at each stage, since complex figures are logically developed from simpler ones. 43 different pieces are explained: place mats, drinking cups, bonbon boxes, sailboats, frogs, roosters, etc. 6 photographic plates. 279 diagrams. 95pp. 5⅜ x 8⅜.
T713 Paperbound **$1.00**

1800 RIDDLES, ENIGMAS AND CONUNDRUMS, Darwin A. Hindman. Entertaining collection ranging from hilarious gags to outrageous puns to sheer nonsense—a welcome respite from sophisticated humor. Children, toastmasters, and practically anyone with a funny bone will find these zany riddles tickling and eminently repeatable. Sample: "Why does Santa Claus always go down the chimney?" "Because it soots him." Some old, some new—covering a wide variety of subjects. New publication. iii + 154pp. 5⅜ x 8½. T1059 Paperbound **$1.00**

EASY-TO-DO ENTERTAINMENTS AND DIVERSIONS WITH CARDS, STRING, COINS, PAPER AND MATCHES, R. M. Abraham. Over 300 entertaining games, tricks, puzzles, and pastimes for children and adults. Invaluable to anyone in charge of groups of youngsters, for party givers, etc. Contains sections on card tricks and games, making things by paperfolding—toys, decorations, and the like; tricks with coins, matches, and pieces of string; descriptions of games; toys that can be made from common household objects; mathematical recreations; word games; and 50 miscellaneous entertainments. Formerly "Winter Nights Entertainments." Introduction by Lord Baden Powell. 329 illustrations. v + 186pp. 5⅜ x 8.
T921 Paperbound **$1.00**

DIVERSIONS AND PASTIMES WITH CARDS, STRING, PAPER AND MATCHES, R. M. Abraham. Another collection of amusements and diversion for game and puzzle fans of all ages. Many new paperfolding ideas and tricks, an extensive section on amusements with knots and splices, two chapters of easy and not-so-easy problems, coin and match tricks, and lots of other parlor pastimes from the agile mind of the late British problemist and gamester. Corrected and revised version. Illustrations. 160pp. 5⅜ x 8½. T1127 Paperbound **$1.00**

STRING FIGURES AND HOW TO MAKE THEM: A STUDY OF CAT'S-CRADLE IN MANY LANDS, Caroline Furness Jayne. In a simple and easy-to-follow manner, this book describes how to make 107 different string figures. Not only is looping and crossing string between the fingers a common youthful diversion, but it is an ancient form of amusement practiced in all parts of the globe, especially popular among primitive tribes. These games are fun for all ages and offer an excellent means for developing manual dexterity and coordination. Much insight also for the anthropological observer on games and diversions in many different cultures. Index. Bibliography. Introduction by A. C. Haddon, Cambridge University. 17 full-page plates. 950 illustrations. xxiii + 407pp. 5⅜ x 8½.
T152 Paperbound **$2.00**

CRYPTANALYSIS, Helen F. Gaines. (Formerly ELEMENTARY CRYPTANALYSIS.) A standard elementary and intermediate text for serious students. It does not confine itself to old material, but contains much that is not generally known, except to experts. Concealment, Transposition, Substitution ciphers; Vigenere, Kasiski, Playfair, multafid, dozens of other techniques. Appendix with sequence charts, letter frequencies in English, 5 other languages, English word frequencies. Bibliography. 167 codes. New to this edition: solution to codes. vi + 230pp. 5⅜ x 8.
T97 Paperbound **$1.95**

MAGIC SQUARES AND CUBES, W. S. Andrews. Only book-length treatment in English, a thorough non-technical description and analysis. Here are nasik, overlapping, pandiagonal, serrated squares; magic circles, cubes, spheres, rhombuses. Try your hand at 4-dimensional magical figures! Much unusual folklore and tradition included. High school algebra is sufficient. 754 diagrams and illustrations. viii + 419pp. 5⅜ x 8. T658 Paperbound **$1.85**

CALIBAN'S PROBLEM BOOK: MATHEMATICAL, INFERENTIAL, AND CRYPTOGRAPHIC PUZZLES, H. Phillips ("Caliban"), S. T. Shovelton, G. S. Marshall. 105 ingenious problems by the greatest living creator of puzzles based on logic and inference. Rigorous, modern, piquant, and reflecting their author's unusual personality, these intermediate and advanced puzzles all involve the ability to reason clearly through complex situations; some call for mathematical knowledge, ranging from algebra to number theory. Solutions. xi + 180pp. 5⅜ x 8.
T736 Paperbound **$1.25**

FICTION

THE LAND THAT TIME FORGOT and THE MOON MAID, Edgar Rice Burroughs. In the opinion of many, Burroughs' best work. The first concerns a strange island where evolution is individual rather than phylogenetic. Speechless anthropoids develop into intelligent human beings within a single generation. The second projects the reader far into the future and describes the first voyage to the Moon (in the year 2025), the conquest of the Earth by the Moon, and years of violence and adventure as the enslaved Earthmen try to regain possession of their planet. "An imaginative tour de force that keeps the reader keyed up and expectant," NEW YORK TIMES. Complete, unabridged text of the original two novels (three parts in each). 5 illustrations by J. Allen St. John. vi + 552pp. 5⅜ x 8½.

T1020 Clothbound **$3.75**
T358 Paperbound **$2.00**

AT THE EARTH'S CORE, PELLUCIDAR, TANAR OF PELLUCIDAR: THREE SCIENCE FICTION NOVELS BY EDGAR RICE BURROUGHS. Complete, unabridged texts of the first three Pellucidar novels. Tales of derring-do by the famous master of science fiction. The locale for these three related stories is the inner surface of the hollow Earth where we discover the world of Pellucidar, complete with all types of bizarre, menacing creatures, strange peoples, and alluring maidens—guaranteed to delight all Burroughs fans and a wide circle of advenutre lovers. Illustrated by J. Allen St. John and P. F. Berdanier. vi + 433pp. 5⅜ x 8½.

T1051 Paperbound **$2.00**

THE PIRATES OF VENUS and LOST ON VENUS: TWO VENUS NOVELS BY EDGAR RICE BURROUGHS. Two related novels, complete and unabridged. Exciting adventure on the planet Venus with Earthman Carson Napier broken-field running through one dangerous episode after another. All lovers of swashbuckling science fiction will enjoy these two stories set in a world of fascinating societies, fierce beasts, 5000-ft. trees, lush vegetation, and wide seas. Illustrations by Fortunino Matania. Total of vi + 340pp. 5⅜ x 8½.   T1053 Paperbound **$1.75**

A PRINCESS OF MARS and A FIGHTING MAN OF MARS: TWO MARTIAN NOVELS BY EDGAR RICE BURROUGHS. "Princess of Mars" is the very first of the great Martian novels written by Burroughs, and it is probably the best of them all; it set the pattern for all of his later fantasy novels and contains a thrilling cast of strange peoples and creatures and the formula of Olympian heroism amidst ever-fluctuating fortunes which Burroughs carries off so successfully. "Fighting Man" returns to the same scenes and cities—many years later. A mad scientist, a degenerate dictator, and an indomitable defender of the right clash— with the fate of the Red Planet at stake! Complete, unabridged reprinting of original editions. Illustrations by F. E. Schoonover and Hugh Hutton. v + 356pp. 5⅜ x 8½.

T1140 Paperbound **$1.75**

THREE MARTIAN NOVELS, Edgar Rice Burroughs. Contains: Thuvia, Maid of Mars; The Chessmen of Mars; and The Master Mind of Mars. High adventure set in an imaginative and intricate conception of the Red Planet. Mars is peopled with an intelligent, heroic human race which lives in densely populated cities and with fierce barbarians who inhabit dead sea bottoms. Other exciting creatures abound amidst an inventive framework of Martian history and geography. Complete unabridged reprintings of the first edition. 16 illustrations by J. Allen St. John. vi + 499pp. 5⅜ x 8½.   T39 Paperbound **$1.85**

THREE PROPHETIC NOVELS BY H. G. WELLS, edited by E. F. Bleiler. Complete texts of "When the Sleeper Wakes" (1st book printing in 50 years), "A Story of the Days to Come," "The Time Machine" (1st complete printing in book form). Exciting adventures in the future are as enjoyable today as 50 years ago when first printed. Predict TV, movies, intercontinental airplanes, prefabricated houses, air-conditioned cities, etc. First important author to foresee problems of mind control, technological dictatorships. "Absolute best of imaginative fiction," N. Y. Times. Introduction. 335pp. 5⅜ x 8.   T605 Paperbound **$1.50**

28 SCIENCE FICTION STORIES OF H. G. WELLS. Two full unabridged novels, MEN LIKE GODS and STAR BEGOTTEN, plus 26 short stories by the master science-fiction writer of all time. Stories of space, time, invention, exploration, future adventure—an indispensable part of the library of everyone interested in science and adventure. PARTIAL CONTENTS: Men Like Gods, The Country of the Blind, In the Abyss, The Crystal Egg, The Man Who Could Work Miracles, A Story of the Days to Come, The Valley of Spiders, and 21 more! 928pp. 5⅜ x 8.

T265 Clothbound **$4.50**

THE WAR IN THE AIR, IN THE DAYS OF THE COMET, THE FOOD OF THE GODS: THREE SCIENCE FICTION NOVELS BY H. G. WELLS. Three exciting Wells offerings bearing on vital social and philosophical issues of his and our own day. Here are tales of air power, strategic bombing, East vs. West, the potential miracles of science, the potential disasters from outer space, the relationship between scientific advancement and moral progress, etc. First reprinting of "War in the Air" in almost 50 years. An excellent sampling of Wells at his storytelling best. Complete, unabridged reprintings. 16 illustrations. 645pp. 5⅜ x 8½.

T1135 Paperbound **$2.00**

SEVEN SCIENCE FICTION NOVELS, H. G. Wells. Full unabridged texts of 7 science-fiction novels of the master. Ranging from biology, physics, chemistry, astronomy to sociology and other studies, Mr. Wells extrapolates whole worlds of strange and intriguing character. "One will have to go far to match this for entertainment, excitement, and sheer pleasure . . . ," NEW YORK TIMES. Contents: The Time Machine, The Island of Dr. Moreau, First Men in the Moon, The Invisible Man, The War of the Worlds, The Food of the Gods, In the Days of the Comet. 1015pp. 5⅜ x 8.   T264 Clothbound **$4.50**

BEST GHOST STORIES OF J. S. LE FANU, Selected and introduced by E. F. Bleiler. LeFanu is deemed the greatest name in Victorian supernatural fiction. Here are 16 of his best horror stories, including 2 nouvelles: "Carmilla," a classic vampire tale couched in a perverse eroticism, and "The Haunted Baronet." Also: "Sir Toby's Will," "Green Tea," "Schalken the Painter," "Ultor de Lacy," "The Familiar," etc. The first American publication of about half of this material: a long-overdue opportunity to get a choice sampling of LeFanu's work. New selection (1964). 8 illustrations. 5⅜ x 8⅜.   T415 Paperbound **$1.85**

THE WONDERFUL WIZARD OF OZ, L. F. Baum. Only edition in print with all the original W. W. Denslow illustrations in full color—as much a part of "The Wizard" as Tenniel's drawings are for "Alice in Wonderland." "The Wizard" is still America's best-loved fairy tale, in which, as the author expresses it, "The wonderment and joy are retained and the heartaches and nightmares left out." Now today's young readers can enjoy every word and wonderful picture of the original book. New introduction by Martin Gardner. A Baum bibliography. 23 full-page color plates. viii + 268pp. 5⅜ x 8.   T691 Paperbound **$1.45**

GHOST AND HORROR STORIES OF AMBROSE BIERCE, Selected and introduced by E. F. Bleiler. 24 morbid, eerie tales—the cream of Bierce's fiction output. Contains such memorable pieces as "The Moonlit Road," "The Damned Thing," "An Inhabitant of Carcosa," "The Eyes of the Panther," "The Famous Gilson Bequest," "The Middle Toe of the Right Foot," and other chilling stories, plus the essay, "Visions of the Night" in which Bierce gives us a kind of rationale for his aesthetic of horror. New collection (1964). xxii + 199pp. 5⅜ x 8⅜.   T767 Paperbound **$1.00**

HUMOR

MR. DOOLEY ON IVRYTHING AND IVRYBODY, Finley Peter Dunne. Since the time of his appearance in 1893, "Mr. Dooley," the fictitious Chicago bartender, has been recognized as America's most humorous social and political commentator. Collected in this volume are 102 of the best Dooley pieces—all written around the turn of the century, the height of his popularity. Mr. Dooley's Irish brogue is employed wittily and penetratingly on subjects which are just as fresh and relevant today as they were then: corruption and hypocrisy of politicans, war preparations and chauvinism, automation, Latin American affairs, superbombs, etc. Other articles range from Rudyard Kipling to football. Selected with an introduction by Robert Hutchinson. xii + 244pp. 5⅜ x 8½.   T626 Paperbound **$1.00**

RUTHLESS RHYMES FOR HEARTLESS HOMES and MORE RUTHLESS RHYMES FOR HEARTLESS HOMES, Harry Graham ("Col. D. Streamer"). A collection of Little Willy and 48 other poetic "disasters." Graham's funniest and most disrespectful verse, accompanied by original illustrations. Nonsensical, wry humor which employs stern parents, careless nurses, uninhibited children, practical jokers, single-minded golfers, Scottish lairds, etc. in the leading roles. A precursor of the "sick joke" school of today. This volume contains, bound together for the first time, two of the most perennially popular books of humor in England and America. Index. vi + 69pp. 5⅜ x 8.   T930 Paperbound **75¢**

A WHIMSEY ANTHOLOGY, Collected by Carolyn Wells. 250 of the most amusing rhymes ever written. Acrostics, anagrams, palindromes, alphabetical jingles, tongue twisters, echo verses, alliterative verses, riddles, mnemonic rhymes, interior rhymes, over 40 limericks, etc. by Lewis Carroll, Edward Lear, Joseph Addison, W. S. Gilbert, Christina Rossetti, Chas. Lamb, James Boswell, Hood, Dickens, Swinburne, Leigh Hunt, Harry Graham, Poe, Eugene Field, and many others. xiv + 221pp. 5⅜ x 8½.   T195 Paperbound **$1.25**

MY PIOUS FRIENDS AND DRUNKEN COMPANIONS and MORE PIOUS FRIENDS AND DRUNKEN COMPANIONS, Songs and ballads of Conviviality Collected by Frank Shay. Magnificently illuminated by John Held, Jr. 132 ballads, blues, vaudeville numbers, drinking songs, cowboy songs, sea chanties, comedy songs, etc. of the Naughty Nineties and early 20th century. Over a third are reprinted with music. Many perennial favorites such as: The Band Played On, Frankie and Johnnie, The Old Grey Mare, The Face on the Bar-room Floor, etc. Many others unlocatable elsewhere: The Dog-Catcher's Child, The Cannibal Maiden, Don't Go in the Lion's Cage Tonight, Mother, etc. Complete verses and introductions to songs. Unabridged republication of first editions, 2 Indexes (song titles and first lines and choruses). Introduction by Frank Shay. 2 volumes bounds as 1. Total of xvi + 235pp. 5⅜ x 8½.   T946 Paperbound **$1.00**

MAX AND MORITZ, Wilhelm Busch. Edited and annotated by H. Arthur Klein. Translated by H. Arthur Klein, M. C. Klein, and others. The mischievous high jinks of Max and Moritz, Peter and Paul, Ker and Plunk, etc. are delightfully captured in sketch and rhyme. (Companion volume to "Hypocritical Helena.") In addition to the title piece, it contians: Ker and Plunk; Two Dogs and Two Boys; The Egghead and the Two Cut-ups of Corinth; Deceitful Henry; The Boys and the Pipe; Cat and Mouse; and others. (Original German text with accompanying English translations.) Afterword by H. A. Klein. vi + 216pp. 5⅜ x 8½.
T181 Paperbound **$1.00**

THROUGH THE ALIMENTARY CANAL WITH GUN AND CAMERA: A FASCINATING TRIP TO THE INTERIOR, Personally Conducted by George S. Chappell. In mock-travelogue style, the amusing account of an imaginative journey down the alimentary canal. The "explorers" enter the esophagus, round the Adam's Apple, narrowly escape from a fierce Amoeba, struggle through the impenetrable Nerve Forests of the Lumbar Region, etc. Illustrated by the famous cartoonist, Otto Soglow, the book is as much a brilliant satire of academic pomposity and professional travel literature as it is a clever use of the facts of physiology for supremely comic purposes. Preface by Robert Benchley. Author's Foreword. 1 Photograph. 17 illustrations by O. Soglow. xii + 114pp. 5⅜ x 8½.
T376 Paperbound **$1.00**

THE BAD CHILD'S BOOK OF BEASTS, MORE BEASTS FOR WORSE CHILDREN, and A MORAL ALPHABET, H. Belloc. Hardly an anthology of humorous verse has appeared in the last 50 years without at least a couple of these famous nonsense verses. But one must see the entire volumes—with all the delightful original illustrations by Sir Basil Blackwood—to appreciate fully Belloc's charming and witty verses that play so subacidly on the platitudes of life and morals that beset his day—and ours. A great humor classic. Three books in one. Total of 157pp. 5⅜ x 8.
T749 Paperbound **$1.00**

THE DEVIL'S DICTIONARY, Ambrose Bierce. Sardonic and irreverent barbs puncturing the pomposities and absurdities of American politics, business, religion, literature, and arts, by the country's greatest satirist in the classic tradition. Epigrammatic as Shaw, piercing as Swift, American as Mark Twain, Will Rogers, and Fred Allen. Bierce will always remain the favorite of a small coterie of enthusiasts, and of writers and speakers whom he supplies with "some of the most gorgeous witticisms of the English language." (H. L. Mencken) Over 1000 entries in alphabetical order. 144pp. 5⅜ x 8.
T487 Paperbound **$1.00**

THE COMPLETE NONSENSE OF EDWARD LEAR. This is the only complete edition of this master of gentle madness available at a popular price. A BOOK OF NONSENSE, NONSENSE SONGS, MORE NONSENSE SONGS AND STORIES in their entirety with all the old favorites that have delighted children and adults for years. The Dong With A Luminous Nose, The Jumblies, The Owl and the Pussycat, and hundreds of other bits of wonderful nonsense. 214 limericks, 3 sets of Nonsense Botany, 5 Nonsense Alphabets. 546 drawings by Lear himself, and much more. 320pp. 5⅜ x 8.
T167 Paperbound **$1.00**

SINGULAR TRAVELS, CAMPAIGNS, AND ADVENTURES OF BARON MUNCHAUSEN, R. E. Raspe, with 90 illustrations by Gustave Doré. The first edition in over 150 years to reestablish the deeds of the Prince of Liars exactly as Raspe first recorded them in 1785—the genuine Baron Munchausen, one of the most popular personalities in English literature. Included also are the best of the many sequels, written by other hands. Introduction on Raspe by J. Carswell. Bibliography of early editions. xliv + 192pp. 5⅜ x 8.
T698 Paperbound **$1.00**

HOW TO TELL THE BIRDS FROM THE FLOWERS, R. W. Wood. How not to confuse a carrot with a parrot, a grape with an ape, a puffin with nuffin. Delightful drawings, clever puns, absurd little poems point out farfetched resemblances in nature. The author was a leading physicist. Introduction by Margaret Wood White. 106 illus. 60pp. 5⅜ x 8.
T523 Paperbound **75¢**

JOE MILLER'S JESTS OR, THE WITS VADE-MECUM. The original Joe Miller jest book. Gives a keen and pungent impression of life in 18th-century England. Many are somewhat on the bawdy side and they are still capable of provoking amusement and good fun. This volume is a facsimile of the original "Joe Miller" first published in 1739. It remains the most popular and influential humor book of all time. New introduction by Robert Hutchinson. xxi + 70pp. 5⅜ x 8½.
T423 Paperbound **$1.00**

Prices subject to change without notice.

Dover publishes books on art, music, philosophy, literature, languages, history, social sciences, psychology, handcrafts, orientalia, puzzles and entertainments, chess, pets and gardens, books explaining science, intermediate and higher mathematics, mathematical physics, engineering, biological sciences, earth sciences, classics of science, etc. Write to:

Dept. catrr.
Dover Publications, Inc.
180 Varick Street, N.Y. 14, N.Y.